**PEARSON**   ALWAYS LEARNING

Allen R. Angel • Christine D. Abbott • Dennis C. Runde

# A Survey of Mathematics with Applications

## Third Custom Edition for Everglades University

Taken from:
*A Survey of Mathematics with Applications*, Ninth Edition
by Allen R. Angel, Christine D. Abbott, and Dennis C. Runde

*Student's Solutions Manual for A Survey of Mathematics with Applications*,
Ninth Edition
by Tamsen Herrick, Allen R. Angel, Christine D. Abbott, and
Dennis C. Runde

Cover Art: Courtesy of Photodisc/Getty Images.

Taken from:

*A Survey of Mathematics with Applications*, Ninth Edition
by Allen R. Angel, Christine D. Abbott, and Dennis C. Runde
Copyright © 2013, 2009, 2005, 2001 by Pearson Education, Inc.
Upper Saddle River, New Jersey 07458

*Student's Solutions Manual for A Survey of Mathematics with Applications*, Ninth Edition
by Tamsen Herrick, Allen R. Angel, Christine D. Abbott, and Dennis C. Runde
Copyright © 2013, 2009, 2005 by Pearson Education, Inc.

This special edition published in cooperation with Pearson Learning Solutions.

All trademarks, service marks, registered trademarks, and registered service marks are the property of their respective owners and are used herein for identification purposes only.

Pearson Learning Solutions, 501 Boylston Street, Suite 900, Boston, MA 02116
A Pearson Education Company
www.pearsoned.com

Printed in the United States of America

2 3 4 5 6 7 8 9 10 V092 16 15 14

000200010271808072

CW

ISBN 10: 1-269-44773-4
ISBN 13: 978-1-269-44773-7

# Contents

# A Survey of Mathematics with Applications

# 2

# Sets

## Why This is Important

A basic human impulse is to sort or classify things. As you will see in this chapter, putting elements into sets helps you order and arrange your world. It allows you to deal with large quantities of information. Set building is a learning tool that helps answer the question, What are the characteristics of this group? For example, when students read a college catalog to determine which courses fulfill their degree requirements, they are looking for courses that are in a particular set. Studying sets is also important because sets underlie other mathematical topics such as logic and abstract algebra.

◄ Children learn how to classify sets, such as shapes and colors, at a very early age.

## SECTION 2.1 Set Concepts

▲ *Many different restaurant categories include McDonald's*

Can you think of a few different categories or groups to which the restaurant McDonald's belongs? One way you could categorize McDonald's is as a fast food restaurant. Another way is as a restaurant selling hamburgers. A third way is as a restaurant selling breakfast. In this section, we will discuss ways to sort or classify objects. We will also discuss different methods that can be used to indicate collections of objects.

Why *This is Important* Set classifications are important in a range of applications from placing students in courses to classifying stars in the universe.

We encounter sets in many different ways every day of our lives. A *set* is a collection of objects, which are called *elements* or *members* of the set. For example, the United States is a collection, or set, of 50 states plus the District of Columbia. The 50 individual states plus the District of Columbia are the members or elements of the set that is called the United States.

A set is *well defined* if its contents can be clearly determined. The set of U.S. presidents is a well-defined set because its contents, the presidents, can be named. The set of the three best movies is not a well-defined set because the word *best* is interpreted differently by different people. In this text, we use only well-defined sets.

Three methods are commonly used to indicate a set: (1) description, (2) roster form, and (3) set-builder notation.

The method of indicating a set by *description* is illustrated in Example 1.

### Example 1 *Description of Sets*

Write a description of the set containing the elements Monday, Tuesday, Wednesday, Thursday, Friday, Saturday, Sunday.

Solution The set is the days of the week. ∎

Listing the elements of a set inside a pair of *braces*, { }, is called *roster form*. The braces are an essential part of the notation because they identify the contents as a set. For example, $\{1, 2, 3\}$ is notation for the set whose elements are 1, 2, and 3, but (1, 2, 3) and [1, 2, 3] are not sets because parentheses and brackets do not indicate a set. For a set written in roster form, commas separate the elements of the set. The order in which the elements are listed is not important.

Sets are generally named with capital letters. For example, the name commonly selected for the set of *natural numbers* or *counting numbers* is $N$.

### Definition: **Natural Numbers**
$$N = \{1, 2, 3, 4, 5, \ldots\}$$

The three dots after the 5, called an *ellipsis*, indicate that the elements in the set continue in the same manner. An ellipsis followed by a last element indicates that the elements continue in the same manner up to and including the last element. This notation is illustrated in Example 2(b).

### Profile in Mathematics

#### Georg Cantor

Georg Cantor (1845–1918), born in St. Petersburg, Russia, is recognized as the founder of set theory. Cantor's creative work in mathematics was nearly lost when his father insisted that he become an engineer rather than a mathematician. His two major books on set theory, *Foundations of General Theory of Aggregates* and *Contributions to the Founding of the Theory of Transfinite Numbers*, were published in 1883 and 1895, respectively. See the Profile in Mathematics on page 85 for more information on Cantor and Leopold Kronecker.

▲ *The planets of Earth's solar system.*

## Example 2 *Roster Form of Sets*

Express the following in roster form.
a) Set *A* is the set of natural numbers less than 6.
b) Set *B* is the set of natural numbers less than or equal to 80.
c) Set *P* is the set of planets in Earth's solar system.

*Solution*

a) The natural numbers less than 6 are 1, 2, 3, 4, and 5. Thus, set *A* in roster form is $A = \{1, 2, 3, 4, 5\}$.
b) $B = \{1, 2, 3, 4, \ldots, 80\}$. The 80 after the ellipsis indicates that the elements continue in the same manner up to and including the number 80.
c) $P = \{$Mercury, Venus, Earth, Mars, Jupiter, Saturn, Uranus, Neptune$\}$ *

## Example 3 *The Word* Inclusive

Express the following in roster form.
a) The set of natural numbers between 7 and 12.
b) The set of natural numbers between 7 and 12, inclusive.

*Solution*

a) $A = \{8, 9, 10, 11\}$
b) $B = \{7, 8, 9, 10, 11, 12\}$. Note that the word *inclusive* indicates that the values of 7 and 12 are included in the set.

The symbol $\in$, read, "is an element of," is used to indicate membership in a set. In Example 3, because 8 is an element of set *A*, we write $8 \in A$. This may also be written $8 \in \{8, 9, 10, 11\}$. We may also write $6 \notin A$, meaning that 6 is not an element of set *A*.

*Set-builder notation* (sometimes called *set-generator notation*) may be used to symbolize a set. Set-builder notation is frequently used in algebra. The following example illustrates its form.

| $D$ | $=$ | $\{$ | $x$ | $\mid$ | Condition(s) $\}$ |
|:---:|:---:|:---:|:---:|:---:|:---:|
| ↑ | ↑ | ↑ | ↑ | ↑ | ↑ |
| Set $D$ | is | the set of | all elements $x$ | such that | the condition(s) $x$ must meet in order to be a member of the set. |

Consider $E = \{x \mid x \in N \text{ and } x > 10\}$. The statement is read: "Set *E* is the set of all the elements *x* such that *x* is a natural number and *x* is greater than 10." The conditions that *x* must meet to be a member of the set are $x \in N$, which means that *x* must be a natural number, and $x > 10$, which means that *x* must be greater than 10. The numbers that meet both conditions are the set of natural numbers greater than 10. Set *E* in roster form is

$$E = \{11, 12, 13, 14, \ldots\}$$

## Example 4 *Using Set-Builder Notation*

a) Write set $B = \{1, 2, 3, 4, 5\}$ in set-builder notation.
b) Write, in words, how you would read set *B* in set-builder notation.

---

*In August 2006, Pluto was reclassified as a dwarf planet.

*Solution*

a) Because set $B$ consists of the natural numbers less than 6, we write

$$B = \{x \mid x \in N \text{ and } x < 6\}$$

Another acceptable answer is $B = \{x \mid x \in N \text{ and } x \leq 5\}$.

b) Set $B$ is the set of all elements $x$ such that $x$ is a natural number and $x$ is less than 6.

## Example 5  *Roster Form to Set-Builder Notation*

a) Write set $C = \{$North America, South America, Europe, Asia, Australia, Africa, Antarctica$\}$ in set-builder notation.

b) Write in words how you would read set $C$ in set-builder notation.

*Solution*

a) $C = \{x \mid x \text{ is a continent}\}$.

b) Set $C$ is the set of all elements $x$ such that $x$ is a continent.

## Example 6  *Set-Builder Notation to Roster Form*

Write set $A = \{x \mid x \in N \text{ and } 2 \leq x < 8\}$ in roster form.

*Solution*  $A = \{2, 3, 4, 5, 6, 7\}$

## Example 7  *Oldest Colleges in the United States*

The table shows the 10 oldest colleges in the United States. Let set $C$ be the set of colleges that are located in Virginia that are among the 10 oldest colleges in the United States. Write set $C$ in roster form.

▲ *Harvard University*

| Ten Oldest Colleges in the United States | State | Year Chartered |
|---|---|---|
| Harvard University | Massachusetts | 1636 |
| College of William and Mary | Virginia | 1692 |
| Yale University | Connecticut | 1701 |
| University of Pennsylvania | Pennsylvania | 1740 |
| Moravian College | Pennsylvania | 1742 |
| Princeton University | New Jersey | 1746 |
| Washington and Lee University | Virginia | 1749 |
| Columbia University | New York | 1754 |
| Brown University | Rhode Island | 1764 |
| Rutgers | New Jersey | 1766 |

Source: National Center for Education Statistics

*Solution*  By examining the table, we find that two colleges located in Virginia appear in the table. They are College of William and Mary and Washington and Lee University. Thus, set $C = \{$College of William and Mary, Washington and Lee University$\}$.

A set is said to be *finite* if it either contains no elements or the number of elements in the set is a natural number. The set $B = \{2, 4, 6, 8, 10\}$ is a finite set because the number of elements in the set is 5, and 5 is a natural number. A set that is not finite is said to be *infinite*. The set of counting numbers is one example of an infinite set. Infinite sets are discussed in more detail in Section 2.6.

Another important concept is equality of sets.

### Definition:  Equal Sets
Set *A* is **equal** to set *B*, symbolized by $A = B$, if and only if set *A* and set *B* contain exactly the same elements.

For example, if set $A = \{1, 2, 3\}$ and set $B = \{3, 1, 2\}$, then $A = B$ because they contain exactly the same elements. The order of the elements in the set is not important. If two sets are equal, both must contain the same number of elements. The number of elements in a set is called its *cardinal number.*

### Definition:  Cardinal Number
The **cardinal number** of set *A*, symbolized by $n(A)$, is the number of elements in set *A*.

Both set $A = \{1, 2, 3\}$ and set $B = \{\text{England, Brazil, Japan}\}$ have a cardinal number of 3; that is, $n(A) = 3$, and $n(B) = 3$. We can say that set *A* and set *B* both have a cardinality of 3.

Two sets are said to be *equivalent* if they contain the same number of elements.

### Definition:  Equivalent Sets
Set *A* is **equivalent** to set *B* if and only if $n(A) = n(B)$.

Any sets that are equal must also be equivalent. Not all sets that are equivalent are equal, however. The sets $D = \{\text{a, b, c}\}$ and $E = \{\text{apple, orange, pear}\}$ are equivalent because both have the same cardinal number, 3. Because the elements differ, however, the sets are not equal.

Two sets that are equivalent or have the same cardinality can be placed in *one-to-one correspondence*. Set *A* and set *B* can be placed in one-to-one correspondence if every element of set *A* can be matched with exactly one element of set *B* and every element of set *B* can be matched with exactly one element of set *A*. For example, there is a one-to-one correspondence between the student names on a class list and the student identification numbers because we can match each student with a student identification number.

Consider set *S*, states, and set *C*, state capitals.

$$S = \{\text{North Carolina, Georgia, South Carolina, Florida}\}$$

$$C = \{\text{Columbia, Raleigh, Tallahassee, Atlanta}\}$$

Two different one-to-one correspondences for sets *S* and *C* follow.

$$S = \{\text{North Carolina, Georgia, South Carolina, Florida}\}$$

$$C = \{\text{Columbia, Raleigh, Tallahassee, Atlanta}\}$$

$$S = \{\text{North Carolina, Georgia, South Carolina, Florida}\}$$

$$C = \{\text{Columbia, Raleigh, Tallahassee, Atlanta}\}$$

Other one-to-one correspondences between sets *S* and *C* are possible. Do you know which capital goes with which state?

## Null or Empty Set

Some sets do not contain any elements, such as the set of zebras that live in your house.

> Definition: **Empty Set**
> The set that contains no elements is called the **empty set** or **null set** and is symbolized by $\{\ \}$ or $\varnothing$.

Note that $\{\varnothing\}$ is not the empty set. This set contains the element $\varnothing$ and has a cardinality of 1. The set $\{0\}$ is also not the empty set because it contains the element 0. It also has a cardinality of 1.

┌─Example **8**   *Natural Number Solutions*

Indicate the set of natural numbers that satisfies the equation $x + 2 = 0$.

*Solution*   The values that satisfy the equation are those natural numbers that make the equation a true statement. Only the number $-2$ satisfies this equation. Because $-2$ is not a natural number, the solution set of this equation is $\{\ \}$ or $\varnothing$.   ∎

## Universal Set

Another important set is a *universal set*.

> Definition: **Universal Set**
> A **universal set**, symbolized by $U$, is a set that contains all the elements for any specific discussion.

When a universal set is given, only the elements in the universal set may be considered when working the problem. If, for example, the universal set for a particular problem is defined as $U = \{1, 2, 3, 4, \ldots, 10\}$, then only the natural numbers 1 through 10 may be used in that problem.

## SECTION 2.1   *Exercises*

### Warm Up Exercises

*In Exercises 1–12, fill in the blank with an appropriate word, phrase, or symbol(s).*

**1.** A collection of objects is called a(n) _____.

**2.** Three dots placed in a set to show that the set continues in the same manner is called a(n) _____.

**3.** The three ways a set can be written are _____, _____, and _____.

**4.** A set that contain no elements or the number of elements in the set is a natural number is called a(n)_____ set.

**5.** A a set that is not finite is called a(n) _____ . set.

**6.** Two sets that contain the same elements are called _____ sets.

**7.** Two sets that contain the same number of elements are called _____ sets.

**8.** The number of elements in a set is called the _____ number.

**9.** The set that contains no elements is called the _____ set.

**10.** The two ways to indicate an empty set are _____ and _____ .

**11.** A set that contains all the elements for any specific discussion is called a(n) _____ set.

**12.** Two sets that have the same cardinal number can be placed in a(n) _____ correspondence.

## Practice the Skills

*In Exercises 13–18, determine whether each set is well defined or not well defined.*

**13.** The set of the best colleges

**14.** The set of the most interesting courses at your school

**15.** The set of states that have a common border with Kansas

**16.** The set of the four states in the United States having the largest population on January 1, 2010

**17.** The set of astronauts who walked on the moon

▲ *Eugene A. Cernan on the moon*

**18.** The set of the most interesting teachers at your school

*In Exercises 19–24, determine whether each set is finite or infinite.*

**19.** $\{1, 3, 5, 7, \dots\}$

**20.** The set of multiples of 4 between 0 and 50

**21.** The set of odd numbers greater than 25

**22.** The set of fractions between 1 and 2

**23.** The set of odd numbers greater than 15

**24.** The set of apple trees in Gro-More Farms Orchards

*In Exercises 25–34, express each set in roster form. You may need to use the Internet or some other reference source.*

**25.** The set of states in the United States whose names begin with the letter M

**26.** The set of countries in Europe whose names begin with S

**27.** The set of natural numbers between 10 and 178

**28.** $C = \{x \mid x + 6 = 10\}$

**29.** $B = \{x \mid x \in N \text{ and } x \text{ is even}\}$

**30.** The set of states west of the Mississippi River that have a common border with the state of Florida

**31.** The set of football players over the age of 70 who are still playing in the National Football League

**32.** The set of states in the United States that have a common border with the state of Washington

**33.** $E = \{x \mid x \in N \text{ and } 14 \le x < 85\}$

**34.** The set of states in the United States that are not in the contiguous 48 states

*In Exercises 35–38, use the following table, which shows the attendance, in millions, at the 10 most visited museums in the world in 2008. Let the 10 museums in the list represent the universal set.*

| Museum | Attendance (in millions) | Location |
|---|---|---|
| 1. Louvre Museum | 8.50 | Paris, France |
| 2. British Museum | 5.93 | London, UK |
| 3. National Gallery of Art | 4.96 | Washington, DC |
| 4. Tate Modern | 4.95 | London, UK |
| 5. Metropolitan Museum of Art | 4.82 | New York, NY |
| 6. Vatican Museums | 4.44 | Vatican City |
| 7. National Gallery | 4.38 | London, UK |
| 8. Musee d'Orsay | 3.03 | Paris, France |
| 9. Musee d'Art Moderne Prado | 2.98 | Paris, France |
| 10. Museum of Modern Art | 2.90 | New York, NY |

Source: The *Art Newspaper*

*Use the list to determine each set in roster form.*

**35.** The set of museums in which the attendance was more than 4.5 million

**36.** The set of museums in which the attendance was less than 3 million

**37.** The set of museums in which the attendance was between 2 million and 4 million

**38.** The set of museums in which the attendance was between 3.5 million and 5.5 million

*In Exercises 39–42, use the graph on page 49, which shows iPod sales, in millions, for the years 2003–2008.*

*Use the graph to determine each set in roster form.*

**39.** The set of years in which iPod sales were more than 52 million

**40.** The set of years in which iPod sales were less than 8 million

**41.** The set of years in which iPod sales were between 8 million and 60 million

**42.** The set of years in which iPod sales were more than 65 million

**iPod Sales**

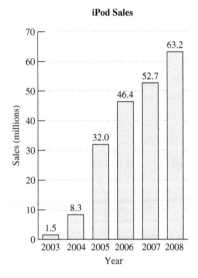

In Exercises 43–50, express each set in set-builder notation.

**43.** $B = \{7, 8, 9, 10, 11, 12, 13, 14\}$

**44.** $A = \{1, 2, 3, 4, 5, 6, 7, 8, 9\}$

**45.** $C = \{3, 6, 9, 12, \ldots\}$

**46.** $D = \{5, 10, 15, 20, \ldots\}$

**47.** $E$ is the set of odd natural numbers.

**48.** $A$ is the set of national holidays in the United States in July.

**49.** $C$ is the set of months that contain less than 30 days.

**50.** $F = \{15, 16, 17, \ldots, 100\}$

In Exercises 51–58, write a description of each set.

**51.** $A = \{1, 2, 3, 4, 5, 6, 7\}$

**52.** $D = \{3, 6, 9, 12, 15, 18, \ldots\}$

**53.** $V = \{a, e, i, o, u\}$

**54.** $S = \{$Bashful, Doc, Dopey, Grumpy, Happy, Sleepy, Sneezy$\}$

▲ Snow White and the Seven Dwarfs

**55.** $T = \{$oak, maple, elm, pine, $\ldots\}$

**56.** $E = \{x \mid x \in N$ and $4 \leq x < 11\}$

**57.** $S = \{$spring, summer, fall, winter$\}$

**58.** $B = \{$John Lennon, Ringo Starr, Paul McCartney, George Harrison$\}$

▲ The Beatles

In Exercises 59–62, use the following list, which shows the 10 countries with the most cellular subscribers, in millions, as of 2008. Let the 10 countries in the list represent the universal set.

| Country | Number of Subscribers |
|---|---|
| 1. China | 649.70 |
| 2. India | 376.12 |
| 3. United States | 260.00 |
| 4. Russia | 172.00 |
| 5. Brazil | 151.90 |
| 6. Indonesia | 115.60 |
| 7. Japan | 102.98 |
| 8. Germany | 101.50 |
| 9. Pakistan | 91.40 |
| 10. United Kingdom | 70.00 |

Source: CIA

Use the list to determine each set in roster form.

**59.** $\{x \mid x$ is a country with at least 250 million cellular subscribers$\}$

**60.** $\{x \mid x$ is a country with fewer than 100 million cellular subscribers$\}$

**61.** $\{x \mid x$ is a country with between 100 million and 200 million cellular subscribers$\}$

**62.** $\{x \mid x$ is a country with between 250 million and 500 million cellular subscribers$\}$

*In Exercises 63–66, use the following graph, which shows the cost of a 30-second commercial during the Super Bowl from 1996 to 2011. Let the 16 years represent the universal set.*

*Use the graph to represent each set in roster form.*

**63.** The set of years in which the cost of a Super Bowl commercial was more than $2.5 million

**64.** The set of years in which the cost of a Super Bowl commercial was less than $2.0 million

**65.** The set of years in which the cost of a Super Bowl commercial was between $2.0 million and $2.5 million

**66.** The set of years in which the cost of a Super Bowl commercial was more than $2.5 million and less then $3 million

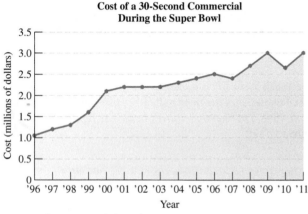

**Cost of a 30-Second Commercial During the Super Bowl**

Source: www.industry.bnet.com

*In Exercises 67–74, state whether each statement is true or false. If false, give the reason.*

**67.** $\{e\} \in \{a, e, i, o, u\}$

**68.** $b \in \{a, b, c, d, e, f\}$

**69.** $h \in \{a, b, c, d, e, f\}$

**70.** Mickey Mouse $\in$ {characters created by Walt Disney}

**71.** 3    $\{x \mid x \in N$ and $x$ is odd$\}$

**72.** Amazon $\in$ {rivers in the United States}

**73.** *Titanic* $\in$ {top 10 motion pictures with the greatest revenues}

**74.** $2 \in \{x \mid x$ is an odd natural number$\}$

*In Exercises 75–78, for the sets $A = \{2, 4, 6, 8\}$, $B = \{1, 3, 7, 9, 13, 21\}$, $C = \{\ \}$, and $D = \{\#, \&, \%, \square, *\}$.*

**75.** Determine $n(A)$.

**76.** Determine $n(B)$.

**77.** Determine $n(C)$.

**78.** Determine $n(D)$.

*In Exercises 79–84, determine whether the pairs of sets are equal, equivalent, both, or neither.*

**79.** $A = \{$algebra, geometry, trigonometry$\}$,
    $B = \{$geometry, trigonometry, algebra$\}$

**80.** $A = \{7, 9, 10\}$, $B = \{a, b, c\}$

**81.** $A = \{$grapes, apples, oranges$\}$,
    $B = \{$grapes, peaches, apples, oranges$\}$

**82.** $A$ is the set of Siamese cats.
    $B$ is the set of cats.

**83.** $A$ is the set of letters in the word *bank*.
    $B$ is the set of letters in the word *post*.

**84.** $A$ is the set of states.
    $B$ is the set of state capitals.

## Problem Solving

**85.** Set-builder notation is often more versatile and efficient than listing a set in roster form. This versatility is illustrated with the following two sets.

$$A = \{x \mid x \in N \text{ and } x > 2\}$$
$$B = \{x \mid x > 2\}$$

   **a)** Write a description of set $A$ and set $B$.

   **b)** Explain the difference between set $A$ and set $B$. (*Hint:* Is $4\frac{1}{2} \in A$? Is $4\frac{1}{2} \in B$?)

   **c)** Write set $A$ in roster form.

   **d)** Can set $B$ be written in roster form? Explain your answer.

**86.** Consider sets $A$ and $B$ below
$$A = \{x \mid 2 < x \le 5 \text{ and } x \in N\}$$
   and
$$B = \{x \mid 2 < x \le 5\}$$

   **a)** Write a description of set $A$ and set $B$.

   **b)** Explain the difference between set $A$ and set $B$.

   **c)** Write set $A$ in roster form.

   **d)** Can set $B$ be written in roster form? Explain your answer.

*A cardinal number answers the question "How many?" An **ordinal number** describes the relative position that an element occupies. For example, Molly's desk is the third desk from the aisle.*

*In Exercises 87–90, determine whether the number used is a cardinal number or an ordinal number.*

**87.** J. K. Rowling has written 7 Harry Potter books.

▲ *J. K. Rowling*

**88.** Study the chart on page 25 in the book.

**89.** Lincoln was the sixteenth president of the United States.

**90.** Emily paid $35 for her new blouse.

**91.** Describe three sets of which you are a member.

**92.** Describe three sets that have no members.

**93.** Write a short paragraph explaining why the universal set and the empty set are necessary in the study of sets.

### Challenge Problem/Group Activity

**94. a)** In a given exercise, a universal set is not specified, but we know that actor Orlando Bloom is a member of the universal set. Describe five different possible universal sets of which Orlando Bloom is a member.

**b)** Write a description of one set that includes all the universal sets in part (a).

### Internet/Research Activity

**95.** Georg Cantor is recognized as the founder and a leader in the development of set theory. Do research and write a paper on his life and his contributions to set theory and to the field of mathematics. References include history of mathematics books, encyclopedias, and the Internet.

## SECTION 2.2 Subsets

▲ *The set of intercollegiate sports includes basketball.*

Consider the following sets. Set $A$ = {baseball, basketball, hockey}. Set $B$ = {baseball, football, basketball, hockey, softball}. Note that each element of set $A$ is also an element of set $B$. In this section, we will discuss how to illustrate the relationship between two sets, $A$ and $B$, when each element of set $A$ is also an element of set $B$.

**Why** *This is Important* The relationship between sets is important throughout life. For example, to gain a promotion at work, you may need to fulfill different sets of criteria.

In our complex world, we often break larger sets into smaller, more manageable sets, called *subsets*. For example, consider the set of people in your class. Suppose we categorize the set of people in your class according to the first letter of their last name (the A's, B's, C's, etc.). When we do so, each of these sets may be considered a subset of the original set. Each of these subsets can be separated further. For example, the set of people whose last name begins with the letter A can be categorized as either male or female or by their age. Each of these collections of people is also a subset. A given set may have many different subsets.

### Definition: **Subset**

Set $A$ is a **subset** of set $B$, symbolized by $A \subseteq B$, if and only if all the elements of set $A$ are also elements of set $B$.

The symbol $A \subseteq B$ indicates that "set $A$ is a subset of set $B$." The symbol $\not\subseteq$ is used to indicate "is not a subset." Thus, $A \not\subseteq B$ indicates that set $A$ is not a subset of set $B$. *To show that set $A$ is not a subset of set $B$, we must find at least one element of set $A$ that is not an element of set $B$.*

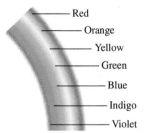
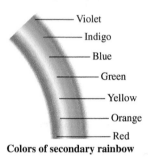
⌐Example **1**  *A Subset?*

Determine whether set *A* is a subset of set *B*.

a) $A = \{\text{rain, snow, sleet}\}$
   $B = \{\text{rain, snow, sleet, hail}\}$
b) $A = \{\text{q, r, s, t}\}$
   $B = \{\text{q, r}\}$
c) $A = \{x \mid x \text{ is a yellow fruit}\}$
   $B = \{x \mid x \text{ is a red fruit}\}$
d) $A = \{\text{vanilla, chocolate, rocky road}\}$
   $B = \{\text{chocolate, vanilla, rocky road}\}$

*Solution*

a) All the elements of set *A* are contained in set *B*, so $A \subseteq B$.
b) The elements *s* and *t* are in set *A* but not in set *B*, so $A \nsubseteq B$ (*A* is not a subset of *B*). In this example, however, all the elements of set *B* are contained in set *A*; therefore, $B \subseteq A$.
c) There are fruits, such as bananas, that are in set *A* that are not in set *B*, so $A \nsubseteq B$.
d) All the elements of set *A* are contained in set *B*, so $A \subseteq B$. Note also that $B \subseteq A$. In fact, set *A* = set *B*.  ∎

## Proper Subsets

**Definition: Proper Subset**

Set *A* is a **proper subset** of set *B*, symbolized by $A \subset B$, if and only if all the elements of set *A* are elements of set *B* and set $A \neq$ set *B* (that is, set *B* must contain at least one element not in set *A*).

Consider the sets $A = \{\text{red, blue, yellow}\}$ and $B = \{\text{red, orange, yellow, green, blue, violet}\}$. Set *A* is a *subset* of set *B*, $A \subseteq B$, because every element of set *A* is also an element of set *B*. Set *A* is also a *proper subset* of set *B*, $A \subset B$, because set *A* and set *B* are not equal. Now consider $C = \{\text{car, bus, train}\}$ and $D = \{\text{train, car, bus}\}$. Set *C* is a subset of set *D*, $C \subseteq D$, because every element of set *C* is also an element of set *D*. Set *C*, however, is not a proper subset of set *D*, $C \not\subset D$, because set *C* and set *D* are equal sets.

⌐Example **2**  *A Proper Subset?*

Determine whether set *A* is a proper subset of set *B*.

a) $A = \{\text{jazz, pop, hip hop}\}$
   $B = \{\text{classical, jazz, pop, rap, hip hop}\}$
b) $A = \{a, b, c, d\}$        $B = \{a, c, b, d\}$

*Solution*

a) All the elements of set *A* are contained in set *B*, and sets *A* and *B* are not equal; thus, $A \subset B$.
b) Set *A* = set *B*, so $A \not\subset B$. (However, $A \subseteq B$.)  ∎

Every set is a subset of itself, but no set is a proper subset of itself. For all sets *A*, $A \subseteq A$, but $A \not\subset A$. For example, if $A = \{1, 2, 3\}$, then $A \subseteq A$ because every element of set *A* is contained in set *A*, but $A \not\subset A$ because set *A* = set *A*.

# MATHEMATICS TODAY

**The Ladder of Life**

In biology, the science of classifying all living things is called *taxonomy*. More than 2000 years ago, Aristotle formalized animal classification with his "ladder of life": higher animals, lower animals, higher plants, lower plants. Today, living organisms are classified into six kingdoms (or sets) called animalia, plantae, archaea, eubacteria, fungi, and protista. Even more general groupings of living things are made according to shared characteristics. The groupings, from most general to most specific, are kingdom, phylum, class, order, family, genus, and species. For example, a zebra, *Equus burchelli*, is a member of the genus *Equus*, as is the horse, *Equus caballus*. Both the zebra and the horse are members of the universal set called the kingdom of animals and the same family, Equidae; they are members of different species (*E. burchelli* and *E. caballus*), however.

**Why** *This is Important* Scientists use sets to classify and catorgize animals, plants, and all forms of life.

Let $A = \{\ \}$ and $B = \{1, 2, 3, 4\}$. Is $A \subseteq B$? To show $A \nsubseteq B$, you must find at least one element of set $A$ that is not an element of set $B$. Because this cannot be done, $A \subseteq B$ must be true. Using the same reasoning, we can show that *the empty set is a subset of every set, including itself.*

## Example 3   *Element or Subset?*

Determine whether the following are true or false.

a) $3 \in \{3, 4, 5\}$   T
b) $\{3\} \in \{3, 4, 5\}$   F
c) $\{3\} \in \{\{3\}, \{4\}, \{5\}\}$   T
d) $\{3\} \subseteq \{3, 4, 5\}$   T
e) $3 \subseteq \{3, 4, 5\}$   F
f) $\{\ \} \subseteq \{3, 4, 5\}$   T

**Solution**

a) $3 \in \{3, 4, 5\}$ is a true statement because 3 is an element of the set $\{3, 4, 5\}$.
b) $\{3\} \in \{3, 4, 5\}$ is a false statement because $\{3\}$ is a set, and the set $\{3\}$ is not an element of the set $\{3, 4, 5\}$.
c) $\{3\} \in \{\{3\}, \{4\}, \{5\}\}$ is a true statement because $\{3\}$ is an element in the set. The elements of the set $\{\{3\}, \{4\}, \{5\}\}$ are themselves sets.
d) $\{3\} \subseteq \{3, 4, 5\}$ is a true statement because every element of the first set is an element of the second set.
e) $3 \subseteq \{3, 4, 5\}$ is a false statement because the 3 is not in braces, so it is not a set and thus cannot be a subset. The 3 is an element of the set as indicated in part (a).
f) $\{\ \} \subseteq \{3, 4, 5\}$ is a true statement because the empty set is a subset of every set. ∎

## Number of Subsets

How many distinct subsets can be made from a given set? The empty set has no elements and has exactly one subset, the empty set. A set with one element has two subsets. A set with two elements has four subsets. A set with three elements has eight subsets. This information is illustrated in Table 2.1.

**Table 2.1** Number of Subsets

| Set | Subsets | Number of Subsets |
|---|---|---|
| $\{\ \}$ | $\{\ \}$ | $1 = 2^0$ |
| $\{a\}$ | $\{a\}$<br>$\{\ \}$ | $2 = 2^1$ |
| $\{a, b\}$ | $\{a, b\}$<br>$\{a\}, \{b\}$<br>$\{\ \}$ | $4 = 2 \times 2 = 2^2$ |
| $\{a, b, c\}$ | $\{a, b, c\}$<br>$\{a, b\}, \{a, c\}, \{b, c\}$<br>$\{a\}, \{b\}, \{c\}$<br>$\{\ \}$ | $8 = 2 \times 2 \times 2 = 2^3$ |

By continuing this table with larger and larger sets, we can develop a general expression for finding the number of distinct subsets that can be made from any given set.

### Number of Distinct Subsets
The **number of distinct subsets** of a finite set $A$ is $2^n$, where $n$ is the number of elements in set $A$.

Every set is a subset of itself, but no set is a proper subset of itself. Thus, the number of proper subsets will always be one less than the number of subsets that can be made from any given set. We summarize this concept in the following expression.

### Number of Distinct Proper Subsets
The **number of distinct proper subsets** of a finite set $A$ is $2^n - 1$, where $n$ is the number of elements in set $A$.

### Example 4  *Distinct Subsets*

a) Determine the number of distinct subsets for the set $\{S, L, E, D\}$.
b) List all the distinct subsets for the set $\{S, L, E, D\}$.
c) How many of the distinct subsets are proper subsets?

**Solution**

a) Since the number of elements in the set is 4, the number of distinct subsets is
$2^4 = 2 \times 2 \times 2 \times 2 = 16$.

b)

| | | | | |
|---|---|---|---|---|
| $\{S, L, E, D\}$ | $\{S, L, E\}$ | $\{S, L\}$ | $\{S\}$ | $\{\ \}$ |
| | $\{S, L, D\}$ | $\{S, E\}$ | $\{L\}$ | |
| | $\{S, E, D\}$ | $\{S, D\}$ | $\{E\}$ | |
| | $\{L, E, D\}$ | $\{L, E\}$ | $\{D\}$ | |
| | | $\{L, D\}$ | | |
| | | $\{E, D\}$ | | |

c) There are 15 proper subsets. Every subset except $\{S, L, E, D\}$ is a proper subset. ∎

### Example 5  *Car Options*

Brigette Martineau is ordering a new car. She can order some, all, or none of the following options: power windows, MP3 player port, leather interior, alarm system, sun roof, and navigation system. How many different variations of the set of options are possible?

**Solution**  Brigette can order the car with no options, any one option, any two options, any three options, and so on, up to six options. One technique used in problem solving is to consider similar problems that you have solved previously. If you think about this problem, you will realize that it is the same as asking how many distinct subsets can be made from a set with six elements. The number of different variations of the set of options is the same as the number of possible subsets of a set that has six elements. There are $2^6$, or 64, possible subsets of a set with six elements. Thus, there are 64 possible variations of the set of options for the car. ∎

## Warm Up Exercises

*In Exercises 1–4, fill in the blank with an appropriate word, phrase, or symbol(s).*

**1.** If all the elements of set *A* are also elements of set *B*, then set *A* is a(n) _____ of set *B*.

**2.** If all the elements of set *A* are also elements of set *B*, and set *A* $\neq$ set *B*, then set *A* is a (n) _____ subset of set *B*.

**3.** The expression for determining the number of distinct subsets for a set with *n* distinct elements is _____ .

**4.** The expression for determining the number of distinct proper subsets for a set with *n* distinct elements is _____ .

## Practice the Skills

*In Exercises 5–26, answer true or false. If false, give the reason.*

**5.** { book } $\subsetneq$ { magazine, newspaper, book }

**6.** { Italy} $\subseteq$ { Italy, Spain, France, Switzerland, Austria }

**7.** { McIntosh, Red Delicious } $\subseteq$ { Empire, Gala, Cortland, Red Delicious }

**8.** { pepper, salt } $\subseteq$ { salt, butter, mayonnaise }

**9.** { motorboat, kayak } $\subset$ { kayak, fishing boat, motorboat, sailboat }

**10.** { polar bear, tiger, lion } $\subset$ { tiger, lion, polar bear, penguin }

**11.** { 4, 2, 7 } $\subset$ { 4, 7, 2 }

**12.** { c, a, r, t } $\subset$ { t, r, a, c }

**13.** Xbox 360 $\in$ { PSIII, Wii, Xbox 360 }

**14.** LaGuardia $\in$ { JFK, LaGuardia, Newark }

**15.** { swimming } $\in$ { sailing, water skiing, swimming }

**16.** { } $\in$ {1, 3, 5, 7 }

**17.** 5 $\notin$ { 2, 4, 6 }

**18.** { } $\subseteq$ { table, chair, sofa }

**19.** { red } $\subset$ { red, blue, green }

**20.** { 3, 5, 9 } $\not\subset$ { 3, 9, 5 }

**21.** { } = { $\varnothing$ }

**22.** $\varnothing$ = { }

**23.** { 0 } = $\varnothing$

**24.** { } $\subseteq$ { }

**25.** 0 = { }

**26.** { 1 } $\in$ { {1}, {2}, {3} }

*In Exercises 27–34, determine whether A = B, A $\subseteq$ B, B $\subseteq$ A, A $\subset$ B, B $\subset$ A, or if none of these applies. (There may be more than one answer.)*

**27.** $A$ = { penny, nickel, dime, quarter }
  $B$ = { penny, quarter }

**28.** $A$ = { $x \mid x \in N$ and $x < 6$ }
  $B$ = { $x \mid x \in N$ and $1 \leq x \leq 5$ }

**29.** Set *A* is the set of states that border the Atlantic Ocean. Set *B* is the set of states east of the Mississippi River.

**30** $A$ = { 1, 3, 5, 7, 9 }
  $B$ = { 3, 9, 5, 7, 6 }

**31.** $A$ = { $x \mid x$ is a brand of soft drink }
  $B$ = { A & W, Coca-Cola, Dr Pepper, Mountain Dew }

**32.** $A$ = { $x \mid x$ is a sport that uses a ball }
  $B$ = { basketball, soccer, tennis }

**33.** Set *A* is the set of natural numbers between 2 and 7. Set *B* is the set of natural numbers greater than 2 and less than 7.

**34.** Set *A* is the set of all cars manufactured by General Motors. Set *B* is the set of sports cars manufactured by General Motors.

*In Exercises 35–38, list all the subsets of the sets given.*

**35.** $D = \varnothing$

**36.** $A = \{\circ\}$

**37.** $B$ = { cow, horse }

**38.** $C = \{$steak, pork, chicken$\}$

## Problem Solving

**39.** For set $A = \{a, b, c, d\}$,

a) list all the subsets of set $A$.

b) state which of the subsets in part (a) are not proper subsets of set $A$.

**40.** A set contains nine elements.

a) How many subsets does it have?

b) How many proper subsets does it have?

*In Exercises 41–52, if the statement is true for all sets A and B, write "true." If it is not true for all sets A and B, write "false." Assume that $A \neq \varnothing$, $U \neq \varnothing$, and $A \subset U$.*

**41.** If $A \subseteq B$, then $A \subset B$.    **42.** If $A \subset B$, then $A \subseteq B$.

**43.** $A \subseteq A$    **44.** $A \subset A$

**45.** $\varnothing \subset A$    **46.** $\varnothing \subseteq A$

**47.** $A \subseteq U$    **48.** $\varnothing \subset \varnothing$

**49.** $\varnothing \subset U$    **50.** $U \subseteq \varnothing$

**51.** $\varnothing \subseteq \varnothing$    **52.** $U \subset \varnothing$

**53.** *Ordering a Pizza* Jasmine Sullivan is ordering a pizza at a Domino's Pizza. She can add any of the following toppings: olives, pepperoni, sausage, onions, green peppers, mushrooms, anchovies, and ham. How many different variations of the pizza and toppings can be made?

**54.** *Building a House* The Jacobsens are planning to build a house in a new development. They can either build the base model offered by the builder or add any of the following options: deck, hot tub, security system, hardwood flooring. How many different variations of the house are possible?

**55.** *Salad Toppings* Donald Wheeler is ordering a salad at a Ruby Tuesday restaurant. He can purchase a salad consisting of just lettuce, or he can add any of the following items: cucumber, onion, tomato, carrot, green pepper, olive, mushroom. How many different variations of a salad are possible?

**56.** *Telephone Features* A customer with Verizon can order telephone service with some, all, or none of the following features: call waiting, call forwarding, caller identification, three-way calling, voice mail, fax line. How many different variations of the set of features are possible?

**57.** If $E \subseteq F$ and $F \subseteq E$, what other relationship exists between $E$ and $F$?

**58.** How can you determine whether the set of boys is equivalent to the set of girls at a roller-skating rink?

**59.** For the set $D = \{a, b, c\}$

a) is $a$ an element of set $D$?

b) is $c$ a subset of set $D$?

c) is $\{a, b\}$ a subset of set $D$?

## Challenge Problem/Group Activity

**60.** *Hospital Expansion* A hospital has four members on the board of directors: Arnold, Benitez, Cathy, and Dominique.

a) When the members vote on whether to add a wing to the hospital, how many different ways can they vote (abstentions are not allowed)? For example, Arnold—yes, Benitez—no, Cathy—no, and Dominique—yes is one of the many possibilities.

b) Make a listing of all the possible outcomes of the vote. For example, the vote described in part (a) could be represented as (YNNY).

c) How many of the outcomes given in part (b) would result in a majority supporting the addition of a wing to the hospital? That is, how many of the outcomes have three or more Y's?

## Recreational Mathematics

**61.** How many elements must a set have if the number of proper subsets of the set is $\frac{1}{2}$ of the total number of subsets of the set?

**62.** If $A \subset B$ and $B \subset C$, must $A \subset C$?

**63.** If $A \subset B$ and $B \subseteq C$, must $A \subset C$?

**64.** If $A \subseteq B$ and $B \subseteq C$, must $A \subset C$?

## Internet/Research Activity

**65.** On page 53, we discussed the ladder of life. Do research and indicate all the different classifications in the Linnaean system, from most general to the most specific, in which a koala belongs.

▲ *Some Laptops have A 14-inch display, some laptops have 4 GB of memory, and some laptops have a 14-inch display and 4 GB of memory.*

Suppose you go to a store to purchase a new laptop and tell a computer salesperson that you wish to purchase a laptop with a 14-inch display *and* 4 GB of memory. The salesperson was a bit distracted and thought you said you wanted to purchase a laptop with a 14-inch display *or* 4 GB of memory. Which laptops are in the set of laptops with a 14-inch display *and* 4 GB of memory? Which laptops are in the set of laptops with a 14-inch display *or* 4 GB of memory? These two questions are quite different. The first involves laptops joined by the word *and*. The second involves laptops joined by the word *or*. In this section, you will learn how to illustrate these and other set relationships.

*Why* **This is Important** Words such as *and* and *or* have important meaning in a variety of everyday applications, such as ordering from a menu or understanding the meaning of a legal document.

**Figure 2.1**

A useful technique for illustrating set relationships is the Venn diagram, named for English mathematician John Venn (1834–1923). Venn invented the diagrams and used them to illustrate ideas in his text on symbolic logic, published in 1881.

In a Venn diagram, a rectangle usually represents the universal set, $U$. The items inside the rectangle may be divided into subsets of the universal set. The subsets are usually represented by circles. In Fig. 2.1, the circle labeled $A$ represents set $A$, which is a subset of the universal set.

Two sets may be represented in a Venn diagram in any of four different ways, as shown in Fig. 2.2. Two sets $A$ and $B$ are *disjoint* when they have no elements in common. Two disjoint sets $A$ and $B$ are illustrated in Fig. 2.2(a). If set $A$ is a proper subset of set $B$, $A \subset B$, the two sets may be illustrated as in Fig. 2.2(b). If set $A$ contains exactly the same elements as set $B$, that is, $A = B$, the two sets may be illustrated as in Fig. 2.2(c). Two sets $A$ and $B$ with some elements in common are shown in Fig. 2.2(d), which is regarded as the most general form of a Venn diagram.

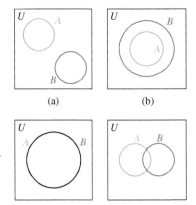

(a)       (b)

(c)       (d)

**Figure 2.2**

If we label the regions of the diagram in Fig. 2.2(d) using I, II, III, and IV, we can illustrate the four possible cases with this one diagram, Fig. 2.3.

**CASE 1: DISJOINT SETS** When sets $A$ and $B$ are disjoint, they have no elements in common. Therefore, region II of Fig. 2.3 is empty.

**CASE 2: SUBSETS** When $A \subseteq B$, every element of set $A$ is also an element of set $B$. Thus, there can be no elements in region I of Fig. 2.3. If $B \subseteq A$, however, then region III of Fig. 2.3 is empty.

**CASE 3: EQUAL SETS** When set $A$ = set $B$, all the elements of set $A$ are elements of set $B$ and all the elements of set $B$ are elements of set $A$. Thus, regions I and III of Fig. 2.3 are empty.

**CASE 4: OVERLAPPING SETS** When sets $A$ and $B$ have elements in common, those elements are in region II of Fig. 2.3. The elements that belong to set $A$ but not to set $B$ are in region I. The elements that belong to set $B$ but not to set $A$ are in region III.

**Figure 2.3**

In each of the four cases, any element belonging to the universal set but not belonging to set $A$ or set $B$ is placed in region IV.

Next we introduce set operations. Venn diagrams will be helpful in understanding set operations. The basic operations of arithmetic are $+$, $-$, $\times$, and $\div$. When we see these symbols, we know what procedure to follow to determine the answer. Some of the operations in set theory are $'$, $\cap$, $\cup$, $-$, and $\times$. They represent complement, intersection, union, difference, and Cartesian product, respectively.

Figure 2.4

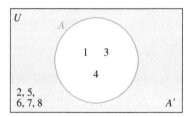

Figure 2.5

Figure 2.6

## Complement

### Definition: Complement

The **complement** of set $A$, symbolized by $A'$, is the set of all the elements in the universal set that are not in set $A$.

In Fig. 2.4, the shaded region outside set $A$ within the universal set represents the complement of set $A$, or $A'$.

### Example 1   *A Set and Its Complement*

Given

$$U = \{1, 2, 3, 4, 5, 6, 7, 8\} \text{ and } A = \{1, 3, 4\}$$

find $A'$ and illustrate the relationship among sets $U$, $A$, and $A'$ in a Venn diagram.

*Solution*   The elements in $U$ that are not in set $A$ are 2, 5, 6, 7, 8. Thus, $A' = \{2, 5, 6, 7, 8\}$. The Venn diagram is illustrated in Fig. 2.5.    ∎

## Intersection

The word *intersection* brings to mind the area common to two crossing streets. The red car in the figure is in the intersection of the two streets. The set operation intersection is defined as follows.

### Definition: Intersection

The **intersection** of sets $A$ and $B$, symbolized by $A \cap B$, is the set containing all the elements that are common to both set $A$ and set $B$.

The shaded region, region II, in Fig. 2.6 represents the intersection of sets $A$ and $B$.

### Example 2   *Sets with Overlapping Regions*

Let the universal set, $U$, represent the 50 states in the United States. Let set $A$ represent the set of states with a population of more than 10 million people as of 2009. Let set $B$ represent the set of states that have at least one city with a population of more than 1 million people, as of 2009 (see the table). Draw a Venn diagram illustrating the relationship between set $A$ and set $B$.

| States with a Population of More Than 10 Million People | States with at Least One City with a Population of More Than 1 Million People |
|---|---|
| California | California |
| Texas | Texas |
| New York | New York |
| Florida | Illinois |
| Illinois | Pennsylvania |
| Pennsylvania | Arizona |
| Ohio | |

Source: Bureau of the U.S. Census

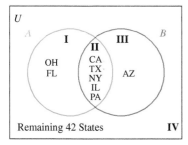

Figure 2.7

**Solution** First determine the intersection of sets $A$ and $B$. The states common to both sets are California, Texas, New York, Illinois, and Pennsylvania. Therefore,

$$A \cap B = \{\text{California, Texas, New York, Illinois, Pennsylvania}\}$$

Place these elements in region II of Fig. 2.7. Complete region I by determining the elements in set $A$ that have not been placed in region II. Therefore, Ohio and Florida are placed in region I. Complete region III by determining the elements in set $B$ that have not been placed in region II. Thus, Arizona is placed in region III. Finally, place those elements in $U$ that are not in either set within the rectangle but are outside both circles. This group includes the remaining 42 states, which are placed in region IV. ∎

---

Example **3** *The Intersection of Sets*

Given

$$U = \{1, 2, 3, 4, 5, 6, 7, 8, 9, 10\}$$
$$A = \{1, 2, 3, 8\}$$
$$B = \{1, 3, 6, 7, 8\}$$
$$C = \{\ \}$$

find

a) $A \cap B.$    b) $A \cap C.$    c) $A' \cap B.$    d) $(A \cap B)'.$

**Solution**

a) $A \cap B = \{1, 2, 3, 8\} \cap \{1, 3, 6, 7, 8\} = \{1, 3, 8\}$. The elements common to both set $A$ and set $B$ are 1, 3, and 8.

b) $A \cap C = \{1, 2, 3, 8\} \cap \{\ \} = \{\ \}$. There are no elements common to both set $A$ and set $C$.

c) To determine $A' \cap B$, we must first determine $A'$.
$$A' = \{4, 5, 6, 7, 9, 10\}$$
$$A' \cap B = \{4, 5, 6, 7, 9, 10\} \cap \{1, 3, 6, 7, 8\}$$
$$= \{6, 7\}$$

d) To find $(A \cap B)'$, first determine $A \cap B$.
$$A \cap B = \{1, 3, 8\} \text{ from part (a)}$$
$$(A \cap B)' = \{1, 3, 8\}' = \{2, 4, 5, 6, 7, 9, 10\}$$
∎

## Union

The word *union* means to unite or join together, as in marriage, and that is exactly what is done when we perform the operation of union.

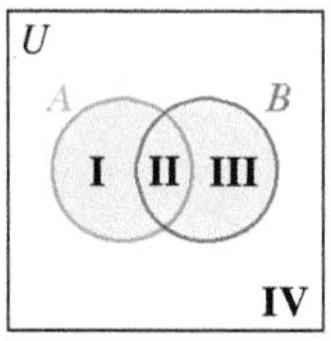

### Definition: **Union**
The **union** of set $A$ and set $B$, symbolized by $A \cup B$, is the set containing all the elements that are members of set $A$ or of set $B$ (or of both sets).

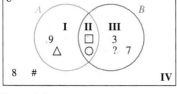

Figure 2.8

The three shaded regions of Fig. 2.8, regions I, II, and III, together represent the union of sets $A$ and $B$. If an element is common to both sets, it is listed only once in the union of the sets.

Example **4** *Determining Sets from a Venn Diagram*

Use the Venn diagram in Fig. 2.9 to determine the following sets.

a) $U$       b) $A$       c) $B'$       d) $A \cap B$
e) $A \cup B$    f) $(A \cup B)'$    g) $n(A \cup B)$

Figure 2.9

*Solution*

a) The universal set consists of all the elements within the rectangle, that is, the elements in regions I, II, III, and IV. Thus, $U = \{9, \triangle, \square, \bigcirc, 3, 7, ?, \#, 8\}$.

b) Set $A$ consists of the elements in regions I and II. Thus, $A = \{9, \triangle, \square, \bigcirc\}$.

c) $B'$ consists of the elements outside set $B$, or the elements in regions I and IV. Thus, $B' = \{9, \triangle, \#, 8\}$.

d) $A \cap B$ consists of the elements that belong to both set $A$ and set $B$ (region II). Thus, $A \cap B = \{\square, \bigcirc\}$.

e) $A \cup B$ consists of the elements that belong to set $A$ or set $B$ (regions I, II, or III). Thus, $A \cup B = \{9, \triangle, \square, \bigcirc, 3, 7, ?\}$.

f) $(A \cup B)'$ consists of the elements in $U$ that are not in $A \cup B$. Thus, $(A \cup B)' = \{\#, 8\}$.

g) $n(A \cup B)$ represents the *number of elements* in the union of sets $A$ and $B$. Thus, $n(A \cup B) = 7$, as there are seven elements in the union of sets $A$ and $B$. ∎

## Example 5   The Union of Sets

Given

$$U = \{1, 2, 3, 4, 5, 6, 7, 8, 9, 10\}$$
$$A = \{1, 2, 4, 6\}$$
$$B = \{1, 3, 6, 7, 9\}$$
$$C = \{\ \}$$

determine each of the following.

a) $A \cup B$     b) $A \cup C$     c) $A' \cup B$     d) $(A \cup B)'$

*Solution*

a) $A \cup B = \{1, 2, 4, 6\} \cup \{1, 3, 6, 7, 9\} = \{1, 2, 3, 4, 6, 7, 9\}$

b) $A \cup C = \{1, 2, 4, 6\} \cup \{\ \} = \{1, 2, 4, 6\}$. Note that $A \cup C = A$.

c) To determine $A' \cup B$, we must determine $A'$.

$$A' = \{3, 5, 7, 8, 9, 10\}$$
$$A' \cup B = \{3, 5, 7, 8, 9, 10\} \cup \{1, 3, 6, 7, 9\}$$
$$= \{1, 3, 5, 6, 7, 8, 9, 10\}$$

d) Determine $(A \cup B)'$ by first determining $A \cup B$, and then find the complement of $A \cup B$.

$$A \cup B = \{1, 2, 3, 4, 6, 7, 9\} \text{ from part (a)}$$
$$(A \cup B)' = \{1, 2, 3, 4, 6, 7, 9\}' = \{5, 8, 10\}$$ ∎

## Example 6   Union and Intersection

Given

$$U = \{a, b, c, d, e, f, g\}$$
$$A = \{a, b, e, g\}$$
$$B = \{a, c, d, e\}$$
$$C = \{b, e, f\}$$

determine each of the following.

a) $(A \cup B) \cap (A \cup C)$     b) $(A \cup B) \cap C'$     c) $A' \cap B'$

> **Solution**
>
> a)  $(A \cup B) \cap (A \cup C) = \{a, b, c, d, e, g\} \cap \{a, b, e, f, g\}$
> $$= \{a, b, e, g\}$$
>
> b)  $(A \cup B) \cap C' = \{a, b, c, d, e, g\} \cap \{a, c, d, g\}$
> $$= \{a, c, d, g\}$$
>
> c)  $A' \cap B' = \{c, d, f\} \cap \{b, f, g\}$
> $$= \{f\}$$

## The Meaning of *and* and *or*

The words *and* and *or* are very important in many areas of mathematics. We use these words in several chapters in this book, including Ch.12, Probability. The word *and* is generally interpreted to mean *intersection*, whereas *or* is generally interpreted to mean *union*. Suppose $A = \{1, 2, 3, 5, 6, 8\}$ and $B = \{1, 3, 4, 7, 9, 10\}$. The elements that belong to set $A$ *and* set $B$ are 1 and 3. These are the elements in the intersection of the sets. The elements that belong to set $A$ *or* set $B$ are 1, 2, 3, 4, 5, 6, 7, 8, 9, and 10. These are the elements in the union of the sets.

## The Relationship Between $n(A \cup B)$, $n(A)$, $n(B)$, and $n(A \cap B)$

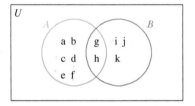

Figure 2.10

Having looked at unions and intersections, we can now determine a relationship between $n(A \cup B)$, $n(A)$, $n(B)$, and $n(A \cap B)$. Suppose set $A$ has eight elements, set $B$ has five elements, and $A \cap B$ has two elements. How many elements are in $A \cup B$? Let's make up some arbitrary sets that meet the criteria specified and draw a Venn diagram. If we let set $A = \{a, b, c, d, e, f, g, h\}$, then set $B$ must contain five elements, two of which are also in set $A$. Let set $B = \{g, h, i, j, k\}$. We construct a Venn diagram by filling in the intersection first, as shown in Fig. 2.10. The number of elements in $A \cup B$ is 11. The elements g and h are in both sets, and if we add $n(A) + n(B)$, we are counting these elements twice.

To find the number of elements in the union of sets $A$ and $B$, we can add the number of elements in sets $A$ and $B$ and then subtract the number of elements common to both sets.

### The Number of Elements in $A \cup B$
For any finite sets $A$ and $B$,
$$n(A \cup B) = n(A) + n(B) - n(A \cap B)$$

### Example 7   *How Many Visitors Speak Spanish or French?*

The results of a survey of visitors at the Grand Canyon showed that 25 speak Spanish, 14 speak French, and 4 speak both Spanish and French. How many speak Spanish or French?

> **Solution**  If we let set $A$ be the set of visitors who speak Spanish and let set $B$ be the set of visitors who speak French, then we need to determine $n(A \cup B)$. We can use the above formula to find $n(A \cup B)$.
>
> $$n(A \cup B) = n(A) + n(B) - n(A \cap B)$$
> $$n(A \cup B) = 25 + 14 - 4$$
> $$= 35$$
>
> Thus, 35 of the visitors surveyed speak either Spanish or French.

## Example 8 *The Number of Elements in Set A*

Of the homes listed for sale with RE/MAX, 39 have either a three-car garage or a fireplace, 31 have a fireplace, and 18 have both a three-car garage and a fireplace. How many of these homes have a three-car garage?

*Solution* If we let set $A$ be the set of homes with a three-car garage and set $B$ be the set of homes with a fireplace, we need to determine $n(A)$. We are given the number of homes with either a three-car garage or a fireplace, which is $n(A \cup B)$. We are also given the number of homes with a fireplace, $n(B)$, and the number of homes that have both a three-car garage and a fireplace, $n(A \cap B)$. We can use the formula $n(A \cup B) = n(A) + n(B) - n(A \cap B)$ to solve for $n(A)$.

$$n(A \cup B) = n(A) + n(B) - n(A \cap B)$$
$$39 = n(A) + 31 - 18$$
$$39 = n(A) + 13$$
$$39 - 13 = n(A) + 13 - 13$$
$$26 = n(A)$$

Thus, the number of homes listed for sale that have a three-car garage is 26. ■

Two other set operations are the difference of two sets and the Cartesian product. We will first discuss the difference of two sets.

## Difference of Two Sets

> **Definition: Difference of Two Sets**
> The **difference of two sets** $A$ and $B$, symbolized $A - B$, is the set of elements that belong to set $A$ but not to set $B$.

Using set-builder notation, the difference of two sets $A$ and $B$ is indicated by $A - B = \{x \mid x \in A \text{ and } x \notin B\}$. The shaded region, region I, in Fig. 2.11 represents the difference of two sets $A$ and $B$, or $A - B$.

Figure 2.11

## Example 9 *The Difference of Two Sets*

Given

$$U = \{a, b, c, d, e, f, g, h, i, j, k\}$$
$$A = \{b, d, e, f, g, h\}$$
$$B = \{a, b, d, h, i\}$$
$$C = \{b, e, g\}$$

determine

a) $A - B$    b) $A - C$    c) $A' - B$    d) $A - C'$

*Solution*

a) $A - B$ is the set of elements that are in set $A$ but not set $B$. The elements that are in set $A$ but not set $B$ are $e, f,$ and $g$. Therefore, $A - B = \{e, f, g\}$.

b) $A - C$ is the set of elements that are in set $A$ but not set $C$. The elements that are in set $A$ but not set $C$ are $d, f,$ and $h$. Therefore, $A - C = \{d, f, h\}$.

c) To determine $A' - B$, we must first determine $A'$.
$$A' = \{a, c, i, j, k\}$$
$A' - B$ is the set of elements that are in set $A'$ but not set $B$. The elements that are in set $A'$ but not set $B$ are $c, j,$ and $k$. Therefore, $A' - B = \{c, j, k\}$.

d) To determine $A - C'$, we must first determine $C'$.
$$C' = \{a, c, d, f, h, i, j, k\}$$
$A - C'$ is the set of elements that are in set $A$ but not set $C'$. The elements that are in set $A$ but not set $C'$ are $b$, $e$, and $g$. Therefore, $A - C' = \{b, e, g\}$.   ∎

Next we discuss the Cartesian product.

## Cartesian Product

> **Definition: Cartesian Product**
>
> The **Cartesian product** of set $A$ and set $B$, symbolized by $A \times B$ and read "$A$ cross $B$," is the set of all possible *ordered pairs* of the form $(a, b)$, where $a \in A$ and $b \in B$.

To determine the ordered pairs in a Cartesian product, select the first element of set $A$ and form an ordered pair with each element of set $B$. Then select the second element of set $A$ and form an ordered pair with each element of set $B$. Continue in this manner until you have used each element of set $A$.

### Example 10   *The Cartesian Product of Two Sets*

Given $A = \{\text{orange, banana, apple}\}$ and $B = \{1, 2\}$, determine the following.
a) $A \times B$     b) $B \times A$     c) $A \times A$     d) $B \times B$

*Solution*

a) $A \times B = \{(\text{orange}, 1), (\text{orange}, 2) (\text{banana}, 1), (\text{banana}, 2), (\text{apple}, 1), (\text{apple}, 2)\}$
b) $B \times A = \{(1, \text{orange}), (1, \text{banana}), (1, \text{apple}), (2, \text{orange}), (2, \text{banana}), (2, \text{apple})\}$
c) $A \times A = \{(\text{orange, orange}), (\text{orange, banana}), (\text{orange, apple}), (\text{banana, orange}),$
$(\text{banana, banana}), (\text{banana, apple}), (\text{apple, orange}), (\text{apple, banana}), (\text{apple, apple})\}$
d) $B \times B = \{(1, 1), (1, 2), (2, 1), (2, 2)\}$   ∎

We can see from Example 10 that, in general, $A \times B \neq B \times A$. The ordered pairs in $A \times B$ are not the same as the ordered pairs in $B \times A$ because (orange, 1) $\neq$ (1, orange).

In general, if a set $A$ has $m$ elements and a set $B$ has $n$ elements, then the number of ordered pairs in $A \times B$ will be $m \times n$. In Example 10, set $A$ contains 3 elements and set $B$ contains 2 elements. Notice that $A \times B$ contains $3 \times 2$ or 6 ordered pairs.

## SECTION 2.3   *Exercises*

### Warm Up Exercises

*In exercises 1–8, fill in the blank with an appropriate word, phrase, or symbol(s).*

**1.** The set of all the elements in the universal set that are not in set $A$ is called the _____ of set $A$.

**2.** The set containing all the elements that are members of set $A$ or of set $B$ or of both sets is called the _____ of set $A$ and set $B$.

**3.** The set containing all the elements that are common to both set $A$ and set $B$ is called the _____ of set $A$ and set $B$.

**4.** The set of elements that belong to set $A$, but not to set $B$, is called the _____ of two sets $A$ and $B$.

**5.** The set of all possible ordered pairs of the form $(a, b)$, where $a \in A$ and $b \in B$, is called the _____ product of set $A$ and set $B$.

**6.** If set $A$ has $m$ elements and set $B$ has $n$ elements, the Cartesian product $A \times B$ has _____ elements.

**7.** Two sets with no elements in common are called _____ sets.

**8.** In a Venn diagram with two overlapping sets there are _____ regions.

## Practice the Skills

*In Exercises 9–13, use Fig. 2.2 as a guide to draw a Venn diagram that illustrates the situation described.*

**9.** Set $A$ and set $B$ are disjoint sets.

**10.** $A \subset B$

**11.** $B \subset A$

**12.** $A = B$

**13.** Set $A$ and set $B$ are overlapping sets.

**14.** Which set operation is the word *or* generally interpreted to mean?

**15.** Which set operation is the word *and* generally interpreted to mean?

**16.** Give the relationship between $n(A \cup B)$, $n(A)$, $n(B)$, and $n(A \cap B)$.

## Problem Solving

**17.** *Cellular Telephones* For the sets $U$, $A$, and $B$, construct a Venn diagram and place the elements in the proper regions.

$U = \{$iPhone, Blackberry, LG, DROID, Samsung, Nokia, Motorola, Sony$\}$

$A = \{$iPhone, Blackberry, LG, Motorola, DROID$\}$

$B = \{$LG, DROID, Nokia, Motorola$\}$

**18.** *National Parks* For the sets $U$, $A$, and $B$, construct a Venn diagram and place the elements in the proper regions.

$U = \{$Badlands, Death Valley, Glacier, Grand Teton, Mammoth Cave, Mount Rainier, North Cascades, Shenandoah, Yellowstone, Yosemite$\}$

$A = \{$Badlands, Glacier, Grand Teton, Mount Rainier, Yellowstone$\}$

$B = \{$Death Valley, Glacier, Mammoth Cave, Mount Rainier, Yosemite$\}$

▲ *Yellowstone National Park*

**19.** *Occupations* The following table shows the fastest-growing occupations for college graduates, based on employment in 2008 and the estimated employment in 2016. Let the occupations in the table represent the universal set.

| Fastest-Growing Occupations for College Graduates, 2008–2016 | | |
|---|---|---|
| | Employment (in thousands of jobs) | |
| **Occupation** | **2008** | **2016** |
| Biomedical engineers (BE) | 16 | 28 |
| Network systems analysts (NSA) | 292 | 448 |
| Financial examiners (FE) | 27 | 38 |
| Medical scientists (MS) | 109 | 154 |
| Physicians assistants (PA) | 75 | 104 |
| Biochemists (B) | 23 | 32 |
| Athletic trainers (AT) | 16 | 22 |
| Dental hygienists (DH) | 174 | 237 |
| Veterinary technicians (VT) | 80 | 108 |
| Computer software engineers (CSE) | 515 | 690 |

Source: U.S. Bureau of Labor Statistics

Let $A$ = the set of fastest-growing occupations for college graduates whose 2008 employment was at least 80,000.

Let $B$ = the set of fastest-growing occupations for college graduates whose estimated employment in 2016 is at least 200,000.

Using the abbreviations listed in the table for each occupation, construct a Venn diagram illustrating the sets.

**20.** *Racing Standings* The following table shows the 2009 NASCAR Sprint Cup Series Final Standings, with the 10 drivers having the highest point total and the number of races won. Let the drivers in the table represent the universal set.

| 2009 NASCAR Sprint Cup Series Final Standings | | |
|---|---|---|
| **Driver** | **Points** | **Wins** |
| Jimmie Johnson | 6652 | 7 |
| Mark Martin | 6511 | 5 |
| Jeff Gordon | 6473 | 1 |
| Kurt Busch | 6446 | 2 |
| Denny Hamlin | 6335 | 4 |
| Tony Stewart | 6309 | 4 |
| Greg Biffle | 6292 | 0 |
| Juan Montoya | 6252 | 0 |
| Ryan Newman | 6175 | 0 |
| Kasey Kahne | 6128 | 2 |

Source: NASCAR

Let $A$ = the set of drivers with more than 6400 points

Let $B$ = the set of drivers with more than 1 win

Construct a Venn diagram illustrating the sets. Use the driver's initials in the Venn diagram.

**21.** Let $U$ represent the set of animals in U.S. zoos. Let $A$ represent the set of animals in the San Diego zoo. Describe $A'$.

▲ *San Diego Zoo*

**22.** Let $U$ represent the set of U.S. colleges and universities. Let $A$ represent the set of U.S. colleges and universities in the state of Mississippi. Describe $A'$.

*In Exercises 23–28,*

$U$ is the set of farms in the United States.

$A$ is the set of farms that produce corn.

$B$ is the set of farms that produce tomatoes.

*Describe each of the following sets in words.*

**23.** $A'$

**24.** $B'$

**25.** $A \cup B$

**26.** $A \cap B$

**27.** $A \cap B'$

**28.** $A \cup B'$

*In Exercises 29–34,*

$U$ is the set of furniture stores.

$A$ is the set of furniture stores that sell mattresses.

$B$ is the set of furniture stores that sell outdoor furniture.

$C$ is the set of furniture stores that sell leather furniture.

*Describe the following sets.*

**29.** $A \cup C$

**30.** $A \cap B$

**31.** $B' \cap C$

**32.** $A \cap B \cap C$

**33.** $A \cup B \cup C$

**34.** $A' \cup C'$

*In Exercises 35–42, use the Venn diagram in Fig. 2.12 to list the set of elements in roster form.*

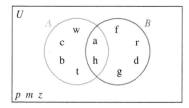

**Figure 2.12**

**35.** $A$          **36.** $B$

**37.** $A \cap B$          **38.** $U$

**39.** $A \cup B$

**40.** $(A \cup B)'$

**41.** $A' \cap B'$

**42.** $(A \cap B)'$

*In Exercises 43–50, use the Venn diagram in Fig. 2.13 to list the set of elements in roster form.*

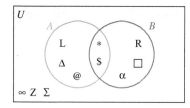

Figure 2.13

**43.** $A$

**44.** $B$

**45.** $U$

**46.** $A \cap B$

**47.** $A' \cup B$

**48.** $A \cup B'$

**49.** $A' \cap B$

**50.** $(A \cup B)'$

*In Exercises 51–60, let*

$$U = \{1, 2, 3, 4, 5, 6, 7, 8\}$$
$$A = \{1, 2, 4, 5, 7\}$$
$$B = \{2, 3, 5, 6\}$$

*Determine the following.*

**51.** $A \cup B$

**52.** $A \cap B$

**53.** $B'$

**54.** $A \cup B'$

**55.** $(A \cup B)'$

**56.** $A' \cap B'$

**57.** $(A \cup B)' \cap B$

**58.** $(A \cup B) \cap (A \cup B)'$

**59.** $(B \cup A)' \cap (B' \cup A')$ **60.** $A' \cup (A \cap B)$

*In Exercises 61–70, let*

$$U = \{a, b, c, d, e, f, g, h, i, j, k\}$$
$$A = \{a, c, d, f, g, i\}$$
$$B = \{b, c, d, f, g\}$$
$$C = \{a, b, f, i, j\}$$

*Determine the following.*

**61.** $B'$

**62.** $B \cup C$

**63.** $A \cap C$

**64.** $A' \cup B'$

**65.** $(A \cap C)'$

**66.** $(A \cap B) \cup C$

**67.** $A \cup (C \cap B)'$

**68.** $A \cup (C' \cup B')$

**69.** $(A' \cup C) \cup (A \cap B)$ **70.** $(C \cap B) \cap (A' \cap B)$

*In Exercises 71–78, let*

$$U = \{1, 2, 3, 4, 5, 6, 7, 8, 9, 10\}$$
$$A = \{1, 2, 4, 6, 9\}$$
$$B = \{1, 3, 4, 5, 8\}$$
$$C = \{4, 5, 9\}$$

*Determine the following.*

**71.** $A - B$

**72.** $A - C$

**73.** $A - B'$

**74.** $A' - C$

**75.** $(A - B)'$

**76.** $(A - B)' - C$

**77.** $C - A'$

**78.** $(C - A)' - B$

*In Exercises 79–84, let*

$$A = \{a, b, c\}$$
$$B = \{1, 2\}$$

**79.** Determine $A \times B$.

**80.** Determine $B \times A$.

**81.** Does $A \times B = B \times A$?

**82.** Determine $n(A \times B)$.

**83.** Determine $n(B \times A)$.

**84.** Does $n(A \times B) = n(B \times A)$?

## Problem Solving

*In Exercises 85–98, let*

$$U = \{x \mid x \in N \text{ and } x < 10\}$$
$$A = \{x \mid x \in N \text{ and } x \text{ is odd and } x < 10\}$$
$$B = \{x \mid x \in N \text{ and } x \text{ is even and } x < 10\}$$
$$C = \{x \mid x \in N \text{ and } x < 6\}$$

*Determine the following.*

**85.** $A \cap B$

**86.** $A \cup B$

**87.** $A' \cup B$

**88.** $(B \cup C)'$

**89.** $A \cap C'$

**90.** $A \cap B'$

**91.** $(B \cap C)'$

**92.** $(A \cup C) \cap B$

**93.** $(C' \cup A) \cap B$

**94.** $(C \cap B) \cup A$

**95.** $(A \cap B)' \cup C$

**96.** $(A' \cup C) \cap B$

**97.** $(A' \cup B') \cap C$

**98.** $(A' \cap C) \cup (A \cap B)$

**99.** When will a set and its complement be disjoint? Explain and give an example.

**100.** When will $n(A \cap B) = 0$? Explain and give an example.

**101.** *Pet Ownership* The results of a survey of customers at PetSmart showed that 27 owned dogs, 38 owned cats, and 16 owned both dogs and cats. How many people owned either a dog or a cat?

**102.** *Student Council and Intramurals* At Madison High School, 46 students participated in student council or intramurals, 30 participated in student council, and 4 participated in student council and intramurals. How many students participated in intramurals?

**103.** Consider the formula

$$n(A \cup B) = n(A) + n(B) - n(A \cap B)$$

**a)** Show that this relation holds for $A = \{a, b, c, d\}$ and $B = \{b, d, e, f, g, h\}$.

**b)** Make up your own sets $A$ and $B$, each consisting of at least six elements. Using these sets, show that the relation holds.

**c)** Use a Venn diagram and explain why the relation holds for any two sets $A$ and $B$.

**104.** The Venn diagram in Fig. 2.14 shows a technique of labeling the regions to indicate membership of elements in a particular region. Define each of the four regions with a set statement. (*Hint:* $A \cap B'$ defines region I.)

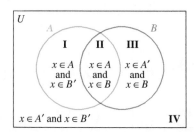

Figure 2.14

*In Exercises 105–114, let* $U = \{0, 1, 2, 3, 4, 5, \dots\}$, $A = \{1, 2, 3, 4, \dots\}$, $B = \{4, 8, 12, 16, \dots\}$, *and* $C = \{2, 4, 6, 8, \dots\}$. *Determine the following.*

**105.** $A \cup B$

**106.** $A \cap B$

**107.** $B \cup C$

**108.** $B \cap C$

**109.** $A \cap C$

**110.** $A' \cap C$

**111.** $B' \cap C$

**112.** $(B \cup C)' \cup C$

**113.** $(A \cap C) \cap B'$

**114.** $U' \cap (A \cup B)$

## Challenge Problems/Group Activities

*In Exercises 115–122, determine whether the answer is* $\varnothing$, $A$, *or* $U$. *(Assume* $A \neq \varnothing, A \neq U$.)

**115.** $A \cap A'$

**116.** $A \cup A'$

**117.** $A \cup \varnothing$

**118.** $A \cap \varnothing$

**119.** $A' \cup U$

**120.** $A \cap U$

**121.** $A \cup U$

**122.** $A \cap A$

*In Exercises 123–128, determine the relationship between set A and set B if*

**123.** $A \cap B = B$.

**124.** $A \cup B = B$.

**125.** $A \cap B = \varnothing$.

**126.** $A \cup B = A$.

**127.** $A \cap B = A$.

**128.** $A \cup B = \varnothing$.

# SECTION 2.4   Venn Diagrams with Three Sets and Verification of Equality of Sets

Suppose a college offers intramurals in basketball, flag football, and softball. Is there a way the director of intramurals can determine which students participate in all three activities or which students participate in exactly two of these activities? The answer is yes by using a *Venn Diagram*. A Venn diagram that can be used to convey important information quickly and efficiently.

**Why** *This is Important*   Classifying sets using diagrams often helps us understand the relationship among various sets.

▲ *Venn diagrams can be used to answer questions regarding the number of people participating in an intramural activity at a college.*

In Section 2.3, we learned how to use Venn diagrams to illustrate two sets. Venn diagrams can also be used to illustrate three sets.

For three sets, *A*, *B*, and *C*, the diagram is drawn so the three sets overlap (Fig. 2.15), creating eight regions. The diagrams in Fig. 2.16 emphasize selected regions of three intersecting sets. *When constructing Venn diagrams with three sets, we generally start with region V and work outward,* as explained in the procedure given on page 69.

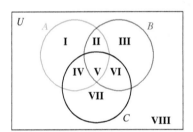

**Figure 2.15**

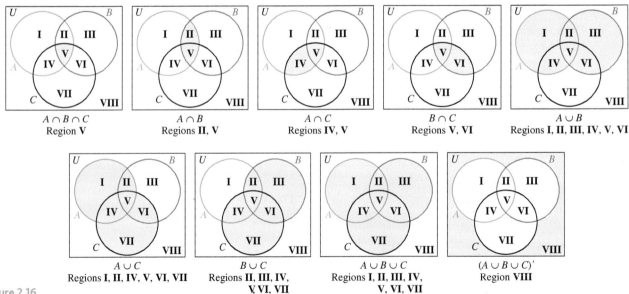

**Figure 2.16**

---

**PROCEDURE**   GENERAL PROCEDURE FOR CONSTRUCTING VENN DIAGRAMS WITH THREE SETS, $A$, $B$, AND $C$

1.  Determine the elements to be placed in region V by finding the elements that are common to all three sets, $A \cap B \cap C$.

2.  Determine the elements to be placed in region II. Find the elements in $A \cap B$. The elements in this set belong in regions II and V. Place the elements in the set $A \cap B$ that are not listed in region V in region II. The elements in regions IV and VI are found in a similar manner.

3.  Determine the elements to be placed in region I by determining the elements in set $A$ that are not in regions II, IV, and V. The elements in regions III and VII are found in a similar manner.

4.  Determine the elements to be placed in region VIII by finding the elements in the universal set that are not in regions I through VII.

---

Example 1 illustrates the general procedure.

Example  **1**  *Constructing a Venn Diagram for Three Sets*

Construct a Venn diagram illustrating the following sets.

$$U = \{1, 2, 3, 4, 5, 6, 7, 8, 9, 10, 11, 12, 13, 14, 15\}$$
$$A = \{1, 4, 8, 9, 10, 12\}$$
$$B = \{2, 4, 5, 9, 10, 13\}$$
$$C = \{1, 3, 4, 8, 9, 11\}$$

*Solution*   First find the intersection of all three sets. Because the elements 4 and 9 are in all three sets, $A \cap B \cap C = \{4, 9\}$. The elements 4 and 9 are placed in region V in Fig. 2.17. Next complete region II by determining the intersection of sets $A$ and $B$.

$$A \cap B = \{4, 9, 10\}$$

$A \cap B$ consists of regions II and V. The elements 4 and 9 have already been placed in region V, so 10 must be placed in region II.

Now determine what numbers go in region IV.

$$A \cap C = \{1, 4, 8, 9\}$$

Since 4 and 9 have already been placed in region V, place the 1 and 8 in region IV. Now determine the numbers to go in region VI.

$$B \cap C = \{4, 9\}$$

Since both the 4 and 9 have been placed in region V, there are no numbers to be placed in region VI. Now complete set $A$. The only element of set $A$ that has not previously been placed in regions II, IV, or V is 12. Therefore, place the element 12 in region I. The element 12 that is placed in region I is only in set $A$ and not in set $B$ or set $C$. Using set $B$, complete region III using the same general procedure used to determine the numbers in region I. Using set $C$, complete region VII by using the same procedure used to complete regions I and III. To determine the elements in region VIII, find the elements in $U$ that have not been placed in regions I–VII. The elements 6, 7, 14, and 15 have not been placed in regions I–VII, so place them in region VIII. ∎

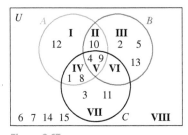

Figure 2.17

Venn diagrams can be used to illustrate and analyze many everyday problems. One example follows.

Example **2** *Blood Types*

Human blood is classified (typed) according to the presence or absence of the specific antigens A, B, and Rh in the red blood cells. Antigens are highly specified proteins and carbohydrates that will trigger the production of antibodies in the blood to fight infection. Blood containing the Rh antigen is labeled positive, $+$, while blood lacking the Rh antigen is labeled negative, $-$. Blood lacking both A and B antigens is called type O. Sketch a Venn diagram with three sets A, B, and Rh and place each type of blood listed in the proper region. A person has only one type of blood.

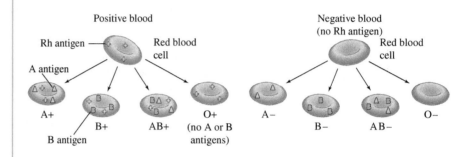

Solution

As illustrated in Chapter 1, the first thing to do is to read the question carefully and make sure you understand what is given and what you are asked to find. There are three antigens A, B, and Rh. Therefore, begin by naming the three circles in a Venn diagram with the three antigens; see Fig. 2.18.

Any blood containing the Rh antigen is positive, and any blood not containing the Rh antigen is negative. Therefore, all blood in the Rh circle is positive, and all blood outside the Rh circle is negative. The intersection of all three sets, region V, is AB+. Region II contains only antigens A and B and is therefore AB−. Region I is A− because it contains only antigen A. Region III is B−, region IV is A+, and region VI is B+. Region VII is O+, containing only the Rh antigen. Region VIII, which lacks all three antigens, is O−.　■

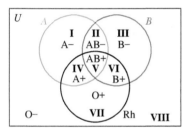

Figure 2.18

## Verification of Equality of Sets

In this chapter, for clarity we may refer to operations on sets, such as $A \cup B'$ or $A \cap B \cap C$, as *statements involving sets* or simply as *statements*. Now we discuss how to determine if two statements involving sets are equal.

Consider the question: Is $A' \cup B = A' \cap B$ *for all sets A and B*? For the specific sets $U = \{1, 2, 3, 4, 5\}$, $A = \{1, 3\}$, and $B = \{2, 4, 5\}$, is $A' \cup B = A' \cap B$? To answer the question, we do the following.

| Find $A' \cup B$ | Find $A' \cap B$ |
|---|---|
| $A' = \{2, 4, 5\}$ | $A' = \{2, 4, 5\}$ |
| $B = \{2, 4, 5\}$ | $B = \{2, 4, 5\}$ |
| $A' \cup B = \{2, 4, 5\}$ | $A' \cap B = \{2, 4, 5\}$ |

For these sets, $A' \cup B = A' \cap B$, because both set statements are equal to $\{2, 4, 5\}$. At this point you may believe that $A' \cup B = A' \cap B$ for all sets A and B.

If we select the sets $U = \{1, 2, 3, 4, 5\}$, $A = \{1, 3, 5\}$, and $B = \{2, 3\}$, we see that $A' \cup B = \{2, 3, 4\}$ and $A' \cap B = \{2\}$. For this case, $A' \cup B \neq A' \cap B$.

Thus, we have proved that $A' \cup B \neq A' \cap B$ for all sets $A$ and $B$ by using a *counterexample*. A counterexample, as explained in Chapter 1, is an example that shows a statement is not true.

In Chapter 1, we explained that proofs involve the use of *deductive reasoning*. Recall that deductive reasoning begins with a general statement and works to a specific conclusion. To verify, or determine whether set statements are equal for any two sets selected, we use deductive reasoning with Venn diagrams. Venn diagrams are used because they can illustrate general cases. To determine if statements that contain sets, such as $(A \cup B)'$ and $A' \cap B'$, are equal for all sets $A$ and $B$, we use the regions of Venn diagrams. If both statements represent the same regions of the Venn diagram, then the statements are equal for all sets $A$ and $B$. See Example 3.

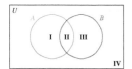

**Figure 2.19**

─Example **3** *Equality of Sets*

Determine whether $(A \cup B)' = A' \cap B'$ for all sets $A$ and $B$.

*Solution* Draw a Venn diagram with two sets $A$ and $B$, as in Fig. 2.19. Label the regions as indicated.

Find $(A \cup B)'$

| Set | Corresponding Regions |
|---|---|
| $A$ | I, II |
| $B$ | II, III |
| $A \cup B$ | I, II, III |
| $(A \cup B)'$ | IV |

Find $A' \cap B'$

| Set | Corresponding Regions |
|---|---|
| $A'$ | III, IV |
| $B'$ | I, IV |
| $A' \cap B'$ | IV |

Both statements are represented by the same region, IV, of the Venn diagram. Thus, $(A \cup B)' = A' \cap B'$ for all sets $A$ and $B$. ∎

In Example 3, when we proved that $(A \cup B)' = A' \cap B'$, we started with two general sets and worked to the specific conclusion that both statements represented the same regions of the Venn diagram. We showed that $(A \cup B)' = A' \cap B'$ *for all sets $A$ and $B$*. No matter what sets we choose for $A$ and $B$, this statement will be true. For example, let $U = \{1, 2, 3, 4, 5, 6, 7, 8, 9, 10\}$, $A = \{3, 4, 6, 10\}$, and $B = \{1, 2, 4, 5, 6, 8\}$.

$$(A \cup B)' = A' \cap B'$$
$$\{1, 2, 3, 4, 5, 6, 8, 10\}' = \{3, 4, 6, 10\}' \cap \{1, 2, 4, 5, 6, 8\}'$$
$$\{7, 9\} = \{1, 2, 5, 7, 8, 9\} \cap \{3, 7, 9, 10\}$$
$$\{7, 9\} = \{7, 9\}$$

We can also use Venn diagrams to prove statements involving three sets.

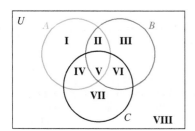

**Figure 2.20**

─Example **4** *Equality of Sets*

Determine whether $A \cup (B \cap C) = (A \cup B) \cap (A \cup C)$ for all sets, $A$, $B$, and $C$.

*Solution* Because the statements include three sets, $A$, $B$, and $C$, three circles must be used. The Venn diagram illustrating the eight regions is shown in Fig. 2.20.

First we will find the regions that correspond to $A \cup (B \cap C)$, and then we will find the regions that correspond to $(A \cup B) \cap (A \cup C)$. If both answers are the same, the statements are equal.

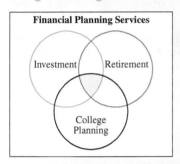
Find $A \cup (B \cap C)$

| Set | Corresponding Regions |
|---|---|
| $A$ | I, II, IV, V |
| $B \cap C$ | V, VI |
| $A \cup (B \cap C)$ | I, II, IV, V, VI |

Find $(A \cup B) \cap (A \cup C)$

| Set | Corresponding Regions |
|---|---|
| $A \cup B$ | I, II, III, IV, V, VI |
| $A \cup C$ | I, II, IV, V, VI, VII |
| $(A \cup B) \cap (A \cup C)$ | I, II, IV, V, VI |

The regions that correspond to $A \cup (B \cap C)$ are I, II, IV, V, and VI, and the regions that correspond to $(A \cup B) \cap (A \cup C)$ are also I, II, IV, V, and VI. The results show that both statements are represented by the same regions, namely, I, II, IV, V, and VI, and therefore $A \cup (B \cap C) = (A \cup B) \cap (A \cup C)$ for all sets $A$, $B$, and $C$.

In Example 4, we proved that $A \cup (B \cap C) = (A \cup B) \cap (A \cup C)$ for all sets $A$, $B$, and $C$. Show that this statement is true for the specific sets $U = \{1, 2, 3, 4, 5, 6, 7, 8, 9, 10\}$, $A = \{1, 2, 3, 7\}$, $B = \{2, 3, 4, 5, 7, 9\}$, and $C = \{1, 4, 7, 8, 10\}$.

## De Morgan's Laws

In set theory, logic, and other branches of mathematics, a pair of related theorems known as De Morgan's laws make it possible to transform statements and formulas into alternative and often more convenient forms. In set theory, *De Morgan's laws* are symbolized as follows.

### De Morgan's Laws

1. $(A \cap B)' = A' \cup B'$
2. $(A \cup B)' = A' \cap B'$

Law 2 was verified in Example 3. We suggest that you verify law 1 at this time. The laws were expressed verbally by William of Ockham in the fourteenth century. In the nineteenth century, Augustus De Morgan expressed them mathematically. De Morgan's laws will be discussed more thoroughly in Chapter 3, Logic.

## SECTION 2.4    *Exercises*

### Warm Up Exercises

*In Exercises 1–4, fill in the blank with an appropriate word, phrase, or symbol(s).*

1. The number of regions created when constructing a Venn diagram with three overlapping sets is _____ .

2. a) When constructing a Venn diagram with three overlapping sets, region _____ is generally completed first.

   b) When constructing a Venn diagram with three overlapping sets, after completing region V, the next regions generally completed are II, IV, and _____ .

3. Complete DeMorgan's laws:

   a) $(A \cup B)' = $ _____

   b) $(A \cap B)' = $ _____

4. When using Venn diagrams to verify or determine whether set statements are equal we use _____ reasoning.

### Practice the Skills/Problem Solving

5. A Venn diagram contains three sets, $A$, $B$, and $C$, as in Fig. 2.15 on page 68. If region V contains 4 elements and there are 12 elements in $B \cap C$, how many elements belong in region VI? Explain.

**6.** A Venn diagram contains three sets, $A$, $B$, and $C$, as in Fig. 2.15 on page 68. If region V contains 4 elements and there are 9 elements in $A \cap B$, how many elements belong in region II? Explain.

**7. a)** For $U = \{1, 2, 3, 4, 5\}$, $A = \{1, 4, 5\}$, and $B = \{1, 4, 5\}$, does $A \cup B = A \cap B$?

   **b)** By observing the answer to part (a), can we conclude that $A \cup B = A \cap B$ for all sets $A$ and $B$? Explain.

   **c)** Using a Venn diagram, determine if $A \cup B = A \cap B$ for all sets $A$ and $B$.

**8.** Construct a Venn diagram illustrating the following sets.
$$U = \{a, b, c, d, e, f, g, h, i, j\}$$
$$A = \{c, d, e, g, h, i\}$$
$$B = \{a, c, d, g\}$$
$$C = \{c, f, i, j\}$$

**9.** Construct a Venn diagram illustrating the following sets.
$U = \{$ *Cinderella, Pinocchio, Ratatouille, Fantasia, Dumbo, Bambi, Pocahontas, Hercules, Mulan, Tarzan, Cars* $\}$

$A = \{$ *Bambi, Hercules, Pocahontas, Tarzan* $\}$

$B = \{$ *Ratatouille, Bambi, Mulan, Hercules* $\}$

$C = \{$ *Pocahontas, Cinderella, Bambi, Ratatouille, Fantasia* $\}$

▲ *Bambi*

**10.** Construct a Venn diagram illustrating the following sets.
$U = \{$ microwave oven, freezer, dishwasher, refrigerator, washer, dryer, toaster, blender, food processor, iron $\}$

$A = \{$ toaster, blender, iron, dishwasher, washer, dryer $\}$

$B = \{$ dishwasher, iron, freezer $\}$

$C = \{$ washer, dryer, iron, freezer, microwave oven $\}$

**11.** Construct a Venn diagram illustrating the following sets.
$U = \{$ American Eagle, Best Buy, Wal-Mart, Kmart, Target, Sears, JCPenney, Costco, Kohl's, Gap, Gap Kids, Foot Locker, Old Navy, Macy's $\}$

$A = \{$ American Eagle, Wal-Mart, Target, JCPenney, Old Navy $\}$

$B = \{$ Best Buy, Target, Costco, Old Navy, Macy's $\}$

$C = \{$ Target, Sears, Kohl's, Gap, JCPenney $\}$

**12.** Construct a Venn diagram illustrating the following sets.
$U = \{$ Louis Armstrong, Glenn Miller, Stan Kenton, Charlie Parker, Duke Ellington, Benny Goodman, Count Basie, John Coltrane, Dizzy Gillespie, Miles Davis, Thelonius Monk $\}$

$A = \{$ Stan Kenton, Count Basie, Dizzy Gillespie, Duke Ellington, Thelonius Monk $\}$

$B = \{$ Louis Armstrong, Glenn Miller, Count Basie, Duke Ellington, Miles Davis $\}$

$C = \{$ Count Basie, Miles Davis, Stan Kenton, Charlie Parker, Duke Ellington $\}$

**13.** *Olympic Medals* Consider the following table, which shows countries that won at least 25 medals in the 2008 Summer Olympics. Let the countries in the table represent the universal set.

| Country | Gold Medals | Silver Medals | Bronze Medals | Total Medals |
| --- | --- | --- | --- | --- |
| United States | 36 | 38 | 36 | 110 |
| China | 51 | 21 | 28 | 100 |
| Russia | 23 | 21 | 28 | 72 |
| Great Britain | 19 | 13 | 15 | 47 |
| Australia | 14 | 15 | 17 | 46 |
| Germany | 16 | 10 | 15 | 41 |
| France | 7 | 16 | 17 | 40 |
| South Korea | 13 | 10 | 8 | 31 |
| Italy | 8 | 10 | 10 | 28 |
| Ukraine | 7 | 5 | 15 | 27 |
| Japan | 9 | 6 | 10 | 25 |

Source: United States Olympic Committee.

Let $A$ = set of countries that won at least 30 gold medals.
Let $B$ = set of countries that won at least 15 silver medals.
Let $C$ = set of countries that won at least 10 bronze medals.

Construct a Venn diagram that illustrates the sets $A$, $B$, and $C$.

**14.** *Popular TV Shows* Construct a Venn diagram illustrating the following sets.

$U = \{$ *American Idol (AI), CSI, Dancing with the Stars (DWS), Family Guy (FG), Gossip Girl (GG), Monday Night Football (MNF), NCIS, Sunday Night Football (SNF), Survivor (S)* $\}$.

$A = \{$ *AI, CSI, DWS, SNF, NCIS* $\}$

$B = \{$ *AI, DWS, SNF, NCIS, MNF* $\}$

$C = \{$ *AI, CSI, SNF, NCIS, MNF, S* $\}$

**Rankings of Fruit-Producing Countries** For Exercises 15–20, use the following table, which shows the top 10 countries for production of apples, oranges, and nuts, The universal set is the set of countries listed in the world.

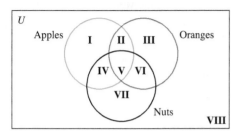

Figure 2.21

| Ranking of Fruit-Producing countries | | |
|---|---|---|
| **Apples** | **Oranges** | **Nuts** |
| 1. China | 1. Brazil | 1. United States |
| 2. United States | 2. United States | 2. Indonesia |
| 3. Iran | 3. Mexico | 3. Mexico |
| 4. Turkey | 4. India | 4. Ethiopia |
| 5. Russia | 5. China | 5. China |
| 6. Italy | 6. Spain | 6. Australia |
| 7. India | 7. Indonesia | 7. Guatemala |
| 8. France | 8. Iran | 8. Portugal |
| 9. Chile | 9. Italy | 9. Thailand |
| 10. Argentina | 10. Egypt | 10. Philippines |

Source: Food and Agriculture of the United Nations

Indicate in which region, I–VIII in Fig. 2.21, each of the following countries belongs.

**15.** Italy  **16.** United States

**17.** Canada  **18.** Portugal

**19.** Spain  **20.** Mexico

**Figures** In Exercises 21–32, indicate in Fig. 2.22 the region in which each of the figures would be placed.

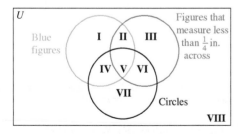

Figure 2.22

**21.**   **22.** ⬡  **23.** ▲

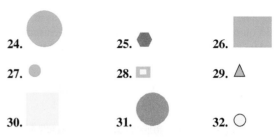

**24.** ⬤  **25.** ⬣  **26.** ⬛

**27.** ⬤  **28.** ◻  **29.** △

**30.** ◻  **31.** ⬤  **32.** ◯

**Senate Bills** During a session of the U.S. Senate, three bills were voted on. The votes of six senators are shown below the figure. Determine in which region of Fig. 2.23 each senator would be placed. The set labeled Bill 1 represents the set of senators who voted yes on Bill 1, and so on.

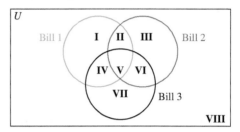

Figure 2.23

| SENATOR | BILL 1 | BILL 2 | BILL 3 |
|---|---|---|---|
| **33.** Hutchinson | yes | no | no |
| **34.** Kerry | no | no | yes |
| **35.** McCain | no | no | no |
| **36.** Mikulski | yes | yes | yes |
| **37.** Rand | no | yes | yes |
| **38.** Reid | no | yes | no |

In Exercises 39–52, use the Venn diagram in Fig. 2.24 to list the sets in roster form.

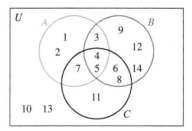

Figure 2.24

**39.** $A$  **40.** $U$

**41.** $B$  **42.** $C$

**43.** $A \cap B$  **44.** $A \cap C$

**45.** $(B \cap C)'$  **46.** $A \cap B \cap C$

**47.** $A \cup B$  **48.** $B \cup C$

**49.** $(A \cup C)'$  **50.** $A \cap (B \cup C)$

**51.** $A'$  **52.** $(A \cup B \cup C)'$

*In Exercises 53–60, use Venn diagrams to determine whether the following statements are equal for all sets A and B.*

**53.** $(A \cap B)'$,        $A' \cup B'$

**54.** $(A \cap B)'$,        $A' \cup B$

**55.** $A' \cup B'$,        $A \cap B$

**56.** $(A \cup B)'$,        $(A \cap B)'$

**57.** $A' \cup B'$,        $(A \cup B)'$

**58.** $A' \cap B'$,        $A \cup B'$

**59.** $(A' \cap B)'$,        $A \cup B'$

**60.** $A' \cap B'$,        $(A' \cap B')'$

*In Exercises 61–70, use Venn diagrams to determine whether the following statements are equal for all sets A, B, and C.*

**61.** $A \cap (B \cup C)$,        $(A \cap B) \cup C$

**62.** $A \cup (B \cap C)$,        $(B \cap C) \cup A$

**63.** $A \cap (B \cup C)$,        $(B \cup C) \cap A$

**64.** $A \cup (B \cap C)'$,        $A' \cap (B' \cup C)$

**65.** $A \cap (B \cup C)$,        $(A \cap B) \cup (A \cap C)$

**66.** $A \cup (B \cap C)$,        $(A \cup B) \cap (A \cup C)$

**67.** $A \cup (B \cup C)'$,        $A \cup (B' \cap C')$

**68.** $(A \cup B) \cap (B \cup C)$,        $B \cup (A \cap C)$

**69.** $(A \cup B)' \cap C$,        $(A' \cup C') \cap (B' \cup C)$

**70.** $(C \cap B)' \cup (A \cap B)'$,        $A \cap (B \cap C)$

*In Exercises 71–74, use set statements to write a description of the shaded area. Use union, intersection and complement as necessary. More than one answer may be possible.*

**71.**

**72.**

**73.**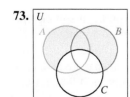

**74.**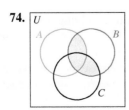

**75.** Let

$$U = \{1, 2, 3, 4, 5, 6, 7, 8, 9, 10\}$$
$$A = \{1, 2, 3, 4\}$$
$$B = \{3, 6, 7\}$$
$$C = \{6, 7, 9\}$$

a) Show that $(A \cup B) \cap C = (A \cap C) \cup (B \cap C)$ for these sets.

b) Make up your own sets $A$, $B$, and $C$. Verify that $(A \cup B) \cap C = (A \cap C) \cup (B \cap C)$ for your sets $A$, $B$, and $C$.

c) Use Venn diagrams to verify that $(A \cup B) \cap C = (A \cap C) \cup (B \cap C)$ for all sets $A$, $B$, and $C$.

**76.** Let

$$U = \{a, b, c, d, e, f, g, h, i\}$$
$$A = \{a, c, d, e, f\}$$
$$B = \{c, d\}$$
$$C = \{a, b, c, d, e\}$$

a) Determine whether $(A \cup C)' \cap B = (A \cap C)' \cap B$ for these sets.

b) Make up your own sets, $A$, $B$, and $C$. Determine whether $(A \cup C)' \cap B = (A \cap C)' \cap B$ for your sets.

c) Determine whether $(A \cup C)' \cap B = (A \cap C)' \cap B$ for all sets $A$, $B$, and $C$.

**77.** *Blood Types* A hematology text gives the following information on percentages of the different types of blood worldwide.

| Type | Positive Blood, % | Negative Blood, % |
| --- | --- | --- |
| A | 37 | 6 |
| O | 32 | 6.5 |
| B | 11 | 2 |
| AB | 5 | 0.5 |

Construct a Venn diagram similar to the one in Example 2 and place the correct percentage in each of the eight regions.

**78.** Define each of the eight regions in Fig. 2.25 using sets $A$, $B$, and $C$ and a set operation. (*Hint:* $A \cap B' \cap C'$ defines region I.)

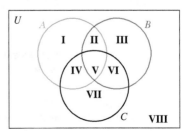

Figure 2.25

**79. Categorizing Contracts** J & C Mechanical Contractors wants to classify its projects. The contractors categorize set A as construction projects, set B as plumbing projects, and set C as projects with a budget greater than $300,000.

**a)** Draw a Venn diagram that can be used to categorize the company projects according to the listed criteria.

**b)** Determine the region of the diagram that contains construction projects and plumbing projects with a budget greater than $300,000. Describe the region using sets A, B, and C with set operations. Use union, intersection, and complement as necessary.

**c)** Determine the region of the diagram that contains plumbing projects with a budget greater than $300,000 that are not construction projects. Describe the region using sets A, B and C with set operations. Use union, intersection, and complement as necessary.

**d)** Determine the region of the diagram that contains construction projects and nonplumbing projects whose budget is less than or equal to $300,000. Describe the region using sets A, B, and C with set operations. Use union, intersection, and complement as necessary.

## Challenge Problem/Group Activity

**80.** We were able to determine the number of elements in the union of two sets with the formula

$$n(A \cup B) = n(A) + n(B) - n(A \cap B).$$

Can you determine a formula for finding the number of elements in the union of three sets? In other words, write a formula to determine $n(A \cup B \cup C)$. [Hint: The formula

will contain each of the following: $n(A)$, $n(B)$, $n(C)$, $n(A \cap B \cap C')$, $n(A \cap B' \cap C)$, $n(A' \cap B \cap C)$, and $2n(A \cap B \cap C)$.

## Recreational Mathematics

**81. a)** Construct a Venn diagram illustrating four sets, A, B, C, and D. (Hint: Four circles cannot be used, and you should end up with 16 distinct regions.) Have fun!

**b)** Label each region with a set statement (see Exercise 78). Check all 16 regions to make sure that each is distinct.

## Internet/Research Activity

**82.** The two Venn diagrams below illustrate what happens when colors are added or subtracted. Do research in an art text, an encyclopedia, the Internet, or another source and write a report explaining the creation of the colors in the Venn diagrams, using such terms as union of colors and subtraction (or difference) of colors.

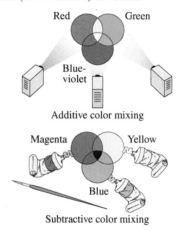

---

# Applications of Sets

▲ We can use a Venn diagram to determine how many members of a health club took a particular fitness class.

The members of a health club were surveyed about taking fitness classes at the club. Suppose the results of the survey show how many members took a yoga class, how many members took a spinning class, and how many members took a class in yoga and a class in spinning. How can the manager of the club use this information to determine how many members took only a yoga class? In this section, we will learn how to use Venn diagrams to answer this type of question.

**Why** *This is Important* As you read through this section, you will see many real-life applications of set theory.

---

We can solve practical problems involving sets by using the problem-solving process discussed in Chapter 1: Understand the problem, devise a plan, carry out the plan, and then examine and check the results. First determine: What is the problem? or What am I looking for? To devise the plan, list all the facts that are given and how they are related. *Look for key words or phrases* such as "only set A," "set A and set B," "set A or set B," "set A and set B and not set C." Remember that *and* means intersection, *or* means union, and *not* means complement. The problems we solve in this section contain two or three sets of elements, which can be represented in a Venn diagram. Our plan will generally include drawing a Venn diagram, labeling the diagram, and filling in the regions of the diagram.

Whenever possible, follow the procedure in Section 2.4 for completing the Venn diagram and then answer the questions. *Remember: When drawing Venn diagrams, we generally start with the intersection of the sets and work outward.*

## Example 1 *Yogurt Taste Test*

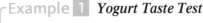

A yogurt company wishes to introduce a new yogurt flavor. The company is considering two flavors: raspberry cheesecake ($R$) and orange creme ($O$). In a survey of 250 people it was found that

180 people liked raspberry cheesecake.

139 people liked orange creme.

82 people liked both flavors.

Of those surveyed, how many people

a) did not like either raspberry cheesecake or orange creme?

b) liked raspberry cheesecake, but not orange creme?

c) liked orange creme, but not raspberry cheesecake?

d) liked either raspberry cheesecake or orange creme?

**Solution** The problem provides the following information.

The number of people surveyed is 250: $n(U) = 250$.

The number of people surveyed who liked raspberry cheesecake is 180: $n(R) = 180$.

The number of people surveyed who liked orange creme is 139: $n(O) = 139$.

The number of people surveyed who liked both raspberry cheesecake and orange creme is 82: $n(R \cap O) = 82$.

We illustrate this information on the Venn diagram shown in Fig. 2.26. We already know that $R \cap O$ corresponds to region II. Because $n(R \cap O) = 82$, we write 82 in region II. Set $R$ consists of regions I and II. We know that set $R$, the number of people who liked raspberry cheesecake, contains 180 people. Therefore, region I contains $180 - 82 = 98$ people. We write the number 98 in region I. Set $O$ consists of regions II and III. Because $n(O) = 139$, the total in these two regions must be 139. Region II contains 82, leaving $139 - 82$, or 57, for region III. We write 57 in region III.

The total number of people surveyed who liked raspberry cheesecake or orange creme is found by adding the numbers in regions I, II, and III. Therefore $n(R \cup O) = 98 + 82 + 57 = 237$. The number in region IV is the difference between $n(U)$ and $n(R \cup O)$. There are $250 - 237$, or 13, members in region IV.

a) The people surveyed who did not like either raspberry cheesecake or orange creme are those people in the universal set who are not contained in set $R$ or set $O$. The 13 people in region IV did not like raspberry cheesecake or orange creme.

b) The 98 people in region I are those people surveyed who liked raspberry cheesecake, but not orange creme.

c) The 57 people in region III are those people surveyed who liked orange creme, but not raspberry cheesecake.

d) The people in regions I, II, or III are those people surveyed who liked either raspberry cheesecake or orange creme. Thus, $98 + 82 + 57$, or 237, people surveyed liked either raspberry cheesecake or orange creme. Notice that the 82 people in region II who like both flavors are included in those people surveyed who liked either raspberry cheesecake or orange creme. ∎

Similar problems involving three sets can be solved, as illustrated in Example 2.

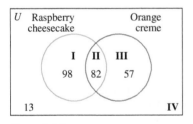

$U$ Raspberry cheesecake    Orange creme

I   II   III

98   82   57

13          IV

Figure 2.26

Example **2**  *Software Purchases*

CompUSA has recorded recent sales for three types of computer software: games, educational software, and utility programs. The following information regarding software purchases was obtained from a survey of 893 customers.

545 purchased games.

497 purchased educational software.

290 purchased utility programs.

297 purchased games and educational software.

196 purchased educational software and utility programs.

205 purchased games and utility programs.

157 purchased all three types of software.

Use a Venn diagram to answer the following questions. How many customers purchased

a) none of these types of software?

b) only games?

c) at least one of these types of software?

d) exactly two of these types of software?

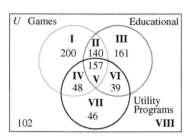

Figure 2.27

**Solution**   Begin by constructing a Venn diagram with three overlapping circles. One circle represents games, another educational software, and the third utilities. See Fig 2.27. Label the eight regions.

Whenever possible, work from the center of the diagram outward. First fill in region V. Since 157 customers purchased all three types of software, we place 157 in region V. Next determine the number to be placed in region II. Regions II and V together represent the customers who purchased both games and educational software. Since 297 customers purchased both of these types of software, the sum of the numbers in these regions must be 297. Since 157 have already been placed in region V, $297 - 157 = 140$ must be placed in region II. Now we determine the number to be placed in region IV. Since 205 customers purchased both games and utility programs, the sum of the numbers in regions IV and V must be 205. Since 157 have already been placed in region V, $205 - 157 = 48$ must be placed in region IV. Now determine the number to be placed in region VI. A total of 196 customers purchased educational software and utility programs. The numbers in regions V and VI must total 196. Since 157 have already been placed in region V, the number to be placed in region VI is $196 - 157 = 39$.

Now that we have determined the numbers for regions V, II, IV, and VI, we can determine the numbers to be placed in regions I, III, and VII. We are given that 545 customers purchased games. The sum of the numbers in regions I, II, IV, and V must be 545. To determine the number to be placed in region I, subtract the amounts in regions II, IV, and V from 545. There must be $545 - 140 - 48 - 157 = 200$ in region I. Determine the numbers to be placed in regions III and VII in a similar manner.

$$\text{Region III} = 497 - 140 - 157 - 39 = 161$$
$$\text{Region VII} = 290 - 48 - 157 - 39 = 46$$

Now that we have determined the numbers in regions I through VII, we can determine the number to be placed in region VIII. Adding the numbers in regions I through VII yields a sum of 791. The difference between the total number of customers surveyed, 893, and the sum of the numbers in regions I through VII must be placed in region VIII.

$$\text{Region VIII} = 893 - 791 = 102$$

Now that we have completed the Venn diagram, we can answer the questions.

a)  One hundred two customers did not purchase any of these types of software. These customers are indicated in region VIII.

**TIMELY TIP**

When constructing a Venn diagram, the most common mistake made by students is forgetting to subtract the number in region V from the respective values in determining the numbers to be placed in regions II, IV, and VI.

b) Region I represents those customers who purchased only games. Thus, 200 customers purchased only games.

c) The words *at least one* mean "one or more." All those in regions I through VII purchased at least one of the types of software. The sum of the numbers in regions I through VII is 791, so 791 customers purchased at least one of the types of software.

d) The customers in regions II, IV, and VI purchased exactly two of the types of software. Summing the numbers in these regions $140 + 48 + 39$ we find that 227 customers purchased exactly two of these types of software. Notice that we did not include the customers in region V. Those customers purchased all three types of software.

The procedure to work problems like those given in Example 2 is generally the same. Start by completing region V. Next complete regions II, IV, and VI. Then complete regions I, III, and VII. Finally, complete region VIII. When you are constructing Venn diagrams, be sure to check your work carefully.

Example 3 *Travel Packages*

Liberty Travel surveyed 125 potential customers. The following information was obtained.

68 wished to travel to Hawaii.

53 wished to travel to Las Vegas.

47 wished to travel to Disney World.

34 wished to travel to Hawaii and Las Vegas.

26 wished to travel to Las Vegas and Disney World.

23 wished to travel to Hawaii and Disney World.

18 wished to travel to all three destinations.

Use a Venn diagram to answer the following questions. How many of those surveyed

a) did not wish to travel to any of these destinations?

b) wished to travel only to Hawaii?

c) wished to travel to Disney World *and* Las Vegas, but not to Hawaii?

d) wished to travel to Disney World *or* Las Vegas, but not to Hawaii?

e) wished to travel to exactly one of these destinations?

▲ *Hawaii*

Solution The Venn diagram is constructed using the procedures we outlined in Example 2. The diagram is illustrated in Fig. 2.28. We suggest you construct the diagram by yourself now and check your diagram with Fig. 2.28.

a) Twenty-two potential customers did not wish to travel to any of these destinations (see region VIII).

b) Twenty-nine potential customers wished to travel only to Hawaii (see region I).

c) Those potential customers in region VI wished to travel to Disney World *and* Las Vegas, but not to Hawaii. Therefore, eight customers satisfied the criteria.

d) The word *or* in this type of problem means one or the other or both. All the potential customers in regions II, III, IV, V, VI, and VII wished to travel to Disney World or Las Vegas. Those in regions II, IV, and V also wished to travel to Hawaii. The potential customers that wished to travel to Disney World or Las Vegas, but not to Hawaii, are found by adding the numbers in regions III, VI, and VII. There are $16 + 8 + 11 = 35$ potential customers who satisfy the criteria.

e) Those potential customers in regions I, III, and VII wished to travel to exactly one of the destinations. Therefore, $29 + 16 + 11 = 56$ customers wished to travel to exactly one of these destinations.

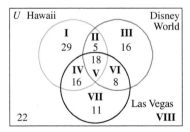

Figure 2.28

## SECTION 2.5    *Exercises*

### Practice The Skills/Problem Solving

*In Exercises 1–15, draw a Venn diagram to obtain the answers.*

1. *Market Purchases* During the fall festival at Wambach's Farmer's market, 200 customers made the following purchases.

   109 purchased pumpkins.

   98 purchased pies.

   61 purchased both pumpkins and pies.

   Of those surveyed,

   a) how many purchased only pumpkins?

   b) how many purchased only pies?

   c) how many did not purchase either of these items?

2. *Landscape Purchases* Agway Lawn and Garden collected the following information regarding purchases from 130 of its customers.

   74 purchased shrubs.

   70 purchased trees.

   41 purchased both shrubs and trees.

   Of those surveyed,

   a) how many purchased only shrubs?

   b) how many purchased only trees?

   c) how many did not purchase either of these items?

3. *Real Estate* The Maiellos are moving to Wilmington, Delaware. Their real estate agent located 83 houses listed for sale, in the Wilmington area, in their price range. Of these houses listed for sale,

   47 had a family room.

   42 had a deck.

   30 had a family room and a deck.

   How many had

   a) a family room but not a deck?

   b) a deck but not a family room?

   c) either a family room or a deck?

4. *Racing* Fleet Foot Racing interviewed 150 long-distance runners to determine the type of races in which they participated. The following information was determined.

   102 participated in a marathon.

   93 participated in a triathlon.

   55 participated in both a marathon and a triathlon.

How many

   a) participated in only a marathon?

   b) participated in only a triathlon?

   c) participated in either a marathon or a triathlon?

   d) had not participated in either a marathon or a triathlon?

5. *Cultural Activities* Thirty-three U.S. cities were researched to determine whether they had a professional sports team, a symphony, or a children's museum. The following information was determined.

   16 had a professional sports team.

   17 had a symphony.

   15 had a children's museum.

   11 had a professional sports team and a symphony.

   7 had a professional sports team and a children's museum.

   9 had a symphony and children's museum.

   5 had all three activities.

How many of the cities surveyed had

   a) only a professional sports team?

   b) a professional sports team and a symphony, but not a children's museum?

   c) a professional sports team or a symphony?

   d) a professional sports team or a symphony, but not a children's museum?

   e) exactly two of the activities?

6. *Amusement Parks* In a survey of 85 amusement parks, it was found that

   24 had a hotel on site.

   55 had water slides.

   38 had a wave pool.

   13 had a hotel on site and water slides.

   10 had a hotel on site and a wave pool.

   19 had water slides and a wave pool.

   7 had all three features.

How many of the amusement parks surveyed had

**a)** only water slides?

**b)** exactly one of these features?

**c)** at least one of these features?

**d)** exactly two of these features?

**e)** none of these features?

7. *Book Purchases*  A survey of 85 customers was taken at Barnes & Noble regarding the types of books purchased. The survey found that

44 purchased mysteries.

33 purchased science fiction.

29 purchased romance novels.

13 purchased mysteries and science fiction.

5 purchased science fiction and romance novels.

11 purchased mysteries and romance novels.

2 purchased all three types of books.

How many of the customers surveyed purchased

**a)** only mysteries?

**b)** mysteries and science fiction, but not romance novels?

**c)** mysteries or science fiction?

**d)** mysteries or science fiction, but not romance novels?

**e)** exactly two types?

8. *Movies*  A survey of 350 customers was taken at Regal Cinemas in Austin, Texas, regarding the type of movies customers liked. The following information was determined.

196 liked dramas.

153 liked comedies.

88 liked science fiction.

59 liked dramas and comedies.

37 liked dramas and science fiction.

32 liked comedies and science fiction.

21 liked all three types of movies.

Of the customers surveyed, how many liked

**a)** none of these types of movies?

**b)** only dramas?

**c)** exactly one of these types of movies?

**d)** exactly two of these types of movies?

**e)** dramas or comedies?

9. *Jobs at a Restaurant*  Panera Bread compiled the following information regarding 30 of its employees. The following was determined.

8 cooked food.

9 washed dishes.

18 operated the cash register.

4 cooked food and washed dishes.

5 washed dishes and operated the cash register.

3 cooked food and operated the cash register.

2 did all three jobs.

How many of the employees

**a)** only cooked food ?

**b)** only operated the cash register?

**c)** washed dishes and operated the cash register but did not cook food?

**d)** washed dishes or operated the cash register but did not cook food?

**e)** did at least two of these jobs?

10. *Electronic Devices*  In a survey of college students, it was found that

356 owned an iPod.

293 owned a laptop.

285 owned a gaming system.

193 owned an iPod and a laptop.

200 owned an iPod and a gaming system.

139 owned a laptop and a gaming system.

68 owned an iPod, a laptop, and a gaming system.

26 owned none of these devices.

**a)** How many college students were surveyed?

Of the college students surveyed, how many owned

**b)** an iPod and a gaming system, but not a laptop?

**c)** a laptop, but neither an iPod nor a gaming system?

**d)** exactly two of these devices?

**e)** at least one of these devices?

11. *Homeowners' Insurance Policies*  A committee of the Florida legislature decided to analyze 350 homeowners' insurance policies to determine if the consumers' homes

were covered for damage due to sinkholes, mold, and floods. The following results were determined.

170 homes were covered for damage due to sinkholes.

172 homes were covered for damage due to mold.

234 homes were covered for damage due to floods.

105 homes were covered for damage due to sinkholes and mold.

115 homes were covered for damage due to mold and floods.

109 homes were covered for damage due to sinkholes and floods.

78 homes were covered for damage due to all three conditions.

How many of the homes

**a)** were covered for damage due to mold but were not covered for damage due to sinkholes?

**b)** were covered for damage due to sinkholes or mold?

**c)** were covered for damage due to mold and floods but were not covered for damage due to sinkholes?

**d)** were not covered for damage due to any of the three conditions?

**12.** *Appetizers Survey* Da Tulio's Restaurant hired Dennis Goldstein to determine what kind of appetizers customers liked. He surveyed 100 people, with the following results: 78 liked shrimp cocktail, 56 liked mozzarella sticks, and 35 liked both shrimp cocktail and mozzarella sticks. Every person interviewed liked one or the other or both kinds of appetizers. Does this result seem correct? Explain your answer.

**13.** *Discovering an Error* An immigration agent sampled cars going from the United States into Canada. In his report, he indicated that of the 85 cars sampled,

35 cars were driven by women.

53 cars were driven by U.S. citizens.

43 cars had two or more passengers.

27 cars were driven by women who are U.S. citizens.

25 cars were driven by women and had two or more passengers.

20 cars were driven by U.S. citizens and had two or more passengers.

15 cars were driven by women who are U.S. citizens and had two or more passengers.

After his supervisor reads the report, she explains to the agent that he made a mistake. Explain how his supervisor knew that the agent's report contained an error.

## Challenge Problems/Group Activities

**14.** *Parks* A survey of 300 parks showed the following.

15 had only camping.

20 had only hiking trails.

35 had only picnicking.

185 had camping.

140 had camping and hiking trails.

125 had camping and picnicking.

210 had hiking trails.

Determine the number of parks that

**a)** had at least one of these features.

**b)** had all three features.

**c)** did not have any of these features.

**d)** had exactly two of these features.

**15.** *Surveying Farmers* A survey of 500 farmers in a midwestern state showed the following.

125 grew only wheat.

110 grew only corn.

90 grew only oats.

200 grew wheat.

60 grew wheat and corn.

50 grew wheat and oats.

180 grew corn.

Determine the number of farmers who

**a)** grew at least one of the three.

**b)** grew all three.

**c)** did not grow any of the three.

**d)** grew exactly two of the three.

**16. *Family Reunion*** When the Montesano family members discussed where their annual reunion should take place, they found that of all the family members,

8 would not go to a park.

7 would not go to a beach.

11 would not go to the family cottage.

3 would go to neither a park nor a beach.

4 would go to neither a beach nor the family cottage.

6 would go to neither a park nor the family cottage.

2 would not go to a park or a beach or to the family cottage.

1 would go to all three places.

What is the total number of family members?

## Recreational Mathematics

**17. *Number of Elements*** A universal set $U$ consists of 12 elements. If sets $A$, $B$, and $C$ are proper subsets of $U$ and $n(U) = 12$, $n(A \cap B) = n(A \cap C) = n(B \cap C) = 6$, $n(A \cap B \cap C) = 4$, and $n(A \cup B \cup C) = 10$, determine

**a)** $n(A \cup B)$

**b)** $n(A' \cup C)$

**c)** $n(A \cap B)'$

---

**SECTION 2.6**    Infinite Sets

▲ *Georg Cantor, founder of set theory*

Which set is larger, the set of integers or the set of even integers? One might argue that because the set of even integers is a subset of the set of integers, the set of integers must be larger than the set of even integers. Yet both sets are infinite sets, so how can we determine which set is larger? This question puzzled mathematicians for centuries until 1874, when Georg Cantor developed a method of determining the cardinal number of an infinite set. In this section, we will discuss infinite sets and how to determine the number of elements in an infinite set.

**Why** *This is Important*    The concept of infinity and which sets contain more elements has led to the expansion and understanding of many mathematical and scientific concepts.

On page 45, we state that a finite set is a set in which the number of elements is zero or the number of elements can be expressed as a natural number. On page 46, we define a one-to-one correspondence. To determine the number of elements in a finite set, we can place the set in a one-to-one correspondence with a subset of the set of counting numbers. For example, the set $A = \{\#, ?, \$\}$ can be placed in one-to-one correspondence with set $B = \{1, 2, 3\}$, a subset of the set of counting numbers.

$$A = \{\#, \ ?, \ \$\}$$
$$\downarrow \ \downarrow \ \downarrow$$
$$B = \{1, \ 2, \ 3\}$$

Because the cardinal number of set $B$ is 3, the cardinal number of set $A$ is also 3. Any two sets, such as set $A$ and set $B$, that can be placed in a one-to-one correspondence must have the same number of elements (therefore the same cardinality) and must be equivalent sets. Note that $n(A)$ and $n(B)$ both equal 3.

German mathematician Georg Cantor (1845–1918), known as the father of set theory, thought about sets that were not bounded. He called an unbounded set an *infinite set* and provided the following definition.

Definition: **Infinite Set**

An **infinite set** is a set that can be placed in a one-to-one correspondence with a proper subset of itself.

In Example 1, we use Cantor's definition of an infinite set to show that the set of counting numbers is infinite.

### Example 1    *The Set of Natural Numbers*

Show that $N = \{1, 2, 3, 4, 5, \ldots, n, \ldots\}$ is an infinite set.

*Solution*    To show that the set $N$ is infinite, we establish a one-to-one correspondence between the counting numbers and a proper subset of itself. By removing the first element from the set of counting numbers, we get the set $\{2, 3, 4, 5, 6, \ldots\}$, which is a proper subset of the set of counting numbers. Now we establish the one-to-one correspondence.

$$\text{Counting numbers} = \{1, 2, 3, 4, 5, \ldots, \quad n, \ldots\}$$
$$\downarrow \downarrow \downarrow \downarrow \downarrow \qquad\qquad \downarrow$$
$$\text{Proper subset} \quad = \{2, 3, 4, 5, 6, \ldots, n + 1, \ldots\}$$

Note that for any number, $n$, in the set of counting numbers, its corresponding number in the proper subset is one greater, or $n + 1$. We have now shown the desired one-to-one correspondence, and thus the set of counting numbers is infinite.    ∎

Note in Example 1 that we showed the pairing of the general terms $n \rightarrow (n + 1)$. Showing a one-to-one correspondence of infinite sets requires showing the pairing of the general terms in the two infinite sets.

In the set of counting numbers, $n$ represents the general term. For any other set of numbers, the general term will be different. The general term in any set should be written in terms of $n$ such that when 1 is substituted for $n$ in the general term, we get the first number in the set; when 2 is substituted for $n$ in the general term, we get the second number in the set; when 6 is substituted for $n$ in the general term, we get the sixth number in the set; and so on.

Consider the set $\{4, 9, 14, 19, \ldots\}$. Suppose we want to write the general term for this set (or sequence) of numbers. What would the general term be? The numbers differ by 5, so the general term will be of the form $5n$ plus or minus some number. Substituting 1 for $n$ yields $5(1)$, or 5. Because the first number in the set is 4, we need to subtract 1 from the 5. Thus, the general term is $5n - 1$. Note that when $n = 1$, the value is $5(1) - 1$ or 4; when $n = 2$, the value is $5(2) - 1$ or 9; when $n = 3$, the value is $5(3) - 1$ or 14; and so on. Therefore, we write the set of numbers with the general term as

$$\{4, 9, 14, 19, \ldots, 5n - 1, \ldots\}$$

Now that you are aware of how to determine the general term of a set of numbers, we can do some more problems involving sets.

### Example 2    *The Set of Even Numbers*

Show that the set of even counting numbers $\{2, 4, 6, 8, \ldots, 2n, \ldots\}$ is an infinite set.

*Solution*   First create a proper subset of the set of even counting numbers by removing the first number from the set. Then establish a one-to-one correspondence.

Even counting numbers: $\{2, 4, 6, 8, \ldots, \quad 2n, \ldots\}$

Proper subset: $\{4, 6, 8, 10, \ldots, 2n + 2, \ldots\}$

A one-to-one correspondence exists between the two sets, so the set of even counting numbers is infinite.

### Example 3   *The Set of Multiples of Five*

Show that the set $\{5, 10, 15, 20, \ldots, 5n, \ldots\}$ is an infinite set.

*Solution*

Given set: $\{5, 10, 15, 20, 25, \ldots, \quad 5n, \ldots\}$

Proper subset: $\{10, 15, 20, 25, 30, \ldots, 5n + 5, \ldots\}$

Therefore, the given set is an infinite set.

## Countable Sets

In his work with infinite sets, Cantor developed ideas on how to determine the cardinal number of an infinite set. He called the cardinal number of infinite sets "transfinite cardinal numbers" or "transfinite powers." He defined a set as *countable* if it is finite or if it can be placed in a one-to-one correspondence with the set of counting numbers. All infinite sets that can be placed in a one-to-one correspondence with the set of counting numbers have cardinal number *aleph-null*, symbolized $\aleph_0$ (the first Hebrew letter, aleph, with a zero subscript, read "null").

### Example 4   *The Cardinal Number of the Set of Even Numbers*

Show that the set of even counting numbers has cardinal number $\aleph_0$.

*Solution*   In Example 2, we showed that the set of even counting numbers is infinite by setting up a one-to-one correspondence between the set and a proper subset of itself.

Now we will show that it is countable and has cardinality $\aleph_0$ by setting up a one-to-one correspondence between the set of counting numbers and the set of even counting numbers.

Counting numbers: $N = \{1, 2, 3, 4, \ldots, n, \ldots\}$

Even counting numbers: $E = \{2, 4, 6, 8, \ldots, 2n, \ldots\}$

For each number $n$ in the set of counting numbers, its corresponding number is $2n$. Since we found a one-to-one correspondence between the set of counting numbers and the set of even counting numbers, the set of even counting numbers is countable. Thus, the cardinal number of the set of even counting numbers is $\aleph_0$; that is, $n(E) = \aleph_0$. As we mentioned earlier, the set of even counting numbers is an infinite set, since it can be placed in a one-to-one correspondence with a proper subset of itself. Therefore, the set of even counting numbers is both infinite and countable.

### Definition: Cardinal Number of Infinite Sets

Any set that can be placed in a one-to-one correspondence with the set of counting numbers has **cardinal number** (or cardinality) $\aleph_0$ and is infinite and is countable.

Example **5**    *The Cardinal Number of the Set of Odd Numbers*

Show that the set of odd counting numbers has cardinality $\aleph_0$.

*Solution*    To show that the set of odd counting numbers has cardinality $\aleph_0$, we need to show a one-to-one correspondence between the set of counting numbers and the set of odd counting numbers.

Counting numbers:    $N = \{1, 2, 3, 4, 5, \ldots, \quad n \ , \ldots\}$

Odd counting numbers:    $O = \{1, 3, 5, 7, 9, \ldots, 2n - 1, \ldots\}$

Since there is a one-to-one correspondence, the odd counting numbers have cardinality $\aleph_0$; that is, $n(O) = \aleph_0$.    ■

We have shown that both the odd and the even counting numbers have cardinality $\aleph_0$. Merging the odd counting numbers with the even counting numbers gives the set of counting numbers, and we may reason that

$$\aleph_0 + \aleph_0 = \aleph_0$$

This result may seem strange, but it is true. What could such a statement mean? Well, consider a hotel with infinitely many rooms. If all the rooms are occupied, the hotel is, of course, full. If more guests appear, wanting accommodations, will they be turned away? The answer is *no,* for if the room clerk were to reassign each guest to a new room with a room number twice that of the present room, all the odd-numbered rooms would become unoccupied and there would be space for infinitely many more guests!

Cantor showed that there are different orders of infinity. Sets that are countable and have cardinal number $\aleph_0$ are the lowest order of infinity. Cantor showed that the set of integers and the set of rational numbers (fractions of the form $p/q$, where $q \neq 0$) are infinite sets with cardinality $\aleph_0$. He also showed that the set of real numbers (discussed in Chapter 5) could not be placed in a one-to-one correspondence with the set of counting numbers and that they have a higher order of infinity.

▲ *. . . where there's always room for one more. . .*

---

*Exercises*

## Warm Up Exercises

*In exercises 1–2, fill in the blank with an appropriate word, phrase, or symbol(s).*

1. A set that can be placed in a one-to-one correspondence with a proper subset of itself is called a(n) _____ set.

2. A set that is finite or can be placed in a one-to-one correspondence with the set of counting numbers is called a(n)_____ set.

## Practice the Skills

*In Exercises 3–12, show that the set is infinite by placing it in a one-to-one correspondence with a proper subset of itself. Be sure to show the pairing of the general terms in the sets.*

3. $\{3, 4, 5, 6, 7, \ldots\}$

4. $\{30, 31, 32, 33, 34, \ldots\}$

5. $\{3, 5, 7, 9, 11, \ldots\}$

6. $\{20, 22, 24, 26, 28, \ldots\}$

7. $\{5, 9, 13, 17, 21, \ldots\}$

8. $\{6, 11, 16, 21, 26, \ldots\}$

9. $\{\frac{1}{2}, \frac{1}{4}, \frac{1}{6}, \frac{1}{8}, \frac{1}{10}, \ldots\}$

10. $\{1, \frac{1}{2}, \frac{1}{3}, \frac{1}{4}, \frac{1}{5}, \ldots\}$

11. $\{\frac{4}{11}, \frac{5}{11}, \frac{6}{11}, \frac{7}{11}, \frac{8}{11}, \ldots\}$

12. $\{\frac{6}{13}, \frac{7}{13}, \frac{8}{13}, \frac{9}{13}, \frac{10}{13}, \ldots\}$

*In Exercises 13–22, show that the set has cardinal number $\aleph_0$ by establishing a one-to-one correspondence between the set of counting numbers and the given set. Be sure to show the pairing of the general terms in the sets.*

**13.** $\{3, 6, 9, 12, 15, \dots\}$  **14.** $\{40, 41, 42, 43, 44, \dots\}$

**15.** $\{4, 6, 8, 10, 12, \dots\}$  **16.** $\{0, 2, 4, 6, 8, \dots\}$

**17.** $\{2, 5, 8, 11, 14, \dots\}$  **18.** $\{7, 11, 15, 19, 23, \dots\}$

**19.** $\{\frac{1}{3}, \frac{1}{6}, \frac{1}{9}, \frac{1}{12}, \frac{1}{15}, \dots\}$  **20.** $\{\frac{1}{2}, \frac{1}{4}, \frac{1}{6}, \frac{1}{8}, \dots\}$

**21.** $\{\frac{1}{3}, \frac{1}{4}, \frac{1}{5}, \frac{1}{6}, \frac{1}{7}, \dots\}$  **22.** $\{\frac{1}{2}, \frac{2}{3}, \frac{3}{4}, \frac{4}{5}, \frac{5}{6}, \dots\}$

## Challenge Problems/Group Activities

*In Exercises 23–26, show that the set has cardinality $\aleph_0$ by establishing a one-to-one correspondence between the set of counting numbers and the given set.*

**23.** $\{1, 4, 9, 16, 25, \dots\}$  **24.** $\{2, 4, 8, 16, 32, \dots\}$

**25.** $\{3, 9, 27, 81, 243, \dots\}$  **26.** $\{\frac{1}{3}, \frac{1}{6}, \frac{1}{12}, \frac{1}{24}, \frac{1}{48}, \dots\}$

## Recreational Mathematics

*In Exercises 27–31, insert the symbol $<$, $>$, or $=$ in the shaded area to make a true statement.*

**27.** $\aleph_0$ \_\_\_ $\aleph_0 + \aleph_0$  **28.** $2\aleph_0$ \_\_\_ $\aleph_0 + \aleph_0$

**29.** $2\aleph_0$ \_\_\_ $\aleph_0$  **30.** $\aleph_0 + 5$ \_\_\_ $\aleph_0 + 3$

**31.** $n(N)$ \_\_\_ $\aleph_0$

**32.** There are a number of paradoxes (a statement that appears to be true and false at the same time) associated with infinite sets and the concept of infinity. One of these, called *Zeno's Paradox,* is named after the mathematician Zeno, born about 496 B.C. in Italy. According to Zeno's paradox, suppose Achelles starts out 1 meter behind a tortoise. Also, suppose Achelles walks 10 times as fast as the tortoise crawls. When Achelles reaches the point where the tortoise started, the tortoise is 1/10 of a meter ahead of Achelles; when Achelles reaches the point where the tortoise was 1/10 of a meter ahead, the tortoise is now 1/100 of a meter ahead; and so on. According to Zeno's Paradox, Achelles gets closer and closer to the tortoise but never catches up to the tortoise.

**a)** Do you believe the reasoning process is sound? If not, explain why not.

**b)** In actuality, if this situation were real, would Achelles ever pass the tortoise?

## Internet/Research Activities

**33.** Do research to explain how Cantor proved that the set of rational numbers has cardinal number $\aleph_0$.

**34.** Do research to explain how it can be shown that the real numbers do not have cardinal number $\aleph_0$.

## CHAPTER 2  *Summary*

### Important Facts and Concepts

### Examples and Discussion

| Section 2.1 | |
|---|---|
| **Methods Used to Indicate a Set** | |
| Description | Example 1, page 43 |
| Roster Form | Examples 2–3, 5–7 pages 44, 45 |
| Set-Builder Notation | Examples 4–6, pages 44–45 |

| Symbol | Meaning | |
|---|---|---|
| $\in$ | is an element of | Examples 4–6, pages 44–45 |
| $\notin$ | is not an element of | |
| $n(A)$ | number of elements in set $A$ | |
| $\varnothing$ or $\{\}$ | the empty set | |
| $U$ | the universal set | |

## Section 2.2

| Symbol | Meaning | |
|---|---|---|
| $\subseteq$ | is a subset of | Examples 1 and 3, pages 52–53 |
| $\not\subseteq$ | is not a subset of | |
| $\subset$ | is a proper subset of | |
| $\not\subset$ | is not a proper subset of | |
| Number of distinct subsets of a finite set with $n$ elements is $2^n$. | | Examples 4 and 5, pages 54 |

## Section 2.3

| Symbol | Meaning | |
|---|---|---|
| $'$ | complement | Examples 1, 3–6, pages 57, 58–61 |
| $\cap$ | intersection | Examples 2, 3, 6, pages 58–61 |
| $\cup$ | union | Examples 4–6, pages 57–61 |
| $-$ | difference of two sets | Example 9, page 62 |
| $\times$ | cartesian product | Example 10, page 63 |
| *And* is generally interpreted to mean *intersection*. | | Examples 7 and 8, pages 61–62 |
| *Or* is generally interpreted to mean *union*. | | Examples 7 and 8, pages 61–62 |
| For any sets $A$ and $B$, | | Examples 7 and 8, pages 61–62 |
| $n(A \cup B) = n(A) + n(B) - n(A \cap B)$ | | |

## Section 2.4

| De Morgan's Laws | |
|---|---|
| $(A \cap B)' = A' \cup B'$ | Example 3, page 71 |
| $(A \cup B)' = A' \cap B'$ | |

## Section 2.6

| | |
|---|---|
| An **infinite set** is a set that can be placed in a one-to-one correspondence with a proper subset of itself. | Examples 1–5, pages 84–86, Discussion pages 83–84 |
| $\aleph_0$      aleph-null | Examples 4–5, pages 85–86 |
| Countable sets | Examples 4–5, pages 85–86 |

## CHAPTER 2   *Review Exercises*

**2.1, 2.2, 2.3, 2.4, 2.6**

*In Exercises 1–14, state whether each statement is true or false. If false, give a reason.*

**1.** The set of cities located in the state of Indiana is a well-defined set.

**2.** The set of the three best movies is a well-defined set.

**3.** maple $\in$ {oak, elm, maple, sycamore}

**4.** { } $\subset \varnothing$

**5.** {3, 6, 9, 12, ... } and {2, 4, 6, 8, ... } are disjoint sets.

**6.** {$a, b, c, 1, 2$} is an example of a set in roster form.

**7.** {purple, green, yellow} = {green, pink, yellow}

**8.** {apple, orange, banana, pear} is equivalent to {tomato, corn, spinach, radish}.

**9.** If $A = $ {a, e, i, o, u}, then $n(A) = 5$.

**10.** $A = $ {1, 3, 5, 7, ... } is a countable set.

**11.** $A = $ {1, 4, 7, 10, ..., 31} is a finite set.

**12.** {2, 5, 7} $\subseteq$ {2, 5, 7, 10}.

**13.** {$x \mid x \in N$ and $3 < x \leq 9$} is a set in set-builder notation.

**14.** {$x \mid x \in N$ and $2 < x \leq 12$} $\subseteq$ {1, 2, 3, 4, 5, ..., 20}

*In Exercises 15–18, express each set in roster form.*

**15.** Set *A* is the set of odd natural numbers between 5 and 16.

**16.** Set *B* is the set of states that border Kansas.

Kansas

**17.** $C = \{x \mid x \in N \text{ and } x < 162\}$

**18.** $D = \{x \mid x \in N \text{ and } 8 < x \le 80\}$

*In Exercises 19–22, express each set in set-builder notation.*

**19.** Set *A* is the set of natural numbers between 50 and 150.

**20.** Set *B* is the set of natural numbers greater than 42.

**21.** Set *C* is the set of natural numbers less than 7.

**22.** Set *D* is the set of natural numbers between 27 and 51, inclusive.

*In Exercises 23–26, express each set with a written description.*

**23.** $A = \{x \mid x \text{ is a capital letter of the English alphabet from E through M inclusive}\}$

**24.** $B = \{\text{penny, nickel, dime, quarter, half-dollar}\}$

**25.** $C = \{a, b, c\}$

**26.** $D = \{x \mid 3 \le x < 9\}$

*In Exercises 27–36, let*

$$U = \{1, 2, 3, 4, \ldots, 10\}$$
$$A = \{1, 3, 5, 7\}$$
$$B = \{3, 7, 9, 10\}$$
$$C = \{1, 7, 10\}$$

*Determine the following.*

**27.** $A \cap B$

**28.** $A \cup B'$

**29.** $A' \cap B$

**30.** $(A \cup B)' \cup C$

**31.** $A - B$

**32.** $A - C'$

**33.** $A \times C$

**34.** $B \times A$

**35.** The number of subsets of set *B*

**36.** The number of proper subsets of set *A*

**37.** For the following sets, construct a Venn diagram and place the elements in the proper region.

$U = \{\text{lion, tiger, leopard, cheetah, puma, lynx, panther, jaguar}\}$
$A = \{\text{tiger, puma, lynx}\}$
$B = \{\text{lion, tiger, jaguar, panther}\}$
$C = \{\text{tiger, lynx, cheetah, panther}\}$

*In Exercises 38–43, use Fig. 2.29 to determine the sets.*

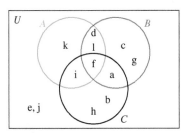

**Figure 2.29**

**38.** $A \cup B$          **39.** $A \cap B'$

**40.** $A \cup B \cup C$

**41.** $A \cap B \cap C$          **42.** $(A \cup B) \cap C$

**43.** $(A \cap B) \cup C$

*Construct a Venn diagram to determine whether the following statements are true for all sets A, B, and C.*

**44.** $(A' \cup B')' = A \cap B$

**45.** $(A \cup B') \cup (A \cup C') = A \cup (B \cap C)'$

In Exercises 46–51, use the following table, which shows the amount of sugar, in grams (g) and caffeine, in milligrams (mg), in an 8-oz serving of selected beverages. Let the beverages listed represent the universal set.

| Beverage | Sugar (grams, g) | Caffeine (milligrams, mg) |
|---|---|---|
| Mountain Dew | 31 | 37 |
| Coca-Cola | 27 | 23 |
| Pepsi | 27 | 25 |
| Sprite | 26 | 0 |
| Brewed coffee | 0 | 108 |
| Brewed tea | 0 | 47 |
| Orange juice | 24 | 0 |
| Grape juice | 40 | 0 |
| Gatorade | 14 | 0 |
| Red Bull | 26 | 76 |
| Vitamin Water | 13 | 17 |
| Water | 0 | 0 |

Source: International Food Information Council

Let A be the set of beverages that contain at least 20 g of sugar.

Let B be the set of beverages that contain at least 20 mg of caffeine.

Indicate in Fig 2.30 in which region, I–IV, each of the following beverages belongs.

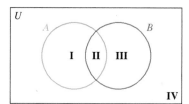

Figure 2.30

46. Pepsi

47. Brewed coffee

48. Orange juice

49. Vitamin Water

50. Gatorade

51. Mountain Dew

52. Red Bull

2.5

53. **Pizza Survey**  A pizza chain was willing to pay $1 to each person interviewed about his or her likes and dislikes of types of pizza crust. Of the people interviewed, 200 liked thin crust, 270 liked thick crust, 70 liked both, and 50 did not like pizza at all. What was the total cost of the survey?

54. **Shopping Preferences**  Visitors to a shopping mall in Atlanta, Georgia, were surveyed to determine their preference for shopping in wholesale warehouse stores. The following information was determined.

58 shopped in BJ's Wholesale Club.
49 shopped in Sam's Club.
45 shopped in Costco.
15 shopped in BJ's Wholesale Club and Sam's Club.
16 shopped in BJ's Wholesale Club and Costco.
12 shopped in Sam's Club and Costco.
 5 shopped in all three stores.
17 did not shop in any of the three stores.

Construct a Venn diagram and then determine how many people

a) completed the survey.

b) shopped only in BJ's Wholesale Club.

c) shopped in BJ's Wholesale Club and Sam's Club, but not Costco.

d) shopped in BJ's Wholesale Club or Costco, but not Sam's Club.

55. **TV Choices** *TV Guide* surveyed 510 subscribers asking which of the following three crime investigation shows they watched on a regular basis: *CSI:Crime Scene Investigation, CSI:Miami,* and *CSI:NY.* The results of the 510 questionnaires that were returned showed that

175 watched *CSI:NY.*
227 watched *CSI:Miami.*
285 watched *CSI:Crime Scene Investigation.*
100 watched *CSI:NY* and *CSI:Miami.*
 96 watched *CSI:NY* and *CSI:Crime Scene Investigation.*
 87 watched *CSI:Miami* and *CSI:Crime Scene Investigation.*
 59 watched all three shows.

Construct a Venn diagram and determine how many people

a) watched only *CSI:NY.*

b) watched exactly one of these shows.

c) watched *CSI:Miami* and *CSI:Crime Scene Investigation,* but not *CSI:NY.*

d) watched *CSI:NY* or *CSI:Crime Scene Investigation,* but not *CSI:Miami.*

e) watched exactly two of these shows.

▲ *Actors from CSI:NY*

**2.6**

*In Exercises 56 and 57, show that the sets are infinite by placing each set in a one-to-one correspondence with a proper subset of itself.*

**56.** $\{2, 4, 6, 8, 10, \dots\}$

**57.** $\{3, 5, 7, 9, 11, \dots\}$

*In Exercises 58 and 59, show that each set has cardinal number $\aleph_0$ by setting up a one-to-one correspondence between the set of counting numbers and the given set.*

**58.** $\{5, 8, 11, 14, 17, \dots\}$

**59.** $\{4, 9, 14, 19, 24, \dots\}$

## CHAPTER 2 ) *Test*

*In Exercises 1–8, state whether each is true or false. If the statement is false, explain why.*

**1.** $\{2, y, \triangle, \$\}$ is equivalent to $\{p, \#, 4, \square\}$.

**2.** $\{3, 5, 9, h\} = \{9, 5, 3, j\}$

**3.** $\{\text{star, moon, sun}\} \subset \{\text{star, moon, sun, planet}\}$

**4.** $\{7\} \subseteq \{x \mid x \in N \text{ and } x < 7\}$

**5.** $\{p, q, r, s\}$ has 15 subsets.

**6.** If $A \cap B = \{\ \}$, then $A$ and $B$ are disjoint sets.

**7.** For any set $A$, $A \cup A' = \{\ \}$.

**8.** For any set $A$, $A \cap U = A$.

*In Exercises 9 and 10, use set*

$$A = \{x \mid x \in N \text{ and } x < 10\}$$

**9.** Write set $A$ in roster form.

**10.** Write a description of set $A$.

*In Exercises 11–16, use the following information.*

$$U = \{3, 5, 7, 9, 11, 13, 15\}$$
$$A = \{3, 5, 7, 9\}$$
$$B = \{7, 9, 11, 13\}$$
$$C = \{3, 11, 15\}$$

*Determine the following.*

**11.** $A \cap B$

**12.** $A \cup C'$

**13.** $A \cap (B \cap C')$

**14.** $n(A \cap B')$

**15.** $A - B$

**16.** $A \times C$

**17.** Using the sets provided for Exercises 11–16, draw a Venn diagram illustrating the relationship among the sets.

**18.** Use a Venn diagram to determine whether

$$A \cap (B \cup C') = (A \cap B) \cup (A \cap C')$$

for all sets $A$, $B$, and $C$. Show your work.

**19.** *Water Activities* A survey of 155 residents of Lake Placid were asked what kind of water activities they participated in on a daily basis during the summer months. The following information was determined.

107 swam.

90 sailed.

76 water skied.

57 swam and sailed.

54 swam and water skied.

52 sailed and water skied.

35 swam, sailed, and water skied.

Construct a Venn diagram and then determine the number of residents who participated in

**a)** exactly one of these activities.

**b)** none of these activities.

**c)** at least two of these activities.

**d)** swimming and sailing, but not water skiing.

**e)** swimming or sailing, but not water skiing.

**f)** only water skiing.

**20.** Show that the following set is infinite by setting up a one-to-one correspondence between the set and a proper subset of itself.

$$\{7, 8, 9, 10, \dots\}$$

## GROUP PROJECTS

### Selecting a Family Pet

1. The Wilcox family is considering buying a dog. They have established several criteria for the family dog: It must be one of the breeds listed in the table, must not shed, must be less than 16 in. tall, and must be good with children.

   a) Using the information in the table,* construct a Venn diagram in which the universal set is the dogs listed. Indicate the set of dogs to be placed in each region of the Venn diagram.

   b) From the Venn diagram constructed in part (a), determine which dogs will meet the criteria set by the Wilcox family. Explain.

| Breed | Sheds | Less than 16 in. | Good with children |
|---|---|---|---|
| Airedale | no | no | no |
| Basset hound | yes | yes | yes |
| Beagle | yes | yes | yes |
| Border terrier | no | yes | yes |
| Cairn terrier | no | yes | no |
| Cocker spaniel | yes | yes | yes |
| Collie | yes | no | yes |
| Dachshund | yes | yes | no |
| Poodle, miniature | no | yes | no |
| Schnauzer, miniature | no | yes | no |
| Scottish terrier | no | yes | no |
| Wirehaired fox terrier | no | yes | no |

### Classification of the Domestic Cat

2. Read the Mathematics Today feature on page 53. Do research and indicate the name of the following groupings to which the domestic cat belongs.

   a) Kingdom

   b) Phylum

   c) Class

   d) Order

   e) Family

   f) Genus

   g) Species

### Who Lives Where

3. On Diplomat Row, an area of Washington, DC, there are five houses. Each owner is a different nationality, each has a different pet, each has a different favorite food, each has a different favorite drink, and each house is painted a different color.

   The green house is directly to the right of the ivory house.
   The Senegalese has the red house.
   The dog belongs to the Spaniard.
   The Afghanistani drinks tea.
   The person who eats cheese lives next door to the fox.
   The Japanese eats fish.
   Milk is drunk in the middle house.
   Apples are eaten in the house next to the horse.
   Ale is drunk in the green house.
   The Norwegian lives in the first house.
   The peach eater drinks whiskey.
   Apples are eaten in the yellow house.
   The banana eater owns a snail.
   The Norwegian lives next door to the blue house.

   For each house find

   a) the color.

   b) the nationality of the occupant.

   c) the owner's favorite food.

   d) the owner's favorite drink.

   e) the owner's pet.

   f) Finally, the crucial question is: Does the zebra's owner drink vodka or ale?

---

*The information is a collection of the opinions of an animal psychologist, Dr. Daniel Tortora, and a group of veterinarians.

# 3
# Logic

## Why This is Important

The study of logic enables us to communicate effectively, make more convincing arguments, and develop patterns of reasoning for decision making. Logic is also used in the programming of modern electronic devices such as cell phones and digital cameras.

◄ *Logic is used in the programming of cell phones and digital cameras.*

## SECTION 3.1    Statements and Logical Connectives

▲ *"Melts in your mouth, not in your hands." Logic symbols can be used to help us analyze statements made by advertisers.*

Advertisements often rely on spoken or written statements that are used to favorably portray the advertised product and form a convincing argument that will persuade us to purchase the product. Some familiar advertising statements are: *Don't leave home without it; It takes a licking and keeps on ticking; Sometimes you feel like a nut, sometimes you don't; When it rains it pours*; and *Melts in your mouth, not in your hands*. In this section, we will learn how to represent statements using logic symbols that may help us better understand the nature of the statement. We will use these symbols throughout the chapter to analyze more complicated statements.

**Why** *This is Important*  Statements appear in everyday life—for example, in legal documents, product instructions, and game rules in addition to advertising.

## History

The ancient Greeks were the first people to systematically analyze the way humans think and arrive at conclusions. Aristotle (384–322 B.C.) organized the study of logic for the first time in a work called *Organon*. As a result of his work, Aristotle is called the father of logic. The logic from this period, called *Aristotelian logic*, has been taught and studied for more than 2000 years.

Since Aristotle's time, the study of logic has been continued by other great philosophers and mathematicians. Gottfried Wilhelm Leibniz (1646–1716) had a deep conviction that all mathematical and scientific concepts could be derived from logic. As a result, he became the first serious student of *symbolic logic*. One difference between symbolic logic and Aristotelian logic is that in symbolic logic, as its name implies, symbols (usually letters) represent written statements. A self-educated English mathematician, George Boole (1815–1864), is considered to be the founder of symbolic logic because of his impressive work in this area. Among Boole's publications are *The Mathematical Analysis of Logic* (1847) and *An Investigation of the Law of Thought* (1854). Mathematician Charles Dodgson, better known as Lewis Carroll, incorporated many interesting ideas from logic into his books *Alice's Adventures in Wonderland* and *Through the Looking Glass* and his other children's stories.

Logic has been studied through the ages to exercise the mind's ability to reason. Understanding logic will enable you to think clearly, communicate effectively, make more convincing arguments, and develop patterns of reasoning that will help you in making decisions. It will also help you to detect the fallacies in the reasoning or arguments of others such as advertisers and politicians. Studying logic has other practical applications, such as helping you to understand wills, contracts, and other legal documents.

The study of logic is also good preparation for other areas of mathematics. If you preview Chapter 12, on probability, you will see formulas for the probability of *A* or *B* and the probability of *A* and *B*, symbolized as *P*(*A* or *B*) and *P*(*A* and *B*), respectively. Special meanings of common words such as *or* and *and* apply to all areas of mathematics. The meaning of these and other special words is discussed in this chapter.

## Logic and the English Language

In reading, writing, and speaking, we use many words such as *and, or,* and *if . . . then . . .* to connect thoughts. In logic we call these words *connectives*. How are these words interpreted in daily communication? A judge announces to a convicted offender, "I hereby sentence you to five months of community service *and* a fine of $100." In this case, we normally interpret the word *and* to indicate that *both* events will take place. That is, the person must perform community service and must also pay a fine.

Now suppose a judge states, "I sentence you to six months in prison *or* 10 months of community service." In this case, we interpret the connective *or* as meaning the convicted person must either spend the time in jail or perform community service, but not both. The word *or* in this case is the *exclusive or*. When the exclusive *or* is used, one or the other of the events can take place, but *not both*.

In a restaurant, a waiter asks, "May I interest you in a cup of soup or a sandwich?" This question offers three possibilities: You may order soup, you may order a sandwich, or you may order both soup and a sandwich. The *or* in this case is the *inclusive or*. When the inclusive *or* is used, one or the other, *or both* events can take place. *In this chapter, when we use the word* or *in a logic statement, it will mean the inclusive* or *unless stated otherwise.*

If–then statements are often used to relate two ideas, as in the bank policy statement "If the average daily balance is greater than $500, then there will be no service charge." If–then statements are also used to emphasize a point or add humor, as in the statement "If the Cubs win, then I will be a monkey's uncle."

Now let's look at logic from a mathematical point of view.

## Statements and Logical Connectives

A sentence that can be judged either true or false is called a *statement*. Labeling a statement true or false is called *assigning a truth value* to the statement. Here are some examples of statements.

1. The Brooklyn Bridge goes over San Francisco Bay.
2. Disney World is in Idaho.
3. The Mississippi River is the longest river in the United States.

In each case, we can say that the sentence is either true or false. Statement 1 is false because the Brooklyn Bridge does not go over San Francisco Bay. Statement 2 is false because Disney World is in Florida. By looking at a map or reading an almanac, we can determine that the Mississippi River is the longest river in the United States; therefore, statement 3 is true.

The three sentences discussed above are examples of *simple statements* because they convey one idea. Sentences combining two or more ideas that can be assigned a truth value are called *compound statements*. Compound statements are discussed shortly.

## Quantifiers

Sometimes it is necessary to change a statement to its opposite meaning. To do so, we use the *negation* of a statement. For example, the negation of the statement "Emily is at home" is "Emily is not at home." The negation of a true statement is always a false statement, and the negation of a false statement is always a true statement. We must use special caution when negating statements containing the words *all*, *none* (or *no*), and *some*. These words are referred to as *quantifiers*.

Consider the statement "All lakes contain fresh water." We know this statement is false because the Great Salt Lake in Utah contains salt water. Its negation must therefore be true. We may be tempted to write its negation as "No lake contains fresh water," but this statement is also false because Lake Superior contains fresh water. Therefore, "No lakes contain fresh water" is not the negation of "All lakes contain fresh water." The correct negation of "All lakes contain fresh water" is "Not all lakes contain fresh water" or "At least one lake does not contain fresh water" or "Some lakes do not contain fresh water." These statements all imply that at least one lake does not contain fresh water, which is a true statement.

▲ *The Brooklyn Bridge in New York City*

96 CHAPTER 3 Logic

George Boole, Augustus De Morgan, and other mathematicians of the nineteenth century were anxious to make logic an abstract science that would operate like algebra but be applicable to all fields. One of the problems logicians faced was that verbal language could be ambiguous and could easily lead to confusion and contradiction. Comedians Bud Abbott and Lou Costello had fun with the ambiguity of language in their skit about the baseball players: "Who's on first, What's on second, I Don't Know is on third—Yeah, but who's on first?"

Now consider the statement "No birds can swim." This statement is false because at least one bird, the penguin, can swim. Therefore, the negation of this statement must be true. We may be tempted to write the negation as "All birds can swim," but because this statement is also false it cannot be the negation. The correct negation of the statement is "Some birds can swim" or "At least one bird can swim," each of which is a true statement.

Now let's consider statements involving the quantifier *some,* as in "Some students have a driver's license." This statement is true, meaning that at least one student has a driver's license. The negation of this statement must therefore be false. The negation is "No student has a driver's license," which is a false statement.

Consider the statement "Some students do not ride motorcycles." This statement is true because it means "At least one student does not ride a motorcycle." The negation of this statement must therefore be false. The negation is "All students ride motorcycles," which is a false statement.

The negation of quantified statements is summarized as follows:

| Form of statement | Form of negation |
| --- | --- |
| All are. | Some are not. |
| None are. | Some are. |
| Some are. | None are. |
| Some are not. | All are. |

The following diagram might help you to remember the statements and their negations:

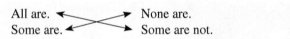

The quantifiers diagonally opposite each other are the negations of each other.

## Example 1 *Write Negations*

Write the negation of each statement.
a) Some telephones can take photographs.
b) All houses have two stories.

**Solution**

a) Since *some* means "at least one," the statement "Some telephones can take photographs" is the same as "At least one telephone can take photographs." Because it is a true statement, its negation must be false. The negation is "No telephones can take photographs," which is a false statement.

b) The statement "All houses have two stories" is a false statement, since some houses have one story, some have three stories, and some may have more than three stories. Its negation must therefore be true. The negation may be written as "Some houses do not have two stories" or "Not all houses have two stories" or "At least one house does not have two stories." Each of these statements is true. ∎

## Compound Statements

Statements consisting of two or more simple statements are called **compound statements**. The connectives often used to join two simple statements are

**and, or, if, … then …, if and only if**

In addition, we consider a simple statement that has been negated to be a compound statement. The word *not* is generally used to negate a statement.

## Sudoku

| | 1 | | 4 | 8 | | 5 | 6 | |
|---|---|---|---|---|---|---|---|---|
| 5 | | | | | 9 | 8 | | |
| | 3 | | | | 1 | 4 | | 7 |
| 8 | 2 | | | 9 | | 1 | | |
| 6 | | | 1 | | 4 | | | 9 |
| | | 3 | | 6 | | | 4 | 5 |
| 9 | | 1 | 5 | | | | 2 | |
| | | 7 | 2 | | | | | 4 |
| | 5 | 2 | | 7 | 8 | | 3 | |

Solving puzzles requires us to use logic. Sudoku is a puzzle that originated in Japan and continues to gain popularity worldwide. To solve the puzzle, you need to place every digit from 1 to 9 exactly one time in each row, in each column, and in each of the nine 3 by 3 boxes. For more information and a daily puzzle see www.websudoku.com. The solution to the puzzle above can be found in the Answers section in the back of this book. For an additional puzzle see Exercise 86 on page 104.

To reduce the amount of writing in logic, it is common to represent each simple statement with a lowercase letter. For example, suppose we are discussing the simple statement "Leland is a farmer." Instead of writing "Leland is a farmer" over and over again, we can let $p$ represent the statement "Leland is a farmer." Thereafter we can simply refer to the statement with the letter $p$. It is customary to use the letters $p$, $q$, $r$, and $s$ to represent simple statements, but other letters may be used instead. Let's now look at the connectives used to make compound statements.

## Not Statements

The negation is symbolized by $\sim$ and read "not." For example, the negation of the statement "Steve is a college student" is "Steve is not a college student." If $p$ represents the simple statement "Steve is a college student," then $\sim p$ represents the compound statement "Steve is not a college student." For any statement $p$, $\sim(\sim p) = p$. For example, the negation of the statement "Steve is not a college student" is "Steve is a college student."

Consider the statement "Inga is not at home." This statement contains the word *not*, which indicates that it is a negation. To write this statement symbolically, we let $p$ represent "Inga *is* at home." Then $\sim p$ would be "Inga is not at home." *We will use this convention of letting letters such as p, q, or r represent statements that are not negated. We will represent negated statements with the negation symbol, $\sim$.*

## And Statements

The *conjunction* is symbolized by $\wedge$ and read "and." The $\wedge$ looks like an A (for And) with the bar missing. Let $p$ and $q$ represent the simple statements.

$p$:  You will perform 5 months of community service.
$q$:  You will pay a $100 fine.

Then the following is the conjunction written in symbolic form.

You will perform 5 months of community service ($p$) and ($\wedge$) you will pay a $100 fine ($q$).

The conjunction is generally expressed as *and*. Other words sometimes used to express a conjunction are *but, however,* and *nevertheless.*

### Example 2  *Write a Conjunction*

Write the following conjunction in symbolic form.
Green Day is not on tour, but Green Day is recording a new CD.

*Solution*  Let $t$ and $r$ represent the simple statements.

$t$:  Green Day is on tour.
$r$:  Green Day is recording a new CD.

In symbolic form, the compound statement is $\sim t \wedge r$.

In Example 2, the compound statement is "Green Day is not on tour, but Green Day is recording a new CD." This statement could also be represented as "Green Day is not on tour, but *they* are recording a new CD." In this problem, it should be clear the word *they* means *Green Day*. Therefore, the statement "Green Day is not on tour, but they are recording a new CD" would also be symbolized as $\sim t \wedge r$.

## Or Statements

The *disjunction* is symbolized by $\vee$ and read "or." The *or* we use in this book (except where indicated in the exercise sets) is the *inclusive or* described on page 95.

### Example 3   *Write a Disjunction*

Let

$p$:   Maria will go to the circus.

$q$:   Maria will go to the zoo.

Write the following statements in symbolic form.

a) Maria will go to the circus or Maria will go to the zoo.

b) Maria will go to the zoo or Maria will not go to the circus.

c) Maria will not go to the circus or Maria will not go to the zoo.

#### Solution

a) $p \vee q$      b) $q \vee \sim p$      c) $\sim p \vee \sim q$

Because *or* represents the *inclusive or,* the statement "Maria will go to the circus or Maria will go to the zoo" in Example 3(a) may mean that Maria will go to the circus, or that Maria will go to the zoo, or that Maria will go to both the circus *and* the zoo. The statement in Example 3(a) could also be written as "Maria will go to the circus or the zoo."

When a compound statement contains more than one connective, a comma can be used to indicate which simple statements are to be grouped together. When we write the compound statement symbolically, *the simple statements on the same side of the comma are to be grouped together within parentheses.*

For example, "Pink is a singer (*p*) or Jennifer Aniston is an actress (*j*), and Dallas is in Texas (*d*)" is written $(p \vee j) \wedge d$. Note that the *p* and *j* are both on the same side of the comma in the written statement. They are therefore grouped together within parentheses. The statement "Pink is a singer, or Jennifer Aniston is an actress and Dallas is in Texas" is written $p \vee (j \wedge d)$. In this case, *j* and *d* are on the same side of the comma and are therefore grouped together within parentheses.

### Example 4   *Understand How Commas Are Used to Group Statements*

Let

$p$:   Dinner includes soup.

$q$:   Dinner includes salad.

$r$:   Dinner includes the vegetable of the day.

Write the following statements in symbolic form.

a) Dinner includes soup, and salad or the vegetable of the day.

b) Dinner includes soup and salad, or the vegetable of the day.

#### Solution

a) The comma tells us to group the statement "Dinner includes salad" with the statement "Dinner includes the vegetable of the day." Note that both statements are on the same side of the comma. The statement in symbolic form is $p \wedge (q \vee r)$.

   In mathematics, we always evaluate the information within the parentheses first. Since the conjunction, $\wedge$, is outside the parentheses and is evaluated *last,* this statement is considered a *conjunction.*

b) The comma tells us to group the statement "Dinner includes soup" with the statement "Dinner includes salad." Note that both statements are on the same side of the comma. The statement in symbolic form is $(p \wedge q) \vee r$. Since the disjunction, $\vee$, is outside the parentheses and is evaluated *last,* this statement is considered a *disjunction.*

The information provided in Example 4 is summarized below.

| Statement | Symbolic representation | Type of statement |
| --- | --- | --- |
| Dinner includes soup, and salad or the vegetable of the day. | $p \wedge (q \vee r)$ | conjunction |
| Dinner includes soup and salad, or the vegetable of the day. | $(p \wedge q) \vee r$ | disjunction |

*A negation symbol has the effect of negating only the statement that directly follows it.* To negate a compound statement, we must use parentheses. When a negation symbol is placed in front of a statement in parentheses, it negates the entire statement in parentheses. The negation symbol in this case is read, "It is not true that … " or "It is false that … "

## Example 5  *Change Symbolic Statements into Words*

Let

> $p$:  The house is for sale.
> $q$:  We can afford to buy the house.

Write the following symbolic statements in words.

a) $p \wedge \sim q$     b) $\sim p \vee \sim q$     c) $\sim(p \wedge q)$

### Solution

a) The house is for sale and we cannot afford to buy the house.
b) The house is not for sale or we cannot afford to buy the house.
c) It is false that the house is for sale and we can afford to buy the house.

Recall that the word *but* may also be used in a conjunction. Therefore, Example 5(a) could also be written "The house is for sale, *but* we cannot afford to buy the house."

Part (b) of Example 5 is a disjunction, since it can be written $(\sim p) \vee (\sim q)$. Part (c), which is $\sim(p \wedge q)$, is a negation since the negation symbol negates the entire statement within parentheses. The similarity of these two statements is discussed in Section 3.4.

Occasionally, we come across a *neither–nor* statement, such as "John is neither handsome nor rich." This statement means that John is not handsome *and* John is not rich. If $p$ represents "John is handsome" and $q$ represents "John is rich," this statement is symbolized by $\sim p \wedge \sim q$.

## If–Then Statements

The *conditional* is symbolized by $\rightarrow$ and is read "if–then." The statement $p \rightarrow q$ is read "If $p$, then $q$."[*] The conditional statement consists of two parts: the part that precedes the arrow is the *antecedent,* and the part that follows the arrow is the *consequent.*[†] In the conditional statement $p \rightarrow q$, the $p$ is the antecedent and the $q$ is the consequent.

---

[*]Some books indicate that $p \rightarrow q$ may also be read "$p$ implies $q$." Many higher-level mathematics books, however, indicate that $p \rightarrow q$ may be read "$p$ implies $q$" only under certain conditions. Implications are discussed in Section 3.3.

[†]Some books refer to the antecedent as the hypothesis or premise and the consequent as the conclusion.

In the conditional statement $\sim(p \vee q) \rightarrow (p \wedge q)$, the antecedent is $\sim(p \vee q)$ and the consequent is $(p \wedge q)$. An example of a conditional statement is "If you drink your milk, then you will grow up to be healthy." A conditional symbol may be placed between any two statements even if the statements are not related.

Sometimes the word *then* in a conditional statement is not explicitly stated. For example, the statement "If you get an A, I will buy you a car" is a conditional statement because it actually means "If you get an A, then I will buy you a car."

▲ *Zoe* by Beth Anderson

### Example 6  *Write Conditional Statements*

Let

$p$:   The portrait is a pastel.

$q$:   The portrait is by Beth Anderson.

Write the following statements symbolically.

a)  If the portrait is a pastel, then the portrait is by Beth Anderson.

b)  If the portrait is by Beth Anderson, then the portrait is not a pastel.

c)  It is false that if the portrait is by Beth Anderson then the portrait is a pastel.

**Solution**

a) $p \rightarrow q$    b) $q \rightarrow \sim p$    c) $\sim(q \rightarrow p)$

### Example 7  *Use Commas When Writing a Symbolic Statement in Words*

Let

$p$:   Jorge is enrolled in calculus.

$q$:   Jorge's major is criminal justice.

$r$:   Jorge's major is engineering.

Write the following symbolic statements in words and indicate whether the statement is a negation, conjunction, disjunction, or conditional.

a) $(q \rightarrow \sim p) \vee r$    b) $q \rightarrow (\sim p \vee r)$

**Solution**  The parentheses indicate where to place the commas in the sentences.

a) "If Jorge's major is criminal justice then Jorge is not enrolled in calculus, or Jorge's major is engineering." This statement is a disjunction because $\vee$ is outside the parentheses.

b) "If Jorge's major is criminal justice, then Jorge is not enrolled in calculus or Jorge's major is engineering." This statement is a conditional because $\rightarrow$ is outside the parentheses.

## If and Only if Statements

The *biconditional* is symbolized by $\leftrightarrow$ and is read "if and only if." The phrase *if and only if* is sometimes abbreviated as "iff." The statement $p \leftrightarrow q$ is read "$p$ if and only if $q$."

### Example 8  *Write Statements Using the Biconditional*

Let

$p$:   Alex plays goalie on the lacrosse team.

$q$:   The Titans win the Champion's Cup.

Write the following symbolic statements in words.

a) $p \leftrightarrow q$    c) $q \leftrightarrow \sim p$    b) $\sim(p \leftrightarrow \sim q)$

*Solution*

a) Alex plays goalie on the lacrosse team if and only if the Titans win the Champion's Cup.

b) The Titans win the Champion's Cup if and only if Alex does not play goalie on the lacrosse team.

c) It is false that Alex plays goalie on the lacrosse team if and only if the Titans do not win the Champion's Cup. ∎

You will learn later that $p \leftrightarrow q$ means the same as $(p \to q) \land (q \to p)$. Therefore, the statement "I will go to college if and only if I can pay the tuition" has the same logical meaning as "If I go to college then I can pay the tuition, and if I can pay the tuition then I will go to college."

A summary of the connectives discussed in this section is given in Table 3.1.

Table 3.1 Logical Connectives

| Formal Name | Symbol | Read | Symbolic Form |
|---|---|---|---|
| Negation | ~ | "Not" | $\sim p$ |
| Conjunction | ∧ | "And" | $p \land q$ |
| Disjunction | ∨ | "Or" | $p \lor q$ |
| Conditional | → | "If-then" | $p \to q$ |
| Biconditional | ↔ | "If and only if" | $p \leftrightarrow q$ |

## SECTION 3.1   *Exercises*

### Warm Up Exercises

*In exercises 1–8, fill in the blanks with an appropriate word, phrase, or symbol(s).*

**1.** A sentence that can be judged either true or false is called a _____.

**2.** A statement that conveys only one idea is called a _____ statement.

**3.** A statement that consists of two or more simple statements is called a _____ statement.

**4.** Words such as *all, none* (or *no*), and *some* are examples of _____.

**5. a)** The negation is symbolized by ~ and is read "_____."

**b)** The conjunction is symbolized by ∧ and is read "_____."

**c)** The disjunction is symbolized by ∨ and is read "_____."

**d)** The conditional is symbolized by → and is read "_____."

**e)** The biconditional is symbolized by ↔ and is read "_____."

**6.** The negation of the statement *Some cars are hybrids* is: _____ cars are hybrids.

**7.** The negation of the statement *All golf courses are green* is: _____ golf courses are not green.

**8.** The negation of the statement *Some drivers are not safe* is: _____ drivers are safe.

## Practice the Skills/Problem Solving

*In Exercises 9–18, indicate whether the statement is a simple statement or a compound statement. If it is a compound statement, indicate whether it is a negation, conjunction, disjunction, conditional, or biconditional by using both the word and its appropriate symbol (for example, "a negation," ~ ).*

**9.** John Waters is scuba diving.

**10.** If you have a cold, then you should eat some chicken soup.

**11.** Time will go backwards if and only if you travel faster than the speed of light.

**12.** Louis Armstrong did not play the drums.

**13.** Bobby Glewen joined the Army and he got married.

**14.** The book was neither a novel nor an autobiography.

**15.** If Cathy Smith walks 4 miles today, then she will be sore tomorrow.

**16.** Inhibor Melendez will be admitted to law school if and only if he earns his bachelor's degree.

**17.** It is false that Jeffery Hilt is a high school teacher and a grade school teacher.

**18.** The hurricane did $400,000 worth of damage to DeSoto County.

*In Exercises 19–28, write the negation of the statement.*

**19.** All butterflies are insects.

**20.** All houses are wired using parallel circuits.

**21.** Some turtles do not have claws.

**22.** No teachers made the roster.

**23.** No bicycles have three wheels.

**24.** All horses have manes.

**25.** Some pedestrians are in the crosswalk.

**26.** Some dogs with long hair do not get cold.

**27.** No Holsteins are Guernseys.

**28.** Some vitamins contain sugar.

*In Exercises 29–34, write the statement in symbolic form.*

*Let*

    *p*:    A panther has a long tail.
    *q*:    A bobcat can purr.

**29.** A panther does not have a long tail.

**30.** A panther has a long tail and a bobcat can purr.

**31.** A bobcat cannot purr or a panther does not have a long tail.

**32.** A bobcat cannot purr if and only if a panther does not have a long tail.

**33.** If a panther does not have a long tail, then a bobcat cannot purr.

**34.** A bobcat cannot purr, but a panther has a long tail.

*In Exercises 35–40, write the statement in symbolic form.*

*Let*

    *p*:  The chili is spicy.
    *q*:  The sour cream is cold.

**35.** The chili is not spicy, but the sour cream is cold.

**36.** Neither is the chili spicy nor is the sour cream cold.

**37.** The sour cream is not cold if and only if the chili is spicy.

**38.** If the chili is spicy, then the sour cream is not cold.

**39.** It is false that the chili is spicy or the sour cream is cold.

**40.** It is false that if the sour cream is not cold then the chili is spicy.

*In Exercises 41–50, write the compound statement in words.*

*Let*

    *p*:  Joe has an iPad.
    *q*:  Brie has a MacBook.

**41.** $\sim q$              **42.** $\sim p$

**43.** $p \wedge q$         **44.** $q \vee p$

**45.** $\sim p \rightarrow q$       **46.** $\sim p \leftrightarrow \sim q$

**47.** $\sim p \vee \sim q$      **48.** $\sim (q \vee p)$

**49.** $\sim (p \wedge q)$      **50.** $\sim p \wedge \sim q$

*In Exercises 51–60, write the statements in symbolic form.*

*Let*

    *p*:  The temperature is 90°.
    *q*:  The air conditioner is working.
    *r*:  The apartment is hot.

**51.** The temperature is 90° and the air conditioner is not working, and the apartment is hot.

**52.** The temperature is not 90° and the air conditioner is working, but the apartment is hot.

**53.** The temperature is 90° and the air conditioner is working, or the apartment is hot.

**54.** If the apartment is hot and the air conditioner is working, then the temperature is 90°.

**55.** If the temperature is 90°, then the air conditioner is working or the apartment is not hot.

**56.** The temperature is not 90° if and only if the air conditioner is not working, or the apartment is not hot.

**57.** The apartment is hot if and only if the air conditioner is working, and the temperature is 90°.

**58.** It is false that if the apartment is hot then the air conditioner is not working.

**59.** If the air conditioner is working, then the temperature is 90° if and only if the apartment is hot.

**60.** The apartment is hot or the air conditioner is not working, if and only if the temperature is 90°.

*In Exercises 61–70, write each symbolic statement in words.*

*Let*

    *p*:  The water is 70°.
    *q*:  The sun is shining.
    *r*:  We go swimming.

**61.** $(p \vee q) \wedge \sim r$     **62.** $(p \wedge q) \vee r$

**63.** $\sim p \wedge (q \vee r)$     **64.** $(q \rightarrow p) \vee r$

**65.** $\sim r \rightarrow (q \wedge p)$    **66.** $(q \wedge r) \rightarrow p$

**67.** $(q \rightarrow r) \wedge p$     **68.** $\sim p \rightarrow (q \vee r)$

**69.** $(q \leftrightarrow p) \wedge r$     **70.** $q \rightarrow (p \leftrightarrow r)$

***Dinner Menu*** *In Exercises 71–74 on page 104, use the following information to arrive at your answers. Many restaurant dinner menus include statements such as the following. All dinners are served with a choice of: Soup or Salad, and Potatoes or Pasta, and Carrots or Peas. Which of the following selections are permissible? If a selection is not permissible, explain why. See the discussion of the* **exclusive** *or on page 95.*

Welcome to
**ANTONIO'S RESTAURANTE**

"All dinners are served
with a choice of:
soup or salad, potatoes
or pasta, and carrots or peas"

**71.** Soup, salad, and peas

**72.** Salad, pasta, and carrots

**73.** Soup, potatoes, pasta, and peas

**74.** Soup, pasta, and potatoes

*In Exercises 75–83, (a) select letters to represent the simple statements and write each statement symbolically by using parentheses and (b) indicate whether the statement is a negation, conjunction, disjunction, conditional, or biconditional.*

**75.** I bought the watch in Tijuana and I did not pay $100.

**76.** If the conference is in Las Vegas, then we can see Blue Man Group or we can play poker.

▲ *Blue Man Group*

**77.** It is false that if your speed is below the speed limit then you will not get pulled over.

**78.** If dinner is ready then we can eat, or we cannot go to the restaurant.

**79.** If the food has fiber or the food has vitamins, then you will be healthy.

**80.** If Corliss is teaching then Faye is in the math lab, if and only if it is not a weekend.

**81.** You may take this course, if and only if you did not fail the previous course or you passed the placement test.

**82.** If the car has gas and the battery is charged, then the car will start.

**83.** The classroom is empty if and only if it is the weekend, or it is 7 A.M.

## Challenge Problems/Group Activities

**84.** *An Ancient Question*  If Zeus could do anything, could he build a wall that he could not jump over? Explain your answer.

**85. a)**  Make up three simple statements and label them *p*, *q*, and *r*. Then write compound statements to represent $(p \vee q) \wedge r$ and $p \vee (q \wedge r)$.

**b)**  Do you think that the statements for $(p \vee q) \wedge r$ and $p \vee (q \wedge r)$ mean the same thing? Explain.

## Recreational Mathematics

**86.** *Sudoku*  Refer to the *Recreational Mathematics* on page 96. Complete the following Sudoku puzzle.

|   | 8 |   |   | 3 |   |   |   |   |
|---|---|---|---|---|---|---|---|---|
| 9 |   |   | 6 | 1 |   |   |   | 4 |
| 5 | 1 | 9 |   |   | 8 | 6 | 3 |   |
|   | 6 |   |   |   | 4 | 8 |   |   |
| 5 |   |   |   |   |   |   |   | 1 |
| 2 | 4 |   |   |   | 5 |   |   |   |
| 4 | 3 | 5 |   | 8 | 1 | 9 |   |   |
| 2 |   | 5 | 1 |   |   | 7 |   |   |
|   |   | 2 |   | 6 |   |   |   |   |

## Internet/Research Activities

**87.** *Legal Documents*  Obtain a legal document such as a will or rental agreement and copy one page of the document. Circle every connective used. Then list the number of times each connective appeared. Be sure to include conditional statements from which the word *then* was omitted from the sentence. Give the page and your listing to your instructor.

**88.** Write a report on the life and accomplishments of George Boole, who was an important contributor to the development of logic. In your report, indicate how his work eventually led to the development of the computer. References include encyclopedias, history of mathematics books, and the Internet.

# Truth Tables for Negation, Conjunction, and Disjunction

Consider the following statement: Subway sells the most sandwiches or Taco Bell sells the most burritos. Under what conditions can the statement be considered true? Under what conditions can the statement be considered false? In this section, we will introduce a tool used to help us analyze such statements.

*Why* This is Important  Understanding when logical statements are true is essential to many different applications in everyday life.

▲ *Under what conditions is the statement Subway sells the most sandwiches or Taco Bell sells the most burritos true?*

A *truth table* is a device used to determine when a compound statement is true or false. Five basic truth tables are used in constructing other truth tables. Three are discussed in this section (Tables 3.2, 3.4, and 3.7), and two are discussed in the next section. Section 3.5 uses truth tables in determining whether a logical argument is valid or invalid.

## Negation

The first truth table is for *negation*. If $p$ is a true statement, then the negation of $p$, "not $p$," is a false statement. If $p$ is a false statement, then "not $p$" is a true statement. For example, if the statement "The shirt is blue" is true, then the statement "The shirt is not blue" is false. These relationships are summarized in Table 3.2. For a simple statement, there are exactly two true–false cases, as shown.

Table 3.2 Negation

|  | $p$ | $\sim p$ |
|---|---|---|
| Case 1 | T | F |
| Case 2 | F | T |

If a compound statement consists of two simple statements $p$ and $q$, there are four possible cases, as illustrated in Table 3.3. Consider the statement "The test is today and the test covers Chapter 5." The simple statement "The test is today" has two possible truth values, true or false. The simple statement "The test covers Chapter 5" also has two truth values, true or false. Thus, for these two simple statements there are four distinct possible true–false arrangements. Whenever we construct a truth table for a compound statement that consists of two simple statements, we begin by listing the four true–false cases shown in Table 3.3.

Table 3.3

|  | $p$ | $q$ |
|---|---|---|
| Case 1 | T | T |
| Case 2 | T | F |
| Case 3 | F | T |
| Case 4 | F | F |

## Conjunction

To illustrate the conjunction, consider the following situation. You have recently purchased a new house. To decorate it, you ordered a new carpet and new furniture from the same store. You explain to the salesperson that the carpet must be delivered before the furniture. He promises that the carpet will be delivered on Thursday and that the furniture will be delivered on Friday.

To help determine whether the salesperson kept his promise, we assign letters to each simple statement. Let $p$ be "The carpet will be delivered on Thursday" and $q$ be "The furniture will be delivered on Friday." The salesperson's statement written in symbolic form is $p \wedge q$. There are four possible true–false situations to be considered (Table 3.4).

Table 3.4 Conjunction

|  | $p$ | $q$ | $p \wedge q$ |
|---|---|---|---|
| Case 1 | T | T | T |
| Case 2 | T | F | F |
| Case 3 | F | T | F |
| Case 4 | F | F | F |

**CASE 1:** $p$ is true and $q$ is true. The carpet is delivered on Thursday and the furniture is delivered on Friday. The salesperson has kept his promise and the compound statement is true. Thus, we put a T in the $p \wedge q$ column.

**CASE 2:** $p$ is true and $q$ is false. The carpet is delivered on Thursday but the furniture is not delivered on Friday. Since the furniture was not delivered as promised, the compound statement is false. Thus, we put an F in the $p \wedge q$ column.

**CASE 3:** $p$ is false and $q$ is true. The carpet is not delivered on Thursday but the furniture is delivered on Friday. Since the carpet was not delivered on Thursday as promised, the compound statement is false. Thus, we put an F in the $p \wedge q$ column.

**CASE 4:** $p$ is false and $q$ is false. The carpet is not delivered on Thursday and the furniture is not delivered on Friday. Since the carpet and furniture were not delivered as promised, the compound statement is false. Thus, we put an F in the $p \wedge q$ column.

Examining the four cases, we see that in only one case did the salesperson keep his promise: in case 1. Therefore, case 1 (T, T) is true. In cases 2, 3, and 4, the salesperson did not keep his promise and the compound statement is false. The results are summarized in Table 3.4, the truth table for the conjunction.

The **conjunction** $p \wedge q$ is true only when both $p$ and $q$ are true.

## Disjunction

Consider the job description in the margin that describes several job requirements. Who qualifies for the job? To help analyze the statement, translate it into symbolic form. Let $p$ be "A requirement for the job is a two-year college degree in civil technology" and $q$ be "A requirement for the job is five years of related experience." The statement in symbolic form is $p \vee q$. For the two simple statements, there are four distinct cases (see Table 3.5).

**CASE 1:** $p$ is true and $q$ is true. A candidate has a two-year college degree in civil technology and five years of related experience. The candidate has both requirements and qualifies for the job. Consider qualifying for the job as a true statement and not qualifying as a false statement. Since the candidate qualifies for the job, we put a T in the $p \vee q$ column.

**CASE 2:** $p$ is true and $q$ is false. A candidate has a two-year college degree in civil technology but does not have five years of related experience. The candidate still qualifies for the job with the two-year college degree. Thus, we put a T in the $p \vee q$ column.

**CASE 3:** $p$ is false and $q$ is true. The candidate does not have a two-year college degree in civil technology but does have five years of related experience. The candidate still qualifies for the job with the five years of related experience. Thus, we put a T in the $p \vee q$ column.

**CASE 4:** $p$ is false and $q$ is false. The candidate does not have a two-year college degree in civil technology and does not have five years of related experience. The candidate does not meet either of the two requirements and therefore does not qualify for the job. Thus, we put an F in the $p \vee q$ column.

In examining the four cases, we see that there is only one case in which the candidate does not qualify for the job: case 4. As this example indicates, an *or* statement will be true in every case, except when both simple statements are false. The results are summarized in Table 3.5, the truth table for the disjunction.

The **disjunction** $p \vee q$ is true when either $p$ is true, $q$ is true, or both $p$ and $q$ are true.

The disjunction $p \vee q$ is false only when $p$ and $q$ are both false.

## Constructing Truth Tables

We will now construct additional truth tables for statements involving the negation, conjunction, and disjunction. We summarize these compound statements on page 107.

---

**Civil Technician**

Municipal program for redevelopment seeks on-site technician. **The applicant must have a two-year college degree in civil technology or five years of related experience**. Interested candidates please call 555-1234.

---

Table 3.5 Disjunction

| $p$ | $q$ | $p \vee q$ |
|-----|-----|------------|
| T   | T   | T          |
| T   | F   | T          |
| F   | T   | T          |
| F   | F   | F          |

### Negation, Conjunction, and Disjunction

- **Negation** $\sim p$ is read "not $p$." If $p$ is true, then $\sim p$ is false; if $p$ is false, then $\sim p$ is true. In other words, $\sim p$ will always have the *opposite* truth value of $p$.
- **Conjunction** $p \wedge q$ is read "$p$ and $q$." $p \wedge q$ is true only when both $p$ and $q$ are true.
- **Disjunction** $p \vee q$ is read "$p$ or $q$." $p \vee q$ is true when either $p$ is true, $q$ is true, or both $p$ and $q$ are true. In other words, $p \vee q$ is false only when both $p$ and $q$ are false.

We will discuss two methods for constructing truth tables. Although the two methods produce tables that will look different, the answer columns will be the same regardless of which method you use.

## Example 1 *Construct a Truth Table*

Construct a truth table for $p \wedge \sim q$.

*Solution*  Because there are two statements, $p$ and $q$, construct a truth table with four cases; see Table 3.6(a). Then write the truth values under the $p$ in the compound statement and label this column 1, as in Table 3.6(b). Copy these truth values directly from the $p$ column on the left. Write the corresponding truth values under the $q$ in the compound statement and call this column 2, as in Table 3.6(c). Copy the truth values for column 2 directly from the $q$ column on the left. Now find the truth values of $\sim q$ by negating the truth values in column 2 and call this column 3, as in

**Table 3.6**

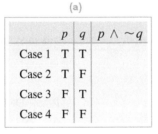

(a)

| | $p$ | $q$ | $p \wedge \sim q$ |
|---|---|---|---|
| Case 1 | T | T | |
| Case 2 | T | F | |
| Case 3 | F | T | |
| Case 4 | F | F | |

(b)

| $p$ | $q$ | $p \wedge \sim q$ |
|---|---|---|
| T | T | T |
| T | F | T |
| F | T | F |
| F | F | F |
| | | 1 |

(c)

| $p$ | $q$ | $p$ | $\wedge$ | $\sim$ | $q$ |
|---|---|---|---|---|---|
| T | T | T | | | T |
| T | F | T | | | F |
| F | T | F | | | T |
| F | F | F | | | F |
| | | 1 | | | 2 |

(d)

| $p$ | $q$ | $p$ | $\wedge$ | $\sim$ | $q$ |
|---|---|---|---|---|---|
| T | T | T | | F | T |
| T | F | T | | T | F |
| F | T | F | | F | T |
| F | F | F | | T | F |
| | | 1 | | 3 | 2 |

(e)

| $p$ | $q$ | $p$ | $\wedge$ | $\sim$ | $q$ |
|---|---|---|---|---|---|
| T | T | T | F | F | T |
| T | F | T | T | T | F |
| F | T | F | F | F | T |
| F | F | F | F | T | F |
| | | 1 | 4 | 3 | 2 |

Table 3.6(d). Use the conjunction table, Table 3.4, and the entries in the columns labeled 1 and 3 to complete the column labeled 4, as in Table 3.6(e). The results in column 4 are obtained as follows:

Row 1: T $\wedge$ F is F.    Row 2: T $\wedge$ T is T.
Row 3: F $\wedge$ F is F.    Row 4: F $\wedge$ T is F.

The answer is always the last column completed. The columns labeled 1, 2, and 3 are only aids in arriving at the answer labeled column 4.

The statement $p \wedge \sim q$ in Example 1 actually means $p \wedge (\sim q)$. In the future, instead of listing a column for $q$ and a separate column for its negation, we will make one column for $\sim q$, which will have the opposite values of those in the $q$ column on the left. Similarly, when we evaluate $\sim p$, we will use the opposite values of those in the $p$ column on the left. This procedure is illustrated in Example 2.

In Example 1, we spoke about *cases* and also *columns*. Consider Table 3.6(e) on page 107. This table has four cases indicated by the four different rows of the two left-hand (unnumbered) columns. The four *cases* are TT, TF, FT, and FF. In every truth table with two letters, we list the four cases (the first two columns) first. Then we complete the remaining columns in the truth table. In Table 3.6(e), after completing the two left-hand columns, we complete the remaining columns in the order indicated by the numbers below the columns. We will continue to place numbers below the columns to show the order in which the columns are completed.

In discussion of the truth table in Example 2, and all following truth tables, if we say column 1, it means the column labeled 1. Column 2 will mean the column labeled 2, and so on.

## Example 2    *Construct and Interpret a Truth Table*

a) Construct a truth table for the following statement: Jo is not an artist and Jo is not a musician.

b) Under which conditions will the compound statement be true?

c) Suppose "Jo is an artist" is a false statement and "Jo is a musician" is a true statement. Is the compound statement given in part (a) true or false?

*Solution*

a) First write the simple statements in symbolic form by using simple nonnegated statements.

Let

$p$:    Jo is an artist.
$q$:    Jo is a musician.

Therefore, the compound statement may be written $\sim p \wedge \sim q$. Now construct a truth table with four cases, as shown in Table 3.7.

Fill in the column labeled 1 by negating the truth values under $p$ on the far left. Fill in the column labeled 2 by negating the values under $q$ in the second column from the left. Fill in the column labeled 3 by using the columns labeled 1 and 2 and the definition of conjunction.

In the first row, to determine the entry for column 3, we use false for $\sim p$ and false for $\sim q$. Since false $\wedge$ false is false (see case 4 of Table 3.4 on page 105), we place an F in column 3, row 1. In the second row, we use false for $\sim p$ and true for $\sim q$. Since false $\wedge$ true is false (see case 3 of Table 3.4), we place an F in column 3, row 2. In the third row, we use true for $\sim p$ and false for $\sim q$. Since true $\wedge$ false is false (see case 2 of Table 3.4), we place an F in column 3, row 3. In the fourth row, we use true for $\sim p$ and true for $\sim q$. Since true $\wedge$ true is true (see case 1 of Table 3.4), we place a T in column 3, row 4.

b) The compound statement in part (a) will be true only in case 4 (circled in blue) when both simple statements, $p$ and $q$, are false, that is, when Jo is not an artist and Jo is not a musician.

c) We are told that $p$, "Jo is an artist," is a false statement and that $q$, "Jo is a musician," is a true statement. From the truth table (Table 3.7), we can determine that when $p$ is false and $q$ is true, the compound statement, case 3 (circled in red), is false.

Table 3.7

| $p$ | $q$ | $\sim p$ | $\wedge$ | $\sim q$ |
|---|---|---|---|---|
| T | T | F | F | F |
| T | F | F | F | T |
| F | T | T | (F) | F |
| F | F | T | (T) | T |
|   |   | 1 | 3 | 2 |

Table 3.8

| p | q | ~ | (~q | ∨ | p) |
|---|---|---|-----|---|-----|
| T | T | F | F | T | T |
| T | F | F | T | T | T |
| F | T | T | F | F | F |
| F | F | F | T | T | F |
|   |   | 4 | 1 | 3 | 2 |

## Example 3 *Truth Table with a Negation*

Construct a truth table for $\sim(\sim q \vee p)$.

*Solution* First construct the standard truth table listing the four cases. Then work within parentheses. The order to be followed is indicated by the numbers below the columns (see Table 3.8). Under $\sim q$, column 1, write the negation of the $q$ column. Then, in column 2, copy the values from the $p$ column. Next, complete the *or* column, column 3, using columns 1 and 2 and the truth table for the disjunction (see Table 3.5 on page 106). The *or* column is false only when both statements are false, as in case 3. Finally, negate the values in the *or* column, column 3, and place these negated values in column 4. By examining the truth table you can see that the compound statement $\sim(\sim q \vee p)$ is true only in case 3, that is, when $p$ is false and $q$ is true. ∎

---

**PROCEDURE** CONSTRUCTING TRUTH TABLES

1. Study the compound statement and determine whether it is a negation, conjunction, disjunction, conditional, or biconditional statement, as was done in Section 3.1. The answer to the truth table will appear under $\sim$ if the statement is a negation, under $\wedge$ if the statement is a conjunction, under $\vee$ if the statement is a disjunction, under $\rightarrow$ if the statement is a conditional, and under $\leftrightarrow$ if the statement is a biconditional.

2. Complete the columns under the simple statements, $p$, $q$, $r$, and their negations, $\sim p$, $\sim q$, $\sim r$, within parentheses, if present. If there are nested parentheses (one pair of parentheses within another pair), work with the innermost pair first.

3. Complete the column under the connective within the parentheses, if present. You will use the truth values of the connective in determining the final answer in step 5.

4. Complete the column under any remaining statements and their negations.

5. Complete the column under any remaining connectives. Recall that the answer will appear under the column determined in step 1. If the statement is a conjunction, disjunction, conditional, or biconditional, you will obtain the truth values for the connective by using the last column completed on the left side and on the right side of the connective. If the statement is a negation, you will obtain the truth values by negating the truth values of the last column completed within the grouping symbols on the right side of the negation. Be sure to circle or highlight your answer column or number the columns in the order they were completed.

---

## Example 4 *Use the General Procedure to Construct a Truth Table*

Table 3.9

Construct a truth table for the statement $(\sim p \vee q) \wedge \sim p$.

| p | q | (~p | ∨ | q) | ∧ | ~p |
|---|---|-----|---|----|---|-----|
| T | T | F | T | T | F | F |
| T | F | F | F | F | F | F |
| F | T | T | T | T | T | T |
| F | F | T | T | F | T | T |
|   |   | 1 | 3 | 2 | 5 | 4 |

*Solution* We will follow the general procedure outlined in the box. This statement is a conjunction, so the answer will be under the conjunction symbol. Complete columns under $\sim p$ and $q$ within the parentheses and call these columns 1 and 2, respectively (see Table 3.9). Complete the column under the disjunction, $\vee$, using the truth values in columns 1 and 2, and call this column 3. Next complete the column under $\sim p$, and call this column 4. The answer, column 5, is determined from the definition of the conjunction and the truth values in column 3, the last column completed on the left side of the conjunction, and column 4. ∎

So far, all the truth tables we have constructed have contained at most two simple statements. Now we will explain how to construct a truth table that consists of three simple statements, such as $(p \wedge q) \wedge r$. When a compound statement consists of three simple statements, there are eight different true–false possibilities,

Table 3.10

|  | *p* | *q* | *r* |
|---|---|---|---|
| Case 1 | T | T | T |
| Case 2 | T | T | F |
| Case 3 | T | F | T |
| Case 4 | T | F | F |
| Case 5 | F | T | T |
| Case 6 | F | T | F |
| Case 7 | F | F | T |
| Case 8 | F | F | F |

as illustrated in Table 3.10. To begin such a truth table, write four Ts and four Fs in the column under *p*. Under the second statement, *q*, pairs of Ts alternate with pairs of Fs. Under the third statement, *r*, T alternates with F. This technique is not the only way of listing the cases, but it ensures that each case is unique and that no cases are omitted.

## Example 5  *Construct a Truth Table with Eight Cases*

a) Construct a truth table for the statement "Santana is home and he is not at his desk, or he is sleeping."

b) Suppose that "Santana is home" is a false statement, that "Santana is at his desk" is a true statement, and that "Santana is sleeping" is a true statement. Is the compound statement in part (a) true or false?

### Solution

a) First we will translate the statement into symbolic form.

Let

$p$:    Santana is home.

$q$:    Santana is at his desk.

$r$:    Santana is sleeping.

In symbolic form, the statement is $(p \wedge {\sim}q) \vee r$.

Since the statement is composed of three simple statements, there are eight cases. Begin by listing the eight cases in the three left-hand columns; see Table 3.11. By examining the statement, you can see that it is a disjunction. Therefore, the answer will be in the $\vee$ column. Fill out the truth table by working in parentheses first. Place values under $p$, column 1, and ${\sim}q$, column 2. Then find the conjunctions of columns 1 and 2 to obtain column 3. Place the values of $r$ in column 4. To obtain the answer, column 5, use columns 3 and 4 and the information for the disjunction contained in Table 3.5 on page 106.

Table 3.11

| *p* | *q* | *r* | (*p* | $\wedge$ | ${\sim}q$) | $\vee$ | *r* |
|---|---|---|---|---|---|---|---|
| T | T | T | T | F | F | T | T |
| T | T | F | T | F | F | F | F |
| T | F | T | T | T | T | T | T |
| T | F | F | T | T | T | T | F |
| F | T | T | F | F | F | (T) | T |
| F | T | F | F | F | F | F | F |
| F | F | T | F | F | T | T | T |
| F | F | F | F | F | T | F | F |
|  |  |  | 1 | 3 | 2 | 5 | 4 |

b) We are given the following:

$p$:    Santana is home—false.

$q$:    Santana is at his desk—true.

$r$:    Santana is sleeping—true.

We need to find the truth value of the following case: false, true, true. In case 5 of the truth table, $p$, $q$, and $r$ are F, T, and T, respectively. Therefore, under these conditions, the original compound statement is true (as circled in the table).  ∎

We have learned that a truth table with one simple statement has two cases, a truth table with two simple statements has four cases, and a truth table with three simple statements has eight cases. In general, *the number of distinct cases in a truth table with n distinct simple statements is* $2^n$. The compound statement $(p \lor q) \lor (r \land \sim s)$ has four simple statements, $p, q, r, s$. Thus, a truth table for this compound statement would have $2^4$, or 16, distinct cases.

When we construct a truth table, we determine the truth values of a compound statement for every possible case. If we want to find the truth value of the compound statement for any specific case when we know the truth values of the simple statements, we do not have to develop the entire table. For example, to determine the truth value for the statement

$$2 + 3 = 5 \quad \text{and} \quad 1 + 1 = 3$$

we let $p$ be $2 + 3 = 5$ and $q$ be $1 + 1 = 3$. Now we can write the compound statement as $p \land q$. We know that $p$ is a true statement and $q$ is a false statement. Thus, we can substitute T for $p$ and F for $q$ and evaluate the statement:

$$p \land q$$
$$T \land F$$
$$F$$

Therefore, the compound statement $2 + 3 = 5$ and $1 + 1 = 3$ is a false statement.

## Alternate Method for Constructing Truth Tables

We now present an alternate method for constructing truth tables. We will use the alternate method to construct truth tables for the same statements we analyzed in Examples 1, 2, and 3.

Example 6  *Use the Alternate Method to Construct a Truth Table*

Construct a truth table for $p \land \sim q$.

Solution  We begin by constructing the first two columns of a truth table with four cases, as shown in Table 3.12 (a). We will add additional columns to Table 3.12(a) to develop our answer column. Since we wish to find the truth table for the compound statement $p \land \sim q$, we need to be able to compare the truth values for $p$ with the truth values for $\sim q$. Table 3.12(a) already has a column showing the truth values for $p$. We next add a column showing the truth values for $\sim q$, as shown in Table 3.12(b). Recall that the values of $\sim q$ are the opposite of those for $q$.

Finally, we add the answer column for the compound statement $p \land \sim q$, as shown as shown in Table 3.12(c). To determine the truth values for the $p \land \sim q$ column, use the $p$ column and the $\sim q$ column, and the conjunction table, Table 3.4,

Table 3.12

(a)

|        | $p$ | $q$ |
|--------|-----|-----|
| Case 1 | T | T |
| Case 2 | T | F |
| Case 3 | F | T |
| Case 4 | F | F |

(b)

| $p$ | $q$ | $\sim q$ |
|-----|-----|----------|
| T | T | F |
| T | F | T |
| F | T | F |
| F | F | T |

(c)

| $p$ | $q$ | $\sim q$ | $p \land \sim q$ |
|-----|-----|----------|------------------|
| T | T | F | F |
| T | F | T | T |
| F | T | F | F |
| F | F | T | F |

Use these columns to determine the answer column

on page 105. Note that the answer column of Table 3.12(c) is the same as the answer column of Table 3.6(e) on page 107.    ■

## Example 7    *Use the Alternate Method to Construct a Truth Table*

Construct a truth table for $\sim p \land \sim q$.

*Solution*    Begin by constructing a truth table with four cases, as shown in Table 3.13(a). Since we wish to find the truth table for the compound statement $\sim p \land \sim q$, we will add a column for $\sim p$ and a column for $\sim q$, as shown in Table 3.13(b).

Table 3.13

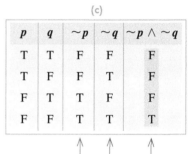

(a)

| $p$ | $q$ |
|---|---|
| T | T |
| T | F |
| F | T |
| F | F |

(b)

| $p$ | $q$ | $\sim p$ | $\sim q$ |
|---|---|---|---|
| T | T | F | F |
| T | F | F | T |
| F | T | T | F |
| F | F | T | T |

(c)

| $p$ | $q$ | $\sim p$ | $\sim q$ | $\sim p \land \sim q$ |
|---|---|---|---|---|
| T | T | F | F | F |
| T | F | F | T | F |
| F | T | T | F | F |
| F | F | T | T | T |

Use these columns to determine the answer column

Finally, we add our answer column for the compound statement $\sim p \land \sim q$. To determine the truth values for the $\sim p \land \sim q$ column, use the $\sim p$ column and the $\sim q$ column, and the conjunction table, Table 3.4, on page 105. Note that the answer column of Table 3.13(c) is the same as the answer column of Table 3.7 on page 108.    ■

## Example 8    *Use the Alternate Method to Construct a Truth Table*

Construct a truth table for $\sim(\sim q \lor p)$.

*Solution*    Begin by constructing a truth table with four cases, as shown in Table 3.14(a). To complete the truth table, we will work within parentheses first. Thus, we next add a column for $\sim q$, as shown in Table 3.14(b). We then will construct a column for the expression within parentheses $\sim q \lor p$ by using the $\sim q$ column and the $p$ column, and the disjunction table, Table 3.5, on page 106.

Table 3.14

(a)

| $p$ | $q$ |
|---|---|
| T | T |
| T | F |
| F | T |
| F | F |

(b)

| $p$ | $q$ | $\sim q$ |
|---|---|---|
| T | T | F |
| T | F | T |
| F | T | F |
| F | F | T |

(c)

| $p$ | $q$ | $\sim q$ | $\sim q \lor p$ |
|---|---|---|---|
| T | T | F | T |
| T | F | T | T |
| F | T | F | F |
| T | F | T | T |

Use these columns to determine the $\sim q \lor p$ column

Table 3.15

| $p$ | $q$ | $\sim q$ | $\sim q \lor p$ | $\sim(\sim q \lor p)$ |
|---|---|---|---|---|
| T | T | F | T | F |
| T | F | T | T | F |
| F | T | F | F | T |
| F | F | T | T | F |

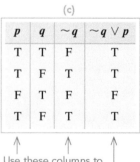

Take the opposite of this column to get the answer column

Finally, we add the answer column for the compound statement, $\sim(\sim q \lor p)$, as shown in Table 3.15. To determine the truth values for the $\sim(\sim q \lor p)$ column, take the opposite values of those shown in the $\sim q \lor p$ column. Note that the answer column of Table 3.15 is the same as the answer column of Table 3.8 on page 109.    ■

We have demonstrated two methods for constructing truth tables. Unless your instructor indicates otherwise, you may use either method. Although both methods will always lead to the correct answer, the alternate method gets more cumbersome and takes up more space as we construct truth tables with more statements. *In the remainder of this chapter, we will demonstrate the construction of truth tables using only the first method.*

## Determine Truth Values Without Constructing a Truth Table

In the remaining examples in this section, we will determine the truth values of compound statements without constructing a truth table.

Example **9**  *Determine the Truth Value of a Compound Statement*

Determine the truth value for each simple statement. Then, using these truth values, determine the truth value of the compound statement.

a)  15 is less than or equal to 9.

b)  George Washington was the first U.S. president or Abraham Lincoln was the second U.S. president, but there has not been a U.S. president born in Antarctica.

Solution

a)  Let

$$p: \quad 15 \text{ is less than 9.}$$
$$q: \quad 15 \text{ is equal to 9.}$$

The statement "15 is less than or equal to 9" means that 15 is less than 9 or 15 is equal to 9. The compound statement can be expressed as $p \lor q$. We know that both $p$ and $q$ are false statements, since 15 is greater than 9, so we substitute F for $p$ and F for $q$ and evaluate the statement:

$$p \lor q$$
$$\text{F} \lor \text{F}$$
$$\text{F}$$

Therefore, the compound statement "15 is less than or equal to 9" is a false statement.

b)  Let

$$p: \quad \text{George Washington was the first U.S. president.}$$
$$q: \quad \text{Abraham Lincoln was the second U.S. president.}$$
$$r: \quad \text{There has been a U.S. president who was born in Antarctica.}$$

The compound statement can be written in symbolic form as $(p \lor q) \land \sim r$. Recall that *but* is used to express a conjunction. We know that $p$ is a true statement and that $q$ is a false statement. We also know that $r$ is a false statement since all U.S. presidents must be born in the United States. Thus, since $r$ is a false statement, the negation, $\sim r$, is a true statement. So we will substitute T for $p$, F for $q$, and T for $\sim r$ and then evaluate the statement:

$$(p \lor q) \land \sim r$$
$$(\text{T} \lor \text{F}) \land \text{T}$$
$$\text{T} \land \text{T}$$
$$\text{T}$$

Therefore, the original compound statement is a true statement.

## Example 10  *Pet Ownership in the United States*

The number of pets owned in the United States in 2009 is shown in Figure 3.1. Use this graph to determine the truth value of the following statement: There are more dogs owned than cats and there are fewer reptiles owned than birds, or the most numerous pets owned are not fish.

**Pets Owned in the United States
(millions)**

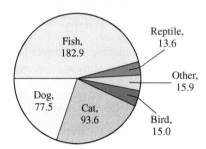

Source: American Pet Products Manufacturing Association

**Figure 3.1**

**Solution**  Let

    $p$:   There are more dogs owned than cats.
    $q$:   There are fewer reptiles owned than birds.
    $r$:   The most numerous pets owned are fish.

The given compound statement can be written in symbolic form as $(p \wedge q) \vee \sim r$. From Fig. 3.1, we see that statement $p$ is false: There are actually more cats owned than dogs. We also see that statement $q$ is true: There are fewer reptiles owned than birds. We also see that statement $r$ is true: The most numerous pets owned are fish. Since $r$ is true, its negation, $\sim r$, is false. Therefore, we substitute F for $p$, T for $q$, and F for $\sim r$, which gives

$$(p \wedge q) \vee \sim r$$
$$(\text{F} \wedge \text{T}) \vee \text{F}$$
$$\text{F} \vee \text{F}$$
$$\text{F}$$

Thus, the original compound statement is a false statement.　■

---

## SECTION 3.2  *Exercises*

### Warm Up Exercises

*In Exercises 1–4, fill in the blanks with an appropriate word, phrase, or symbol(s).*

**1.** The negation $\sim p$ will always have the _____ truth value of $p$.

**2.** The conjunction $p \wedge q$ is true only when both $p$ and $q$ are _____.

**3.** The disjunction $p \vee q$ is false only when both $p$ and $q$ are _____.

**4.** A truth table for a compound statement with

  **a)** one distinct simple statement will have _____ cases.

  **b)** two distinct simple statements will have _____ cases.

  **c)** three distinct simple statements will have _____ cases.

## Practice the Skills/Problem Solving

*In Exercises 5–18, construct a truth table for the statement.*

**5.** $p \wedge \sim p$

**6.** $p \vee \sim p$

**7.** $q \vee \sim p$

**8.** $p \wedge \sim q$

**9.** $\sim p \vee \sim q$

**10.** $\sim (p \vee \sim q)$

**11.** $\sim (p \wedge \sim q)$

**12.** $\sim (\sim p \wedge \sim q)$

**13.** $\sim q \vee (p \wedge r)$

**14.** $(p \vee \sim q) \wedge r$

**15.** $r \vee (p \wedge \sim q)$

**16.** $(r \wedge q) \wedge \sim p$

**17.** $(r \vee \sim p) \wedge \sim q$

**18.** $\sim p \wedge (q \vee r)$

*In Exercises 19–26, write the statement in symbolic form and construct a truth table.*

**19.** Train recorded *Hey, Soul Sister* and The Black Eyed Peas recorded *Where Is the Love?*

▲ *The Black Eyed Peas*

**20.** We can eat at McDonald's, but we cannot eat breakfast.

**21.** I have worked all week, but I have not been paid.

**22.** It is false that Robert A. Farinelli is the president or that Pauline Chow is the treasurer.

**23.** It is false that Jasper Adams is a tutor and Mark Russo is a secretary.

**24.** Mike made pizza and Dennis made a chef salad, but Gil burned the lemon squares.

**25.** The copier is out of toner, or the lens is dirty or the corona wires are broken.

**26.** I am hungry, and I want to eat a healthy lunch and I want to eat in a hurry.

*In Exercises 27–36, determine the truth value of the statement if*

 **a)** $p$ is true, $q$ is false, and $r$ is true.

 **b)** $p$ is false, $q$ is true, and $r$ is true.

**27.** $(p \vee q) \wedge \sim r$

**28.** $p \vee (q \wedge \sim r)$

**29.** $(\sim p \wedge \sim q) \vee \sim r$

**30.** $\sim p \wedge (\sim q \vee \sim r)$

**31.** $(p \vee \sim q) \wedge \sim (p \wedge \sim r)$

**32.** $(p \wedge \sim q) \vee r$

**33.** $(\sim r \wedge p) \vee q$

**34.** $\sim q \vee (r \wedge p)$

**35.** $(\sim p \vee \sim q) \vee (\sim r \vee q)$

**36.** $(\sim r \wedge \sim q) \wedge (\sim r \vee \sim p)$

*In Exercises 37–44, determine the truth value for each simple statement. Then use these truth values to determine the truth value of the compound statement. (You may have to use a reference source such as the Internet or an encyclopedia.)*

**37.** $8 + 7 = 20 - 5$ and $63 \div 7 = 3 \cdot 3$

**38.** $0 < -3$ or $5 \geq 10$

**39.** Florida is in Canada or Texas borders Mexico.

**40.** Washington, DC is west of the Mississippi River and Virginia is an island in the Pacific Ocean.

**41.** Quentin Tarantino is a movie director and Zac Efron is an actor, but Scarlett Johansson is not an actress.

▲ *Scarlett Johansson*

**42.** Quebec is in Texas or Toronto is in California, and Cedar Rapids is in Iowa.

**43.** Iraq is in Africa or Iran is in South America, and Syria is in the Middle East.

**44.** Holstein is a breed of cattle and collie is a breed of dogs, or beagle is not a breed of cats.

*Number of Movies Produced In Exercises 45–48, use the table to determine the truth value of each simple statement. Then determine the value of the compound statement.*

| Countries with the Highest Number of Feature Films Produced in 2008 | |
|---|---|
| **Country** | **Number of Films** |
| India | 1325 |
| United States | 520 |
| Japan | 418 |
| China | 406 |
| France | 240 |

Source: Screen Digest Magazine

**45.** India produced more feature films than the United States and China produced more feature films than Japan.

**46.** India produced more than twice as many feature films as the United States and India produced more feature films than Japan, China, and France combined.

**47.** The United States produced more feature films than Japan, but Japan produced more feature films than China.

**48.** The United States produced more than twice as many feature films as France or Japan produced more feature films than India.

*Sleep Time  In Exercises 49–52, use the graph, which shows the number of hours Americans sleep, to determine the truth value of each simple statement. Then determine the truth value of the compound statement.*

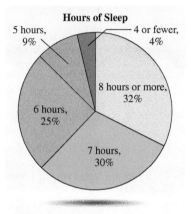

**Hours of Sleep**

5 hours, 9%
4 or fewer, 4%
8 hours or more, 32%
6 hours, 25%
7 hours, 30%

**49.** It is false that 30% of Americans get 6 hours of sleep each night and 9% get 5 hours of sleep each night.

**50.** Twenty-five percent of Americans get 6 hours of sleep each night, and 30% get 7 hours of sleep each night or 9% do not get 5 hours of sleep each night.

**51.** Thirteen percent of Americans get 5 or fewer hours of sleep each night or 32% get 6 or more hours of sleep each night, and 30% get 8 or more hours of sleep each night.

**52.** Over one-half of all Americans get 7 or fewer hours of sleep each night, and over one-quarter get 6 or fewer hours of sleep each night.

*In Exercises 53–56, let*

> $p$:   Tanisha owns a convertible.
>
> $q$:   Joan owns a Volvo.

*Translate each statement into symbols. Then construct a truth table for each compound statement and indicate under what conditions the compound statement is true.*

**53.** Tanisha owns a convertible and Joan does not own a Volvo.

**54.** Tanisha does not own a convertible, but Joan owns a Volvo.

**55.** Tanisha owns a convertible or Joan does not own a Volvo.

**56.** Tanisha does not own a convertible or Joan does not own a Volvo.

*In Exercises 57–60 on page 117, let*

> $p$:   The house is owned by an engineer.
>
> $q$:   The heat is solar generated.
>
> $r$:   The car is run by electric power.

*Translate each statement into symbols. Then construct a truth table for each and indicate under what conditions the compound statement is true.*

**57.** The car is run by electric power or the heat is solar generated, but the house is owned by an engineer.

**58.** The house is owned by an engineer and the heat is solar generated, or the car is run by electric power.

**59.** The heat is solar generated, or the house is owned by an engineer and the car is not run by electric power.

**60.** The house is not owned by an engineer, and the car is not run by electric power and the heat is solar generated.

***Obtaining a Loan*** *In Exercises 61 and 62, read the requirements and each applicant's qualifications for obtaining a loan.*

   **a)** Identify which of the applicants would qualify for the loan.

   **b)** For the applicants who do not qualify for the loan, explain why.

**61.** To qualify for a loan of $40,000, an applicant must have a gross income of $28,000 if single, $46,000 combined income if married, and assets of at least $6,000.

   Mrs. Rusinek, married with three children, earns $42,000. Mr. Rusinek does not have an income. The Rusineks have assets of $42,000.

   Mr. Duncan is not married, works in sales, and earns $31,000. He has assets of $9000.

   Mrs. Tuttle and her husband have total assets of $43,000. One earns $35,000, and the other earns $23,500.

**62.** To qualify for a loan of $45,000, an applicant must have a gross income of $30,000 if single, $50,000 combined income if married, and assets of at least $10,000.

   Mr. Argento, married with two children, earns $37,000. Mrs. Argento earns $15,000 at a part-time job. The Argentos have assets of $25,000.

   Ms. McVey, single, has assets of $19,000. She works in a store and earns $25,000.

   Mr. Siewert earns $24,000 and Ms. Fox, his wife, earns $28,000. Their assets total $8000.

**63.** ***Airline Special Fares*** An airline advertisement states, "To get the special fare you must purchase your tickets between January 1 and February 15 and fly round trip between March 1 and April 1. You must depart on a Monday, Tuesday, or Wednesday, and return on a Tuesday, Wednesday, or Thursday, and stay over at least one Saturday."

   **a)** Determine which of the following individuals will qualify for the special fare.

   **b)** If the person does not qualify for the special fare, explain why.

      Wing Park plans to purchase his ticket on January 15, depart on Monday, March 3, and return on Tuesday, March 18.

Gina Vela plans to purchase her ticket on February 1, depart on Wednesday, March 12, and return on Thursday, April 3.

Kara Shavo plans to purchase her ticket on February 14, depart on Tuesday, March 4, and return on Monday, March 19.

Christos Supernaw plans to purchase his ticket on January 4, depart on Monday, March 10, and return on Thursday, March 13.

Alex Chang plans to purchase his ticket on January 1, depart on Monday, March 3, and return on Monday, March 10.

▲ *See Exercise 63*

## Problem Solving/Group Activities

*In Exercises 64 and 65, construct a truth table for the symbolic statement.*

**64.** $\sim[(\sim(p \lor q)) \lor (q \land r)]$

**65.** $[(q \land \sim r) \land (\sim p \lor \sim q)] \lor (p \lor \sim r)$

**66.** On page 111, we indicated that a compound statement consisting of $n$ simple statements had $2^n$ distinct true–false cases.

   **a)** How many distinct true–false cases does a truth table containing simple statements $p$, $q$, $r$, and $s$ have?

   **b)** List all possible true–false cases for a truth table containing the simple statements $p$, $q$, $r$, and $s$.

   **c)** Use the list in part (b) to construct a truth table for $(q \land p) \lor (\sim r \land s)$.

   **d)** Construct a truth table for $(\sim r \land \sim s) \land (\sim p \lor q)$.

**67.** Must $(p \land \sim q) \lor r$ and $(q \land \sim r) \lor p$ have the same number of trues in their answer columns? Explain.

## Internet/Research Activities

**68.** Do research and write a report on each of the following.

   **a)** The relationship between *negation* in logic and *complement* in set theory.

   **b)** The relationship between *conjunction* in logic and *intersection* in set theory.

   **c)** The relationship between *disjunction* in logic and *union* in set theory.

# Truth Tables for the Conditional and Biconditional

▲ *Under what conditions is the statement* If you get an A, then I will buy you a car *true?*

Suppose I said to you, "If you get an A, then I will buy you a car." As we discussed in Section 3.1, this statement is called a *conditional* statement. In this section, we will discuss under what conditions a conditional statement is true and under what conditions a conditional statement is false.

**Why** *This is Important*  Understanding when conditional statements are true is essential to understanding logic and real-life documents such as wills, trusts, and contracts.

## Conditional

In Section 3.1, we mentioned that the statement preceding the conditional symbol is called the *antecedent* and that the statement following the conditional symbol is called the *consequent*. For example, consider $(p \lor q) \to [\sim(q \land r)]$. In this statement, $(p \lor q)$ is the antecedent and $[\sim(q \land r)]$ is the consequent.

To develop a truth table for the conditional statement, consider the statement "If you get an A, then I will buy you a car." Assume this statement is true except when I have actually broken my promise to you.

Let

  $p$:   You get an A.

  $q$:   I buy you a car.

Translated into symbolic form, the statement becomes $p \to q$. Let's examine the four cases shown in Table 3.16.

**CASE 1: (T, T)**  You get an A, and I buy a car for you. I have met my commitment, and the statement is true.

**CASE 2: (T, F)**  You get an A, and I do not buy a car for you. I have broken my promise, and the statement is false.

What happens if you don't get an A? If you don't get an A, I no longer have a commitment to you, and therefore I cannot break my promise.

**CASE 3: (F, T)**  You do not get an A, and I buy you a car. I have not broken my promise, and therefore the statement is true.

**CASE 4: (F, F)**  You do not get an A, and I don't buy you a car. I have not broken my promise, and therefore the statement is true.

The conditional statement is false when the antecedent is true and the consequent is false. In every other case the conditional statement is true.

> The **conditional statement** $p \to q$ is true in every case except when $p$ is a true statement and $q$ is a false statement.

Table 3.16  Conditional

| $p$ | $q$ | $p \to q$ |
|-----|-----|-----------|
| T | T | T |
| T | F | F |
| F | T | T |
| F | F | T |

## Example 1  *A Truth Table with a Conditional*

Construct a truth table for the statement $\sim p \to \sim q$.

**Solution**  Because this statement is a conditional, the answer will lie under the $\to$. Fill out the truth table by placing the appropriate truth values under $\sim p$, column 1,

Table 3.17

| p | q | ~p | → | ~q |
|---|---|----|---|----|
| T | T | F | T | F |
| T | F | F | T | T |
| F | T | T | F | F |
| F | F | T | T | T |
|   |   | 1 | 3 | 2 |

Table 3.18

| p | q | r | p | → | (~q | ∧ | r) |
|---|---|---|---|---|-----|---|----|
| T | T | T | T | F | F | F | T |
| T | T | F | T | F | F | F | F |
| T | F | T | T | T | T | T | T |
| T | F | F | T | F | T | F | F |
| F | T | T | F | T | F | F | T |
| F | T | F | F | T | F | F | F |
| F | F | T | F | T | T | T | T |
| F | F | F | F | T | T | F | F |
|   |   |   | 4 | 5 | 1 | 3 | 2 |

and under ~q, column 2 (see Table 3.17). Then, using the information given in the truth table for the conditional (Table 3.16 on page 118) and the truth values in columns 1 and 2, determine the solution, column 3. In row 1, the antecedent, ~p, is false and the consequent, ~q, is also false. Row 1 is F → F, which according to row 4 of Table 3.16, is T. Likewise, row 2 of Table 3.17 is F → T, which is T. Row 3 is T → F, which is F. Row 4 is T → T, which is T.

## Example 2  *A Conditional Truth Table with Three Simple Statements*

Construct a truth table for the statement $p \rightarrow (\sim q \wedge r)$.

*Solution*  Because this statement is a conditional, the answer will lie under the →. Work within the parentheses first. Place the truth values under ~q, column 1, and r, column 2 (Table 3.18). Then take the conjunction of columns 1 and 2 to obtain column 3. Next, place the truth values under p in column 4. To determine the answer, column 5, use columns 3 and 4 and the information of the conditional statement given in Table 3.16. Column 4 represents the truth values of the antecedent, and column 3 represents the truth values of the consequent. Remember that the conditional is false only when the antecedent is true and the consequent is false, as in cases (rows) 1, 2, and 4 of column 5.

## Example 3  *Examining an Advertisement*

An advertisement for Perky Morning coffee makes the following claim: "If you drink Perky Morning coffee, then you will not be sluggish and you will have a great day." Translate the statement into symbolic form and construct a truth table.

*Solution*  Let

    p:  You drink Perky Morning coffee.
    q:  You will be sluggish.
    r:  You will have a great day.

In symbolic form, the claim is

$$p \rightarrow (\sim q \wedge r)$$

This symbolic statement is identical to the statement in Table 3.18, and the truth tables are the same. Column 3 represents the truth values of $(\sim q \wedge r)$, which corresponds to the statement "You will not be sluggish and you will have a great day." Note that column 3 is true in cases (rows) 3 and 7. In case 3, since p is true, you drank Perky Morning coffee. In case 7, however, since p is false, you did not drink Perky Morning coffee. From this information we can conclude that it is possible for you to not be sluggish and for you to have a great day without drinking Perky Morning coffee.

A truth table cannot by itself determine whether a compound statement is true or false. However, a truth table does allow us to examine all possible cases for compound statements.

## Biconditional

The *biconditional statement* $p \leftrightarrow q$ means that $p \rightarrow q$ and $q \rightarrow p$, or, symbolically, $(p \rightarrow q) \wedge (q \rightarrow p)$. To determine the truth table for $p \leftrightarrow q$, we will construct the truth table for $(p \rightarrow q) \wedge (q \rightarrow p)$ (Table 3.19 on page 120). Table 3.20 on page 120 shows the truth values for the biconditional statement.

Table 3.19

| p | q | (p | → | q) | ∧ | (q | → | p) |
|---|---|---|---|---|---|---|---|---|
| T | T | T | T | T | T | T | T | T |
| T | F | T | F | F | F | F | T | T |
| F | T | F | T | T | F | T | F | F |
| F | F | F | T | F | T | F | T | F |
|   |   | 1 | 3 | 2 | 7 | 4 | 6 | 5 |

Table 3.20  Biconditional

| p | q | p ↔ q |
|---|---|---|
| T | T | T |
| T | F | F |
| F | T | F |
| F | F | T |

From Table 3.20 we see that the biconditional statement is true when the antecedent and the consequent have the same truth value and false when the antecedent and consequent have different truth values.

The **biconditional statement** $p \leftrightarrow q$ is true only when $p$ and $q$ have the same truth value, that is, when both are true or both are false.

## Example 4  *A Truth Table Using a Biconditional*

Construct a truth table for the statement $\sim p \leftrightarrow (\sim q \rightarrow r)$.

*Solution*  Since there are three letters, there must be eight cases. The parentheses indicate that the answer must be under the biconditional, as shown in Table 3.21. Use columns 1 and 4 to obtain the answer in column 5. When columns 1 and 4 have the same truth values, place a T in column 5. When columns 1 and 4 have different truth values, place an F in column 5.

Table 3.21

| p | q | r | ~p | ↔ | (~q | → | r) |
|---|---|---|----|---|-----|---|----|
| T | T | T | F | F | F | T | T |
| T | T | F | F | F | F | T | F |
| T | F | T | F | F | T | T | T |
| T | F | F | F | T | T | F | F |
| F | T | T | T | T | F | T | T |
| F | T | F | T | T | F | T | F |
| F | F | T | T | T | T | T | T |
| F | F | F | T | F | T | F | F |
|   |   |   | 1 | 5 | 2 | 4 | 3 |

In Section 3.2, we showed that finding the truth value of a compound statement for a specific case does not require constructing an entire truth table. Examples 5 and 6 illustrate this technique for the conditional and the biconditional.

## Example 5  *Determine the Truth Value of a Compound Statement*

Determine the truth value of the statement $(\sim p \leftrightarrow q) \rightarrow (\sim q \leftrightarrow r)$ when $p$ is false, $q$ is true, and $r$ is false.

*Solution*  Substitute the truth value for each simple statement:

$$(\sim p \leftrightarrow q) \rightarrow (\sim q \leftrightarrow r)$$
$$(T \leftrightarrow T) \;\rightarrow\; (F \leftrightarrow F)$$
$$T \quad\rightarrow\quad T$$
$$T$$

For this specific case, the statement is true.                ◼

## Example 6  *Determine the Truth Value of a Compound Statement*

Determine the truth value for each simple statement. Then use the truth values to determine the truth value of the compound statement.

a) If 15 is an even number, then 29 is an even number.
b) Vanderbilt University is in Tennessee and Wake Forest University is in Alaska, if and only if Syracuse University is in Alabama.

*Solution*

a) Let

$p$:   15 is an even number.
$q$:   29 is an even number.

Then the statement "If 15 is an even number, then 29 is an even number" can be written $p \rightarrow q$. Since 15 is not an even number, $p$ is a false statement. Also, since 29 is not an even number, $q$ is a false statement. We substitute F for $p$ and F for $q$ and evaluate the statement:

$$p \rightarrow q$$
$$F \rightarrow F$$
$$T$$

Therefore, "If 15 is an even number, then 29 is an even number" is a true statement.

b) Let

$p$:   Vanderbilt University is in Tennessee.
$q$:   Wake Forest University is in Alaska.
$r$:   Syracuse University is in Alabama.

The original compound statement can be written $(p \wedge q) \leftrightarrow r$. By checking the Internet or other references we can find that Vanderbilt University is in Tennessee, Wake Forest University is in North Carolina, and Syracuse University is in New York. Therefore, $p$ is a true statement, but $q$ and $r$ are false statements. We will substitute T for $p$, F for $q$, and F for $r$ and evaluate the compound statement:

$$(p \wedge q) \leftrightarrow r$$
$$(T \wedge F) \leftrightarrow F$$
$$F \quad \leftrightarrow F$$
$$T$$

Therefore, the original compound statement is true.                ◼

▲ *Vanderbilt University*

## Example 7  *Using Real Data in Compound Statements*

The graph in Fig. 3.2 on page 122 represents the student population by age group in 2009 for the State College of Florida (SCF). Use this graph to determine the truth value of the following compound statements.

## Satisfiability Problems

Suppose you are hosting a dinner party for seven people: Yasumasa, Marie, Albert, Stephen, Leonhard, Karl, and Emmy. You need to develop a seating plan around your circular dining room table that would satisfy all your guests. Albert and Emmy are great friends and must sit together. Yasumasa and Karl haven't spoken to each other in years and cannot sit by each other. Leonhard must sit by Marie or by Albert, but he cannot sit by Karl. Stephen insists he sit by Albert. Can you come up with a plan that would satisfy all your guests? Now imagine the difficulty of such a problem as the list of guests, and their demands, grows.

Problems such as this are known as *satisfiability* problems. The symbolic logic you are studying in this chapter allows computer scientists to represent these problems with symbols and solve the problems using computers. Even with the fastest computers, some satisfiability problems take an enormous amount of time to solve.

One solution to the problem posed above is shown upside down below. Exercises 79 and 80 on page 127 have other satisfiability problems.

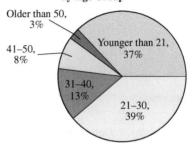

**State College of Florida Population
by Age Group**

Source: www.scf.edu

**Figure 3.2**

a) If 37% of the SCF population is younger than 21 or 26% of the SCF population is age 21–30, then 13% of the SCF population is age 31–40.

b) 3% of the SCF population is older than 50 and 8% of the SCF population is age 41–50, if and only if 19% of the SCF population is age 21–30.

*Solution*

a) Let

> $p$: 37% of the SCF population is younger than 21.
> $q$: 26% of the SCF population is age 21–30.
> $r$: 13% of the SCF population is age 31–40.

Then the original statement can be written $(p \lor q) \to r$. We can see from Fig. 3.2 that both $p$ and $r$ are true statements and that $q$ is a false statement. Substitute T for $p$, F for $q$, and T for $r$ and evaluate the statement:

$$(p \lor q) \to r$$
$$(T \lor F) \to T$$
$$T \quad \to T$$
$$T$$

Therefore, "If 37% of the SCF population is younger than 21 or 26% of the SCF population is age 21–30, then 13% of the SCF population is age 31–40" is a true statement.

b) Let

> $p$: 3% of the SCF population is older than 50.
> $q$: 8% of the SCF population is age 41–50.
> $r$: 19% of the SCF population is age 21–30.

Then the original statement can be written $(p \land q) \leftrightarrow r$. We can see from Fig. 3.2 that $p$ and $q$ are both true statements and $r$ is a false statement. Substitute T for $p$, T for $q$, and F for $r$ and evaluate the statement:

$$(p \land q) \leftrightarrow r$$
$$(T \land T) \leftrightarrow F$$
$$T \quad \leftrightarrow F$$
$$F$$

Therefore, the original statement, "3% of the SCF population is older than 50 and 8% of the SCF population is age 41–50, if and only if 19% of the SCF population is age 21–30," is a false statement.

## Self-Contradictions, Tautologies, and Implications

Two special situations can occur in the truth table of a compound statement: The statement may always be false, or the statement may always be true. We give such statements special names.

### Definition: Self-contradiction

A **self-contradiction** is a compound statement that is always false.

When every truth value in the answer column of the truth table is false, then the statement is a self-contradiction.

Table 3.22

| $p$ | $q$ | $(p \leftrightarrow q)$ | $\land$ | $(p$ | $\leftrightarrow$ | $\sim q)$ |
|-----|-----|------|------|------|------|------|
| T | T | T | F | T | F | F |
| T | F | F | F | T | T | T |
| F | T | F | F | F | T | F |
| F | F | T | F | F | F | T |
| | | 1 | 5 | 2 | 4 | 3 |

### Example 8 *All Falses, a Self-Contradiction*

Construct a truth table for the statement $(p \leftrightarrow q) \land (p \leftrightarrow \sim q)$.

*Solution* See Table 3.22. In this example, the truth values are false in each case of column 5. This statement is an example of a self-contradiction or a *logically false statement*.

### Definition: Tautology

A **tautology** is a compound statement that is always true.

When every truth value in the answer column of the truth table is true, the statement is a tautology.

### Example 9 *All Trues, a Tautology*

Construct a truth table for the statement $(p \land q) \rightarrow (p \lor r)$.

*Solution* The answer is given in column 3 of Table 3.23. The truth values are true in every case. Thus, the statement is an example of a tautology or a *logically true statement*.

Table 3.23

| $p$ | $q$ | $r$ | $(p \land q)$ | $\rightarrow$ | $(p \lor r)$ |
|-----|-----|-----|------|------|------|
| T | T | T | T | T | T |
| T | T | F | T | T | T |
| T | F | T | F | T | T |
| T | F | F | F | T | T |
| F | T | T | F | T | T |
| F | T | F | F | T | F |
| F | F | T | F | T | T |
| F | F | F | F | T | F |
| | | | 1 | 3 | 2 |

The conditional statement $(p \land q) \rightarrow (p \lor r)$ is a tautology. Conditional statements that are tautologies are called *implications*. In Example 9, we can say that $p \land q$ implies $p \lor r$.

▲ *"Heads I win, tails you lose." Do you think that this statement is a tautology, self-contradiction, or neither? See Exercise 77 on page 126.*

## Definition: Implication
An **implication** is a conditional statement that is a tautology.

In any implication the antecedent of the conditional statement implies the consequent. In other words, if the antecedent is true, then the consequent must also be true. That is, the consequent will be true whenever the antecedent is true.

Table 3.24

| $p$ | $q$ | $[(p \land q)$ | $\land$ | $p]$ | $\rightarrow$ | $q$ |
|---|---|---|---|---|---|---|
| T | T | T | T | T | T | T |
| T | F | F | F | T | T | F |
| F | T | F | F | F | T | T |
| F | F | F | F | F | T | F |
| | | 1 | 3 | 2 | 5 | 4 |

## Example 10 *An Implication?*

Determine whether the conditional statement $[(p \land q) \land p] \rightarrow q$ is an implication.

*Solution*  If the conditional statement is a tautology, the conditional statement is an implication. Because the conditional statement is a tautology (see Table 3.24), the conditional statement is an implication. The antecedent $[(p \land q) \land p]$ implies the consequent $q$. Note that the antecedent is true only in case 1 and that the consequent is also true in case 1.

## SECTION 3.3    *Exercises*

### Warm Up Exercises

*In Exercises 1–6, fill in the blanks with an appropriate word, phrase, or symbol(s).*

1. The conditional statement $p \rightarrow q$ is _____ only when $p$ is true and $q$ is false.

2. In the conditional statement $p \rightarrow q$,

   a) The lower-case letter $p$ represents the _____.

   b) The lower-case letter $q$ represents the _____.

3. The biconditional statement $p \leftrightarrow q$ is _____ only when $p$ and $q$ have the same truth value.

4. A compound statement that is always true is known as a _____.

5. A compound statement that is always false is known as a _____.

6. A conditional statement that is a tautology is known as an _____.

### Practice the Skills

*In Exercises 7–16, construct a truth table for the statement.*

7. $\sim p \rightarrow q$

8. $\sim p \rightarrow \sim q$

9. $\sim(p \rightarrow \sim q)$

10. $\sim(\sim p \leftrightarrow q)$

11. $\sim q \leftrightarrow p$

12. $(p \leftrightarrow q) \rightarrow p$

13. $p \leftrightarrow (q \lor p)$

14. $(\sim q \land p) \rightarrow \sim q$

15. $q \rightarrow (p \rightarrow \sim q)$

16. $(p \lor q) \leftrightarrow (p \land q)$

*In Exercises 17–24, construct a truth table for the statement.*

17. $\sim p \rightarrow (q \land r)$

18. $q \lor (p \rightarrow \sim r)$

19. $(q \lor \sim r) \leftrightarrow \sim p$

20. $(p \land r) \rightarrow (q \lor r)$

21. $(\sim r \lor \sim q) \rightarrow p$

22. $[r \land (q \lor \sim p)] \leftrightarrow \sim p$

23. $(p \rightarrow q) \leftrightarrow (\sim q \rightarrow \sim r)$

24. $(\sim p \leftrightarrow \sim q) \rightarrow (\sim q \leftrightarrow r)$

*In Exercises 25–30, write the statement in symbolic form. Then construct a truth table for the symbolic statement.*

**25.** If it is raining, then the baseball game is canceled and we can eat dinner together.

**26.** We advance in the tournament if and only if Max plays, or Pondo does not show up.

**27.** The election was fair if and only if the polling station stayed open until 8 P.M., or we will request a recount.

**28.** If the dam holds then we can go fishing, if and only if the pole is not broken.

**29.** If Mary Andrews does not send me an e-mail then we can call her, or we can write to Mom.

**30.** It is false that if Eileen Jones went to lunch, then she cannot take a message and we will have to go home.

*In Exercises 31–36, determine whether the statement is a tautology, self-contradiction, or neither.*

**31.** $\sim p \rightarrow p$

**32.** $(\sim p \vee q) \leftrightarrow \sim q$

**33.** $\sim p \wedge (q \leftrightarrow \sim q)$

**34.** $(p \wedge \sim q) \rightarrow q$

**35.** $(\sim q \rightarrow p) \vee \sim q$

**36.** $[(p \rightarrow q) \vee r] \leftrightarrow [(p \wedge q) \rightarrow r]$

*In Exercises 37–42, determine whether the statement is an implication.*

**37.** $\sim p \rightarrow p$

**38.** $p \rightarrow (p \vee q)$

**39.** $\sim p \rightarrow \sim (p \wedge q)$

**40.** $(p \vee q) \rightarrow (p \vee \sim r)$

**41.** $[(p \rightarrow q) \wedge (q \rightarrow p)] \rightarrow (p \leftrightarrow q)$

**42.** $[(p \vee q) \wedge r] \rightarrow (p \vee q)$

*In Exercises 43–52, if p is true, q is false, and r is true, find the truth value of the statement.*

**43.** $p \rightarrow (q \rightarrow r)$

**44.** $(p \wedge \sim q) \rightarrow \sim r$

**45.** $(p \wedge q) \leftrightarrow (q \vee r)$

**46.** $r \rightarrow (\sim p \leftrightarrow \sim q)$

**47.** $(\sim p \wedge \sim q) \vee \sim r$

**48.** $\sim [p \rightarrow (q \wedge r)]$

**49.** $(\sim p \leftrightarrow r) \vee (\sim q \leftrightarrow r)$

**50.** $(r \rightarrow \sim p) \wedge (q \rightarrow \sim r)$

**51.** $\sim [(p \vee q) \leftrightarrow (p \rightarrow \sim r)]$

**52.** $[(\sim r \rightarrow \sim q) \vee (p \wedge \sim r)] \rightarrow q$

## Problem Solving

*In Exercises 53–60, determine the truth value for each simple statement. Then, using the truth values, determine the truth value of the compound statement.*

**53.** If $\sqrt{25} = 5$, then $\sqrt{49} = 7$.

**54.** If $5 < 1$, then $7 > 10$.

**55.** If a cat has whiskers or a fish can swim, then a dog lays eggs.

**56.** If Dallas is in Texas and St. Louis is in Missouri, then Detroit is in California.

**57.** Apple makes computers, if and only if Nike makes sports shoes or Rolex makes watches.

**58.** Spike Lee is a movie director, or if Halle Berry is a school teacher then George Clooney is a circus clown.

**59.** Mother's Day is in May and Father's Day is in December, if and only if Thanksgiving is in April.

**60.** Honda makes automobiles or Honda makes motorcycles, if and only if Toyota makes cereal.

In Exercises 61–64, use the information provided about the moons for the planets Jupiter and Saturn to determine the truth values of the simple statements. Then determine the truth value of the compound statement.

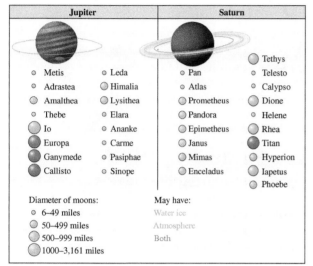

| Jupiter | | Saturn | |
|---|---|---|---|
| ○ Metis | ○ Leda | ○ Pan | ○ Tethys |
| ○ Adrastea | ○ Himalia | ○ Atlas | ○ Telesto |
| ○ Amalthea | ○ Lysithea | ○ Prometheus | ○ Calypso |
| ○ Thebe | ○ Elara | ○ Pandora | ○ Dione |
| ○ Io | ○ Ananke | ○ Epimetheus | ○ Helene |
| ○ Europa | ○ Carme | ○ Janus | ○ Rhea |
| ○ Ganymede | ○ Pasiphae | ○ Mimas | ○ Titan |
| ○ Callisto | ○ Sinope | ○ Enceladus | ○ Hyperion |
| | | | ○ Iapetus |
| | | | ○ Phoebe |

Diameter of moons:
○ 6–49 miles
○ 50–499 miles
○ 500–999 miles
○ 1000–3,161 miles

May have:
Water ice
Atmosphere
Both

Source: Data from *Time* Magazine

**61. *Jupiter's Moons*** Io has a diameter of 1000–3161 miles or Thebe may have water, and Io may have atmosphere.

**62. *Moons of Saturn*** Titan may have water and Titan may have atmosphere, if and only if Janus may have water.

**63. *Moon Comparisons*** Phoebe has a larger diameter than Rhea if and only if Callisto may have water ice, and Calypso has a diameter of 6–49 miles.

**64. *Moon Comparisons*** If Jupiter has 16 moons or Saturn does not have 18 moons, then Saturn has 7 moons that may have water ice.

***College Credits*** In Exercises 65 and 66, use the graph to determine the truth value of each simple statement. Then determine the truth value of the compound statement.

The following graph shows the number of credits in various categories needed by Jose Silva to earn his Associate in Arts degree from Keiser University.

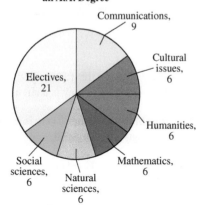

**Credits Needed for an A.A. Degree**

**65.** The number of communications credits needed is more than the number of mathematics credits needed and the number of cultural issues credits needed is equal to the number of humanities credits needed, if and only if the number of social sciences credits needed is more than the number of natural sciences credits needed.

**66.** If the number of elective credits needed is 21 or the number of communications credits needed is 15, then the number of humanities credits needed is equal to the number of mathematics credits needed.

In Exercises 67–72, suppose both of the following statements are false.

p:   Muhundan spoke at the teachers' conference.
q:   Muhundan received the outstanding teacher award.

Find the truth values of each compound statement.

**67.** If Muhundan received the outstanding teacher award, then Muhundan spoke at the teachers' conference.

**68.** If Muhundan spoke at the teachers' conference, then Muhundan did not receive the outstanding teacher award.

**69.** If Muhundan did not receive the outstanding teacher award, then Muhundan spoke at the teachers' conference.

**70.** Muhundan did not receive the outstanding teacher award if and only if Muhundan spoke at the teachers' conference.

**71.** Muhundan received the outstanding teacher award if and only if Muhundan spoke at the teachers' conference.

**72.** If Muhundan did not receive the outstanding teacher award, then Muhundan did not speak at the teachers' conference.

**73. *A New Computer*** Your parents make the following statement to your sister, "If you get straight A's this semester, then we will buy you a new computer." At the end of the semester your parents buy your sister a new computer. Can you conclude that your sister got straight A's? Explain.

**74. *Job Interview*** Consider the statement "If your interview goes well, then you will be offered the job." If you are interviewed and then offered the job, can you conclude that your interview went well? Explain.

## Challenge Problems/Group Activities

In Exercises 75 and 76, construct truth tables for the symbolic statement.

**75.** $[p \vee (q \rightarrow \sim r)] \leftrightarrow (p \wedge \sim q)$

**76.** $[(r \rightarrow \sim q) \rightarrow \sim p] \vee (q \leftrightarrow \sim r)$

**77.** Is the statement "Heads I win, tails you lose" a tautology, a self-contradiction, or neither? Explain your answer.

**78.** Construct a truth table for

**a)** $(p \vee q) \rightarrow (r \wedge s)$.

**b)** $(q \rightarrow \sim p) \vee (r \leftrightarrow s)$.

## Recreational Mathematics

**79.** *Satisfiability Problem* Refer to the Recreational Mathematics box on page 122 and then solve the following satisfiability problem. Allen, Booker, Chris, and Dennis all were born in the same year—one in January, one in February, one in March, and one in April. Chris was born before Dennis. Dennis was born two months after Booker. Booker was born after Allen, but before Chris. Find out who was born in each month.

**80.** *Cat Puzzle* Solve the following puzzle. The Joneses have four cats. The parents are Tiger and Boots, and the kittens are Sam and Sue. Each cat insists on eating out of its own bowl. To complicate matters, each cat will eat only its own brand of cat food. The colors of the bowls are red, yellow, green, and blue. The different types of cat food are Whiskas, Friskies, Nine Lives, and Meow Mix. Tiger will eat Meow Mix if and only if it is in a yellow bowl. If Boots is to eat her food, then it must be in a yellow bowl.

Mrs. Jones knows that the label on the can containing Sam's food is the same color as his bowl. Boots eats Whiskas. Meow Mix and Nine Lives are packaged in a brown paper bag. The color of Sue's bowl is green if and only if she eats Meow Mix. The label on the Friskies can is red. Match each cat with its food and the bowl of the correct color.

**81.** *The Youngest Triplet* The Barr triplets have an annoying habit: Whenever a question is asked of the three of them, two tell the truth and the third lies. When I asked them which of them was born last, they replied as follows.

> *Mary:* Katie was born last.
> *Katie:* I am the youngest.
> *Annie:* Mary is the youngest.

Which of the Barr triplets was born last?

## Internet/Research Activity

**82.** Select an advertisement from the Internet, a newspaper, or a magazine that makes or implies a conditional statement. Analyze the advertisement to determine whether the consequent necessarily follows from the antecedent. Explain your answer. (See Example 3.)

---

## SECTION 3.4   Equivalent Statements

▲ *Which statement is equivalent to* If it is sunny, then we go to the beach?

Suppose your friend makes the following statements:

> If it is sunny, then we go to the beach.
>
> If we go to the beach, then it is sunny.
>
> If it is not sunny, then we do not go to the beach.
>
> If we do not go to the beach, then it is not sunny.

Are these statements all saying the same thing, or does each one say something completely different from the others? In this section, we will study how we can answer this question by using logic symbols and truth tables. We also will learn to identify variations of conditional statements.

**Why** *This is Important* Understanding when two statements are equivalent is important to understanding advertisers' claims, political statements, and legal documents.

---

Equivalent statements are an important concept in the study of logic.

### Definition: Equivalent

Two statements are **equivalent**, symbolized ⇔,* if both statements have exactly the same truth values in the answer columns of the truth tables.

Sometimes the words *logically equivalent* are used in place of the word *equivalent*.

---

*The symbol ≡ is also used to indicate equivalent statements.

To determine whether two statements are equivalent, construct a truth table for each statement and compare the answer columns of the truth tables. If the answer columns are identical, the statements are equivalent. If the answer columns are not identical, the statements are not equivalent.

## Example 1  Equivalent Statements

Determine whether the following two statements are equivalent.

$$p \wedge (q \vee r)$$
$$(p \wedge q) \vee (p \wedge r)$$

**Solution**  Construct a truth table for each statement (see Table 3.25).

Table 3.25

| $p$ | $q$ | $r$ | $p$ | $\wedge$ | $(q \vee r)$ | $(p \wedge q)$ | $\vee$ | $(p \wedge r)$ |
|---|---|---|---|---|---|---|---|---|
| T | T | T | T | T | T | T | T | T |
| T | T | F | T | T | T | T | T | F |
| T | F | T | T | T | T | F | T | T |
| T | F | F | T | F | F | F | F | F |
| F | T | T | F | F | T | F | F | F |
| F | T | F | F | F | T | F | F | F |
| F | F | T | F | F | T | F | F | F |
| F | F | F | F | F | F | F | F | F |
| | | | 1 | 3 | 2 | 1 | 3 | 2 |

Because the truth tables have the same answer (column 3 for both tables), the statements are equivalent. Therefore, we can write

$$p \wedge (q \vee r) \Leftrightarrow (p \wedge q) \vee (p \wedge r)$$

## Example 2  Are the Following Equivalent Statements?

Determine whether the following statements are equivalent.
a)  If your homework is finished and you have washed the dishes, then you can watch television.
b)  If your homework is not finished or you have not washed the dishes, then you cannot watch television.

**Solution**  First write each statement in symbolic form, then construct a truth table for each statement. If the answer columns of both truth tables are identical, then the statements are equivalent. If the answer columns are not identical, then the statements are not equivalent.

Let

$p$:  Your homework is finished.
$q$:  You have washed the dishes.
$r$:  You can watch television.

In symbolic form, the statements are

a)  $(p \wedge q) \to r$.    b)  $(\sim p \vee \sim q) \to \sim r$.

The truth tables for these statements are given in Tables 3.26 and 3.27, respectively. The answers in the columns labeled 5 are not identical, so the statements are not equivalent.

Table 3.26

| $p$ | $q$ | $r$ | $(p$ | $\wedge$ | $q)$ | $\to$ | $r$ |
|---|---|---|---|---|---|---|---|
| T | T | T | T | T | T | T | T |
| T | T | F | T | T | T | F | F |
| T | F | T | T | F | F | T | T |
| T | F | F | T | F | F | T | F |
| F | T | T | F | F | T | T | T |
| F | T | F | F | F | T | T | F |
| F | F | T | F | F | F | T | T |
| F | F | F | F | F | F | T | F |
| | | | 1 | 3 | 2 | 5 | 4 |

Table 3.27

| $p$ | $q$ | $r$ | $(\sim p$ | $\vee$ | $\sim q)$ | $\to$ | $\sim r$ |
|---|---|---|---|---|---|---|---|
| T | T | T | F | F | F | T | F |
| T | T | F | F | F | F | T | T |
| T | F | T | F | T | T | F | F |
| T | F | F | F | T | T | T | T |
| F | T | T | T | T | F | F | F |
| F | T | F | T | T | F | T | T |
| F | F | T | T | T | T | F | F |
| F | F | F | T | T | T | T | T |
| | | | 1 | 3 | 2 | 5 | 4 |

Example **3** *Which Statements Are Logically Equivalent?*

Determine which statement is logically equivalent to "It is not true that the tire is both out of balance and flat."

a) If the tire is not flat, then the tire is not out of balance.

b) The tire is not out of balance or the tire is not flat.

c) The tire is not flat and the tire is not out of balance.

d) If the tire is not out of balance, then the tire is not flat.

**Solution** To determine whether any of the choices are equivalent to the given statement, first write the given statement and the choices in symbolic form. Then construct truth tables and compare the answer columns of the truth tables.

Let

$$p:\quad \text{The tire is out of balance.}$$
$$q:\quad \text{The tire is flat.}$$

The given statement may be written "It is not true that the tire is out of balance and the tire is flat." The statement is expressed in symbolic form as $\sim(p \wedge q)$. Using $p$ and $q$ as indicated, choices (a) through (d) may be expressed symbolically as

a) $\sim q \to \sim p$.   b) $\sim p \vee \sim q$.   c) $\sim q \wedge \sim p$.   d) $\sim p \to \sim q$.

Now construct a truth table for the given statement (Table 3.28) and for each statement (a) through (d), given in Table 3.29 (a) through (d). By examining the truth tables, we see that the given statement, $\sim(p \wedge q)$, is logically equivalent to choice (b), $\sim p \vee \sim q$. Therefore, the correct answer is "The tire is not out of balance or the tire is not flat." This statement is logically equivalent to the statement "It is not true that the tire is both out of balance and flat."

Table 3.28

| $p$ | $q$ | $\sim$ | $(p$ | $\wedge$ | $q)$ |
|---|---|---|---|---|---|
| T | T | F | T | T | T |
| T | F | T | T | F | F |
| F | T | T | F | F | T |
| F | F | T | F | F | F |
|   |   | 4 | 1 | 3 | 2 |

Table 3.29    (a)      (b)      (c)      (d)

| $p$ | $q$ | $\sim q$ | $\to$ | $\sim p$ | $\sim p$ | $\vee$ | $\sim q$ | $\sim q$ | $\wedge$ | $\sim p$ | $\sim p$ | $\to$ | $\sim q$ |
|---|---|---|---|---|---|---|---|---|---|---|---|---|---|
| T | T | F | T | F | F | F | F | F | F | F | F | T | F |
| T | F | T | F | F | F | T | T | T | F | F | F | T | T |
| F | T | F | T | T | T | T | F | F | F | T | T | F | F |
| F | F | T | T | T | T | T | T | T | T | T | T | T | T |

## De Morgan's Laws

Example 3 showed that a statement of the form $\sim(p \wedge q)$ is equivalent to a statement of the form $\sim p \vee \sim q$. Thus, we may write $\sim(p \wedge q) \Leftrightarrow \sim p \vee \sim q$. This equivalent statement is one of two special laws called De Morgan's laws. The laws, named after Augustus De Morgan, an English mathematician, were first introduced in Section 2.4, where they applied to sets.

**De Morgan's Laws**

**1.** $\sim(p \wedge q) \Leftrightarrow \sim p \vee \sim q$

**2.** $\sim(p \vee q) \Leftrightarrow \sim p \wedge \sim q$

You can demonstrate that De Morgan's second law is true by constructing and comparing truth tables for $\sim(p \vee q)$ and $\sim p \wedge \sim q$. Do so now.

When using De Morgan's laws, if it becomes necessary to negate an already negated statement, use the fact that $\sim(\sim p)$ is equivalent to $p$. For example, the negation of the statement "Today is not Monday" is "Today is Monday."

### Example 4   *Use De Morgan's Laws*

Select the statement that is logically equivalent to "I do not have investments, but I do not have debts."

a) I do not have investments or I do not have debts.

b) It is false that I have investments and I have debts.

c) It is false that I have investments or I have debts.

d) I have investments or I have debts.

**Solution**   To determine which statement is equivalent, write each statement in symbolic form.

Let

$p$:   I have investments.

$q$:   I have debts.

The statement "I do not have investments, but I do not have debts" written symbolically is $\sim p \wedge \sim q$. Recall that the word *but* means the same thing as *and*. Now, write parts (a) through (d) symbolically.

a) $\sim p \vee \sim q$    b) $\sim(p \wedge q)$    c) $\sim(p \vee q)$    d) $p \vee q$

De Morgan's law shows that $\sim p \wedge \sim q$ is equivalent to $\sim(p \vee q)$. Therefore, the answer is (c): "It is false that I have investments or I have debts." ∎

### Example 5   *Using De Morgan's Laws to Write an Equivalent Statement*

Write a statement that is logically equivalent to "It is not true that tomatoes are poisonous or eating peppers cures the common cold."

**Solution**   Let

$p$:   Tomatoes are poisonous.

$q$:   Eating peppers cures the common cold.

The given statement is of the form $\sim(p \vee q)$. Using the second of De Morgan's laws, we see that an equivalent statement in symbols is $\sim p \wedge \sim q$. Therefore, an equivalent statement in words is "Tomatoes are not poisonous and eating peppers does not cure the common cold." ∎

Consider $\sim(p \wedge q) \Leftrightarrow \sim p \vee \sim q$, one of De Morgan's laws. To go from $\sim(p \wedge q)$ to $\sim p \vee \sim q$, we negate both the $p$ and the $q$ within parentheses; change the conjunction, $\wedge$, to a disjunction, $\vee$; and remove the negation symbol preceding the left parentheses and the parentheses themselves. We can use a similar procedure to obtain equivalent statements. For example,

$$\sim(\sim p \wedge q) \Leftrightarrow p \vee \sim q$$
$$\sim(p \wedge \sim q) \Leftrightarrow \sim p \vee q$$

We can use a similar procedure to obtain equivalent statements when a disjunction is within parentheses. Note that

$$\sim(\sim p \vee q) \Leftrightarrow p \wedge \sim q$$
$$\sim(p \vee \sim q) \Leftrightarrow \sim p \wedge q$$

▲ *Taylor Swift*

## Profile In Mathematics

### Augustus De Morgan

Augustus De Morgan (1806–1871), the son of a member of the East India Company, was born in India and educated at Trinity College, Cambridge (UK). One of the great reformers of logic in the nineteenth century, De Morgan made his greatest contribution to the subject by realizing that logic as it had come down from Aristotle was narrow in scope and could be applied to a wider range of arguments. His work laid the foundation for modern, symbolic logic.

---

Example **6**  *Using De Morgan's Laws to Write an Equivalent Statement*

Use De Morgan's laws to write a statement logically equivalent to "Taylor Swift did not win an Academy of Country Music award, but she had a top-selling record."

**Solution**  Let

$p:$    Taylor Swift won an Academy of Country Music award.

$q:$    Taylor Swift had a top-selling record.

The statement written symbolically is $\sim p \ \wedge \ q$. Earlier we showed that

$$\sim p \ \wedge \ q \Leftrightarrow \ \sim (p \ \vee \sim q)$$

Therefore, the statement "It is false that Taylor Swift won an Academy of Country Music award or Taylor Swift did not have a top-selling record" is logically equivalent to the given statement.

---

There are strong similarities between the topics of sets and logic. We can see them by examining De Morgan's laws for sets and logic.

| De Morgan's laws: set theory | De Morgan's laws: logic |
|---|---|
| $(A \cap B)' = A' \cup B'$ | $\sim (p \wedge q) \Leftrightarrow \ \sim p \vee \sim q$ |
| $(A \cup B)' = A' \cap B'$ | $\sim (p \vee q) \Leftrightarrow \ \sim p \wedge \sim q$ |

The complement in set theory, $'$, is similar to the negation, $\sim$, in logic. The intersection, $\cap$, is similar to the conjunction, $\wedge$; and the union, $\cup$, is similar to the disjunction, $\vee$. If we were to interchange the set symbols with the logic symbols, De Morgan's laws would remain, but in a different form.

Both $'$ and $\sim$ can be interpreted as *not*.

Both $\cap$ and $\wedge$ can be interpreted as *and*.

Both $\cup$ and $\vee$ can be interpreted as *or*.

For example, the set statement $A' \cup B$ can be written as a statement in logic as $\sim a \vee b$.

---

Statements containing connectives other than *and* and *or* may have equivalent statements. To illustrate this point, construct truth tables for $p \rightarrow q$ and for $\sim p \vee q$. The truth tables will have the same answer columns and therefore the statements are equivalent. We summarize this as follows.

### The Conditional Statement Written As a Disjunction

$$p \rightarrow q \Leftrightarrow \ \sim p \vee q$$

With these equivalent statements, we can write a conditional statement as a disjunction or a disjunction as a conditional statement. For example, the statement "If the game is polo, then you ride a horse" can be equivalently stated as "The game is not polo or you ride a horse."

To change a conditional statement to a disjunction, negate the antecedent, change the conditional symbol to a disjunction symbol, and keep the consequent the same. To change a disjunction statement to a conditional statement, negate the first statement, change the disjunction symbol to a conditional symbol, and keep the second statement the same.

Example **7**  *Rewriting a Disjunction as a Conditional Statement*

Write a conditional statement that is logically equivalent to "The Oregon Ducks will win or the Oregon State Beavers will lose." Assume that the negation of winning is losing.

*Solution* Let

$p$: The Oregon Ducks will win.

$q$: The Oregon State Beavers will win.

The original statement may be written symbolically as $p \lor \sim q$. To write an equivalent conditional statement, negate the first statement, $p$, change the disjunction symbol to a conditional symbol, and keep the second statement the same. Symbolically, the equivalent statement is $\sim p \to \sim q$. The equivalent statement in words is "If the Oregon Ducks lose, then the Oregon State Beavers will lose." ∎

## Negation of the Conditional Statement

Now we will discuss how to negate a conditional statement. To negate a conditional statement we use the fact that $p \to q \Leftrightarrow \sim p \lor q$ and De Morgan's laws. Examples 8 and 9 show the process.

Example **8** *The Negation of a Conditional Statement*

Determine a statement equivalent to $\sim(p \to q)$.

*Solution* Begin with $p \to q \Leftrightarrow \sim p \lor q$, negate both statements, and use De Morgan's laws.

$$p \to q \Leftrightarrow \sim p \lor q$$
$$\sim(p \to q) \Leftrightarrow \sim(\sim p \lor q) \qquad \text{Negate both statements.}$$
$$\Leftrightarrow p \land \sim q \qquad \text{De Morgan's laws}$$

Therefore, $\sim(p \to q)$ is equivalent to $p \land \sim q$. ∎

We summarize the result of Example 8 as follows.

**The Negation of the Conditional Statement Written As a Conjunction**

$$\sim(p \to q) \Leftrightarrow p \land \sim q$$

Example **9** *Write an Equivalent Statement*

Write a statement that is equivalent to "It is false that if you hang the picture then it will be crooked."

*Solution* Let

$p$: You hang the picture.

$q$: The picture will be crooked.

The given statement can be represented symbolically as $\sim(p \to q)$. We illustrated in Example 8 that $\sim(p \to q)$ is equivalent to $p \land \sim q$. Therefore, an equivalent statement is "You hang the picture and the picture will not be crooked." ∎

Using the fact that $\sim(p \to q) \Leftrightarrow p \land \sim q$, can you determine what $\sim(p \to \sim q)$ is equivalent to as a conjunction? If you answered $p \land q$ you answered correctly.

## Variations of the Conditional Statement

We know that $p \rightarrow q$ is equivalent to $\sim p \vee q$. Are any other statements equivalent to $p \rightarrow q$? Yes, there are many. Now let's look at the variations of the conditional statement to determine whether any are equivalent to the conditional statement. *The variations of the conditional statement are made by switching and/or negating the antecedent and the consequent of a conditional statement.* The variations of the conditional statement are the *converse* of the conditional, the *inverse* of the conditional, and the *contrapositive* of the conditional.

Listed here are the variations of the conditional with their symbolic form and the words we say to read each one.

### Variations of the Conditional Statement

| Name | Symbolic form | Read |
|------|---------------|------|
| Conditional | $p \rightarrow q$ | "If $p$, then $q$" |
| Converse of the conditional | $q \rightarrow p$ | "If $q$, then $p$" |
| Inverse of the conditional | $\sim p \rightarrow \sim q$ | "If not $p$, then not $q$" |
| Contrapositive of the conditional | $\sim q \rightarrow \sim p$ | "If not $q$, then not $p$" |

> **TIMELY TIP**
>
> The contrapositive statement is always equivalent to the original conditional statement.

To write the converse of the conditional statement, switch the order of the antecedent and the consequent. To write the inverse, negate both the antecedent and the consequent. To write the contrapositive, switch the order of the antecedent and the consequent and then negate both of them.

Are any of the variations of the conditional statement equivalent? To determine the answer, we can construct a truth table for each variation, as shown in Table 3.30. It reveals that *the conditional statement is equivalent to the contrapositive statement and that the converse statement is equivalent to the inverse statement.*

Table 3.30

| $p$ | $q$ | Conditional $p \rightarrow q$ | Contrapositive $\sim q \rightarrow \sim p$ | Converse $q \rightarrow p$ | Inverse $\sim p \rightarrow \sim q$ |
|-----|-----|-------------------------------|--------------------------------------------|----------------------------|-------------------------------------|
| T | T | T | T | T | T |
| T | F | F | F | T | T |
| F | T | T | T | F | F |
| F | F | T | T | T | T |

## Example 10  *The Converse, Inverse, and Contrapositive*

For the conditional statement "If the song contains sitar music, then the song was written by George Harrison," write the

a) converse.   b) inverse.   c) contrapositive.

*Solution*

a) Let

$p$:  The song contains sitar music.

$q$:  The song was written by George Harrison.

The conditional statement is of the form $p \rightarrow q$, so the converse must be of the form $q \rightarrow p$. Therefore, the converse is "If the song was written by George Harrison, then the song contains sitar music."

▲ *A sitar.*

b) The inverse is of the form $\sim p \rightarrow \sim q$. Therefore, the inverse is "If the song does not contain sitar music, then the song was not written by George Harrison."

c) The contrapositive is of the form $\sim q \rightarrow \sim p$. Therefore, the contrapositive is "If the song was not written by George Harrison, then the song does not contain sitar music."

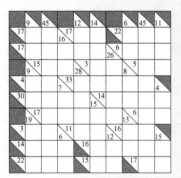
## Example 11   Determine the Truth Values

Let

$p$:   The number is divisible by 10.
$q$:   The number is divisible by 5.

Write the following statements and determine which are true.
a) The conditional statement, $p \rightarrow q$
b) The converse of $p \rightarrow q$
c) The inverse of $p \rightarrow q$
d) The contrapositive of $p \rightarrow q$

### Solution

a) The conditional statement in symbols is $p \rightarrow q$. Therefore, in words the conditional statement is *If the number is divisible by 10, then the number is divisible by 5.* This statement is true. A number divisible by 10 must also be divisible by 5, since 5 is a divisor of 10.

b) The converse of the conditional statement in symbols is $q \rightarrow p$. Therefore, in words the converse is *If the number is divisible by 5, then the number is divisible by 10.* This statement is false. For example, 15 is divisible by 5, but 15 is not divisible by 10.

c) The inverse of the conditional statement in symbols is $\sim p \rightarrow \sim q$. Therefore, in words the inverse is *If the number is not divisible by 10, then the number is not divisible by 5.* This statement is false. For example, 25 is not divisible by 10, but 25 is divisible by 5.

d) The contrapositive of the conditional statement in symbols is $\sim q \rightarrow \sim p$. Therefore, in words the contrapositive is *If the number is not divisible by 5, then the number is not divisible by 10.* This statement is true. Any number that is not divisible by 5 cannot be divisible by 10, since 5 is a divisor of 10.

Because the contrapositive statement is always equivalent to the original conditional statement, in Example 11 d) we should have expected the answer to be a true statement because the original conditional statement was also a true statement.

## Example 12   Use the Contrapositive

Use the contrapositive to write a statement logically equivalent to "If you don't eat your meat, then you can't have any pudding."

### Solution   Let

$p$:   You do eat your meat.
$q$:   You can have any pudding.

The given statement written symbolically is

$$\sim p \rightarrow \sim q$$

**Fuzzy Logic**

$M$ any modern computers work solely with two values, 1 or 0. This constraint makes it difficult for a computer to evaluate vague concepts that human beings deal with on a regular basis, such as *bright, slow*, and *light*. More and more computers are becoming more capable of handling such vague concepts, thanks to the introduction of *fuzzy logic*. Unlike the traditional computer logic, fuzzy logic is based on the assignment of a value between 0 and 1, inclusively, that can vary from setting to setting. For example, a camera using fuzzy logic may assign *bright* a value of 0.9 on a sunny day, 0.4 on a cloudy day, and 0.1 at night. Fuzzy logic also makes use of logical statements like those studied in this chapter. One such statement is "If X and Y, then Z." For example, a computer chip in a camera programmed with fuzzy logic may use the rule "If the day is *bright* and the film speed is *slow*, then let in less *light*." Fuzzy logic is discussed further in Exercises 81 and 82 on page 139.

**Why** *This is Important* Fuzzy logic is increasingly used in many devices that are part of everyday life.

The contrapositive of the statement is

$$q \rightarrow p$$

Therefore, an equivalent statement is "If you can have any pudding, then you do eat your meat."

The contrapositive of the conditional is very important in mathematics. Consider the statement "If $a^2$ is not a whole number, then $a$ is not a whole number." Is this statement true? You may find this question difficult to answer. Writing the statement's contrapositive may enable you to answer the question. The contrapositive is "If $a$ is a whole number, then $a^2$ is a whole number." Since the contrapositive is a true statement, the original statement must also be true.

### Example 13 *Which Are Equivalent?*

Determine which, if any, of the following statements are equivalent. You may use De Morgan's laws, the fact that $p \rightarrow q \Leftrightarrow {\sim}p \vee q$, information from the variations of the conditional, or truth tables.

a) If you leave by 9 A.M., then you will get to your destination on time.

b) You do not leave by 9 A.M. or you will get to your destination on time.

c) It is false that you will get to your destination on time or you did not leave by 9 A.M.

d) If you do not get to your destination on time, then you did not leave by 9 A.M.

**Solution** Let

$p$: You leave by 9 A.M.
$q$: You will get to your destination on time.

In symbolic form, the four statements are

a) $p \rightarrow q$.    b) ${\sim}p \vee q$.    c) ${\sim}(q \vee {\sim}p)$.    d) ${\sim}q \rightarrow {\sim}p$.

Which of these statements are equivalent? Earlier in this section, you learned that $p \rightarrow q$ is equivalent to ${\sim}p \vee q$. Therefore, statements (a) and (b) are equivalent. Statement (d) is the contrapositive of statement (a). Therefore, statement (d) is also equivalent to statement (a) and statement (b). Statements (a), (b), and (d) all have the same truth table (Table 3.31).

Table 3.31

| | | (a) | (b) | (d) |
|---|---|---|---|---|
| $p$ | $q$ | $p \rightarrow q$ | ${\sim}p \vee q$ | ${\sim}q \rightarrow {\sim}p$ |
| T | T | T | T | T |
| T | F | F | F | F |
| F | T | T | T | T |
| F | F | T | T | T |

Now let's look at statement (c). To determine whether ${\sim}(q \vee {\sim}p)$ is equivalent to the other statements, we will construct its truth table (Table 3.32) and compare the answer column with the answer columns in Table 3.31.

Table 3.32       (c)

| $p$ | $q$ | ${\sim}$ | $(q$ | $\vee$ | ${\sim}p)$ |
|---|---|---|---|---|---|
| T | T | F | T | T | F |
| T | F | T | F | F | F |
| F | T | F | T | T | T |
| F | F | F | F | T | T |
| | | 4 | 1 | 3 | 2 |

None of the three answer columns of the truth table in Table 3.31 is the same as the answer column of the truth table in Table 3.32. Therefore $\sim (q \vee \sim p)$ is not equivalent to any of the other statements. Therefore, only statements (a), (b), and (d) are equivalent to each other. ∎

## SECTION 3.4    *Exercises*

### Warm Up Exercises

*In Exercises 1–8, fill in the blanks with an appropriate word, phrase, or symbol(s).*

1. Statements that have exactly the same truth values in the answer columns of their truth tables are called _____ statements.

2. DeMorgan's laws state that

   a) $\sim (p \wedge q)$ is equivalent to _____, and

   b) $\sim (p \vee q)$ is equivalent to _____.

3. The conditional statement $p \rightarrow q$ is equivalent to the following disjunction statement: _____.

4. The negation of the conditional statement $\sim (p \rightarrow q)$ is equivalent to the following conjunction statement: _____.

5. Given the conditional statement $p \rightarrow q$, the converse of the conditional statement in symbolic form is _____.

6. Given the conditional statement $p \rightarrow q$, the inverse of the conditional statement in symbolic form is _____.

7. Given the conditional statement $p \rightarrow q$, the contrapositive of the conditional statement in symbolic form is _____.

8. Of the converse, inverse, and contrapositive, only the contrapositive of the conditional statement is _____ to the conditional statement.

### Practice the Skills

*In Exercises 9–18, use De Morgan's laws to determine whether the two statements are equivalent.*

9. $\sim (p \wedge q), \sim p \wedge \sim q$

10. $\sim (p \wedge q), \sim p \vee \sim q$

11. $\sim (p \vee q), \sim p \wedge \sim q$

12. $\sim (p \vee q), \sim p \vee \sim q$

13. $\sim (\sim p \wedge q), p \wedge \sim q$

14. $\sim (\sim p \wedge q), p \vee \sim q$

15. $(\sim p \vee \sim q) \rightarrow r, \sim (p \wedge q) \rightarrow r$

16. $q \rightarrow \sim (p \wedge \sim r), q \rightarrow \sim p \vee r$

17. $\sim (p \rightarrow \sim q), p \wedge q$

18. $\sim (\sim p \rightarrow q), \sim p \wedge \sim q$

*In Exercises 19–30, use a truth table to determine whether the two statements are equivalent.*

19. $p \rightarrow q, \sim p \vee q$

20. $\sim (p \rightarrow q), p \wedge \sim q$

21. $\sim q \rightarrow \sim p, p \rightarrow q$

22. $q \rightarrow p, \sim p \rightarrow \sim q$

23. $(p \vee q) \vee r, p \vee (q \vee r)$

24. $p \vee (q \wedge r), \sim p \rightarrow (q \wedge r)$

25. $p \wedge (q \vee r), (p \wedge q) \vee r$

26. $\sim (q \rightarrow p) \vee r, (p \vee q) \wedge \sim r$

27. $(p \rightarrow q) \wedge (q \rightarrow p), (p \leftrightarrow q)$

28. $[\sim (p \rightarrow q)] \wedge [\sim (q \rightarrow p)], \sim (p \leftrightarrow q)$

### Problem Solving

*In Exercises 29–34, use De Morgan's laws to write an equivalent statement for the sentence.*

29. It is false that Oregon borders the Atlantic Ocean and Delaware borders the Pacific Ocean.

30. It is false that Greg Dietrich selects formulas or Moana Karsteter applies concepts.

31. The dog was neither a bulldog nor was the dog a boxer.

32. The pot roast is hot, but it is not well done.

33. If Ashley Tabai takes the new job, then she will not move or she will buy a new house in town.

**34.** If Phil Murphy buys us dinner, then we will not go to the top of the CN Tower but we will be able to walk to the Red Bistro Restaurant.

*In Exercises 35–40, use the fact that $p \rightarrow q$ is equivalent to $\sim p \vee q$ to write an equivalent form of the given statement.*

**35.** If Janette Campbell buys a new car, then she sells her old car.

**36.** Byron Dyce did not walk to the meeting or we started late.

**37.** Bob the Tomato visited the nursing home or he did not visit the Cub Scout meeting.

**38.** If Joanne Ernst goes to the Lightning game, then she will not go to the Rays game.

**39.** Chase is not hiding or the pitcher is broken.

**40.** If Weezer is not on the radio, then Tim Ollendick is working.

*In Exercises 41–48, use the fact that $\sim (p \rightarrow q)$ is equivalent to $p \wedge \sim q$ to write the statement in an equivalent form.*

**41.** It is false that if we go to Chicago, then we will go to Navy Pier.

▲ *Navy Pier in Chicago*

**42.** It is false that if General Electric makes the telephone, then the telephone is made in the United States.

**43.** I am cold and the heater is not working.

**44.** The Badgers beat the Nittany Lions and the Bucks beat the 76ers.

**45.** It is not true that if Amazon has a sale then we will buy $100 worth of books.

**46.** Thompson is sick today but Allen didn't go to school.

**47.** John Deere will hire new workers and the city of Dubuque will retrain the workers.

**48.** My cell phone is not a Blackberry but my cell phone has a keyboard.

*In Exercises 49–54, write the converse, inverse, and contrapositive of the statement. (For Exercise 54, use De Morgan's laws.)*

**49.** If Nanette Berry teaches macramé, then she needs extra yarn.

**50.** If the water is running, then Linus is getting a drink.

**51.** If I go to Mexico, then I buy silver jewelry.

**52.** If Bob Dylan records a new CD, then he will go on tour.

**53.** If that annoying paper clip shows up on my computer screen, then I will scream.

**54.** If the sun is shining, then we will go down to the marina and we will take out the sailboat.

*In Exercises 55–60, write the contrapositive of the statement. Use the contrapositive to determine whether the conditional statement is true or false.*

**55.** If a natural number is divisible by 14, then the natural number is divisible by 7.

**56.** If the quadrilateral is a parallelogram, then the opposite sides are parallel.

**57.** If a natural number is divisible by 3, then the natural number is divisible by 6.

**58.** If $1/n$ is not a natural number, then $n$ is not a natural number.

**59.** If two lines do not intersect in at least one point, then the two lines are parallel.

**60.** If $\dfrac{m \cdot a}{m \cdot b} \neq \dfrac{a}{b}$, then $m$ is not a counting number.

*In Exercises 61–74, determine which, if any, of the three statements are equivalent (see Example 13).*

**61.** **a)** If the ball lands in foul territory, then the runner returns to the base.

   **b)** If the runner returns to the base, then the ball lands in foul territory.

   **c)** The runner does not return to the base or the ball lands in foul territory.

**62. a)** If Fido is our dog's name, then Rex is not our dog's name.

**b)** It is false that Fido is our dog's name and Rex is not our dog's name.

**c)** Fido is not our dog's name or Rex is our dog's name.

**63. a)** The office is not cool and the copier is jammed.

**b)** If the office is not cool, then the copier is not jammed.

**c)** It is false that the office is cool or the copier is not jammed.

**64. a)** The test is not written or the review sheet is not ready.

**b)** If the test is written, then the review sheet is ready.

**c)** It is false that the review sheet is ready and the test is not written.

**65. a)** Today is not Sunday or the library is open.

**b)** If today is Sunday, then the library is not open.

**c)** If the library is open, then today is not Sunday.

**66. a)** If you are fishing at 1 P.M., then you are driving a car at 1 P.M.

**b)** You are not fishing at 1 P.M. or you are driving a car at 1 P.M.

**c)** It is false that you are fishing at 1 P.M. and you are not driving a car at 1 P.M.

**67. a)** The grass grows and the trees are blooming.

**b)** If the trees are blooming, then the grass does not grow.

**c)** The trees are not blooming or the grass does not grow.

**68. a)** Johnny Patrick is chosen as department chair if and only if he is the only candidate.

**b)** If Johnny Patrick is chosen as department chair then he is the only candidate, and if Johnny Patrick is the only candidate then he is chosen as department chair.

**c)** Johnny Patrick is not chosen as department chair and he is not the only candidate.

**69. a)** If the corn bag goes in the hole, then you are awarded three points.

**b)** It is false that the corn bag goes in the hole and you are awarded three points.

**c)** The corn bag does not go in the hole and you are not awarded three points.

**70. a)** Fitz and the Tantrums will not go on tour if and only if James King does not play the saxophone.

**b)** It is false that Fitz and the Tantrums will go on tour if and only if James King does not play the saxophone.

**c)** If Fitz and the Tantrums go on tour, then James King plays saxophone.

**71. a)** If the pay is good and today is Monday, then I will take the job.

**b)** If I do not take the job, then it is false that the pay is good or today is Monday.

**c)** The pay is good and today is Monday, or I will take the job.

**72. a)** If you are 18 years old and a citizen of the United States, then you can vote in the presidential election.

**b)** You can vote in the presidential election, if and only if you are a citizen of the United States and you are 18 years old.

**c)** You cannot vote in the presidential election, or you are 18 years old and you are not a citizen of the United States.

**73. a)** The package was sent by Federal Express, or the package was not sent by United Parcel Service but the package arrived on time.

**b)** The package arrived on time, if and only if it was sent by Federal Express or it was not sent by United Parcel Service.

**c)** If the package was not sent by Federal Express, then the package was not sent by United Parcel Service but the package arrived on time.

**74. a)** The mortgage rate went down, if and only if Tim purchased the house and the down payment was 10%.

**b)** The down payment was 10%, and if Tim purchased the house then the mortgage rate went down.

**c)** If Tim purchased the house, then the mortgage rate went down and the down payment was not 10%.

## Concept/Writing Exercises

**75.** If $p$ and $q$ represent two simple statements, and if $p \rightarrow q$ is a false statement, what must be the truth value of the converse, $q \rightarrow p$? Explain.

**76.** If $p$ and $q$ represent two simple statements, and if $p \rightarrow q$ is a false statement, what must be the truth value of the inverse, $\sim p \rightarrow \sim q$? Explain.

**77.** If $p$ and $q$ represent two simple statements, and if $p \rightarrow q$ is a false statement, what must be the truth value of the contrapositive, $\sim q \rightarrow \sim p$? Explain.

**78.** If $p$ and $q$ represent two simple statements, and if $p \rightarrow q$ is a true statement, what must be the truth value of the contrapositive, $\sim q \rightarrow \sim p$? Explain.

## Challenge Problems/Group Activities

**79.** We learned that $p \rightarrow q \Leftrightarrow \sim p \vee q$. Determine a conjunction that is equivalent to $p \rightarrow q$. (*Hint:* There are many answers.)

**80.** Determine whether $\sim[\sim(p \vee \sim q)] \Leftrightarrow p \vee \sim q$. Explain the method(s) you used to determine your answer.

**81.** In an appliance or device that uses fuzzy logic, a change in one condition causes a change in a second condition. For example, in a camera, if the brightness increases, the lens aperture automatically decreases to get the proper exposure. Name at least 10 appliances or devices that make use of fuzzy logic and explain how fuzzy logic is used in each appliance or device. See the *Mathematics Today* box on page 135.

**82.** In symbolic logic, a statement is either true or false (consider true to have a value of 1 and false a value of 0). In fuzzy logic, nothing is true or false, but everything is a matter of degree. For example, consider the statement "The sun is shining." In fuzzy logic, this statement may have a value between 0 and 1 and may be constantly changing. For example, if the sun is partially blocked by clouds, the value of this statement may be 0.25. In fuzzy logic, the values of connective statements are found as follows for statements $p$ and $q$.

Not $p$ has a truth value of $1 - p$.

$p \wedge q$ has a truth value equal to the lesser of $p$ and $q$.

$p \vee q$ has a truth value equal to the greater of $p$ and $q$.

$p \rightarrow q$ has a truth value equal to the lesser of 1 and $1 - p + q$.

$p \leftrightarrow q$ has a truth value equal to $1 - |p - q|$, that is, 1 minus the absolute value* of $p$ minus $q$.

Suppose the statement "$p$: The sun is shining" has a truth value of 0.25 and the statement "$q$: Mary is getting a tan" has a truth value of 0.20. Find the truth value of

**a)** $\sim p$      **b)** $\sim q$

**c)** $p \wedge q$      **d)** $p \vee q$

**e)** $p \rightarrow q$      **f)** $p \leftrightarrow q$

*Absolute values are discussed in Section 13.8.

## Recreational Exercises

**83. *Kakuro*** Refer to the *Recreational Mathematics* box on page 134. Complete the following Kakuro puzzle.

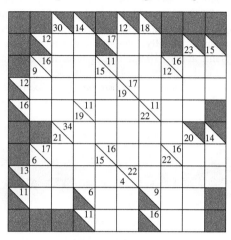

## Internet/Research Activities

**84.** Do research and write a report on fuzzy logic.

**85.** Read one of Lewis Carroll's books and write a report on how he used logic in the book. Give at least five specific examples.

**86.** Do research and write a report on the life and achievements of Augustus De Morgan. Indicate in your report his contributions to sets and logic.

---

# SECTION 3.5    Symbolic Arguments

▲ *The Who plays during halftime of Super Bowl XLIV.*

Consider the following statements.

If Carrie Underwood sings the national anthem, then The Who will play at halftime.

Carrie Underwood sings the national anthem.

If you accept these two statements as true, then what logical conclusion could you draw? Do you agree that you can logically conclude that The Who will play at halftime? In this section, we will use our knowledge of logic to study the structure of such statements to draw logical conclusions.

**Why** *This is Important* Drawing logical conclusions from a given set of statements is an important application of logic. Also, we use logic daily in decision making after considering all the facts we know to be true.

---

Previously in this chapter, we used symbolic logic to determine the truth value of a compound statement. We now extend those basic ideas to determine whether we can draw logical conclusions from a set of given statements. Consider once again the two statements.

If Carrie Underwood sings the national anthem, then The Who will play at halftime.

Carrie Underwood sings the national anthem.

These statements in the following form constitute what we will call a *symbolic argument*.

*Premise 1:*    If Carrie Underwood sings the national anthem, then The Who will play at halftime.

*Premise 2:*    Carrie Underwood sings the national anthem

*Conclusion:*    The Who will play at halftime.

In the case of the disappearance of the racehorse Silver Blaze, Sherlock Holmes demonstrated that sometimes the absence of a clue is itself a clue. The local police inspector asked him, "Is there any point to which you would wish to draw my attention?" Holmes replied, "To the curious incident of the dog in the nighttime." The inspector, confused, asked: "The dog did nothing in the nighttime." "That was the curious incident," remarked Sherlock Holmes. From the lack of the dog's bark, Holmes concluded that the horse had been "stolen" by a stablehand. How did Holmes reach his conclusion?

A *symbolic argument* consists of a set of *premises* and a *conclusion*. It is called a symbolic argument because we generally write it in symbolic form to determine its validity.

### Definition: Valid and Invalid Arguments

An **argument is valid** when its conclusion necessarily follows from a given set of premises.

An **argument is invalid** or a **fallacy** when the conclusion does not necessarily follow from the given set of premises.

An argument that is not valid is invalid. The argument just presented is an example of a valid argument, as the conclusion necessarily follows from the premises. Now we will discuss a procedure to determine whether an argument is valid or invalid. We begin by writing the argument in symbolic form. To write the argument in symbolic form, we let $p$ and $q$ be

$p$:    Carrie Underwood sings the national anthem.

$q$:    The Who will play at halftime.

Symbolically, the argument is written

Premise 1:      $p \rightarrow q$
Premise 2:      $p$
Conclusion      $\therefore q$      (The three-dot-triangle is read "therefore.")

Write the argument in the following form.

If      [*premise 1*   **and**   *premise 2*]   **then**   *conclusion*
        $[(p \rightarrow q)$      $\wedge$      $p]$      $\rightarrow$      $q$

Then construct a truth table for the statement $[(p \rightarrow q) \wedge p] \rightarrow q$ (Table 3.33). *If the truth table answer column is true in every case, then the statement is a tautology, and the argument is valid. If the truth table is not a tautology, then the argument is invalid.* Since the statement is a tautology (see column 5), the conclusion necessarily follows from the premises and the argument is valid.

Table 3.33

| $p$ | $q$ | $[(p \rightarrow q)$ | $\wedge$ | $p]$ | $\rightarrow$ | $q$ |
|---|---|---|---|---|---|---|
| T | T | T | T | T | T | T |
| T | F | F | F | T | T | F |
| F | T | T | F | F | T | T |
| F | F | T | F | F | T | F |
| | | 1 | 3 | 2 | 5 | 4 |

Once we have demonstrated that an argument in a particular form is valid, all arguments with exactly the same form will also be valid. In fact, many of these forms have been assigned names. The argument form just discussed,

$$p \rightarrow q$$
$$p$$
$$\therefore q$$

is called the *law of detachment*, or *modus ponens*.

▲ *Alaska*

**Example 1** *Determining Validity Without a Truth Table*

Determine whether the following argument is valid or invalid.

> If Canada is north of the United States, then Alaska is in Mexico.
> Canada is north of the United States.
> ─────────────────────────────────
> ∴ Alaska is in Mexico.

**Solution**  Translate the argument into symbolic form.

Let

> $c$:   Canada is north of the United States.
> $a$:   Alaska is in Mexico.

In symbolic form, the argument is

$$c \rightarrow a$$
$$\underline{c}$$
$$\therefore a$$

This argument is also the law of detachment. Therefore, it is a valid argument.  ▪

Note that the argument in Example 1 is valid even though the conclusion, "Alaska is in Mexico," is a false statement. It is also possible to have an invalid argument in which the conclusion is a true statement. *When an argument is valid, the conclusion necessarily follows from the premises. It is not necessary for the premises or the conclusion to be true statements in an argument.*

---

**PROCEDURE**   TO DETERMINE WHETHER AN ARGUMENT IS VALID

1. Write the argument in symbolic form.
2. Compare the form of the argument with forms that are known to be valid or invalid. If there are no known forms to compare it with, or you do not remember the forms, go to step 3.
3. If the argument contains two premises, write a conditional statement of the form

   [(premise 1) ∧ (premise 2)] → conclusion

4. Construct a truth table for the statement in step 3.
5. If the answer column of the truth table has all trues, the statement is a tautology, and the argument is valid. If the answer column does not have all trues, the argument is invalid.

---

Examples 1 through 4 contain two premises. When an argument contains more than two premises, step 3 of the procedure will change slightly, as will be explained shortly.

**Example 2** *Determining the Validity of an Argument With a Truth Table*

Determine whether the following argument is valid or invalid.

> If you watch *Good Morning America*, then you see Robin Roberts.
> You did not see Robin Roberts.
> ─────────────────────────────────
> ∴ You did not watch *Good Morning America*.

▲ *Robin Roberts*

*Solution*  We first write the argument in symbolic form.

Let

> *p*:  You watch *Good Morning America*.
> *q*:  You see Robin Roberts.

In symbolic form, the argument is

$$p \rightarrow q$$
$$\sim q$$
$$\overline{\therefore \sim p}$$

As we have not tested an argument in this form, we will construct a truth table to determine whether the argument is valid or invalid. We write the argument in the form $[(p \rightarrow q) \wedge \sim q] \rightarrow \sim p$, and construct a truth table (Table 3.34). Since the answer, column 5, has all T's, the argument is valid.

Table 3.34

| *p* | *q* | $[(p \rightarrow q)$ | $\wedge$ | $\sim q]$ | $\rightarrow$ | $\sim p$ |
|---|---|---|---|---|---|---|
| T | T | T | F | F | T | F |
| T | F | F | F | T | T | F |
| F | T | T | F | F | T | T |
| F | F | T | T | T | T | T |
| | | 1 | 3 | 2 | 5 | 4 |

The argument form in Example 2 is an example of the *law of contraposition*, or *modus tollens*.

## Example 3  *Another Symbolic Argument*

Determine whether the following argument is valid or invalid.

> The grass is green or the grass is full of weeds.
> The grass is not green.
> ∴ The grass is full of weeds.

*Solution*  Let

> *p*:  The grass is green.
> *q*:  The grass is full of weeds.

In symbolic form, the argument is

$$p \vee q$$
$$\sim p$$
$$\overline{\therefore q}$$

As this form is not one of those we are familiar with, we will construct a truth table. We write the argument in the form $[(p \vee q) \wedge \sim p] \rightarrow q$. Next we construct a truth table, as shown in Table 3.35 on page 144. The answer to the truth table, column 5, is true in *every case*. Therefore, the statement is a tautology, and the argument is valid.

Table 3.35

| $p$ | $q$ | $[(p \lor q)$ | $\land$ | $\sim p]$ | $\rightarrow$ | $q$ |
|---|---|---|---|---|---|---|
| T | T | T | F | F | T | T |
| T | F | T | F | F | T | F |
| F | T | T | T | T | T | T |
| F | F | F | F | T | T | F |
|   |   | 1 | 3 | 2 | 5 | 4 |

The argument form in Example 3 is an example of a *disjunctive syllogism*. Other standard forms of arguments are given in the following chart.

### Standard Forms of Arguments

| **Valid Arguments** | *Law of Detachment* | *Law of Contraposition* | *Law of Syllogism* | *Disjunctive Syllogism* |
|---|---|---|---|---|
| | $p \rightarrow q$ | $p \rightarrow q$ | $p \rightarrow q$ | $p \lor q$ |
| | $\underline{p\qquad}$ | $\underline{\sim q\qquad}$ | $\underline{q \rightarrow r}$ | $\underline{\sim p\qquad}$ |
| | $\therefore q$ | $\therefore \sim p$ | $\therefore p \rightarrow r$ | $\therefore q$ |

| **Invalid Arguments** | *Fallacy of the Converse* | *Fallacy of the Inverse* | | |
|---|---|---|---|---|
| | $p \rightarrow q$ | $p \rightarrow q$ | | |
| | $\underline{q\qquad}$ | $\underline{\sim p\qquad}$ | | |
| | $\therefore p$ | $\therefore \sim q$ | | |

As we saw in Example 1, it is not always necessary to construct a truth table to determine whether or not an argument is valid. The next two examples will show how we can identify an argument as one of the standard arguments given in the chart above.

### Example 4   *Identifying a Standard Argument*

Determine whether the following argument is valid or invalid.

> If you are on Facebook, then you see my pictures.
> If you see my pictures, then you know I have a dog.
> —————————————————————————
> ∴ If you are on Facebook, then you know I have a dog.

**Solution**  Let

$p$:   You are on Facebook.
$q$:   You see my pictures.
$r$:   You know I have a dog.

In symbolic form, the argument is

$$p \rightarrow q$$
$$q \rightarrow r$$
$$\overline{\therefore p \rightarrow r}$$

The argument is in the form of the law of syllogism. Therefore, the argument is valid, and there is no need to construct a truth table.

## Example 5 *Identifying Common Fallacies in Arguments*

Determine whether the following arguments are valid or invalid.

a)

> If it is snowing, then we put salt on the driveway.
> We put salt on the driveway.
> _____
> ∴ It is snowing.

b)

> If it is snowing, then we put salt on the driveway.
> It is not snowing.
> _____
> ∴ We do not put salt on the driveway.

*Solution*

a) Let

$$p: \text{It is snowing.}$$
$$q: \text{We put salt on the driveway.}$$

In symbolic form, the argument is

$$p \rightarrow q$$
$$q$$
$$\overline{\therefore p}$$

This argument is in the form of the fallacy of the converse. Therefore, the argument is a fallacy, or invalid.

b) Using the same symbols defined in the solution to part (a), in symbolic form, the argument is

$$p \rightarrow q$$
$$\sim p$$
$$\overline{\therefore \sim q}$$

This argument is in the form of the fallacy of the inverse. Therefore, the argument is a fallacy, or invalid.

**TIMELY TIP**
If you are not sure whether an argument with two premises is one of the standard forms or if you do not remember the standard forms, you can always determine whether a given argument is valid or invalid by using a truth table. To do so, follow the boxed procedure on page 142.

In Example 5(b), if you did not recognize that this argument was of the same form as the fallacy of the inverse you could construct the truth table for the conditional statement

$$[(p \rightarrow q) \wedge \sim p] \rightarrow \sim q$$

The true–false values under the conditional column, $\rightarrow$, would be T, T, F, T. Since the statement is not a tautology, the argument is invalid.

Now we consider an argument that has more than two premises. When an argument contains more than two premises, the statement we test, using a truth table, is formed by taking the conjunction of all the premises as the antecedent of a conditional statement and the conclusion as the consequent of the conditional statement. One example is an argument of the form

$$p_1$$
$$p_2$$
$$p_3$$
$$\overline{\therefore c}$$

We evaluate the truth table for $[p_1 \wedge p_2 \wedge p_3] \rightarrow c$. When we evaluate $[p_1 \wedge p_2 \wedge p_3]$, it makes no difference whether we evaluate $[(p_1 \wedge p_2) \wedge p_3]$ or $[p_1 \wedge (p_2 \wedge p_3)]$ because both give the same answer. In Example 6, we evaluate $[p_1 \wedge p_2 \wedge p_3]$ from left to right; that is, $[(p_1 \wedge p_2) \wedge p_3]$.

Example 6    *An Argument with Three Premises*

Use a truth table to determine whether the following argument is valid or invalid.

> If my cell phone company is Verizon, then I can call you free of charge.
> I can call you free of charge or I can send you a text message.
> I can send you a text message or my cell phone company is Verizon.
> _____
> ∴ My cell phone company is Verizon.

Solution    This argument contains three simple statements.

Let

| | |
|---|---|
| $p$: | My cell phone company is Verizon. |
| $q$: | I can call you free of charge. |
| $r$: | I can send you a text message. |

In symbolic form, the argument is

$$p \rightarrow q$$
$$q \vee r$$
$$r \vee p$$
$$\overline{\phantom{xxxxx}}$$
$$\therefore p$$

Write the argument in the form

$$[(p \rightarrow q) \wedge (q \vee r) \wedge (r \vee p)] \rightarrow p.$$

Now construct the truth table (Table 3.36). The answer, column 7, is not true in every case. Thus, the argument is a fallacy, or invalid.

Table 3.36

| $p$ | $q$ | $r$ | $[(p \rightarrow q)$ | $\wedge$ | $(q \vee r)$ | $\wedge$ | $(r \vee p)]$ | $\rightarrow$ | $p$ |
|---|---|---|---|---|---|---|---|---|---|
| T | T | T | T | T | T | T | T | T | T |
| T | T | F | T | T | T | T | T | T | T |
| T | F | T | F | F | T | F | T | T | T |
| T | F | F | F | F | F | F | T | T | T |
| F | T | T | T | T | T | T | T | F | F |
| F | T | F | T | T | T | F | F | T | F |
| F | F | T | T | T | T | T | T | F | F |
| F | F | F | T | F | F | F | F | T | F |
| | | | 1 | 3 | 2 | 5 | 4 | 7 | 6 |

Let's now investigate how we can arrive at a valid conclusion from a given set of premises.

Example 7    *Determine a Logical Conclusion*

Determine a logical conclusion that follows from the given statements. "If the price of gas is below \$4.00 per gallon, then we will drive to the Offspring concert. We will not drive to the Offspring concert. Therefore …"

Solution    If you recognize a specific form of an argument, you can use your knowledge of that form to draw a logical conclusion.

Let

$p$:    The price of gas is below \$4.00 per gallon.

$q$:    We will drive to the Offspring concert.

The argument is of the following form.

$$p \rightarrow q$$
$$\sim q$$
$$\overline{\therefore \ ?}$$

If the question mark is replaced with a $\sim p$, this argument is of the form of the law of contraposition. Thus, a logical conclusion is "Therefore, the price of gas is not below \$4.00 per gallon."

## SECTION 3.5  *Exercises*

### Warm Up Exercises

*In Exercises 1–6, fill in the blanks with an appropriate word, phrase, or symbol(s).*

1. When the conclusion of an argument necessarily follows from the given set of premises it is a(n) _____ argument.

2. When the conclusion of an argument does not necessarily follow from the given set of premises it is a(n) _____ argument.

3. An argument that is invalid is also known as a(n) _____.

4. To determine the validity of an argument with two premises, construct a truth table for a conditional statement of the form [(premise 1) $\wedge$ (premise 2)] $\rightarrow$ _____.

5. If the conditional statement referred to in Exercise 4 is a tautology, then the argument is a(n) _____ argument.

6. If the conditional statement referred to in Exercise 4 is not a tautology, then the argument is a(n) _____ argument.

*For Exercises 7–12, identify the standard form of the argument.*

7. $p \rightarrow q$    Fallacy of the _____.
$$\sim p$$
$$\overline{\therefore \ \sim q}$$

8. $p \rightarrow q$    Law of _____.
$$p$$
$$\overline{\therefore \ q}$$

9. $p \ \vee \ q$    Disjunctive _____.
$$\sim p$$
$$\overline{\therefore \ q}$$

10. $p \rightarrow q$    Fallacy of the _____.
$$q$$
$$\overline{\therefore \ p}$$

11. $p \rightarrow q$    Law of _____.
$$q \rightarrow r$$
$$\overline{\therefore \ p \rightarrow r}$$

12. $p \rightarrow q$    Law of _____.
$$\sim q$$
$$\overline{\therefore \ \sim p}$$

### Practice the Skills

*In Exercises 13–32, determine whether the argument is valid or invalid. You may compare the argument to a standard form, given on page 144, or use a truth table.*

13. $a \rightarrow b$
$$\sim a$$
$$\overline{\therefore \ \sim b}$$

14. $c \vee d$
$$\sim c$$
$$\overline{\therefore \ d}$$

15. $e \rightarrow f$
$$e$$
$$\overline{\therefore \ f}$$

16. $g \rightarrow h$
$$h \rightarrow i$$
$$\overline{\therefore \ g \rightarrow i}$$

17. $j \vee k$
$$\sim k$$
$$\overline{\therefore \ j}$$

18. $l \rightarrow m$
$$\sim m$$
$$\overline{\therefore \ \sim l}$$

19. $n \rightarrow o$
$$o$$
$$\overline{\therefore \ n}$$

20. $r \rightarrow s$
$$r$$
$$\overline{\therefore \ s}$$

**21.** $t \rightarrow u$
$\sim t$
∴ $\sim u$

**22.** $v \rightarrow w$
$w$
∴ $v$

**23.** $x \rightarrow y$
$y \rightarrow z$
∴ $x \rightarrow z$

**24.** $x \rightarrow y$
$\sim x$
∴ $\sim y$

**25.** $p \leftrightarrow q$
$q \wedge r$
∴ $p \vee r$

**26.** $p \leftrightarrow q$
$q \rightarrow r$
∴ $\sim r \rightarrow \sim p$

**27.** $r \leftrightarrow p$
$\sim p \wedge q$
∴ $p \wedge r$

**28.** $p \vee q$
$r \wedge p$
∴ $q$

**29.** $p \rightarrow q$
$q \vee r$
$r \vee p$
∴ $p$

**30.** $p \rightarrow q$
$q \rightarrow r$
$r \rightarrow p$
∴ $q \rightarrow p$

**31.** $p \rightarrow q$
$r \rightarrow \sim p$
$p \vee r$
∴ $q \vee \sim p$

**32.** $p \leftrightarrow q$
$p \vee r$
$q \rightarrow r$
∴ $q \vee r$

## Problem Solving

*In Exercises 33–48, (a) translate the argument into symbolic form and (b) determine if the argument is valid or invalid. You may compare the argument to a standard form or use a truth table.*

**33.** If the lighthouse works, then the boat can stay out late.

The boat cannot stay out late.

∴ The lighthouse does not work.

**34.** If the car is a Road Runner, then the car is fast.

The car is fast.

∴ The car is a Road Runner.

**35.** If the baby is a boy, then we will name him Alexander Martin.

The baby is a boy.

∴ We will name him Alexander Martin.

**36.** If I can get my child to preschool by 8:45 A.M., then I can take the 9:00 A.M. class.

If I can take the 9:00 A.M. class, then I can be done by 2:00 P.M.

∴ If I can get my child to preschool by 8:45 A.M., then I can be done by 2:00 P.M.

**37.** If the guitar is a Les Paul model, then the guitar is made by Gibson.

The guitar is not made by Gibson.

∴ The guitar is not a Les Paul model.

**38.** We will go for a bike ride or we will go shopping.

We will not go shopping.

∴ We will go for a bike ride.

**39.** If we planted the garden by the first Friday in April, then we will have potatoes by the Fourth of July.

We will have potatoes by the Fourth of July.

∴ We planted the garden by the first Friday in April.

**40.** If you pass general chemistry, then you can take organic chemistry.

You pass general chemistry.

∴ You can take organic chemistry.

**41.** Erica Kane will marry Samuel Woods or Erica Kane will marry David Hayward.

Erica Kane will not marry Samuel Woods.

∴ Erica Kane will marry David Hayward.

**42.** If Nicholas Thompson teaches this course, then I will get a passing grade.

I did not get a passing grade.

∴ Nicholas Thompson did not teach this course.

**43.** If it is cold, then graduation will be held indoors.

If graduation is held indoors, then the fireworks will be postponed.

∴ If it is cold, then the fireworks will be postponed.

**44.** If the canteen is full, then we can go for a walk.
We can go for a walk and we will not get thirsty.
∴ If we go for a walk, then the canteen is not full.

**45.** Marie works at the post office and Jim works for Target.
If Jim works for Target, then Tommy gets an internship.
∴ If Tommy gets an internship, then Marie works at the post office.

**46.** Vitamin C helps your immune system or niacin helps reduce cholesterol.
If niacin helps reduce cholesterol, then vitamin E enhances your skin.
∴ Vitamin C helps your immune system and vitamin E enhances your skin.

**47.** It is snowing and I am going skiing.
If I am going skiing, then I will wear a coat.
∴ If it is snowing, then I will wear a coat.

**48.** The garden has vegetables or the garden has flowers.
If the garden does not have flowers, then the garden has vegetables.
∴ The garden has flowers or the garden has vegetables.

*In Exercises 49–58, translate the argument into symbolic form. Then determine whether the argument is valid or invalid.*

**49.** If you read *The Order of the Phoenix* then you can understand *The Half-Blood Prince*. You cannot understand *The Half-Blood Prince*. Therefore, you did not read *The Order of the Phoenix*.

**50.** The printer has a clogged nozzle or the printer does not have toner. The printer has toner. Therefore, the printer has a clogged nozzle.

**51.** Max is playing Game Boy with the sound off or Max is wearing headphones. Max is not playing Game Boy with the sound off. Therefore, Max is wearing headphones.

**52.** If the cat is in the room, then the mice are hiding. The mice are not hiding. Therefore, the cat is not in the room.

**53.** The test was easy and I received a good grade. The test was not easy or I did not receive a good grade. Therefore, the test was not easy.

**54.** If Bonnie passes the bar exam, then she will practice law. Bonnie will not practice law. Therefore, Bonnie did not pass the bar exam.

**55.** The baby is crying but the baby is not hungry. If the baby is hungry then the baby is crying. Therefore, the baby is hungry.

**56.** If the car is new, then the car has air conditioning. The car is not new and the car has air conditioning. Therefore, the car is not new.

**57.** If you liked *This Is Spinal Tap* then you liked *Best in Show*. If you liked *Best in Show* then you did not like *A Mighty Wind*. Therefore, if you liked *This Is Spinal Tap* then you liked *A Mighty Wind*.

**58.** The engineering courses are difficult and the chemistry labs are long. If the chemistry labs are long, then the art tests are easy. Therefore, the engineering courses are difficult and the art tests are not easy.

*In Exercises 59–64, using the standard forms of arguments and other information you have learned, supply what you believe is a logical conclusion to the argument. Verify that the argument is valid for the conclusion you supplied.*

**59.** If you throw more than 60 pitches, then you must rest for three days. You throw more than 60 pitches.
Therefore, …

**60.** If the temperature hits 100°, then we will go swimming.
We did not go swimming.
Therefore, …

**61.** I am stressed out or I have the flu.
I do not have the flu.
Therefore, …

**62.** If I can get Nick to his piano lesson by 3:30 P.M., then I can do my shopping.
If I can do my shopping, then we do not need to order pizza again.
Therefore, …

**63.** If you close the deal, then you will get a commission.
You did not get a commission.
Therefore, …

**64.** If Katherine is at her ballet lesson, then Allyson will take a nap.
Katherine is at her ballet lesson.
Therefore, …

## Concept/Writing Exercises

**65.** Is it possible for an argument to be invalid if its conclusion is true? Explain your answer.

**66.** Is it possible for an argument to be valid if its conclusion is false? Explain your answer.

**67.** Is it possible for an argument to be invalid if the premises are all true? Explain your answer.

**68.** Is it possible for an argument to be valid if the premises are all false? Explain your answer.

## Challenge Problems/Group Activities

**69.** Determine whether the argument is valid or invalid.

If Lynn wins the contest or strikes oil, then she will be rich.

If Lynn is rich, then she will stop working.
_____
∴ If Lynn does not stop working, then she did not win the contest.

**70.** Is it possible for an argument to be invalid if the conjunction of the premises is false in every case of the truth table? Explain your answer.

## Recreational Mathematics

**71.** René Descartes was a seventeenth-century French mathematician and philosopher. One of his most memorable statements is, "I think, therefore, I am." This statement is the basis for the following joke.

Descartes walks into an inn. The innkeeper asks Descartes if he would like something to drink. Descartes replies, "I think not," and promptly vanishes into thin air!

This joke can be summarized in the following argument: If I think, then I am. I think not. Therefore, I am not.

**a)** Represent this argument symbolically.

**b)** Is it a valid argument?

**c)** Explain your answer using either a standard form of argument or using a truth table.

## Internet/Research Activities

**72.** Show how logic is used in advertising. Discuss several advertisements and show how logic is used to persuade the reader.

**73.** Find examples of valid (or invalid) arguments in printed matter such as newspaper or magazine articles. Explain why the arguments are valid (or invalid).

---

## SECTION 3.6    Euler Diagrams and Syllogistic Arguments

▲ Ben Stiller

While trying to select a movie to watch, you think, "All Ben Stiller movies are comedies. Ben Stiller is in the movie *The Hardy Men*. Therefore, *The Hardy Men* is a comedy." This type of argument will be discussed in this section.

**Why** *This is Important*   Understanding arguments is an important part of the study of logic, and it is useful in making real-life decisions.

---

In Section 3.5, we showed how to determine the validity of *symbolic arguments* using truth tables and comparing the arguments to standard forms. This section presents another form of argument called a *syllogistic argument*, better known by the shorter name *syllogism*. The validity of a syllogistic argument is determined by using Euler (pronounced "oiler") diagrams, as is explained shortly.

Syllogistic logic, a deductive process of arriving at a conclusion, was developed by Aristotle in about 350 B.C. Aristotle considered the relationships among the four types of statements that follow.

All _____ are _____.
No _____ are _____.
Some _____ are _____.
Some _____ are not _____.

Examples of these statements are as follows: *All doctors are tall. No doctors are tall. Some doctors are tall. Some doctors are not tall.* Since Aristotle's time, other types of statements have been added to the study of syllogistic logic, two of which are

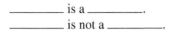

_____ is a _____.
_____ is not a _____.

Examples of these statements are as follows: *Maria is a doctor. Maria is not a doctor.*

The difference between a symbolic argument and a syllogistic argument can be seen in the following chart. Symbolic arguments use the connectives *and, or, not, if–then,* and *if and only if.* Syllogistic arguments use the quantifiers *all, some,* and *none,* which were discussed in Section 3.1.

### Symbolic Arguments Versus Syllogistic Arguments

|  | *Words or phrases used* | *Method of determining validity* |
|---|---|---|
| *Symbolic argument* | and, or, not, if–then, if and only if | Truth tables or by comparison with standard forms of arguments |
| *Syllogistic argument* | all are, some are, none are, some are not | Euler diagrams |

As with symbolic logic, the premises and the conclusion together form an argument. An example of a syllogistic argument is

> All German shepherds are dogs.
> All dogs bark.
> _____
> ∴ All German shepherds bark.

This is an example of a valid argument. Recall from Section 3.5 that an argument is *valid* when its conclusion necessarily follows from a given set of premises. Recall that an argument in which the conclusion does not necessarily follow from the given premises is said to be an *invalid argument* or a *fallacy.*

Before we give another example of a syllogism, let's review the Venn diagrams discussed in Section 2.3 in relationship with Aristotle's four statements.

| All *A*s are *B*s | No *A*s are *B*s | Some *A*s are *B*s | Some *A*s are not *B*s |
|---|---|---|---|
|  |  |  |  |
| If an element is in set *A*, then it is in set *B*. | If an element is in set *A*, then it is not in set *B*. | There is at least one element that is in both set *A* and set *B*. | There is at least one element that is in set *A* that is not in set *B*. |

One method used to determine whether an argument is valid or is a fallacy is by means of an *Euler diagram*, named after Leonhard Euler, who used circles to represent sets in syllogistic arguments. The technique of using Euler diagrams is illustrated in Example 1.

## Example 1    *Using an Euler Diagram*

Determine whether the following syllogism is valid or invalid.

> All keys are made of brass.
> All things made of brass are valuable.
> _____
> ∴ All keys are valuable.

*Solution*    To determine whether this syllogism is valid or not valid, we will construct an Euler diagram. We begin with the first premise, "All keys are made of brass." As shown in Fig. 3.3, the inner blue circle labeled *K* represents the set of all keys and the outer red circle labeled *B* represents the set of all brass objects. The first premise requires that the inner blue circle must be entirely contained within the outer red circle. Next, we will represent the second premise, "All things made of brass are valuable." As shown in Fig. 3.4, the outermost black circle labeled *V* represents the set of all valuable objects. The second premise dictates that the red circle, representing the set of brass objects, must be entirely contained within the black circle, representing the set of valuable objects. Now, examine the completed Euler diagram in Fig. 3.4. Note that the premises force the set of keys to be within the set of valuable objects. Therefore, the argument is valid since the conclusion, "All keys are valuable," necessarily follows from the set of premises.    ∎

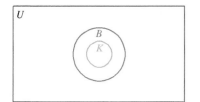

Figure 3.3

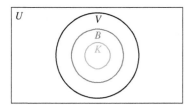

Figure 3.4

The syllogism in Example 1 is valid even though the conclusion, "All keys are valuable," is not a true statement. Similarly, a syllogism can be invalid, or a fallacy, even if the conclusion is a true statement.

When we determine the validity of an argument, we are determining whether the conclusion necessarily follows from the premises. When we say that an argument is valid, we are saying that if all the premises are true statements, then the conclusion must also be a true statement.

The form of the argument determines its validity, not the particular statements. For example, consider the syllogism

> All Earth people have two heads.
> All people with two heads can fly.
> _____
> ∴ All Earth people can fly.

The form of this argument is the same as that of the previous valid argument in Example 1. Therefore, this argument is also valid.

## Example 2    *Analyzing a Syllogism*

Determine whether the following syllogism is valid or invalid.

> All patriots are Americans.
> Betsy is a patriot.
>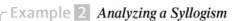
> ∴ Betsy is an American.

*Solution*    The statement "All patriots are Americans" is illustrated in Fig. 3.5. Note that the *P* circle must be completely inside the *A* circle. The second premise, "Betsy is a patriot," tells us that Betsy must be placed in the inner circle labeled *P* (Fig. 3.6). The Euler diagram illustrates, that by placing Betsy inside the *P* circle, Betsy must also be inside the *A* circle. Therefore, the conclusion "Betsy is an American" necessarily follows from the premises and the argument is valid.    ∎

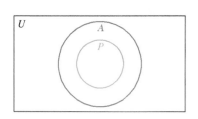

Figure 3.5

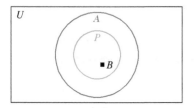

Figure 3.6

In both Example 1 and Example 2, we had no choice as to where the second premise was to be placed in the Euler diagram. In Example 1, the set of brass objects had to be placed inside the set of valuable objects. In Example 2, Betsy had to be placed inside the set of patriots. Often when determining the truth value of a syllogism, a premise can be placed in more than one area in the diagram. *We always try to draw the Euler diagram so that the conclusion **does not necessarily** follow from the premises. If that can be done, then the conclusion **does not necessarily** follow from the premises and the argument is invalid.* If we cannot show that the argument is invalid, only then do we accept the argument as valid. We illustrate this process in Example 3.

### Example 3  *Ballerinas and Athletes*

Determine whether the following syllogism is valid or is invalid.

> All ballerinas are athletic.
> Keyshawn is athletic.
> ──────────────────────
> ∴ Keyshawn is a ballerina.

*Solution*    The premise "All ballerinas are athletic" is illustrated in Fig. 3.7(a). The next premise, "Keyshawn is athletic," tells us that Keyshawn must be placed in the set of athletic people. Two diagrams in which both premises are satisfied are shown in Fig. 3.7(b) and (c). By examining Fig. 3.7(b), however, we see that Keyshawn is not a ballerina. Therefore, the conclusion "Keyshawn is a ballerina" does not necessarily follow from the set of premises. Thus, the argument is invalid, or a fallacy.

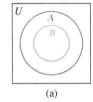 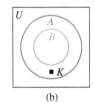 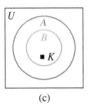

| (a) | (b) | (c) |

**Figure 3.7**

### Example 4  *Parrots and Chickens*

Determine whether the following syllogism is valid or invalid.

> No parrots eat chicken.
> Fletch does not eat chicken.
> ──────────────────────
> ∴ Fletch is a parrot.

*Solution*    The first premise tells us that parrots and things that eat chicken are disjoint sets—that is, sets that do not intersect. The diagram in Fig. 3.8 satisfies the two given premises and also shows that Fletch is not a parrot. Therefore, the argument is invalid, or is a fallacy.

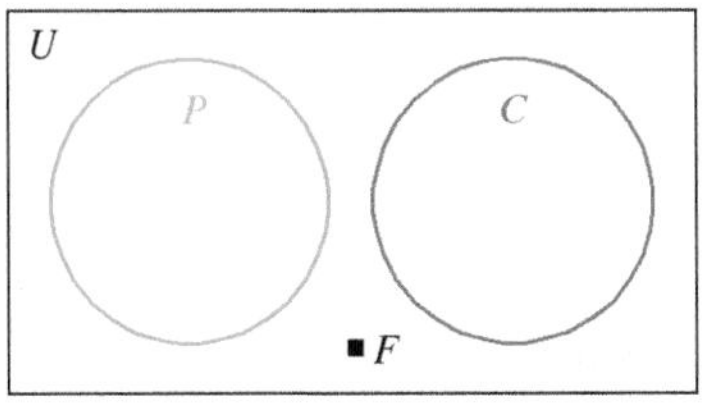

### Example 5  *A Syllogism Involving the Word Some*

Determine whether the following syllogism is valid or invalid.

> All *A*s are *B*s.
> Some *B*s are *C*s.
> ──────────────────────
> ∴ Some *A*s are *C*s.

**Figure 3.8**

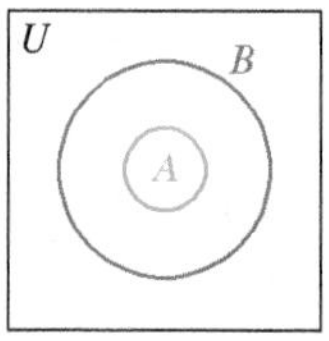

Figure 3.9

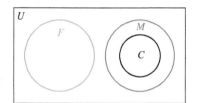

Figure 3.11

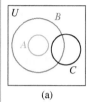 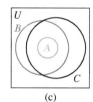 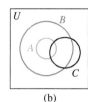 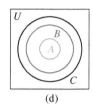

(a)                    (b)                    (c)                    (d)

Figure 3.10

*Solution*   The premise "All *A*s are *B*s" is illustrated in Fig. 3.9. The premise "Some *B*s are *C*s" means that there is at least one *B* that is a *C*. We can illustrate this set of premises in four ways, as illustrated in Fig. 3.10.

In all four illustrations, we see that (1) all *A*s are *B*s and (2) some *B*s are *C*s. The conclusion is "Some *A*s are *C*s." Since at least one of the illustrations, Fig. 3.10(a), shows that the conclusion does not necessarily follow from the given premises, the argument is invalid.                                                                                 ■

─ Example **6**   *Fish and Cows*

Determine whether the following syllogism is valid or invalid.

> No fish are mammals.
> All cows are mammals.
> ──────────────────
> ∴ No fish are cows.

*Solution*   The first premise tells us that fish and mammals are disjoint sets, as shown in Fig. 3.11. The second premise tells us that the set of cows is a subset of the set of mammals. Therefore, the circle representing the set of cows must go within the circle representing the set of mammals.

Note that the set of fish and the set of cows cannot be made to intersect without violating a premise. Thus, the conclusion "No fish are cows" necessarily follows from the premises and the argument is valid. Note that we did not say that this conclusion is true, only that the argument is valid.                                                      ■

## SECTION 3.6    *Exercises*

### Warm Up Exercises

*In Exercises 1–6, fill in the blanks with an appropriate word, phrase, or symbol(s).*

**1.** The validity of a syllogistic argument can be determined using a(n) _____ diagram.

**2.** If an Euler diagram can only be drawn in a way in which the conclusion necessarily follows from the premises, the syllogistic argument is a(n) _____ argument.

**3.** If an Euler diagram can be drawn in a way in which the conclusion does not necessarily follow from the premises, the syllogistic argument is a(n) _____ argument.

**4.** The following Euler diagram can represent the statement _____ *A*s are *B*s.

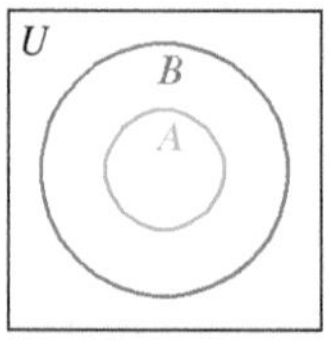

**5.** The following Euler diagram can represent the statement _____ *A*s are *B*s.

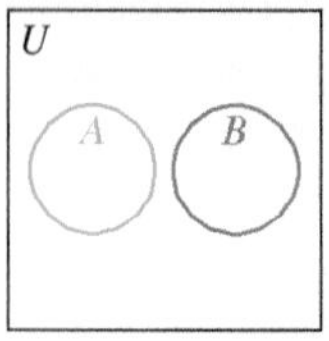

**6.** The following Euler diagram can represent the statement _____ As are Bs.

## Practice the Skills/Problem Solving

*In Exercises 7–28, use an Euler diagram to determine whether the syllogism is valid or invalid.*

**7.** All gingerbread men can sing.

Gingy is a gingerbread man.

∴ Gingy can sing.

**8.** All cats have whiskers.

All things with whiskers are dogs.

∴ All cats are dogs.

**9.** No PCs are Macs.

All Dells are PCs.

∴ No Dells are Macs.

**10.** All dolphins are mammals.

All mammals are vertebrates.

∴ All dolphins are vertebrates.

**11.** All fishermen wear boots.

Percy wears boots.

∴ Percy is a fisherman.

**12.** All golfers have rain gear.

John Pearse has rain gear.

∴ John Pearse is a golfer.

**13.** No horses buck.

Palominos are horses.

∴ Palominos do not buck.

**14.** No jockeys weigh more than 200 pounds.

Deb Otto is not a jockey.

∴ Deb Otto weighs more than 200 pounds.

**15.** Some mushrooms are poisonous.

A morel is a mushroom.

∴ A morel is poisonous.

**16.** Some skunks are tame.

Pepé is a skunk.

∴ Pepé is not tame.

**17.** Some stamps are collectors' items.

Some collectors' items are valuable.

∴ Some stamps are valuable.

**18.** Some professional golfers give golf lessons.

All people who belong to the PGA are professional golfers.

∴ All people who belong to the PGA give golf lessons.

**19.** No lawn weeds are flowers.

Sedge is not a flower.

∴ Sedge is a lawn weed.

**20.** Some caterpillars are furry.

All furry things are mammals.

∴ Some caterpillars are mammals.

**21.** Some flowers love sunlight.

All things that love sunlight love water.

∴ Some flowers love water.

**22.** Some CD players are MP3 players.

All iPods are MP3 players.

∴ Some CD players are iPods.

**23.** No scarecrows are tin men.

No tin men are lions.

∴ No scarecrows are lions.

**24.** All pilots can fly.
All astronauts can fly.
———————————
∴ Some pilots are astronauts.

**25.** Some dogs wear glasses.
Fido wears glasses.
———————————
∴ Fido is a dog.

**26.** All rainy days are cloudy.
Today it is cloudy.
———————————
∴ Today is a rainy day.

**27.** All sweet things taste good.
All things that taste good are fattening.
All things that are fattening put on pounds.
———————————
∴ All sweet things put on pounds.

**28.** All books have red covers.
All books that have red covers contain 200 pages.
Some books that contain 200 pages are novels.
———————————
∴ All books that contain 200 pages are novels.

**29.** Can an argument be valid if the conclusion is a false statement? Explain your answer.

**30.** Can an argument be invalid if the conclusion is a true statement? Explain.

Challenge Problem/Group Activity

**31.** *Sets and Logic* Statements in logic can be translated into set statements: For example, $p \wedge q$ is similar to $P \cap Q$; $p \vee q$ is similar to $P \cup Q$; and $p \rightarrow q$ is equivalent to $\sim p \vee q$, which is similar to $P' \cup Q$. Euler diagrams can also be used to show that arguments similar to those discussed in Section 3.5 are valid or invalid. Use Euler diagrams to show that the following symbolic argument is invalid.

$$p \rightarrow q$$
$$\underline{p \vee q}$$
$$\therefore \sim p$$

Internet/Research Activity

**32.** Leonhard Euler is considered one of the greatest mathematicians of all time. Do research and write a report on Euler's life. Include information on his contributions to sets and to logic. Also indicate other areas of mathematics in which he made important contributions. References include encyclopedias, history of mathematics books, and the Internet.

---

## SECTION 3.7    Switching Circuits

▲ *What must be true for a lamp to produce light?*

Suppose you are sitting at your desk and want to turn on a lamp so you can read a book. If a wall switch controls the power to the outlet that the lamp is plugged into and the lamp has an on/off switch, what conditions must be true for the lamp's bulb to light? The wiring in our homes can be explained and described using logic.

*Why This is Important* Analyzing electrical circuits is one of the most important applications of logic.

## Using Symbolic Statements to Represent Circuits

A common application of logic is switching circuits. To understand the basic concepts of switching circuits, let us examine a few simple circuits that are common in most homes. The typical lamp has a cord, which is plugged into a wall outlet. Somewhere between the bulb in the lamp and the outlet is a switch to turn the lamp on and off. A switch is often referred to as being on or off. When the switch is in the *on* position, the current flows through the switch and the bulb lights up. When the switch is in the *on* position, we can say that the switch is *closed* and that current will flow through the switch. When the switch is in the *off* position, the current does not flow through the switch and the bulb does not light. When the switch is in the *off* position, we can say that the switch is *open*, and the current does not flow through the switch. The basic configuration of a switch is shown in Fig. 3.12.

Figure 3.12

Table 3.37

| Switch | Lightbulb |
|--------|-----------|
| T | on (switch closed) |
| F | off (switch open) |

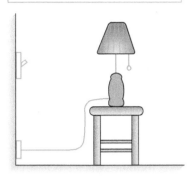

Figure 3.13

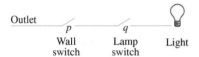

Figure 3.14

Table 3.38

| $p$ | $q$ | *Light* | $p \wedge q$ |
|-----|-----|---------|--------------|
| T | T | on (T) | T |
| T | F | off (F) | F |
| F | T | off (F) | F |
| F | F | off (F) | F |

Figure 3.15

Table 3.39

| $p$ | $q$ | *Light* | $p \vee q$ |
|-----|-----|---------|------------|
| T | T | on (T) | T |
| T | F | on (T) | T |
| F | T | on (T) | T |
| F | F | off (F) | F |

Electric circuits can be expressed as logical statements. We represent switches as letters, using T to represent a closed switch (or current flow) and F to represent an open switch (or no current flow). This relationship is indicated in Table 3.37.

Occasionally, we have a wall switch connected to a wall outlet and a lamp plugged into the wall outlet (Fig. 3.13). We then say that the wall switch and the switch on the lamp are in *series*, meaning that for the bulb in the lamp to light, both switches must be on at the same time (Fig. 3.14). On the other hand, the bulb will not light if either switch is off or if both switches are off. In either of these conditions, the electricity will not flow through the circuit. In a *series circuit*, the current can take only one path. If any switch in the path is open, the current cannot flow.

To illustrate this situation symbolically, let $p$ represent the wall switch and $q$ the lamp switch. The letter T will be used to represent both a closed switch and the bulb lighting. The letter F will represent an open switch and the bulb not lighting. Thus, we have four possible cases.

**CASE 1:** Both switches are closed; that is, $p$ is T and $q$ is T. The light is on, T.

**CASE 2:** Switch $p$ is closed and switch $q$ is open; that is, $p$ is T and $q$ is F. The light is off, F.

**CASE 3:** Switch $p$ is open and switch $q$ is closed; that is, $p$ is F and $q$ is T. The light is off, F.

**CASE 4:** Both switches are open; that is, $p$ is F and $q$ is F. The light is off, F.

Table 3.38 summarizes the results. The on–off results are the same as the truth table for the conjunction p ∧ q if we think of "on" as true and "off" as false.

### Series Circuits
Switches in **series** will always be represented with a conjunction, ∧.

Another type of electric circuit used in the home is the *parallel circuit*, in which there are two or more paths that the current can take. If the current can pass through either path or both (see Fig. 3.15), the light will go on. The letter T will be used to represent both a closed switch and the bulb lighting. The letter F will represent an open switch and the bulb not lighting. Thus, we have four possible cases.

**CASE 1:** Both switches are closed; that is, $p$ is T and $q$ is T. The light is on, T.

**CASE 2:** Switch $p$ is closed and switch $q$ is open; that is, $p$ is T and $q$ is F. The light is on, T.

**CASE 3:** Switch $p$ is open and switch $q$ is closed; that is, $p$ is F and $q$ is T. The light is on, T.

**CASE 4:** Both switches are open; that is, $p$ is F and $q$ is F. The light is off, F.

Table 3.39 summarizes the results. The on–off results are the same as the $p \vee q$ truth table if we think of "on" as true and "off" as false.

### Parallel Circuits
Switches in **parallel** will always be represented with a disjunction, ∨.

Sometimes it is necessary to have two or more switches in the same circuit that will both be open at the same time and both be closed at the same time. In such circuits, we will use the same letter to represent both switches. For example, in the circuit shown in Fig. 3.16, there are two switches labeled *p*. Therefore, both of these switches must be open at the same time and both must be closed at the same time. One of the *p* switches cannot be open at the same time the other *p* switch is closed.

We can now combine some of these basic concepts to analyze more circuits.

Figure 3.16

## Example 1  *Representing a Switching Circuit with Symbolic Statements*

a) Write a symbolic statement that represents the circuit shown in Fig. 3.16.

b) Construct a truth table to determine when the light will be on.

> **Solution**
>
> a) In Fig. 3.16, there is a blue switch *p* on the left, and to the right there is a branch containing a red switch *p* and a switch *q*. The current must flow through the blue switch *p* into the branch on its right. Therefore, the blue switch *p* is in series with the branch containing the red switch *p* and switch *q*. After the current flows through the blue switch *p* it reaches the branch on its right. At this point, the current has the option of flowing into the red switch *p*, switch *q*, or both of these switches. Therefore, the branch containing the red switch *p* and switch *q* is a parallel branch. We say these two switches are in parallel. The entire circuit in symbolic form is $p \wedge (p \vee q)$. Note that the parentheses are very important. Without parentheses, the symbolic statement could be interpreted as $(p \wedge p) \vee q$. The diagram for $(p \wedge p) \vee q$ is illustrated in Fig. 3.17. We shall see later in this section that the circuits in Fig. 3.16 and Fig. 3.17 are not the same.
>
> b) The truth table for the statement (Table 3.40) indicates that the light will be on only in the cases in which *p* is true or when switch *p* is closed. ∎

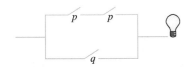

Figure 3.17

Table 3.40

| *p* | *q* | *p* | ∧ | (*p* ∨ *q*) |
|-----|-----|-----|---|-------------|
| T | T | T | T | T |
| T | F | T | T | T |
| F | T | F | F | T |
| F | F | F | F | F |
|   |   | 1 | 3 | 2 |

## Example 2  *Representing a Switching Circuit with Symbolic Statements*

a) Write a symbolic statement that represents the circuit in Fig. 3.18.

b) Construct a truth table to determine when the light will be on.

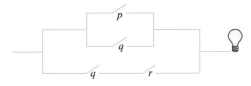

Figure 3.18

> **Solution**
>
> a) The upper branch of the circuit contains two switches, *p* and *q*, in parallel. We can represent that branch with the statement $p \vee q$. The lower branch of the circuit has two switches, *q* and *r*, in series. We can represent that branch with the statement $q \wedge r$. The upper branch is in parallel with the lower branch. Putting the two branches together, we get the statement $(p \vee q) \vee (q \wedge r)$.
>
> b) The truth table for the statement (Table 3.41 on page 159) shows that cases 7 and 8 are false. Thus, the light will be off in these two cases and on in all the other cases. In examining the truth values, we see that the statement is false only in the cases in which both *p* and *q* are false, or when both switches *p* and *q* are open. By examining the diagram or truth table, we can see that the current will flow if switch *p* is closed or switch *q* is closed.

Table 3.41

| $p$ | $q$ | $r$ | $(p \lor q)$ | $\lor$ | $(q \land r)$ |
|---|---|---|---|---|---|
| T | T | T | T | T | T |
| T | T | F | T | T | F |
| T | F | T | T | T | F |
| T | F | F | T | T | F |
| F | T | T | T | T | T |
| F | T | F | T | T | F |
| F | F | T | F | F | F |
| F | F | F | F | F | F |
| | | | 1 | 3 | 2 |

## Drawing Switching Circuits that Represent Symbolic Statements

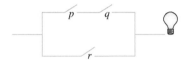

Figure 3.19

We will next study how to draw a switching circuit that represents a given symbolic statement. Suppose we are given the statement $(p \land q) \lor r$ and are asked to construct a circuit corresponding to it. Remember that $\land$ indicates a series branch and $\lor$ indicates a parallel branch. Working first within parentheses, we see that switches $p$ and $q$ are in series. This series branch is in parallel with switch $r$, as indicated in Fig. 3.19.

Occasionally, it is necessary to have two switches in the same circuit such that when one switch is open, the other switch is closed; and when one switch is closed, the other switch is open. Therefore, the two switches will never both be open together and never be closed together. This situation can be represented by using $p$ for one of the switches and $\bar{p}$ for the other switch. The switch labeled $\bar{p}$ corresponds to $\sim p$ in a logic statement. For example, in a series circuit, $p \land \sim p$ would be represented by Fig. 3.20. In this case, the light would never go on; the switches would counteract each other. When switch $p$ is closed, switch $\bar{p}$ is open; and when $p$ is open, $\bar{p}$ is closed.

Figure 3.20

### Example 3 *Representing a Symbolic Statement as a Switching Circuit*

Draw a switching circuit that represents $[(p \land \sim q) \lor (r \lor q)] \land s$.

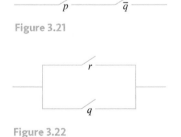

Figure 3.21

Figure 3.22

**Solution** In the statement, $p$ and $\sim q$ have $\land$ between them, so switches $p$ and $\bar{q}$ are in series, as represented in Fig. 3.21. Also in the statement, $r$ and $q$ have $\lor$ between them, so switches $r$ and $q$ are in parallel, as represented in Fig. 3.22.

Because $(p \land \sim q)$ and $(r \lor q)$ are connected with $\lor$, the two branches are in parallel with each other. The parallel branches are represented in Fig. 3.23. Finally, $s$ in the statement is connected to the rest of the statement with $\land$. Therefore, switch $s$ is in series with the entire rest of the circuit, as illustrated in Fig. 3.24.

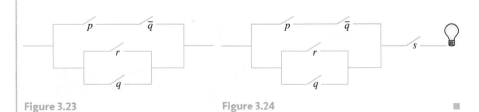

Figure 3.23                          Figure 3.24

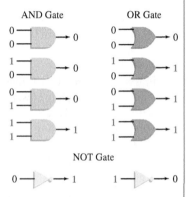
## Equivalent Circuits

Sometimes two circuits that look very different will actually have the exact same conditions under which the light will be on. If we were to analyze the truth tables for the corresponding symbolic statements for such circuits, we would find that they have identical answer columns. In other words, the corresponding symbolic statements are equivalent.

### Definition: Equivalent Circuits
**Equivalent circuits** are two circuits that have equivalent corresponding symbolic statements.

To determine whether two circuits are equivalent, we will analyze the answer columns of the truth tables of their corresponding symbolic statements. If the answer columns from their corresponding symbolic statements are identical, then the circuits are equivalent.

### Example 4    *Are the Circuits Equivalent?*

Determine whether the two circuits are equivalent.

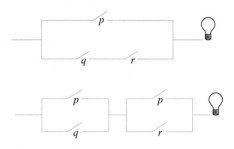

**Solution**  The symbolic statement that represents the first circuit is $p \vee (q \wedge r)$. The symbolic statement that represents the second circuit is $(p \vee q) \wedge (p \vee r)$. The truth tables for these statements are shown in Table 3.42.

Table 3.42

| $p$ | $q$ | $r$ | $p$ | $\vee$ | $(q \wedge r)$ | $(p \vee q)$ | $\wedge$ | $(p \vee r)$ |
|---|---|---|---|---|---|---|---|---|
| T | T | T | T | T | T | T | T | T |
| T | T | F | T | T | F | T | T | T |
| T | F | T | T | T | F | T | T | T |
| T | F | F | T | T | F | T | T | T |
| F | T | T | F | T | T | T | T | T |
| F | T | F | F | F | F | T | F | F |
| F | F | T | F | F | F | F | F | T |
| F | F | F | F | F | F | F | F | F |

Note that the answer columns for the two statements are identical. Therefore, $p \vee (q \wedge r)$ is equivalent to $(p \vee q) \wedge (p \vee r)$ and the two circuits are equivalent.  ∎

SECTION 3.7 *Exercises*

## Warm Up Exercises

*In Exercises 1–4, fill in the blanks with an appropriate word, phrase, or symbol(s).*

**1.** A conjunction, ∧, is used to represent switches in a(n) _____ circuit.

**2.** A disjunction, ∨, is used to represent switches in a(n) _____ circuit.

**3.** When a switch labeled as $p$ is open, a switch labeled as $\bar{p}$ is _____.

**4.** Two circuits are equivalent if they have equivalent _____ statements.

## Practice the Skills/Problem Solving

*In Exercises 5–12, (a) write a symbolic statement that represents the circuit and (b) construct a truth table to determine when the lightbulb will be on. That is, determine which switches must be open and which switches must be closed for the lightbulb to be on.*

**5.**

**6.**

**7.**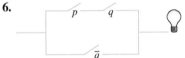

**8.**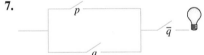

**9.**

**10.**

**11.**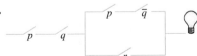

**12.**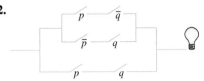

*In Exercises 13–20, draw a switching circuit that represents the symbolic statement.*

**13.** $p \wedge q$

**14.** $p \vee (q \wedge r)$

**15.** $(p \vee q) \wedge r$

**16.** $\sim p \wedge (q \vee r)$

**17.** $(p \vee q) \wedge (r \vee s)$

**18.** $(p \wedge q) \vee (r \wedge s)$

**19.** $[(p \vee q) \vee (r \wedge q)] \wedge (\sim p)$

**20.** $[(p \vee q) \wedge r] \vee (\sim p \wedge q)$

*In Exercises 21–26, represent each circuit with a symbolic statement. Then use a truth table to determine if the circuits are equivalent.*

**21.**

**22.**

**23.**

**24.**

**25.**

**26.**

## Concept/Writing Exercises

**27.** Explain why the lightbulb will never go on in the following circuit.

**28.** Explain why the lightbulb will always be on in the following circuit.

## Challenge Problems/Group Activities

**29.** Design a circuit that can be represented by

**a)** $p \rightarrow q$         **b)** $\sim (p \rightarrow q)$

(*Hint*: See Section 3.4.)

**30.** Design two circuits that each involve switches labeled $p$, $q$, $r$, and $s$ that appear to be different but are actually equivalent circuits.

## Internet/Research Activities

**31.** Digital computers use gates that work like switches to perform calculations. (See *Did You Know?* box on page 160.) Information is fed into the gates and information leaves the gates, according to the type of gate. The three basic gates used in computers are the NOT gate, the AND gate, and or OR gate. Do research on the three types of gates.

**a)** Explain how each gate works.

**b)** Explain the relationship between each gate and the corresponding logic connectives *not*, *and*, and *or*.

**c)** Illustrate how two or more gates can be combined to form a more complex gate.

---

## CHAPTER 3    *Summary*

## Important Facts and Concepts

## Examples

### Section 3.1

**Quantifiers**

Example 1, page 96

| Form of Statement | Form of Negation |
|---|---|
| All are. | Some are not. |
| None are. | Some are. |
| Some are. | None are. |
| Some are not. | All are. |

**Summary of Connectives**

Examples 2–8, pages 97–101

| Formal Name | Symbol | Read | Symbolic Form |
|---|---|---|---|
| Negation | $\sim$ | not | $\sim p$ |
| Conjunction | $\wedge$ | and | $p \wedge q$ |
| Disjunction | $\vee$ | or | $p \vee q$ |
| Conditional | $\rightarrow$ | if–then | $p \rightarrow q$ |
| Biconditional | $\leftrightarrow$ | if and only if | $p \leftrightarrow q$ |

### Section 3.2 & Section 3.3

**Basic Truth Tables**

Examples 1–10, pages 107–114
Examples 1–10, pages 118–124

| Negation | | Conjunction | Disjunction | Conditional | Biconditional |
|---|---|---|---|---|---|
| $p$ | $\sim p$ | $p$ | $q$ | $p \wedge q$ | $p \vee q$ | $p \rightarrow q$ | $p \leftrightarrow q$ |

| $p$ | $\sim p$ | $p$ | $q$ | $p \wedge q$ | $p \vee q$ | $p \rightarrow q$ | $p \leftrightarrow q$ |
|---|---|---|---|---|---|---|---|
| T | F | T | T | T | T | T | T |
| F | T | T | F | F | T | F | F |
| | | F | T | F | T | T | F |
| | | F | F | F | F | T | T |

### Section 3.4

**De Morgan's Laws**

Examples 4–6, pages 130–131

$$\sim (p \wedge q) \Leftrightarrow \sim p \vee \sim q$$
$$\sim (p \vee q) \Leftrightarrow \sim p \wedge \sim q$$

## Section 3.4
### Other Equivalent Forms

$$p \rightarrow q \Leftrightarrow \sim p \lor q$$
$$\sim (p \rightarrow q) \Leftrightarrow p \land \sim q$$
$$p \leftrightarrow q \Leftrightarrow [(p \rightarrow q) \land (q \rightarrow p)]$$

Examples 7–9, pages 131–132

### Variations of the Conditional Statement

Examples 10–12, pages 133–135

| Name | Symbolic Form | Read |
|---|---|---|
| Conditional | $p \rightarrow q$ | If $p$, then $q$. |
| Converse of the conditional | $q \rightarrow p$ | If $q$, then $p$. |
| Inverse of the conditional | $\sim p \rightarrow \sim q$ | If not $p$, then not $q$. |
| Contrapositive of the conditional | $\sim q \rightarrow \sim p$ | If not $q$, then not $p$. |

## Section 3.5
### Standard Forms of Valid Arguments

Examples 1–4, pages 142–144

| Law of Detachment | Law of Contraposition | Law of Syllogism | Disjunctive Syllogism |
|---|---|---|---|
| $p \rightarrow q$ | $p \rightarrow q$ | $p \rightarrow q$ | $p \lor q$ |
| $p$ | $\sim q$ | $q \rightarrow r$ | $\sim p$ |
| $\therefore q$ | $\therefore \sim p$ | $\therefore p \rightarrow r$ | $\therefore q$ |

### Standard Forms of Invalid Arguments

Example 5, page 145

| Fallacy of the Converse | Fallacy of the Inverse |
|---|---|
| $p \rightarrow q$ | $p \rightarrow q$ |
| $q$ | $\sim p$ |
| $\therefore p$ | $\therefore \sim q$ |

## Section 3.5 & Section 3.6
### Symbolic Argument vs. Syllogistic Argument

Examples 1–5, pages 142–145
Examples 1–6, pages 152–154

| | Words or Phrases Used | Method of Determining Validity |
|---|---|---|
| *Symbolic argument* | and, or, not, if–then, if and only if | Truth tables or by comparison with standard forms of arguments |
| *Syllogistic argument* | all are, some are, none are, some are not | Euler diagrams |

## Section 3.7
### Switching Circuits as Symbolic Statements

Examples 1–4, pages 158–160

Switches in series will always be represented with a conjunction, $\land$.

Switches in parallel will always be represented with a disjunction, $\lor$.

## CHAPTER 3   Review Exercises

### 3.1

*In Exercises 1–4, write the negation of the statement.*

**1.** All Scions are Toyotas.

**2.** No pets are allowed in this park.

**3.** Some women are presidents.

**4.** Some pine trees are not green.

*In Exercises 5–10, write each compound statement in words.*

$p$:    The coffee is Maxwell House.
$q$:    The coffee is hot.
$r$:    The coffee is strong.

**5.** $p \vee q$

**6.** $\sim q \wedge r$

**7.** $q \rightarrow (r \wedge \sim p)$

**8.** $p \leftrightarrow \sim r$

**9.** $\sim p \leftrightarrow (r \wedge \sim q)$

**10.** $(p \vee \sim q) \wedge \sim r$

### 3.2

*In Exercises 11–16, use the statements for p, q, and r as in Exercises 5–10 to write the statement in symbolic form.*

**11.** The coffee is Maxwell House or the coffee is strong.

**12.** If the coffee is strong, then the coffee is not Maxwell House.

**13.** If the coffee is strong then the coffee is hot, or the coffee is not Maxwell House.

**14.** The coffee is hot if and only if the coffee is Maxwell House, and the coffee is not strong.

**15.** The coffee is strong and the coffee is hot, or the coffee is not Maxwell House.

**16.** It is false that the coffee is strong and the coffee is hot.

*In Exercises 17–22, construct a truth table for the statement.*

**17.** $(p \vee q) \wedge \sim p$

**18.** $q \leftrightarrow (p \vee \sim q)$

**19.** $(p \vee q) \leftrightarrow (p \vee r)$

**20.** $p \wedge (\sim q \vee r)$

**21.** $p \rightarrow (q \wedge \sim r)$

**22.** $(p \wedge q) \rightarrow \sim r$

### 3.2, 3.3

*In Exercises 23–26, determine the truth value of the statement. You may need to use a reference such as the Internet or an encyclopedia.*

**23.** If ESPN is a sports network then CNN is a news network, if and only if Nickelodeon is a cooking network.

**24.** President's Day is in February, or Memorial Day is in May and Labor Day is in December.

**25.** If Oregon borders the Pacific Ocean or California borders the Atlantic Ocean, then Minnesota is south of Texas.

**26.** $15 - 7 = 22$ or $4 + 9 = 13$, and $9 - 8 = 1$.

### 3.3

*In Exercises 27–30, determine the truth value of the statement when p is T, q is F, and r is F.*

**27.** $(\sim p \rightarrow q) \wedge \sim (q \vee r)$

**28.** $(p \leftrightarrow q) \rightarrow (\sim p \vee r)$

**29.** $\sim r \leftrightarrow [(p \vee q) \leftrightarrow \sim p]$

**30.** $\sim [(q \wedge r) \rightarrow (\sim p \vee r)]$

## 3.4

*In Exercises 31–34, determine whether the pairs of statements are equivalent. You may use De Morgan's laws, the fact that $(p \rightarrow q) \Leftrightarrow (\sim p \vee q)$, the fact that $\sim(p \rightarrow q) \Leftrightarrow (p \wedge \sim q)$, truth tables, or equivalent forms of the conditional statement.*

**31.** $\sim(p \wedge \sim q), \sim p \wedge q$

**32.** $p \vee q, \sim p \rightarrow q$

**33.** $\sim p \vee (q \wedge r), \quad (\sim p \vee q) \wedge (\sim p \vee r)$

**34.** $(\sim q \rightarrow p) \wedge p, \quad \sim(\sim p \leftrightarrow q) \vee p$

*In Exercises 35–39, use De Morgan's laws, the fact that $(p \rightarrow q) \Leftrightarrow (\sim p \vee q)$, or the fact that $\sim(p \rightarrow q) \Leftrightarrow (p \wedge \sim q)$, to write an equivalent statement for the given statement.*

**35.** Lady Gaga sang "Poker Face" and Jay-Z did not sing "Beamer, Benz, or Bentley."

**36.** Lynn Swann played for the Steelers or Jack Tatum played for the Raiders.

**37.** It is not true that Altec Lansing only produces speakers or Harman Kardon only produces stereo receivers.

**38.** Travis Tritt did not win an Academy Award and Randy Jackson does not do commercials for Milk Bone Dog Biscuits.

**39.** If the temperature is not above 32°, then we will go ice fishing at O'Leary's Lake.

*In Exercises 40–44, write the (a) converse, (b) inverse, and (c) contrapositive for the given statement.*

**40.** If you listen to Jim Rome, then you know Jay Stu.

**41.** If we take the table to *Antiques Roadshow*, then we will learn the table's value.

**42.** If you do not advertise, then you do not sell more doughnuts.

**43.** If the desk is made by Winner's Only and the desk is in the Rose catalog, then we will not buy a desk at Miller's Furniture.

**44.** If you get straight A's on your report card, then I will let you attend the prom.

*In Exercises 45–48, determine which, if any, of the three statements are equivalent.*

**45. a)** If you swim every day, then you lose five pounds.

   **b)** You do not swim every day or you lose five pounds.

   **c)** It is false that you swim every day and you do not lose five pounds.

**46. a)** The screwdriver is on the workbench if and only if the screwdriver is not on the counter.

   **b)** If the screwdriver is not on the counter, then the screwdriver is not on the workbench.

   **c)** It is false that the screwdriver is on the counter and the screwdriver is not on the workbench.

**47. a)** If $2 + 3 = 6$, then $3 + 1 = 5$.

   **b)** $2 + 3 = 6$ if and only if $3 + 1 \neq 5$.

   **c)** If $3 + 1 \neq 5$, then $2 + 3 \neq 6$.

**48. a)** If the sale is on Tuesday and I have money, then I will go to the sale.

   **b)** If I go to the sale, then the sale is on Tuesday and I have money.

   **c)** I go to the sale, or the sale is on Tuesday and I have money.

## 3.5

*In Exercises 49–52, determine whether the argument is valid or invalid. You may compare the argument to a standard form or use a truth table.*

**49.** $p \rightarrow q$

$q$

$\therefore p$

**50.** $p \wedge q$

$q \rightarrow r$

$\therefore p \rightarrow r$

**51.** If Jose Macias is the manager, then Kevin Geis is the coach.

If Kevin Geis is the coach, then Tim Weisman is the umpire.

$\therefore$ If Jose Macias is the manager, then Tim Weisman is the umpire.

**52.** If the astronaut visits the space station, then the astronaut uses the space shuttle. The astronaut uses the space shuttle or the astronaut uses the Soyuz spacecraft. Therefore, the astronaut does not use the Soyuz spacecraft.

▲ *The International Space Station*

## 3.6

*In Exercises 53–56, use an Euler diagram to determine whether the argument is valid or invalid.*

**53.** All registered nurses went to college.

Some bookkeepers went to college.

$\therefore$ Some bookkeepers are registered nurses.

**54.** All hackysack players are students.

Joel Knutson is a hackysack player.

$\therefore$ Joel Knutson is a student.

**55.** No Beatles are Rolling Stones.

Some Rolling Stones are Small Faces.

$\therefore$ No Beatles are Small Faces.

**56.** All bears are furry.

Teddy is furry.

$\therefore$ Teddy is a bear.

## 3.7

**57. a)** Write the corresponding symbolic statement of the circuit shown.

**b)** Construct a truth table to determine when the lightbulb will be on.

**58.** Construct a diagram of a circuit that corresponds to the symbolic statement $(p \vee q) \vee (p \wedge q)$.

**59.** Determine whether the circuits shown are equivalent.

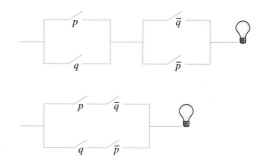

## CHAPTER 3 ) Test

*In Exercise 1–3, write the statement in symbolic form*

    *p*: Phobos is a moon of Mars.
    *q*: Callisto is a moon of Jupiter.
    *r*: Rosalind is a moon of Uranus.

▲ *Callisto, a moon of Jupiter*

**1.** Phobos is a moon of Mars and Rosalind is a moon of Uranus, or Callisto is not a moon of Jupiter.

**2.** If Rosalind is a moon of Uranus then Callisto is a moon of Jupiter, or Phobos is not a moon of Mars.

**3.** It is false that Rosalind is a moon of Uranus if and only if Callisto is not a moon of Jupiter.

*In Exercises 4 and 5, use p, q, and r as above to write each symbolic statement in words.*

**4.** $(\sim p \wedge r) \leftrightarrow \sim q$      **5.** $(p \vee \sim q) \rightarrow r$

*In Exercises 6 and 7, construct a truth table for the given statement.*

**6.** $[\sim(p \rightarrow r)] \wedge q$      **7.** $(q \leftrightarrow \sim r) \vee p$

*In Exercises 8 and 9, find the truth value of the statement.*

**8.** $2 + 6 = 8$ or $7 - 12 = 5$.

**9.** Harrison Ford is an actor or Gerald Ford was a president, if and only if the Mississippi is a river.

*In Exercises 10 and 11, given that p is true, q is false, and r is true, determine the truth value of the statement.*

**10.** $(r \vee q) \leftrightarrow (p \wedge \sim q)$

**11.** $[\sim(r \rightarrow \sim p)] \wedge (q \rightarrow p)$

**12.** Determine whether the pair of statements are equivalent.

$$\sim p \vee q, \quad \sim(p \wedge \sim q)$$

*In Exercises 13 and 14, determine which, if any, of the three statements are equivalent.*

**13. a)** If the bird is red, then it is a cardinal.

   **b)** The bird is not red or it is a cardinal.

   **c)** If the bird is not red, then it is not a cardinal.

**14. a)** It is not true that the test is today or the concert is tonight.

   **b)** The test is not today and the concert is not tonight.

   **c)** If the test is not today, then the concert is not tonight.

**15.** *Translate the following argument into symbolic form. Determine whether the argument is valid or invalid by comparing the argument to a recognized form or by using a truth table.*
    If the soccer team wins the game, then Sue played fullback. If Sue played fullback, then the team is in second place. Therefore, if the soccer team wins the game, then the team is in second place.

**16.** *Use an Euler diagram to determine whether the syllogism is valid or is a fallacy.*

    All living things contain carbon.
    Roger contains carbon.

    ∴ Therefore, Roger is a living thing.

*In Exercises 17 and 18, write the negation of the statement.*

**17.** All highways are roads.

**18.** Nick played football and Max played baseball.

**19.** Write the converse, inverse, and contrapositive of the conditional statement "If the garbage truck comes, then today is Saturday."

**20.** Construct a diagram of a circuit that corresponds to $(p \wedge q) \vee (\sim p \vee \sim q)$

## GROUP PROJECTS

### Computer Gates

1. Gates in computers work on the same principles as switching circuits. The three basic types of gate are the NOT gate, the AND gate, and the OR gate. Each is illustrated along with a table that indicates current flow entering and exiting the gate. If current flows into a NOT gate, then no current exits, and vice versa. Current exits an AND gate only when both inputs have a current flow. Current exits an OR gate if current flows through either, or both, inputs. In the table, a 1 represents a current flow and a 0 indicates no current flow. For example, in the AND gate, if there is a current flow in input $A$ ($I_a$ has a value of 1) and no current flow in input $B$ ($I_b$ has a value of 0), there is no current flow in the output ($O$ has a value of 0); see row 2 of the AND Gate table.

**NOT gate**

Input —▷o— Output

NOT gate

| I | O |
|---|---|
| 1 | 0 |
| 0 | 1 |

**AND gate**

Input $A$ —⊐D— Output
Input $B$ —

AND gate

| $I_a$ | $I_b$ | $O$ |
|-------|-------|-----|
| 1 | 1 | 1 |
| 1 | 0 | 0 |
| 0 | 1 | 0 |
| 0 | 0 | 0 |

**OR gate**

Input $A$ —⊃D— Output
Input $B$ —

OR gate

| $I_a$ | $I_b$ | $O$ |
|-------|-------|-----|
| 1 | 1 | 1 |
| 1 | 0 | 1 |
| 0 | 1 | 1 |
| 0 | 0 | 0 |

a) If 1 is considered true and 0 is considered false, explain how these tables are similar to the *not, and,* and *or* truth tables.

   For the inputs indicated in the following figures determine whether the output is 1 or 0.

b)
$I_a$ — 1
$I_b$ — 0 —⊃D—▷o— Output

c)
$I_a$ — 1
$I_b$ — 0 —▷o— —⊐D— Output

d)
$I_a$ — 1
$I_b$ — 1
—▷o—
—▷o—
—⊐D— Output

e) What values for $I_a$ and $I_b$ will give an output of 1 in the figure in part (d)? Explain how you determined your answer.

f) Construct a truth table using 1's and 0's for the following gate. Your truth table should have columns $I_a$, $I_b$, and $O$ and should indicate the four possible cases for the inputs and each corresponding output.

$I_a$ —▷o— —⊃D— Output
$I_b$ —

### Logic Game

2. a) Shown is a photograph of a logic game at the Ontario Science Centre. There are 12 balls on top of the game board, numbered from left to right, with ball 1 on the extreme left and ball 12 on the extreme right. On the platform in front of the players are 12 buttons. Button 1 corresponds to ball 1, button 2 corresponds to ball 2, and so on. When 6 buttons are pushed, the 6 respective balls are released. When 1 or 2 balls reach an *and* gate or an *or* gate, a single ball may or may not pass through the gate. The object of the game is to select a proper combination of 6 buttons that will allow 1 ball to reach the bottom. Using your knowledge of *and* and *or*, select a combination of 6 buttons that will result in a win. (There is more than one answer.) Explain how you determined your answer.

   b) Construct a game similar to this one where 15 balls are at the top and 8 balls must be selected to allow 1 ball to reach the bottom.

   c) Indicate all solutions to the game you constructed in part (c).

# 9

# Geometry

◄ *Baseballs and baseball diamonds are examples of geometric objects.*

## What You Will Learn

- Points, lines, planes, and angles
- Polygons, similar figures, and congruent figures
- Perimeter and area
- Pythagorean theorem
- Circles
- Volume
- Transformational geometry, symmetry, and tessellations
- The Möbius strip, Klein bottle, and maps
- Non-Euclidean geometry and fractal geometry

## Why This is Important

Many objects we encounter each day can be described in terms of geometry. Spherical baseballs hit on square baseball "diamonds," cylindrical cans of soda, and rectangular computer screens are all examples of geometric objects we frequently encounter. In addition to these items, scientists also use geometry to conduct research and create items that improve our lives. For example, the antenna on your cell phone is an example of a geometric object known as a *fractal*. In this chapter, we will study many geometric objects that we see in our everyday lives.

**SECTION 9.1** Points, Lines, Planes, and Angles

▲ *Billiard games involve many geometric concepts.*

## Profile In Mathematics

### Euclid

Euclid (320–275 B.C.) lived in Alexandria, Egypt, and was a teacher and scholar at Alexandria's school called the *Museum*. It was here that Euclid collected and arranged many of the mathematical results known at the time. This collection of works became his 13-volume masterpiece known as *Elements*. Beginning with a list of definitions, postulates, and axioms, Euclid proved one theorem after another, using only previously proven results. This method of proof became a model of mathematical and scientific investigation that survives today. Remarkably, the geometry in *Elements* does not rely on making exact geometric measurements using a ruler or protractor. Rather, the work is developed using only an unmarked straightedge and a drawing compass. Next to the Bible, Euclid's *Elements* may be the most translated, published, and studied of all the books produced in the Western world.

Playing billiards involves many geometric concepts. In this section, we will introduce the geometric terms *points*, *lines*, *planes*, and *angles*. In a typical billiard game, each of these terms is evident. The billiard balls rest on specific points on the table, which is part of a plane. After being struck with a cue, the ball travels along a path that is part of a line. Angles are involved in the path the ball takes when the ball hits a table bumper or another ball. The concepts we will discuss in this section form an important basis for the study of geometry.

**Why** *This is Important* Geometry is used in our everyday lives to describe the world around us. An understanding of fundamental geometric concepts can help us better understand our world.

Human beings recognized shapes, sizes, and physical forms long before geometry was developed. Geometry as a science is said to have begun in the Nile Valley of ancient Egypt. The Egyptians used geometry to measure land and to build pyramids and other structures.

The word *geometry* is derived from two Greek words: *ge*, meaning earth, and *metron*, meaning measure. Thus, geometry means "earth measure" or "measurement of the earth."

Unlike the Egyptians, the Greeks were interested in more than just the applied aspects of geometry. The Greeks attempted to apply their knowledge of logic to geometry. In about 600 B.C., Thales of Miletus was the first to be credited with using deductive methods to develop geometric concepts. Another outstanding Greek mathematician, Pythagoras, continued the systematic development of geometry that Thales had begun.

In about 300 B.C., Euclid (see *Profile in Mathematics* in the margin) collected and summarized much of the Greek mathematics of his time. In a set of 13 books called *Elements*, Euclid laid the foundation for plane geometry, which is also called *Euclidean geometry*.

Euclid is credited with being the first mathematician to use the *axiomatic method* in developing a branch of mathematics. First, Euclid introduced *undefined terms* such as point, line, plane, and angle. He related these to physical space by such statements as "A line is length without breadth" so that we may intuitively understand them. Because such statements play no further role in his system, they constitute primitive or undefined terms.

Second, Euclid introduced certain *definitions*. The definitions are introduced when needed and are often based on the undefined terms. Some terms that Euclid introduced and defined include triangle, right angle, and hypotenuse.

Third, Euclid stated certain primitive propositions called *postulates* (now called *axioms**) about the undefined terms and definitions. The reader is asked to accept these statements as true on the basis of their "obviousness" and their relationship with the physical world. For example, the Greeks accepted all right angles as being equal, which is Euclid's fourth postulate.

Fourth, Euclid proved, using deductive reasoning (see Section 1.1), other propositions called *theorems*. One theorem that Euclid proved is known as the Pythagorean

---

*The concept of the axiom has changed significantly since Euclid's time. Now any statement may be designated as an axiom, whether it is self-evident or not. All axioms are *accepted* as true. A set of axioms forms the foundation for a mathematical system.

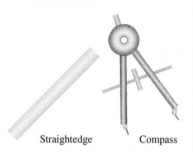
theorem: "The sum of the areas of the squares constructed on the arms of a right triangle is equal to the area of the square constructed on the hypotenuse." He also proved that the sum of the angles of a triangle is 180°.

Using only 10 axioms, Euclid deduced 465 propositions (or theorems) in plane and solid geometry, number theory, and Greek geometric algebra.

## Point and Line

Three basic terms in geometry are *point*, *line*, and *plane*. These three terms are not given a formal definition, but we recognize points, lines, and planes when we see them.

Let's consider some properties of a line. Assume that a line means a straight line unless otherwise stated.

1. A line is a set of points. Each point is on the line and the line passes through each point. When we wish to refer to a specific point, we will label it with a single capital letter. For example, in Fig. 9.1(a) three points are labeled $A$, $B$, and $C$, respectively.

2. Any two distinct points determine a unique line. Figure 9.1(a) illustrates a line. The arrows at both ends of the line indicate that the line continues in each direction. The line in Fig. 9.1(a) may be symbolized with any two points on the line by placing a line with a double-sided arrow above the letters that correspond to the points, such as $\overleftrightarrow{AB}$, $\overleftrightarrow{BA}$, $\overleftrightarrow{AC}$, $\overleftrightarrow{CA}$, $\overleftrightarrow{BC}$, or $\overleftrightarrow{CB}$.

3. Any point on a line separates the line into three parts: the point itself and two *half lines* (neither of which includes the point). For example, in Fig. 9.1(a) point $B$ separates the line into the point $B$ and two half lines. Half line $BA$, symbolized $\overset{\circ}{\overrightarrow{BA}}$, is illustrated in Fig. 9.1(b). The open circle above the $B$ indicates that point $B$ is not included in the half line. Figure 9.1(c) illustrates half line $BC$, symbolized $\overset{\circ}{\overrightarrow{BC}}$.

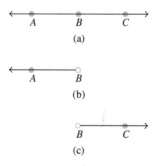

Figure 9.1

Look at the half line $\overset{\circ}{\overrightarrow{AB}}$ in Fig. 9.2(b) on page 481. If the *end point*, A, is included with the set of points on the half line, the result is called a *ray*. Ray $AB$, symbolized $\overrightarrow{AB}$, is illustrated in Fig. 9.2(c). Ray $BA$, symbolized $\overrightarrow{BA}$, is illustrated in Fig. 9.2(d).

A *line segment* is that part of a line between two points, including the end points. Line segment $AB$, symbolized $\overline{AB}$, is illustrated in Fig. 9.2(e).

An open line segment is the set of points on a line between two points, excluding the end points. Open line segment $AB$, symbolized $\overset{\circ\circ}{AB}$, is illustrated in Fig. 9.2(f).

Figure 9.2(g) illustrates two half open line segments, symbolized $\overline{AB}\!\overset{\circ}{}$ and $\overset{\circ}{}\overline{AB}$.

Recall from Chapter 2 that the intersection (symbolized $\cap$) of two sets is the set of elements (points in this case) common to both sets. Consider the rays $\overrightarrow{AB}$ and $\overrightarrow{BA}$ in Fig. 9.3(a) on page 481. The intersection of $\overrightarrow{AB}$ and $\overrightarrow{BA}$ is $\overline{AB}$. Thus, $\overrightarrow{AB} \cap \overrightarrow{BA} = \overline{AB}$.

| Description | Diagram | Symbol |
|---|---|---|
| (a) Line $AB$ | | $\overleftrightarrow{AB}$ |
| (b) Half line $AB$ | | $\overset{\circ\rightarrow}{AB}$ |
| (c) Ray $AB$ | | $\overrightarrow{AB}$ |
| (d) Ray $BA$ | | $\overleftarrow{BA}$ |
| (e) Line segment $AB$ | | $\overline{AB}$ |
| (f) Open line segment $AB$ | | $\overset{\circ\ \circ}{AB}$ |
| (g) Half open line segments $AB$ | | $\overset{\circ}{\overline{AB}}$ <br> $\overset{\ \ \circ}{\overline{AB}}$ |

**Figure 9.2**

Also recall from Chapter 2 that the union (symbolized $\cup$) of two sets is the set of elements (points in this case) that belong to either of the sets or both sets. The union of $\overrightarrow{AB}$ and $\overrightarrow{BA}$ is $\overleftrightarrow{AB}$ (Fig. 9.3b). Thus, $\overrightarrow{AB} \cup \overrightarrow{BA} = \overleftrightarrow{AB}$.

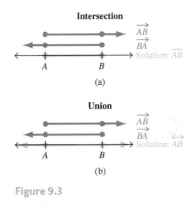

**Figure 9.3**

## Example 1  Unions and Intersections of Parts of a Line

Using line $AD$, determine the solution to each part.

a) $\overrightarrow{AB} \cap \overrightarrow{DC}$    b) $\overrightarrow{AB} \cup \overrightarrow{DC}$    c) $\overrightarrow{AB} \cap \overrightarrow{CD}$    d) $\overline{AD} \cup \overset{\circ\rightarrow}{CA}$

**Solution**

a) $\overrightarrow{AB} \cap \overrightarrow{DC}$

Ray $AB$ and ray $DC$ are shown below. The intersection of these two rays is that part of line $AD$ that is a part of *both* ray $AB$ *and* ray $DC$. The intersection of ray $AB$ and ray $DC$ is line segment $AD$.

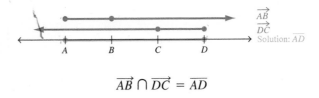

$$\overrightarrow{AB} \cap \overrightarrow{DC} = \overline{AD}$$

b) $\overrightarrow{AB} \cup \overrightarrow{DC}$

Once again ray $AB$ and ray $DC$ are shown below. The union of these two rays is that part of line $AD$ that is part of *either* ray $AB$ or ray $DC$. The union of ray $AB$ and ray $DC$ is the entire line $AD$.

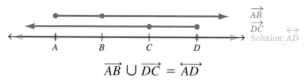

$$\overrightarrow{AB} \cup \overrightarrow{DC} = \overleftrightarrow{AD}$$

c) $\overline{AB} \cap \overrightarrow{CD}$

Line segment $AB$ and ray $CD$ have no points in common, so their intersection is empty.

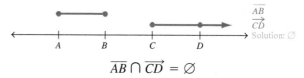

$$\overline{AB} \cap \overrightarrow{CD} = \varnothing$$

d) $\overline{AD} \cup \overset{\circ}{CA}$

The union of line segment $AD$ and half line $CA$ is ray $DA$ (or equivalently, $\overrightarrow{DB}$ or $\overrightarrow{DC}$).

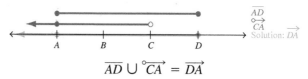

$$\overline{AD} \cup \overset{\circ}{CA} = \overrightarrow{DA}$$

## Plane

The term *plane* is one of Euclid's undefined terms. For our purposes, we can think of a plane as a two-dimensional surface that extends infinitely in both directions, like an infinitely large blackboard. Euclidean geometry is called *plane geometry* because it is the study of two-dimensional figures in a plane.

Two lines in the same plane that do not intersect are called *parallel lines*. Figure 9.4(a) illustrates two parallel lines in a plane ($\overleftrightarrow{AB}$ is parallel to $\overleftrightarrow{CD}$).

Properties of planes include the following:

1. Any three points that are not on the same line (noncollinear points) determine a unique plane (Fig. 9.4b).
2. A line in a plane divides the plane into three parts, the line and two half planes (Fig. 9.4c).
3. Any line and a point not on the line determine a unique plane.
4. The intersection of two distinct planes is a line (Fig. 9.4d).

Two planes that do not intersect are said to be *parallel planes*. For example, in Fig. 9.5 plane $ABE$ is parallel to plane $GHF$.

Two lines that do not lie in the same plane and do not intersect are called *skew lines*. Figure 9.5 illustrates many skew lines (for example, $\overleftrightarrow{AB}$ and $\overleftrightarrow{CD}$).

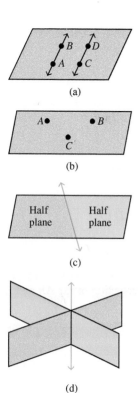

Figure 9.4

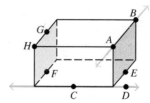

Figure 9.5

## Angles

An *angle*, denoted ∡, is the union of two rays with a common end point (Fig. 9.6):

$$\overrightarrow{BA} \cup \overrightarrow{BC} = ∡ABC \text{ (or } ∡CBA)$$

An angle can be formed by the rotation of a ray about a point. An angle has an initial side and a terminal side. The initial side indicates the position of the ray prior to rotation; the terminal side indicates the position of the ray after rotation. The point common to both rays is called the *vertex* of the angle. The letter designating the vertex is always the middle one of the three letters designating an angle. The rays that make up the angle are called its *sides*.

There are several ways to name an angle. The angle in Fig. 9.6 may be denoted

$$∡ABC, \qquad ∡CBA, \qquad \text{or} \qquad ∡B$$

An angle divides a plane into three distinct parts: the angle itself, its interior, and its exterior. In Fig. 9.6, the angle is represented by the blue lines, the interior of the angle is shaded pink, and the exterior is shaded green.

The *measure of an angle*, symbolized $m$, is the amount of rotation from its initial side to its terminal side. In Fig. 9.6, the letter $x$ represents the measure of $∡ABC$; therefore, we may write $m∡ABC = x$.

Angles can be measured in *degrees*, radians, or gradients. In this text, we will discuss only the degree unit of measurement. An angle of 45 degrees is written 45°. A *protractor* is used to measure angles. The angle shown being measured by the protractor in Fig. 9.7 is 50°.

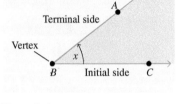

Figure 9.6

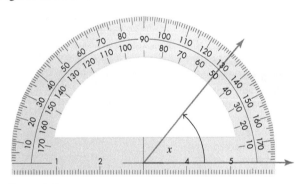

Figure 9.7

---

⌐ Example **2**  *Union and Intersection*

Refer to Fig. 9.8. Determine the following.

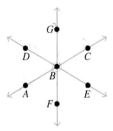

Figure 9.8

a) $\overrightarrow{BC} \cup \overrightarrow{BG}$      b) $\overrightarrow{AB} \cap \overrightarrow{CB}$      c) $\overrightarrow{BE} \cap \overrightarrow{BF}$      d) $∡DBG \cap ∡ABD$

**Solution**

a) $\overrightarrow{BC} \cup \overrightarrow{BG} = ∡CBG$ or $∡GBC$      b) $\overrightarrow{AB} \cap \overrightarrow{CB} = \overline{AC}$

c) $\overrightarrow{BE} \cap \overrightarrow{BF} = \{B\}$      d) $∡DBG \cap ∡ABD = \overrightarrow{BD}$   ∎

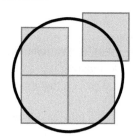
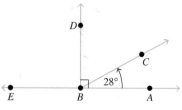

**Figure 9.10**

Consider a circle whose circumference is divided into 360 equal parts. If we draw a line from each mark on the circumference to the center of the circle, we get 360 wedge-shaped pieces. The measure of an angle formed by the straight sides of each wedge-shaped piece is defined to be 1°.

Angles are classified by their degree measurement, as shown in the following summary. A *right angle* has a measure of 90°, an *acute angle* has a measure less than 90°, an *obtuse angle* has a measure greater than 90° but less than 180°, and a *straight angle* has a measure of 180°.

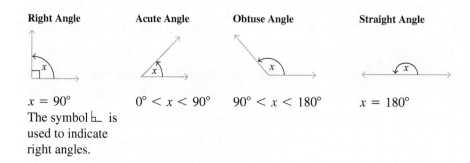

| Right Angle | Acute Angle | Obtuse Angle | Straight Angle |
|---|---|---|---|
| $x = 90°$ | $0° < x < 90°$ | $90° < x < 180°$ | $x = 180°$ |

The symbol ∟ is used to indicate right angles.

Two angles in the same plane are *adjacent angles* when they have a common vertex and a common side but no common interior points. In Fig. 9.9, $\angle DBC$ and $\angle CBA$ are adjacent angles, but $\angle DBA$ and $\angle CBA$ are not adjacent angles.

Two angles are called *complementary angles* if the sum of their measures is 90°. Two angles are called *supplementary angles* if the sum of their measures is 180°.

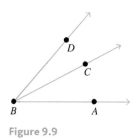

**Figure 9.9**

## Example 3  *Determining Complementary and Supplementary Angles*

In Fig. 9.10, we see that $m\angle ABC = 28°$.

a) $\angle ABC$ and $\angle CBD$ are complementary angles. Determine $m\angle CBD$.

b) $\angle ABC$ and $\angle CBE$ are supplementary angles. Determine $m\angle CBE$.

**Solution**

a) The sum of two complementary angles must be 90°, so

$$m\angle ABC + m\angle CBD = 90°$$
$$28° + m\angle CBD = 90°$$
$$m\angle CBD = 90° - 28° = 62°$$

Subtract 28° from each side of the equation.

b) The sum of two supplementary angles must be 180°, so

$$m\angle ABC + m\angle CBE = 180°$$
$$28° + m\angle CBE = 180°$$
$$m\angle CBE = 180° - 28° = 152°$$

Subtract 28° from each side of the equation.

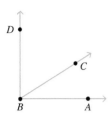

Figure 9.11

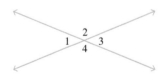

Figure 9.12

## Example 4  *Determining Complementary Angles*

If $\angle ABC$ and $\angle CBD$ are complementary angles and $m\angle ABC$ is 26° less than $m\angle CBD$, determine the measure of each angle (Fig. 9.11).

**Solution** Let $m\angle CBD = x$. Then $m\angle ABC = x - 26$ since it is 26° less than $m\angle CBD$. Because these angles are complementary, we have

$$m\angle CBD + m\angle ABC = 90°$$
$$x + (x - 26) = 90°$$
$$2x - 26 = 90°$$
$$2x = 116°$$
$$x = 58°$$

Therefore, $m\angle CBD = 58°$ and $m\angle ABC = 58° - 26°$, or 32°. Note that $58° + 32° = 90°$, which is what we expected. ■

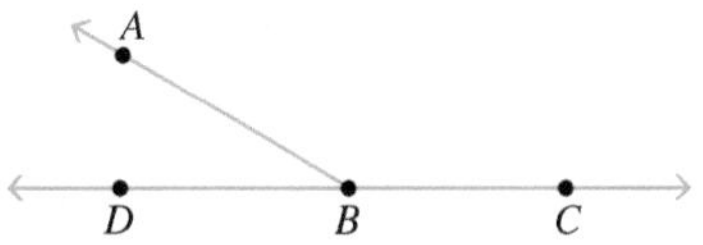

## Example 5  *Determining Supplementary Angles*

If $\angle ABC$ and $\angle ABD$ are supplementary and $m\angle ABC$ is five times larger than $m\angle ABD$, determine $m\angle ABC$ and $m\angle ABD$ (Fig. 9.12).

**Solution** Let $m\angle ABD = x$, then $m\angle ABC = 5x$. Since these angles are supplementary, we have

$$m\angle ABD + m\angle ABC = 180°$$
$$x + 5x = 180°$$
$$6x = 180°$$
$$x = 30°$$

Thus, $m\angle ABD = 30°$ and $m\angle ABC = 5(30°) = 150°$. Note that $30° + 150° = 180°$, which is what we expected. ■

When two straight lines intersect, the nonadjacent angles formed are called *vertical angles*. In Fig. 9.13, $\angle 1$ and $\angle 3$ are vertical angles, and $\angle 2$ and $\angle 4$ are vertical angles. We can show that vertical angles have the same measure; that is, they are equal. For example, Fig. 9.13 shows that

$$m\angle 1 + m\angle 2 = 180°. \qquad \text{Why?}$$
$$m\angle 2 + m\angle 3 = 180°. \qquad \text{Why?}$$

Since $\angle 2$ has the same measure in both cases, $m\angle 1$ must equal $m\angle 3$.

**Vertical Angles**
Vertical angles have the same measure.

A line that intersects two different lines, $l_1$ and $l_2$, at two different points is called a *transversal*. Figure 9.14 illustrates that when two parallel lines are cut by a transversal, eight angles are formed. Angles 3, 4, 5, and 6 are called *interior angles*, and angles 1, 2, 7, and 8 are called *exterior angles*. Eight pairs of supplementary angles are formed. Can you list them?

Special names are given to the angles formed by a transversal crossing two parallel lines. We describe these angles on page 486.

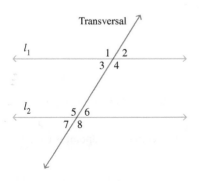

Figure 9.13

Figure 9.14

| Name | Description | Illustration | Pairs of Angles Meeting Criteria |
|------|-------------|--------------|----------------------------------|
| **Alternate interior angles** | Interior angles on opposite sides of the transversal | | ∢3 and ∢6 <br> ∢4 and ∢5 |
| **Alternate exterior angles** | Exterior angles on opposite sides of the transversal | | ∢1 and ∢8 <br> ∢2 and ∢7 |
| **Corresponding angles** | One interior and one exterior angle on the same side of the transversal | | ∢1 and ∢5 <br> ∢2 and ∢6 <br> ∢3 and ∢7 <br> ∢4 and ∢8 |

## Parallel Lines Cut by a Transversal

When two parallel lines are cut by a transversal,
1. alternate interior angles have the same measure.
2. alternate exterior angles have the same measure.
3. corresponding angles have the same measure.

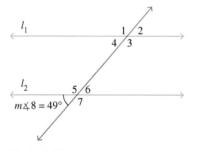

Figure 9.15

Example **6**  *Determining Angle Measures*

Figure 9.15 shows two parallel lines cut by a transversal. Determine the measure of ∢1 through ∢7.

*Solution*

| | |
|---|---|
| $m∢6 = 49°$ | ∢8 and ∢6 are vertical angles. |
| $m∢5 = 131°$ | ∢8 and ∢5 are supplementary angles. |
| $m∢7 = 131°$ | ∢5 and ∢7 are vertical angles. |
| $m∢1 = 131°$ | ∢1 and ∢7 are alternate exterior angles. |
| $m∢4 = 49°$ | ∢4 and ∢6 are alternate interior angles. |
| $m∢2 = 49°$ | ∢6 and ∢2 are corresponding angles. |
| $m∢3 = 131°$ | ∢3 and ∢1 are vertical angles. |

In Example 6, the angles could have been determined in alternate ways. For example, we mentioned $m∢1 = 131°$ because ∢1 and ∢7 are alternate exterior angles. We could have also stated that $m∢1 = 131°$ because ∢1 and ∢5 are corresponding angles.

## SECTION 9.1

## *Exercises*

### Warm Up Exercises

*In Exercises 1–12, fill in the blanks with an appropriate word, phrase, or symbol(s).*

**1.** Two lines in the same plane that do not intersect are called _____ lines.

**2.** Two lines that do not lie in the same plane and do not intersect are called _____ lines.

**3.** The union of two rays with a common endpoint is called a(n) _____.

**4.** Two angles, the sum of whose measures is 90°, are called _____ angles.

**5.** Two angles, the sum of whose measures is 180°, are called _____ angles.

**6.** Two angles in the same plane that have a common vertex and a common side, but no common interior points, are called _____ angles.

**7.** An angle whose measure is 180° is called a(n) _____ angle.

**8.** An angle whose measure is 90° is called a(n) _____ angle.

**9.** An angle whose measure is greater than 90° but less than 180° is called a(n) _____ angle.

**10.** An angle whose measure is less than 90° is called a(n) _____ angle.

**11.** When two straight lines intersect, the nonadjacent angles formed are called _____ angles.

**12.** A line that intersects two different lines at two different points is called a(n) _____.

## Practice the Skills

*In Exercises 13–20, identify the figure as a line, half line, ray, line segment, open line segment, or half open line segment. Denote the figure by its appropriate symbol.*

**13.**
A          B

**14.**
A          B

**15.**
A          B

**16.**
A          B

**17.**
A          B

**18.**
A          B

**19.**
A          B

**20.**
A          B

*In Exercises 21–32, use the figure to find the following:*

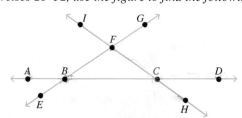

**21.** $\overrightarrow{AB} \cap \overrightarrow{DC}$

**22.** $\overset{\circ}{FE} \cup \overrightarrow{FG}$

**23.** $\overset{\circ}{BC} \cup \overset{\circ}{CD}$

**24.** $\overline{AB} \cup \overline{BD}$

**25.** $\angle ICA \cap \overleftrightarrow{EG}$

**26.** $\angle IFG \cap \angle EFH$

**27.** $\overset{\circ}{AB} \cap \overrightarrow{HC}$

**28.** $\overset{\circ}{BD} \cap \overset{\circ}{CB}$

**29.** $\overrightarrow{BC} \cup \overrightarrow{BF}$

**30.** $\overline{BC} \cup \overline{CF} \cup \overline{FB}$

**31.** $\overset{\circ}{BD} \cup \overset{\circ}{CB}$

**32.** $\{C\} \cap \overset{\circ}{CH}$

*In Exercises 33–44, use the figure to find the following.*

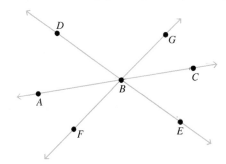

**33.** $\overrightarrow{DB} \cup \overrightarrow{EB}$

**34.** $\angle ABD \cap \angle CBG$

**35.** $\angle GBC \cap \angle CBE$

**36.** $\overleftrightarrow{DE} \cup \overset{\circ}{BE}$

**37.** $\angle ABE \cup \overset{\circ}{AB}$

**38.** $\overset{\circ}{BF} \cup \overline{BE}$

**39.** $\overrightarrow{FG} \cap \overrightarrow{BF}$

**40.** $\overline{BE} \cup \overline{BD}$

**41.** $\overset{\circ}{AC} \cap \overline{AC}$

**42.** $\overset{\circ}{AC} \cap \overset{\circ}{BE}$

**43.** $\overrightarrow{EB} \cap \overrightarrow{BE}$

**44.** $\overline{FB} \cup \overline{BG}$

*In Exercises 45–52, classify the angle as acute, right, straight, obtuse, or none of these angles.*

**45.**

**46.**

**47.**

**48.**

**49.**

**50.**

**51.**

**52.**

*In Exercises 53–58, find the complementary angle of the given angle.*

**53.** 10°

**54.** 15°

**55.** $32\frac{3}{4}°$

**56.** $31\frac{2}{5}°$

**57.** 64.7°

**58.** 0.01°

*In Exercises 59–64, find the supplementary angle of the given angle.*

**59.** 80°                **60.** 150°

**61.** 20.5°              **62.** 148.7°

**63.** $43\frac{5}{7}°$         **64.** $64\frac{7}{16}°$

*In Exercises 65–70, match the names of the angles with the corresponding figure in parts (a)–(f).*

**65.** Complementary angles    **66.** Supplementary angles

**67.** Vertical angles        **68.** Corresponding angles

**69.** Alternate exterior angles  **70.** Alternate interior angles

**a)**

**b)**
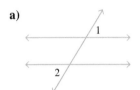

**c)**
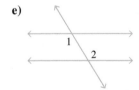

**d)**
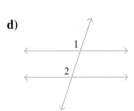

**e)**
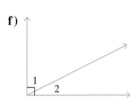

**f)**

## Problem Solving

**71. MODELING - *Complementary Angles*** If ∡1 and ∡2 are complementary angles and if the measure of ∡1 is five times the measure of ∡2, determine the measures of ∡1 and ∡2.

**72. MODELING - *Complementary Angles*** The difference between the measures of two complementary angles is 22°. Determine the measures of the two angles.

**73. MODELING - *Supplementary Angles*** The difference between the measures of two supplementary angles is 88°. Determine the measures of the two angles.

**74. MODELING - *Supplementary Angles*** If ∡1 and ∡2 are supplementary angles and if the measure of ∡2 is 17 times the measure of ∡1, determine the measures of the two angles.

*In Exercises 75–78, parallel lines are cut by the transversal shown. Determine the measures of ∡1 through ∡7.*

**75.**
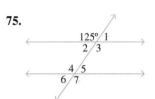

**76.**
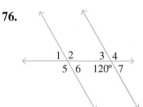

**77.**
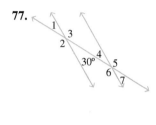

**78.**
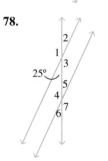

*In Exercises 79–82, the angles are complementary angles. Determine the measures of ∡1 and ∡2.*

**79.**

**80.**

**81.**
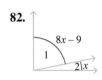

**82.**

*In Exercises 83–86, the angles are supplementary angles. Determine the measures of ∡1 and ∡2.*

**83.**
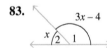

**84.**
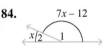

**85.**
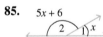

**86.**
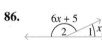

*The figure below suggests a number of lines and planes. The lines may be described by naming two points, and the planes may be described by naming three points. In Exercises 87–94, use the figure to name the following.*

**87.** Two parallel planes

**88.** Two parallel lines

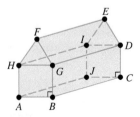

**89.** Two lines that intersect at right angles

**90.** Two planes that intersect at right angles

**91.** Three planes whose intersection is a single point

**92.** Three planes whose intersection is a line

**93.** A line and a plane whose intersection is a point

**94.** A line and a plane whose intersection is a line

## Concept/Writing Exercises

**95. a)** What are the four key parts in the axiomatic method used by Euclid?

   **b)** Discuss each of the four parts.

**96.** What is the difference between an axiom and a theorem?

**97. a)** How many lines can be drawn through a given point?

   **b)** How many planes can be drawn through a given point?

**98.** What is the intersection of two distinct nonparallel planes?

**99.** How many planes can be drawn through a given line?

**100. a)** Will three noncollinear points *A*, *B*, and *C* always determine a plane? Explain.

   **b)** Is it possible to determine more than one plane with three noncollinear points? Explain.

   **c)** How many planes can be constructed through three collinear points?

*In Exercises 101–106, determine whether the statement is always true, sometimes true, or never true. Explain your answer.*

**101.** Two lines that are both parallel to a third line must be parallel to each other.

**102.** A triangle contains exactly two acute angles.

**103.** Vertical angles are complementary angles.

**104.** Alternate exterior angles are supplementary angles.

**105.** Alternate interior angles are complementary angles.

**106.** A triangle contains two obtuse angles.

## Challenge Problems/Group Activities

**107.** Use a straightedge and a compass to construct a triangle with sides of equal length (an equilateral triangle) by doing the following:

   **a)** Use the straightedge to draw a line segment of any length and label the end points *A* and *B* (Fig. a).

**b)** Place one end of the compass at point *A* and the other end at point *B* and draw an arc as shown (Fig. b).

**c)** Now turn the compass around and draw another arc as shown. Label the point of intersection of the two arcs *C* (Fig. c).

**d)** Draw line segments *AC* and *BC*. This completes the construction of equilateral triangle *ABC* (Fig. d).

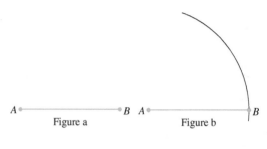

Figure a                    Figure b

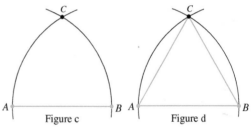

Figure c                    Figure d

**108.** If lines *l* and *m* are parallel lines and if lines *l* and *n* are skew lines, is it true that lines *m* and *n* must also be skew? (*Hint:* Look at Fig. 9.5 on page 482.) Explain your answer and include a sketch to support your answer.

**109.** Two lines are *perpendicular* if they intersect at right angles. If lines *l* and *m* are perpendicular and if lines *m* and *n* are perpendicular, is it true that lines *l* and *n* must also be perpendicular? Explain your answer and include a sketch to support your answer.

**110.** Suppose you have three distinct lines, all lying in the same plane. Find all the possible ways in which the three lines can be related. Sketch each case (four cases).

**111.** If two straight lines intersect at a point, determine the sum of the measures of the 4 angles formed.

**112.** ∡*ABC* and ∡*CBD* are complementary and *m*∡*CBD* is twice the *m*∡*ABC*. ∡*ABD* and ∡*DBE* are supplementary angles.

   **a)** Draw a sketch illustrating ∡*ABC*, ∡*CBD*, and ∡*DBE*.

   **b)** Determine *m*∡*ABC*.

   **c)** Determine *m*∡*CBD*.

   **d)** Determine *m*∡*DBE*.

## Internet/Research Activities

**113.** Using the Internet and other sources, write a research paper on Euclid's contributions to geometry.

**114.** Using the Internet and other sources, write a research paper on the three classic geometry problems of Greek antiquity (see the *Did You Know?* on page 484).

**115.** Search the Internet or other sources such as a geometry textbook to study the geometric constructions that use a straightedge and a compass only. Prepare a poster demonstrating five of these basic constructions.

---

▲ *The shapes of these road signs are examples of polygons.*

What shape would you use to best describe the following road signs: a stop sign, a yield sign, a speed limit sign? In this section, we will study the shapes of these and other geometric figures that can be classified as *polygons*.

**Why** *This is Important* Polygons appear in many aspects of our daily lives. The properties of polygons can be used in many problem-solving applications.

---

A *polygon* is a closed figure in a plane determined by three or more straight line segments. Examples of polygons are given in Fig. 9.16.

The straight line segments that form the polygon are called its *sides*, and a point where two sides meet is called a *vertex* (plural, *vertices*). The union of the sides of a polygon and its interior is called a *polygonal region*. A *regular polygon* is one whose sides are all the same length and whose interior angles all have the same measure. Figures 9.16(b) and (d) are regular polygons.

(a)            (b)            (c)            (d)

Figure 9.16

Polygons are named according to their number of sides. The names of some polygons are given in Table 9.1.

Table 9.1

| Number of Sides | Name | Number of Sides | Name |
|---|---|---|---|
| 3 | Triangle | 8 | Octagon |
| 4 | Quadrilateral | 9 | Nonagon |
| 5 | Pentagon | 10 | Decagon |
| 6 | Hexagon | 12 | Dodecagon |
| 7 | Heptagon | 20 | Icosagon |

One of the most important polygons is the triangle. The sum of the measures of the interior angles of a triangle is 180°. To illustrate, consider triangle *ABC* given in Fig. 9.17. The triangle is formed by drawing two transversals through two parallel lines $l_1$ and $l_2$ with the two transversals intersecting at a point on $l_1$.

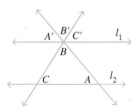

Figure 9.17

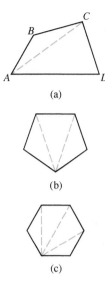

(a)

(b)

(c)

Figure 9.18

In Fig. 9.17, notice that $\angle A$ and $\angle A'$ are corresponding angles. Recall from Section 9.1 that corresponding angles are equal, so $m\angle A = m\angle A'$. Also, $\angle C$ and $\angle C'$ are corresponding angles; therefore, $m\angle C = m\angle C'$. Next, we notice that $\angle B$ and $\angle B'$ are vertical angles. In Section 9.1, we learned that vertical angles are equal; therefore, $m\angle B = m\angle B'$. Figure 9.17 shows that $\angle A'$, $\angle B'$, and $\angle C'$ form a straight angle; therefore, $m\angle A' + m\angle B' + m\angle C' = 180°$. Since $m\angle A = m\angle A'$, $m\angle B = m\angle B'$, and $m\angle C = m\angle C'$, we can reason that $m\angle A + m\angle B + m\angle C = 180°$. This example illustrates that the sum of the interior angles of a triangle is 180°.

Consider the quadrilateral $ABCD$ (Fig. 9.18a). Drawing a straight line segment between any two vertices forms two triangles. Since the sum of the measures of the angles of a triangle is 180°, the sum of the measures of the interior angles of a quadrilateral is $2 \cdot 180°$, or 360°.

Now let's examine a pentagon (Fig. 9.18b). We can draw two straight line segments to form three triangles. Thus, the sum of the measures of the interior angles of a five-sided figure is $3 \cdot 180°$, or 540°. Figure 9.18(c) shows that four triangles can be drawn in a six-sided figure. Table 9.2 summarizes this information.

Table 9.2

| Sides | Triangles | Sum of the Measures of the Interior Angles |
|---|---|---|
| 3 | 1 | 1(180°) = 180° |
| 4 | 2 | 2(180°) = 360° |
| 5 | 3 | 3(180°) = 540° |
| 6 | 4 | 4(180°) = 720° |

If we continue this procedure, we can see that for an $n$-sided polygon the sum of the measures of the interior angles is $(n-2)180°$.

### Sum of the Measures of Interior Angles
The **sum** of the measures of the interior angles of an $n$-sided polygon is $(n-2)180°$.

Figure 9.19

## Example 1 *Angles of a Hexagon*

The surfaces of the heads of many bolts are in the shape of regular hexagons. A regular hexagon is a six-sided figure with all the sides the same length and all interior angles with the same measure. See Fig. 9.19. Determine

a) the measure of an interior angle.

b) the measure of exterior $\angle 1$.

*Solution*

a) Using the formula $(n-2)180°$, we can determine the sum of the measures of the interior angles of a hexagon as follows.

$$\text{Sum} = (6-2)180°$$
$$= 4(180°)$$
$$= 720°$$

The measure of an interior angle of a regular polygon can be determined by dividing the sum of the interior angles by the number of angles.
The measure of an interior angle of a regular hexagon is determined as follows:

$$\text{Measure} = \frac{720°}{6} = 120°$$

b) Since $\angle 1$ is the supplement of an interior angle,

$$m\angle 1 = 180° - 120° = 60°$$

To discuss area in the next section, we must be able to identify various types of triangles and quadrilaterals. The following is a summary of certain types of triangles and their characteristics.

### Triangles

| | | |
|---|---|---|
| **Acute Triangle** | **Obtuse Triangle** | **Right Triangle** |
|  |  |  hypotenuse |
| All angles are acute angles. | One angle is obtuse. | One angle is a right angle. |
| **Isosceles Triangle** | **Equilateral Triangle** | **Scalene Triangle** |
|  |  |  |
| Two equal sides Two equal angles | Three equal sides Three equal angles (60° each) | No two sides are equal in length. |

## Similar Figures

In everyday living, we often have to deal with geometric figures that have the "same shape" but are of different sizes. For example, an architect will make a small-scale drawing of a floor plan or a photographer will make an enlargement of a photograph. Figures that have the same shape but may be of different sizes are called *similar figures*. Two similar figures are illustrated in Fig. 9.20.

Similar figures have *corresponding angles* and *corresponding sides*. In Fig. 9.20, triangle *ABC* has angles *A*, *B*, and *C*. Their respective corresponding angles in triangle *DEF* are angles *D*, *E*, and *F*. Sides $\overline{AB}$, $\overline{BC}$, and $\overline{AC}$ in triangle *ABC* have corresponding sides $\overline{DE}$, $\overline{EF}$, and $\overline{DF}$, respectively, in triangle *DEF*.

> **Definition:** **Similar Figures**
> Two figures are **similar** if their corresponding angles have the same measure and the lengths of their corresponding sides are in proportion.

In Figure 9.20, $\angle A$ and $\angle D$ have the same measure, $\angle B$ and $\angle E$ have the same measure, and $\angle C$ and $\angle F$ have the same measure. Also, the lengths of corresponding sides of similar triangles are in proportion.

When we refer to the line segment *AB*, we place a line over the *AB* and write $\overline{AB}$. **When we refer to the *length* of a line segment, we do not place a bar above the two letters**. For example, if we write $AB = 12$, we are indicating the length of line segment $\overline{AB}$ is 12. The proportion below shows that the lengths of the corresponding sides of the similar triangles in Fig. 9.20 are in proportion.

$$\frac{AB}{DE} = \frac{BC}{EF} = \frac{AC}{DF}$$

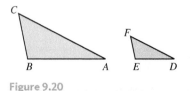

Figure 9.20

## Did You Know?

**Buckyballs**

The molecular structure of $C_{60}$ resembles the patterns found on a soccer ball.

Buckminsterfullerenes, known as buckyballs, are a class of pure carbon molecules. Along with graphite and diamond, buckyballs are the only naturally occurring forms of pure carbon. Named after American architect–engineer F. Buckminster Fuller, who designed hemispherical geodesic domes from hexagonal and pentagonal faces, fullerenes are the most spherical molecules known. Discovered in 1985 at Rice University, buckyballs are used primarily as microscopic lubricant and have potential applications in molecular medical engineering, electrical superconductivity, and computer chip design. The most common form of buckminsterfullerene contains 60 carbon atoms and has the chemical symbol $C_{60}$. The molecular structure of $C_{60}$ contains 12 pentagons and 20 hexagons arranged in a pattern similar to that found on a soccer ball.

## Example 2 *Similar Figures*

Consider the similar figures in Fig. 9.21.

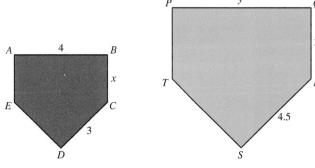

**Figure 9.21**

Determine

a) the length of side $\overline{BC}$.    b) the length of side $\overline{PQ}$.

**Solution**

a) We will represent the length of side $\overline{BC}$ with the variable $x$. Because the corresponding sides of similar figures must be in proportion, we can write a proportion (as explained in Section 6.2) to determine the length of side $\overline{BC}$. Corresponding sides $\overline{CD}$ and $\overline{RS}$ are known, so we use them as one ratio in the proportion. The side corresponding to $\overline{BC}$ is $\overline{QR}$.

$$\frac{BC}{QR} = \frac{CD}{RS}$$

$$\frac{x}{3} = \frac{3}{4.5}$$

Now we solve for $x$.

$$x \cdot 4.5 = 3 \cdot 3$$
$$4.5x = 9$$
$$x = 2$$

Thus, the length of side $\overline{BC}$ is 2 units.

b) We will represent the length of side $\overline{PQ}$ with the variable $y$. The side corresponding to $\overline{PQ}$ is $\overline{AB}$. We will work part (b) in a manner similar to part (a).

$$\frac{PQ}{AB} = \frac{RS}{CD}$$

$$\frac{y}{4} = \frac{4.5}{3}$$

$$y \cdot 3 = 4 \cdot 4.5$$
$$3y = 18$$
$$y = 6$$

Thus, the length of side $\overline{PQ}$ is 6 units.

## Example 3 *Using Similar Triangles to Find the Height of a Tree*

Monique Currie plans to remove a tree from her backyard. She needs to know the height of the tree. Monique is 6 ft tall and determines that when her shadow is 9 ft long, the shadow of the tree is 45 ft long (see Fig. 9.22 on page 494). How tall is the tree?

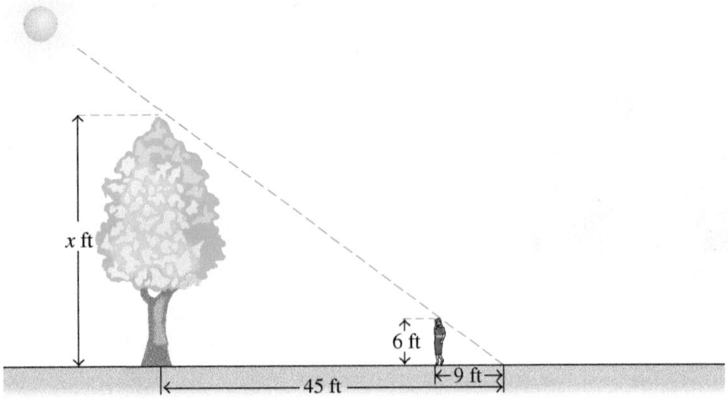

**Figure 9.22**

*Solution* We will let $x$ represent the height of the tree. From Fig. 9.22, we can see that the triangle formed by the sun's rays, Monique, and her shadow is similar to the triangle formed by the sun's rays, the tree, and its shadow. To find the height of the tree, we will set up and solve the following proportion:

$$\frac{\text{height of the tree}}{\text{height of Monique}} = \frac{\text{length of tree's shadow}}{\text{length of Monique's shadow}}$$

$$\frac{x}{6} = \frac{45}{9}$$

$$9x = 270$$

$$x = 30$$

Therefore, the tree is 30 ft tall.    ■

## Congruent Figures

If the corresponding sides of two similar figures are the same length, the figures are called *congruent figures*. Corresponding angles of congruent figures have the same measure, and the corresponding sides are equal in length. Two congruent figures coincide when placed one upon the other.

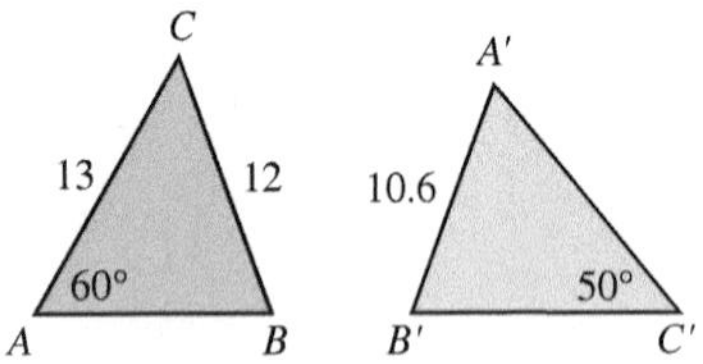

**Figure 9.23**

┌ Example **4**  *Congruent Triangles*

Triangles $ABC$ and $A'B'C'$ in Fig. 9.23 are congruent. Determine
a) the length of side $A'C'$.         b) the length of side $\overline{AB}$.
c) $m\angle C'A'B'$.                  d) $m\angle ACB$.
e) $m\angle ABC$.

*Solution* Because $\triangle ABC$ is congruent to $\triangle A'B'C'$, we know that the corresponding side lengths are equal and corresponding angle measures are equal.
a) $A'C' = AC = 13$              b) $AB = A'B' = 10.6$
c) $m\angle C'A'B' = m\angle CAB = 60°$     d) $m\angle ACB = m\angle A'C'B' = 50°$
e) The sum of the angles of a triangle is 180°. Since $m\angle BAC = 60°$ and $m\angle ACB = 50°$, $m\angle ABC = 180° - 60° - 50° = 70°$.    ■

Earlier we learned that *quadrilaterals* are four-sided polygons, the sum of whose interior angles is 360°. Quadrilaterals may be classified according to their characteristics, as illustrated in the summary box on page 495.

## Quadrilaterals

| Trapezoid | Parallelogram | Rhombus |
|---|---|---|
|  |  |  |
| Two sides are parallel. | Both pairs of opposite sides are parallel. Both pairs of opposite sides are equal in length. | Both pairs of opposite sides are parallel. The four sides are equal in length. |

| Rectangle | Square |
|---|---|
|  |  |
| Both pairs of opposite sides are parallel. Both pairs of opposite sides are equal in length. The angles are right angles. | Both pairs of opposite sides are parallel. The four sides are equal in length. The angles are right angles. |

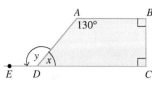

Figure 9.24

## Example 5 *Angles of a Trapezoid*

Trapezoid *ABCD* is shown in Fig. 9.24.

a) Determine the measure of the interior angle, *x*.

b) Determine the measure of the exterior angle, *y*.

**Solution**

a) We know that each of the two right angles in trapezoid *ABCD* has a measure of 90°. We also know that the sum of the interior angles in any quadrilateral is 360°. Therefore, we have

$$m\angle DAB + m\angle ABC + m\angle BCD + m\angle x = 360°$$

$$130° + 90° + 90° + m\angle x = 360°$$

$$310° + m\angle x = 360°$$

$$m\angle x = 50°$$

Thus, the measure of the interior angle, *x*, is 50°.

b) Angle *x* and angle *y* are supplementary angles. Therefore, $m\angle x + m\angle y = 180°$ and $m\angle y = 180° - m\angle x = 180° - 50° = 130°$. Thus, the measure of the exterior angle, *y*, is 130°.  ∎

Note that in Example 5 part (b) we could also have determined the measure of angle *y* as follows. By the definition of a trapezoid, sides $\overline{AB}$ and $\overline{CD}$ must be parallel. Therefore, side $\overline{AD}$ may be considered a transversal and $\angle BAD$ and $\angle ADE$ are alternate interior angles. Recall from Section 9.1 that alternate interior angles are equal. Thus, $m\angle BAD = m\angle ADE$ and $m\angle y = 130°$.

## SECTION 9.2  Exercises

### Warm Up Exercises

*In Exercises 1–6, fill in the blanks with an appropriate word, phrase, or symbol(s).*

1. A closed figure in a plane determined by three or more straight line segments is called a(n) _____.

2. A polygon whose sides are all the same length and whose interior angles all have the same measure is called a(n) _____ polygon.

3. Two polygons are similar if their corresponding angles have the same measure and the lengths of their corresponding sides are in _____.

4. The sum of the measures of the interior angles of a triangle is _____.

5. If the corresponding sides of two similar figures are the same length, the figures are called _____ figures.

6. The sum of the measures of the interior angles of a quadrilateral is _____.

*In Exercises 7–14, (a) name the polygon. If the polygon is a quadrilateral, give its specific name. (b) State whether or not the polygon is a regular polygon.*

7.

8.

9.

10.

11.

12.

13.

14.

*In Exercises 15–22, identify the triangle as (a) scalene, isosceles, or equilateral and as (b) acute, obtuse, or right. The*

parallel markings (the two small parallel lines) on two or more sides indicate that the marked sides are of equal length.

15.

16.

17.

18.

19.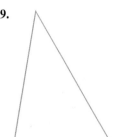

20.

21.

22.

*In Exercises 23–28, identify the quadrilateral.*

23.

24.

25.

26.

27.

28.

*In Exercises 29–32, find the measure of ∡x.*

29.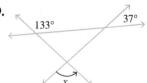
133°    37°

x

**30.**

105°
133°  *x*

**31.**

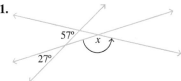

57°  *x*
27°

**32.**

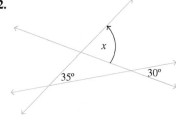

*x*
35°     30°

*In Exercises 33–34, lines l₁ and l₂ are parallel. Determine the measures of ∢1 through ∢12.*

**33.**        **34.**

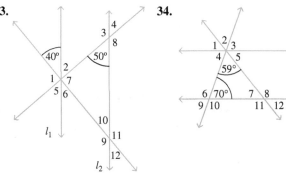

**In Exercises 35–40, determine the sum of the measures of the interior angles of the indicated polygon.**

**35.** Pentagon    **36.** Heptagon    **37.** Nonagon

**38.** Decagon    **39.** Icosagon    **40.** Dodecagon

*In Exercises 41–46, (a) determine the measure of an interior angle of the named regular polygon. (b) If a side of the polygon is extended, determine the supplementary angle of an interior angle. See Example 1.*

**41.** Triangle            **42.** Quadrilateral

**43.** Octagon            **44.** Nonagon

**45.** Decagon            **46.** Icosagon

*In Exercises 47–52, the figures are similar. Find the length of side x and side y.*

**47.**

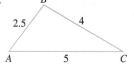

B
2.5     4
A     5     C     B'  *y*
1
A'  *x*  C'

**48.**

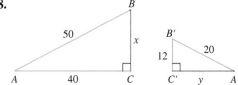

B
50     *x*
A     40     C
B'
12     20
C'  *y*  A'

**49.**

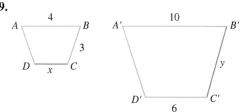

A  4  B          A'  10  B'
3
D  *x*  C          D'        C'
y
6

**50.**

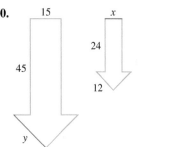

15          *x*
24
45
12
*y*

**51.**

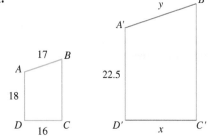

B'
*y*
A'
17  B
22.5
A
18
D  16  C          D'  *x*  C'

**52.**

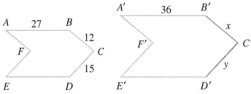

A  27  B          A'  36  B'
12          *x*
F     C          F'          C'
15          *y*
E     D          E'          D'

*In Exercises 53–56, triangles ABC and DEC are similar figures. Determine the length of*

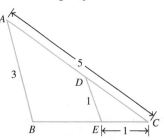

A
5
3
D
1
B     E |←— 1 —→| C

**53.** side $\overline{BC}$.            **54.** side $\overline{DC}$.

**55.** side $\overline{AD}$.            **56.** side $\overline{BE}$.

*In Exercises 57–62, find the length of the sides and the measures of the angles for the congruent triangles ABC and A′B′C′.*

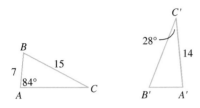

**57.** The length of side $\overline{AC}$    **58.** The length of side $\overline{A'B'}$

**59.** The length of side $\overline{B'C'}$    **60.** ∡$B'A'C'$

**61.** ∡$ACB$    **62.** ∡$ABC$

*In Exercises 63–68, determine the length of the sides and the measures of the angles for the congruent quadrilaterals ABCD and A′B′C′D′.*

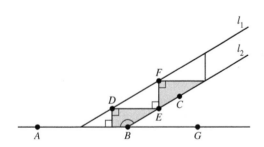

**63.** The length of side $\overline{AD}$    **64.** The length of side $\overline{B'C'}$

**65.** The length of side $\overline{A'B'}$    **66.** ∡$BCD$

**67.** ∡$A'D'C'$    **68.** ∡$DAB$

## Problem Solving

*In Exercises 69–72, determine the measure of the angle. In the figure, ∡ABC makes an angle of 125° with the floor and $l_1$ and $l_2$ are parallel.*

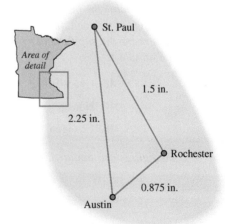

**69.** ∡$GBC$    **70.** ∡$EDF$

**71.** ∡$DFE$    **72.** ∡$DEC$

**73.** *Height of a Silo*  Steve Runde is buying a farm and needs to determine the height of a silo on the farm. Steve, who is 6 ft tall, notices that when his shadow is 9 ft long, the shadow of the silo is 105 ft long (see diagram above and to the right). How tall is the silo? Note that the diagram is not to scale.

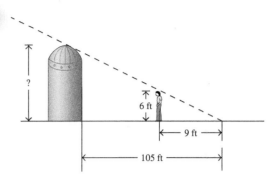

**74.** *Angles on a Picnic Table*  The legs of a picnic table form an isosceles triangle as indicated in the figure. If ∡$ABC = 80°$, determine $m∡x$ and $m∡y$ so that the top of the table will be parallel to the ground.

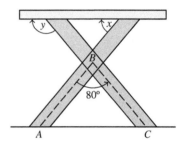

**75.** *Distances in Minnesota*  A triangle can be formed by drawing line segments on a map of Minnesota connecting the cities of Austin, Rochester, and St. Paul (see figure below). If the actual distance from Austin to Rochester is approximately 44 miles, use the lengths of the line segments indicated in the figure along with similar triangles to approximate

**a)** the actual distance from St. Paul to Austin.

**b)** the actual distance from St. Paul to Rochester.

**76.** *Distances in Illinois* A triangle can be formed by drawing line segments on a map of Illinois connecting the cities of Rockford, Chicago, and Bloomington (see figure below). If the actual distance from Chicago to Rockford is approximately 90 miles, use the lengths of the line segments indicated in the figure along with similar triangles to approximate

**a)** the actual distance from Chicago to Bloomington.

**b)** the actual distance from Bloomington to Rockford.

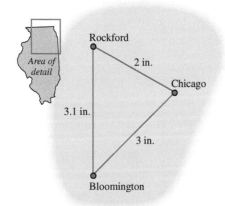

## Concept/Writing Exercises

**77.** List six different types of triangles and in your own words describe the characteristics of each.

**78.** List five different types of quadrilaterals and in your own words describe the characteristics of each.

## Challenge Problems/Group Activities

*Scaling Factor In Exercises 79 and 80 we use a scaling factor. Examine the similar triangles ABC and A'B'C' in the figure below.*

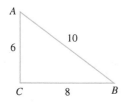

*If we calculate the ratios $\dfrac{AB}{A'B'}$, $\dfrac{BC}{B'C'}$, and $\dfrac{CA}{C'A'}$, we see that each of these ratios is equal to 2. We call this common ratio the* **scaling factor** *of $\triangle ABC$ with respect to $\triangle A'B'C'$. If we calculate the reciprocal ratios $\dfrac{A'B'}{AB}$, $\dfrac{B'C'}{BC}$, and $\dfrac{C'A'}{CA}$, we see that each of these ratios is equal to $\frac{1}{2}$. We call this common ratio the scaling factor of $\triangle A'B'C'$ with respect to $\triangle ABC$. Every pair of similar figures has two*

*scaling factors that show the relationship between the corresponding side lengths. Notice that the length of each side of $\triangle ABC$ is two times the length of the corresponding side in $\triangle A'B'C'$. We can also state that the length of each side of $\triangle A'B'C'$ is one-half the length of the corresponding side of $\triangle ABC$.*

**79.** In the figure, $\triangle DEF$ is similar to $\triangle D'E'F'$. The length of the sides of $\triangle DEF$ is shown in the figure. If the scaling factor of $\triangle DEF$ with respect to $\triangle D'E'F'$ is 3, determine the length of the sides of triangle $\triangle D'E'F'$.

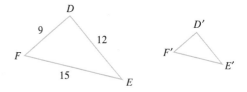

**80.** In the figure, quadrilateral *EFGH* is similar to quadrilateral *E'F'G'H'*. The length of the sides of quadrilateral *EFGH* is shown in the figure. If the scaling factor of quadrilateral *E'F'G'H'* with respect to quadrilateral *EFGH* is $\frac{1}{3}$, determine the length of the sides of quadrilateral *E'F'G'H'*.

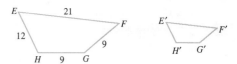

**81.** *Height of a Wall* You are asked to measure the height of an inside wall of a warehouse. No ladder tall enough to measure the height is available. You borrow a mirror from a salesclerk and place it on the floor. You then move away from the mirror until you can see the reflection of the top of the wall in it, as shown in the figure.

**a)** Explain why triangle *HFM* is similar to triangle *TBM*. (*Hint:* In the reflection of light the angle of *incidence*, $\angle HMF$, equals the angle of *reflection*, $\angle TMB$. Thus, $\angle HMF = \angle TMB$.)

**b)** If your eyes are $5\frac{1}{2}$ ft above the floor and you are $2\frac{1}{2}$ ft from the mirror and the mirror is 20 ft from the wall, how high is the wall?

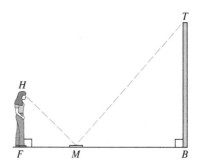

## Recreational Mathematics

**82.** *Distance Across a Lake*

**a)** In the figure, $m\angle CED = m\angle ABC$. Explain why triangles *ABC* and *DEC* must be similar.

**b)** Determine the distance across the lake, *DE*.

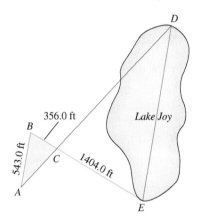

## Internet/Research Activities

**83.** Using the Internet and history of mathematics texts, write a paper on the history and use of the theodolite, a surveying instrument.

**84.** Using the Internet and other sources, write a paper on the use of geometry in the photographic process. Include discussions on the use of similar figures.

---

## SECTION 9.3    Perimeter and Area

▲ We will study the perimeter and area of rectangles, such as those on which volleyball games are played.

If you were to walk around the outside edge of a volleyball court, how far would you walk? If you had to place floor tiles that each measured 1 foot by 1 foot on a basketball court, how many tiles would you need? In this section, we will study the geometric concepts of perimeter and area that are used to answer these and other questions.

**Why** *This is Important* The concepts of area and perimeter are involved in many real-life applications of geometry. These include calculating the cost of flooring for your home, calculating the amount of fencing needed for your yard, and determining the best value when purchasing pizza!

---

## Perimeter and Area

The *perimeter*, *P*, of a two-dimensional figure is the sum of the lengths of the sides of the figure. In Figs. 9.25 and 9.26, the sums of the lengths of the red line segments are the perimeters. Perimeters are measured in the same units as the sides. For example, if the sides of a figure are measured in feet, the perimeter will be measured in feet.

The *area*, *A*, is the region within the boundaries of the figure. The blue color in Figs. 9.25 and 9.26 indicates the areas of the figures. Area is measured in square units. For example, if the sides of a figure are measured in inches, the area of the

Figure 9.25

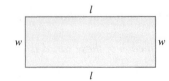

Figure 9.26

figure will be measured in square inches (in.$^2$). (See Table 8.7 on page 465 for common units of area in the U.S. customary and metric systems.)

Consider the rectangle in Fig. 9.26 on page 500. Two sides of the rectangle have length $l$, and two sides of the rectangle have width $w$. Thus, if we add the lengths of the four sides to get the perimeter, we find $P = l + w + l + w = 2l + 2w$.

### Perimeter of a Rectangle

$$P = 2l + 2w$$

Figure 9.27

Consider a rectangle of length 5 units and width 3 units (Fig. 9.27). Counting the number of 1-unit by 1-unit squares within the figure, we obtain the area of the rectangle, 15 square units. The area can also be obtained by multiplying the number of units of length by the number of units of width, or 5 units × 3 units = 15 square units. We can find the area of a rectangle by the formula area = length × width.

### Area of a Rectangle

$$A = l \times w$$

Using the formula for the area of a rectangle, we can determine the formulas for the areas of other figures.

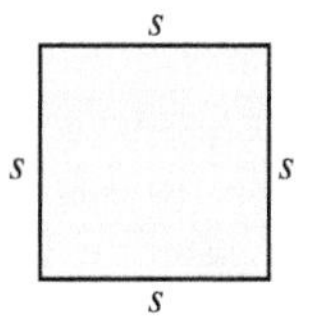

A square (Fig. 9.28) is a rectangle that contains four equal sides. Therefore, the length equals the width. If we call both the length and the width of the square $s$, then

$$A = l \times w, \quad \text{so} \quad A = s \times s = s^2$$

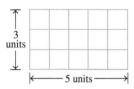

Figure 9.28

### Area of a Square

$$A = s^2$$

A parallelogram with height $h$ and base $b$ is shown in Fig. 9.29(a).

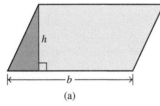 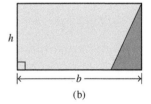

(a) (b)

Figure 9.29

If we were to cut off the red portion of the parallelogram on the left, Fig. 9.29(a), and attach it to the right side of the figure, the resulting figure would be a rectangle, Fig. 9.29(b). Since the area of the rectangle is $b \times h$, the area of the parallelogram is also $b \times h$.

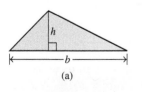

(a)

### Area of a Parallelogram

$$A = b \times h$$

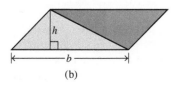

(b)

Figure 9.30

Consider the triangle with height, $h$, and base, $b$, shown in Fig. 9.30(a). Using this triangle and a second identical triangle, we can construct a parallelogram, Fig. 9.30(b). The area of the parallelogram is $bh$. The area of the triangle is one-half that of the parallelogram. Therefore, the area of the triangle is $\frac{1}{2}$ × base × height.

## Area of a Triangle

$$A = \tfrac{1}{2}bh$$

Now consider the trapezoid shown in Fig. 9.31(a). We can partition the trapezoid into two triangles by drawing diagonal $\overline{DB}$, as in Fig. 9.31(b). One triangle has base $\overline{AB}$ (called $b_2$) with height $\overline{DE}$, and the other triangle has base $\overline{DC}$ (called $b_1$) with height $\overline{FB}$. Note that the line used to measure the height of the triangle need not be inside the triangle. Because heights $\overline{DE}$ and $\overline{FB}$ are equal, both triangles have the same height, $h$. The area of triangles $DCB$ and $ADB$ are $\frac{1}{2}b_1 h$ and $\frac{1}{2}b_2 h$, respectively. The area of the trapezoid is the sum of the areas of the triangles, $\frac{1}{2}b_1 h + \frac{1}{2}b_2 h$, which can be written $\frac{1}{2}h(b_1 + b_2)$.

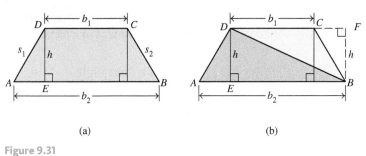

(a)                                    (b)

Figure 9.31

## Area of a Trapezoid

$$A = \tfrac{1}{2}h(b_1 + b_2)$$

Following is a summary of the perimeters and areas of selected figures.

## Perimeters and Areas

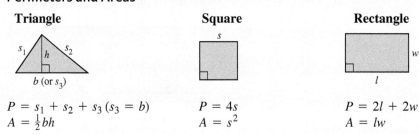

**Triangle**

$P = s_1 + s_2 + s_3 \ (s_3 = b)$
$A = \frac{1}{2}bh$

**Square**

$P = 4s$
$A = s^2$

**Rectangle**

$P = 2l + 2w$
$A = lw$

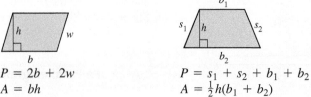

**Parallelogram**

$P = 2b + 2w$
$A = bh$

**Trapezoid**

$P = s_1 + s_2 + b_1 + b_2$
$A = \frac{1}{2}h(b_1 + b_2)$

## Example 1  *Sodding a Lacrosse Field*

Rob Marshall wishes to replace the grass (sod) on a lacrosse field. One pallet of Bethel Farms sod costs $175 and covers 450 square feet. If the area to be covered is a rectangle with a length of 330 feet and a width of 270 feet, determine

a) the area to be covered with sod.

b) how many pallets of sod Rob needs to purchase.

c) the cost of the sod purchased.

**Solution**

a) The area to be covered is

$$A = l \cdot w = 330 \cdot 270 = 89{,}100 \text{ ft}^2$$

The area to be covered is in square feet because both the length and the width are measured in feet.

b) To determine the number of pallets of sod Rob needs, divide the area to be covered by the area covered by one pallet of sod.

$$\frac{\text{Area to be covered}}{\text{Area covered by one pallet}} = \frac{89{,}100}{450} = 198$$

Rob needs 198 pallets of sod.

c) The cost of 198 pallets of sod is $198 \times \$175$, or $\$34{,}650$.

## Pythagorean Theorem

We introduced the Pythagorean theorem in Chapter 5. Because this theorem is an important tool for finding the perimeter and area of triangles, we restate it here.

### Pythagorean Theorem

The sum of the squares of the lengths of the legs of a right triangle equals the square of the length of the hypotenuse.

$$\text{leg}^2 + \text{leg}^2 = \text{hypotenuse}^2$$

Symbolically, if $a$ and $b$ represent the lengths of the legs and $c$ represents the length of the hypotenuse (the side opposite the right angle), then

$$a^2 + b^2 = c^2$$

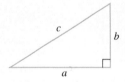

### Example 2 *Crossing a Moat*

The moat surrounding a castle is 18 ft wide and the wall by the moat of the castle is 24 ft high (see Fig. 9.32). If an invading army wishes to use a ladder to cross the moat and reach the top of the wall, how long must the ladder be?

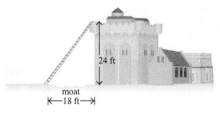

**Figure 9.32**

**Solution** The moat, the castle wall, and the ladder form a right triangle. The moat and the castle wall form the legs of the triangle (sides $a$ and $b$), and the ladder forms the hypotenuse (side $c$). By the Pythagorean theorem,

$$c^2 = a^2 + b^2$$
$$c^2 = (18)^2 + (24)^2$$
$$c^2 = 324 + 576$$
$$c^2 = 900$$
$$\sqrt{c^2} = \sqrt{900} \qquad \text{Take the square root of both sides of the equation.}$$
$$c = 30$$

Therefore, the ladder would need to be at least 30 ft long. ∎

## Circles

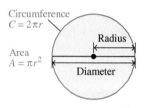

Circumference
$C = 2\pi r$

Radius

Area
$A = \pi r^2$

Diameter

**Figure 9.33**

A commonly used plane figure that is not a polygon is a *circle*. A *circle* is a set of points equidistant from a fixed point called the center. A *radius*, $r$, of a circle is a line segment from the center of the circle to any point on the circle (Fig. 9.33). A *diameter*, $d$, of a circle is a line segment through the center of a circle with both end points on the circle. Note that the diameter of the circle is twice its radius. The *circumference* is the length of the simple closed curve that forms the circle. The formulas for the area and circumference of a circle are given in the box below.

**Circumference and Area of a Circle**

$r$

$$C = 2\pi r$$
$$A = \pi r^2$$

The symbol pi, $\pi$, was introduced in Chapter 5. Recall that $\pi$ is approximately 3.14. However, when solving problems, you should use the $\boxed{\pi}$ key on your calculator to get a more accurate answer.

## Example 3  *Comparing Pizzas*

Victoria Montoya wishes to order a large cheese pizza. She can choose among three pizza parlors in town: Antonio's, Steve's, and Dorsey's. Antonio's large cheese pizza is a round 16-in.-diameter pizza that sells for $15. Steve's large cheese pizza is a round 14-in.-diameter pizza that sells for $12. Dorsey's large cheese pizza is a square 12-in. by 12-in. pizza that sells for $10. All three pizzas have the same thickness. To get the most for her money, from which pizza parlor should Victoria order her pizza?

**Solution** To determine the best value, we will calculate the cost per square inch of pizza for each of the three pizzas. To do so, we will divide the cost of each pizza by its area. The areas of the two round pizzas can be determined using the formula for the area of a circle, $A = \pi r^2$. Since the radius is half the diameter,

we will use $r = 8$ and $r = 7$ for Antonio's and Steve's large pizzas, respectively, and we will use the $\boxed{\pi}$ key on our calculator. The area for the square pizza can be determined using the formula for the area of a square, $A = s^2$. We will use $s = 12$.

$$\text{Area of Antonio's pizza} = \pi r^2 = \pi(8)^2 = \pi(64) \approx 201.06 \text{ in.}^2$$
$$\text{Area of Steve's pizza} = \pi r^2 = \pi(7)^2 = \pi(49) \approx 153.94 \text{ in.}^2$$
$$\text{Area of Dorsey's pizza} = s^2 = (12)^2 = 144 \text{ in.}^2$$

Now, to find the cost per square inch of pizza, we will divide the cost of the pizza by the area of the pizza.

$$\text{Cost per square inch of Antonio's pizza} \approx \frac{\$15}{201.06 \text{ in.}^2} \approx \$0.0746$$

Thus, Antonio's pizza costs about $0.0746, or about 7.5 cents, per square inch.

$$\text{Cost per square inch of Steve's pizza} \approx \frac{\$12}{153.94 \text{ in.}^2} \approx \$0.0780$$

Thus, Steve's pizza costs about $0.0780, or about 7.8 cents, per square inch.

$$\text{Cost per square inch of Dorsey's pizza} = \frac{\$10}{144 \text{ in.}^2} \approx \$0.0694$$

Thus, Dorsey's pizza costs about $0.0694, or about 6.9 cents, per square inch.

Since the cost per square inch of pizza is the lowest for Dorsey's pizza, Victoria would get the most pizza for her money by ordering her pizza from Dorsey's.  ∎

## Example 4   *Determining the Shaded Area*

Determine the shaded area. Use the $\boxed{\pi}$ key on your calculator and round your answer to the nearest hundredth.

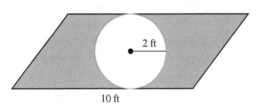

10 ft

*Solution*   To determine the area of the shaded region, we will first determine the area of the parallelogram and then subtract the area of the circle. Notice that the height of the parallelogram is equal to the diameter of the circle. Since the diameter of a circle is twice its radius, the height of the parallelogram = 2 · 2 feet, or 4 feet.

$$\text{Area of the parallelogram} = bh = 10 \cdot 4 = 40 \text{ ft}^2$$
$$\text{Area of the circle} = \pi r^2 = \pi(2)^2 = \pi \cdot 4 \approx 12.57 \text{ ft}^2$$
$$\text{Area of the shaded region} = \text{Area of the parallelogram} - \text{Area of the circle}$$
$$\approx 40 - 12.57 \approx 27.43 \text{ ft}^2$$

Thus, the area of the shaded region is approximately 27.43 ft$^2$.  ∎

## Example 5   *Applying Lawn Fertilizer*

Altay Özgener plans to fertilize his lawn. The shapes and dimensions of his lot, house, driveway, pool, and rose garden are shown in Fig. 9.34 on page 506. One bag of fertilizer costs $29.95 and covers 5000 ft$^2$. Determine how many bags of fertilizer Altay needs and the total cost of the fertilizer.

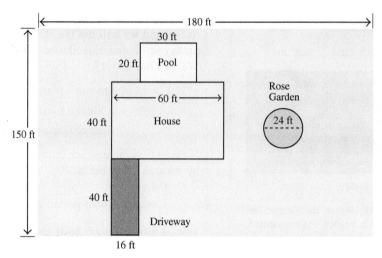

**Figure 9.34**

*Solution*  The total area of the lot is $150 \cdot 180$, or $27,000 \text{ ft}^2$. To determine the area to be fertilized, subtract the area of house, driveway, pool, and rose garden from the total area.

$$\text{Area of house} = 60 \cdot 40 = 2400 \text{ ft}^2$$
$$\text{Area of driveway} = 40 \cdot 16 = 640 \text{ ft}^2$$
$$\text{Area of pool} = 20 \cdot 30 = 600 \text{ ft}^2$$

The diameter of the rose garden is 24 ft, so its radius is 12 ft.

$$\text{Area of rose garden} = \pi r^2 = \pi(12)^2 = \pi(144) \approx 452.39 \text{ ft}^2$$

The total area of the house, driveway, pool, and rose garden is approximately $2400 + 640 + 600 + 452.39$, or $4092.39 \text{ ft}^2$. The area to be fertilized is $27,000 - 4092.39 \text{ ft}^2$, or $22,907.61 \text{ ft}^2$. The number of bags of fertilizer is found by dividing the total area to be fertilized by the number of square feet covered per bag.

The number of bags of fertilizer is $\dfrac{22,907.61}{5000}$, or about 4.58 bags. Therefore, Altay needs five bags. At \$29.95 per bag, the total cost is $5 \times \$29.95$, or \$149.75. ∎

### Example 6  *Converting Between Square Feet and Square Inches*

a) Convert $1 \text{ ft}^2$ to square inches.    b) Convert $37 \text{ ft}^2$ to square inches.
c) Convert $432 \text{ in}^2$ to square feet.    d) Convert $2196 \text{ in}^2$ to square feet.

*Solution*

a) $1 \text{ ft} = 12 \text{ in.}$ Therefore, $1 \text{ ft}^2 = 12 \text{ in.} \times 12 \text{ in.} = 144 \text{ in}^2$.

b) From part (a), we know that $1 \text{ ft}^2 = 144 \text{ in}^2$. Therefore, $37 \text{ ft}^2 = 37 \times 144 \text{ in}^2 = 5328 \text{ in}^2$.

c) In part (b), we converted from square feet to square inches by *multiplying* the number of square feet by 144. Now, to convert from square inches to square feet we will *divide* the number of square inches by 144. Therefore, $432 \text{ in}^2 = \frac{432}{144} \text{ ft}^2 = 3 \text{ ft}^2$.

d) As in part (c), we will divide the number of square inches by 144. Therefore, $2196 \text{ in}^2 = \frac{2196}{144} \text{ ft}^2 = 15.25 \text{ ft}^2$. ∎

Example **7** *Installing Ceramic Tile*

Rebecca Williams wishes to purchase ceramic tile for her family room, which measures 30 ft × 27 ft. The cost of the tile, including installation, is $72 per square yard.

a) Find the area of Rebecca's family room in square *yards*.

b) Determine Rebecca's cost of the ceramic tile for her family room.

**Solution**

a) The area of the family room in square feet is $30 \cdot 27 = 810 \text{ ft}^2$. Since 1 yd = 3 ft, $1 \text{ yd}^2 = 3 \text{ ft} \times 3 \text{ ft} = 9 \text{ ft}^2$. To find the area of the family room in square yards, divide the area in square feet by $9 \text{ ft}^2$.

$$\text{Area in square yards} = \frac{810}{9} = 90$$

Therefore, the area is $90 \text{ yd}^2$.

b) The cost of $90 \text{ yd}^2$ of ceramic tile, including installation, is $90 \cdot \$72 = \$6480$. ∎

*When multiplying units of length, be sure that the units are the same.* You can multiply feet by feet to get square feet or yards by yards to get square yards. However, you cannot get a valid answer if you multiply numbers expressed in feet by numbers expressed in yards.

---

**SECTION 9.3**

*Exercises*

## Warm Up Exercises

*In Exercises 1–4, fill in the blanks with an appropriate word, phrase, or symbol(s).*

**1. a)** The sum of the lengths of the sides of a two-dimensional figure is called the _____ of the figure.

**b)** The region within the boundaries of a two-dimensional figure is called the _____ of the figure.

**2.** In a right triangle, the side that is opposite the right angle is called the _____.

**3.** A set of points equidistant from a fixed point is called a(n) _____.

**4. a)** A line segment from the center of a circle to any point on the circle is called the _____ of the circle.

**b)** A line segment through the center of the circle with both endpoints on the circle is called the _____ of the circle.

**c)** The length of the simple closed curve that forms a circle is called the _____ of the circle.

## Practice the Skills

*In Exercises 5–8, determine the area of the triangle.*

**5.**
4 cm
6 cm

**6.**
9 ft
1 ft

**7.**
5 cm
|←— 7 cm —→|

**8.**
2 m
$\sqrt{3}$ m

*In Exercises 9–14, determine (a) the area and (b) the perimeter of the quadrilateral.*

**9.**

5 ft
10 ft

**10.**

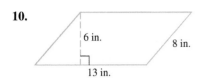

6 in.
8 in.
13 in.

**11.**

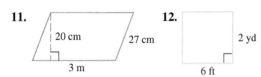

20 cm
27 cm
3 m

**12.**

2 yd
6 ft

**13.**

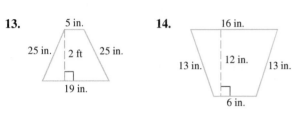

5 in.
25 in.    2 ft    25 in.
19 in.

**14.**

16 in.
13 in.    12 in.    13 in.
6 in.

*In Exercises 15–18, determine (a) the area and (b) the circumference of the circle. Use the ☐π☐ key on your calculator and round your answer to the nearest hundredth.*

**15.**

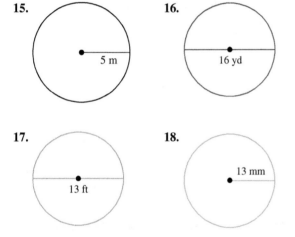

5 m

**16.**

16 yd

**17.**

13 ft

**18.**

13 mm

*In Exercises 19–22, (a) use the Pythagorean theorem to determine the length of the unknown side of the triangle, (b) determine the perimeter of the triangle, and (c) determine the area of the triangle.*

**19.**

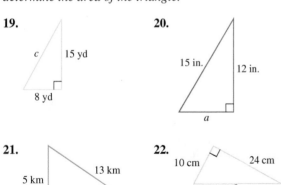

c    15 yd
8 yd

**20.**

15 in.    12 in.
a

**21.**

13 km
5 km
b

**22.**

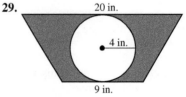

10 cm    24 cm
c

## Problem Solving

*In Exercises 23–32, determine the shaded area. When appropriate, use the ☐π☐ key on your calculator and round your answer to the nearest hundredth.*

**23.**

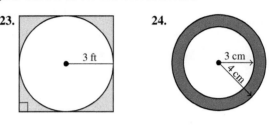

3 ft

**24.**

3 cm
4 cm

**25.**

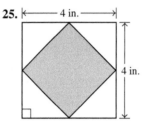

4 in.
4 in.

**26.**

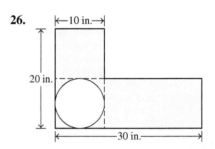

10 in.
20 in.
30 in.

**27.**

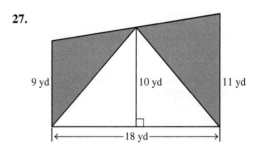

9 yd    10 yd    11 yd
18 yd

**28.**

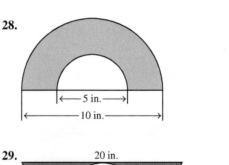

5 in.
10 in.

**29.**

20 in.
4 in.
9 in.

**30.**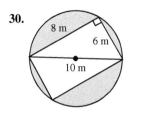

**31.**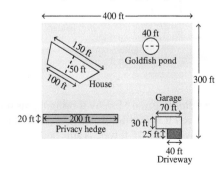

**32.**

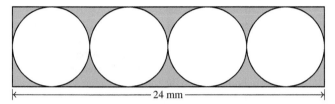

*In Exercises 33–36, one square yard equals 9 ft². Use this information to convert the following.*

**33.** 72 ft² to square yards  **34.** 153 ft² to square yards

**35.** 14.7 yd² to square feet  **36.** 15.2 yd² to square feet

*In Exercises 37–40, one square meter equals 10,000 cm². Use this information to convert the following.*

**37.** 5 m² to square centimeters

**38.** 0.25 m² to square centimeters

**39.** 8625 cm² to square meters

**40.** 608 cm² to square meters

*In Exercises 41–46, Nancy Wallin has just purchased a new house that is in need of new flooring. Use the measurements given on the floor plans of Nancy's house to obtain the answer.*

**41.** *Cost of Hardwood Flooring* The cost of Thomasville Walnut hardwood flooring is $9.99 per square foot if Nancy installs the flooring herself or $11.99 per square foot if she has the flooring installed by the flooring company. Determine the cost for hardwood flooring in the living/dining room if

**a)** Nancy installs it herself.

**b)** Nancy has it installed by the flooring company.

**42.** *Cost of Laminate Flooring* The cost of Prestige August Oak laminate flooring is $2.29 per square foot if Nancy installs the flooring herself or $4.29 per square foot if she has the flooring installed by the flooring company. Determine the cost for the flooring in the living/dining room if

**a)** Nancy installs it herself.

**b)** Nancy has it installed by the flooring company.

**43.** *Cost of Ceramic Tile* The cost of Mohawk Porcelain ceramic tile is $8.99 per square foot. This price includes the cost of installation. Determine the cost for Nancy to have this ceramic tile installed in the kitchen and in both bathrooms.

**44.** *Cost of Linoleum* The cost of Armstrong Marmorette Parchment linoleum is $2.59 per square foot. This price includes the cost of installation. Determine the cost for Nancy to have this linoleum installed in the kitchen and in both bathrooms.

**45.** *Cost of Berber Carpeting* The cost of Shaw Golden Wheat Berber carpeting is $7.99 per square foot. This price includes the cost of installation. Determine the cost for Nancy to have this carpeting installed in all three bedrooms.

**46.** *Cost of Saxony Carpeting* The cost of DuPont Stainmaster Saxony carpeting is $6.99 per square foot. This price includes the cost of installation. Determine the cost for Nancy to have this carpeting installed in all three bedrooms.

**47.** *Cost of a Lawn Service* Clarence and Rose Cohen's home lot is illustrated here. Clarence and Rose wish to hire Picture Perfect Lawn Service to cut their lawn. How much will it cost Clarence and Rose to have their lawn cut if Picture Perfect charges $0.02 per square yard?

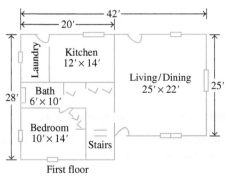

**48.** *Cost of a Lawn Service*  Jim and Wendy Scott's home lot is illustrated here. The Scotts wish to hire a lawn service to cut their lawn. M&M Lawn Service charges $0.02 per square yard of lawn. How much will it cost the Scotts to have their lawn cut?

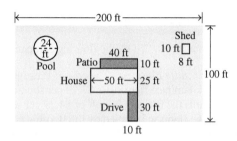

**49.** *Area of a Basketball Court*  A National Basketball Association (NBA) basketball court is a rectangle that is 94 ft long and 50 ft wide.

**a)** If you were to walk around the outside edge of a basketball court, how far would you walk?

**b)** If you had to place floor tiles that each measured 1 foot by 1 foot on a basketball court, how many tiles would you need?

**50.** *Quartz Countertops*  Larry Shedden wishes to have three Cambria Windsor quartz countertops installed in his new kitchen. The countertops are rectangular and have the following dimensions: $3\frac{1}{2}$ ft × 6 ft, $2\frac{1}{2}$ ft × 8 ft, and 3 ft × $11\frac{1}{2}$ ft. The cost of the countertops is $75 per square foot, which includes the cost of installation.

**a)** Determine the total area of the three countertops.

**b)** Determine the total cost to have all three countertops installed.

**51.** *Ladder on a Wall*  Lorrie Morgan places a 29-ft ladder against the side of a building with the bottom of the ladder 20 ft away from the building (see figure). How high up on the wall does the ladder reach?

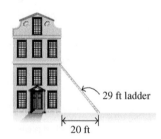

**52.** *Docking a Boat*  Brian Murphy is bringing his boat into a dock that is 9 ft above the water level (see figure above and to the right). If a 41-ft rope is attached to the dock on one side and to the boat on the other side, determine the horizontal distance from the dock to the boat.

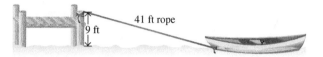

**53.** *The Green Monster*  In Fenway Park, home of baseball's Boston Red Sox, the left field wall is known as the *Green Monster*. The distance from home plate down the third baseline to the bottom of the wall is 310 feet (see photo). In left field, at the end of the baseline, the Green Monster is perpendicular to the ground and is 37 feet tall. Determine the distance from home plate to the top of the Green Monster along the third baseline. Round your answer to the nearest foot.

**54.** *Plasma Television*  The screen of a plasma television is in the shape of a rectangle with a diagonal of length 43 in. If the height of the screen is 21 in., determine the width of the screen.

## Challenge Problems/Group Activities

**55.** *Doubling the Sides of a Square*  In the figure below, an original square with sides of length *s* is shown. Also shown is a larger square with sides double in length, or 2*s*.

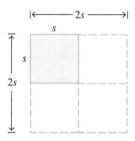

**a)** Express the area of the original square in terms of *s*.

**b)** Express the area of the larger square in terms of *s*.

**c)** How many times larger is the area of the square in part (b) than the area of the square in part (a)?

**56.** *Doubling the Sides of a Parallelogram* In the figure below, an original parallelogram with base $b$ and height $h$ is shown. Also shown is a larger parallelogram with base and height double in length, or $2b$ and $2h$, respectively.

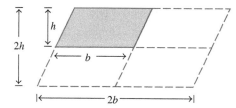

a) Express the area of the original parallelogram in terms of $b$ and $h$.

b) Express the area of the larger parallelogram in terms of $b$ and $h$.

c) How many times larger is the area of the parallelogram in part (b) than the area of the parallelogram in part (a)?

**57.** *Heron's Formula* A second formula for determining the area of a triangle (called Heron's formula) is

$$A = \sqrt{s(s - a)(s - b)(s - c)}$$

where $s = \frac{1}{2}(a + b + c)$ and $a$, $b$, and $c$ are the lengths of the sides of the triangle. Use Heron's formula to determine the area of right triangle $ABC$ and check your answer using the formula $A = \frac{1}{2}ab$.

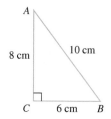

**58.** *Expansion of $(a + b)^2$* In the figure, one side of the largest square has length $a + b$. Therefore, the area of the largest square is $(a + b)^2$. Answer the following questions to find a formula for the expansion of $(a + b)^2$.

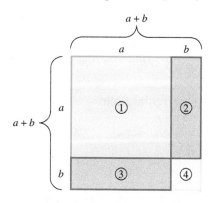

a) What is the area of the square marked ①?

b) What is the area of the rectangle marked ②?

c) What is the area of the rectangle marked ③?

d) What is the area of the square marked ④?

e) Add the four areas found in parts (a) through (d) to write a formula for the expansion of $(a + b)^2$.

## Recreational Mathematics

**59.** *Sports Areas* Use the Internet to research the official dimensions of the playing surface of your favorite sport and determine the area of the playing surface. Choices may include a basketball court, volleyball court, tennis court, racquetball court, hockey rink, football field, soccer field, lacrosse field, and a baseball diamond.

**60.** *Scarecrow's Error* In the movie *The Wizard of Oz*, once the scarecrow gets his diploma he states the following: "In an isosceles triangle, the sum of the square roots of the two equal sides is equal to the square root of the third side." Discuss why this statement is incorrect.

## Internet/Research Activities

*For Exercises 61–63, references include the Internet, history of mathematics textbooks, and encyclopedias.*

**61.** Research the proof of the Pythagorean theorem provided by President James Garfield. Write a brief paper and make a poster of this proof and the associated diagrams.

**62.** The early Babylonians and Egyptians did not know about $\pi$ and had to devise techniques to approximate the area of a circle. Do research and write a paper on the techniques these societies used to approximate the area of a circle.

**63.** Write a paper on the contributions of Heron of Alexandria to geometry.

On the label of a can of Color Place paint is the following sentence: "One gallon will cover about 400 sq. ft." This sentence refers to the two main geometric topics that we will cover in this section. *One gallon* refers to volume of the paint in the can, and *400 sq. ft* refers to the surface area that the paint will cover.

**Why** *This is Important* The concepts of volume and surface area have many real-life applications. These include calculating the volume of a freezer, the displacement of an engine, and the amount of paint needed to paint a room.

▲ *The amount of paint in a can refers to volume, and the amount of wall space that the paint covers refers to surface area.*

When discussing a one-dimensional figure such as a line, we can find its length. When discussing a two-dimensional figure such as a rectangle, we can find its area and its perimeter. When discussing a three-dimensional figure such as a cube, we can find its volume and its surface area. *Volume* is a measure of the capacity of a three-dimensional figure. *Surface area* is the sum of the areas of the surfaces of a three-dimensional figure. Volume refers to the amount of material that you can put *inside* a three-dimensional figure, and surface area refers to the total area that is on the *outside* surface of the figure.

   *Solid geometry* is the study of three-dimensional solid figures, also called *space figures*. Volumes of three-dimensional figures are measured in cubic units such as cubic feet or cubic meters. Surface areas of three-dimensional figures are measured in square units such as square feet or square meters.

## Rectangular Solids, Cylinders, Cones, and Spheres

### Rectangular Solid

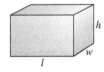

If the length of a *rectangular solid* is 5 units, the width is 2 units, and the height is 3 units, the total number of cubes is 30 (Fig. 9.35). Thus, the volume is 30 cubic units. The volume of a rectangular solid can also be found by multiplying its length times width times height; in this case, 5 units $\times$ 2 units $\times$ 3 units = 30 cubic units. In general, the volume of any rectangular solid is $V = l \times w \times h$.

   The surface area of the rectangular solid in Fig. 9.35 is the sum of the area of the surfaces of the rectangular solid. Notice that each surface of the rectangular solid is a rectangle. The left and right side of the rectangular solid each has an area of 5 units $\times$ 3 units, or 15 square units. The front and back sides of the rectangular solid each has an area of 2 units $\times$ 3 units, or 6 square units. The top and bottom sides of the rectangular solid each has an area of 5 units $\times$ 2 units, or 10 square units. Therefore, the surface area of the rectangular solid is $2(5 \times 3) + 2(2 \times 3) + 2(5 \times 2) = 2(15) + 2(6) + 2(10) = 30 + 12 + 20 = 62$ square units. In general, the surface area of any rectangular solid is $SA = 2lw + 2wh + 2lh$ (see the figure to the left).

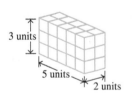

Figure 9.35

**Volume and Surface Area of a Rectangular Solid**

$$V = lwh \qquad SA = 2lw + 2wh + 2lh$$

### Cube

A *cube* is a rectangular solid with the same length, width, and height. If we call the length of the side of the cube $s$ and use the volume and surface area formulas for a rectangular solid, substituting $s$ in for $l$, $w$, and $h$, we obtain $V = s \cdot s \cdot s = s^3$ and $SA = 2 \cdot s \cdot s + 2 \cdot s \cdot s + 2 \cdot s \cdot s = 2s^2 + 2s^2 + 2s^2 = 6s^2$ (see the figure to the left).

### Volume and Surface Area of a Cube

$$V = s^3 \qquad SA = 6s^2$$

## Cylinder

Now consider the right circular cylinder shown in Fig. 9.36(a). When we use the term *cylinder* in this book, we mean a right circular cylinder. The volume of the cylinder is found by multiplying the area of the circular base, $\pi r^2$, by the height, $h$, to get $V = \pi r^2 h$.

The surface area of the cylinder is the sum of the area of the top, the area of the bottom, and the area of the side of the cylinder. Both the top and bottom of the cylinder are circles with an area of $\pi r^2$. To determine the area of the side of the cylinder, examine Fig. 9.36(b) and (c).

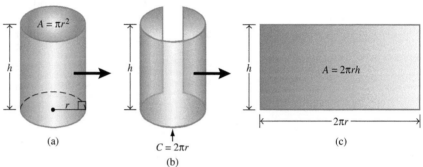

**Figure 9.36**

Notice how when flattened, the side of the cylinder is a rectangle whose length is the circumference of the base of the cylinder and whose width is the height of the cylinder. Thus, the side of the cylinder has an area of $2\pi r \cdot h$, or $2\pi rh$. Therefore, the surface area of the cylinder is $\pi r^2 + \pi r^2 + 2\pi rh$, or $SA = 2\pi rh + 2\pi r^2$.

### Volume and Surface Area of a Cylinder

$$V = \pi r^2 h \qquad SA = 2\pi rh + 2\pi r^2$$

Now consider the right circular cone illustrated in Fig. 9.37. When we use the term *cone* in this book, we mean a right circular cone. The volume of a cone is less than the volume of a cylinder that has the same base and the same height. In fact, the volume of the cone is one-third the volume of the cylinder. The formula for the surface area of a cone is the sum of the area of the circular base of the cone, $\pi r^2$, and the area of the side of the cone, $\pi r\sqrt{r^2 + h^2}$, or $SA = \pi r^2 + \pi r\sqrt{r^2 + h^2}$. The derivation of the area of the side of the cone is beyond the scope of this book.

**Figure 9.37**

### Volume and Surface Area of a Cone

$$V = \tfrac{1}{3}\pi r^2 h \qquad SA = \pi r^2 + \pi r\sqrt{r^2 + h^2}$$

## Sphere

Baseballs, tennis balls, and so on have the shape of a *sphere*. The formulas for the volume and surface area of a sphere are as follows. The derivation of the volume and surface area of a sphere are beyond the scope of this book (see the figure to the left).

### Volume and Surface Area of a Sphere

$$V = \tfrac{4}{3}\pi r^3 \qquad SA = 4\pi r^2$$

Following is a summary of the formulas for the volumes and surface areas of the three-dimensional figures we have discussed thus far.

## Volumes and Surface Areas

**Rectangular Solid**

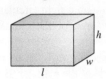

$V = lwh$
$SA = 2lw + 2wh + 2lh$

**Cube**

$V = s^3$
$SA = 6s^2$

**Cylinder**

$V = \pi r^2 h$
$SA = 2\pi rh + 2\pi r^2$

**Cone**

$V = \frac{1}{3}\pi r^2 h$
$SA = \pi r^2 + \pi r\sqrt{r^2 + h^2}$

**Sphere**

$V = \frac{4}{3}\pi r^3$
$SA = 4\pi r^2$

## Example 1  *Volume and Surface Area*

Determine the volume and surface area of each of the following three-dimensional figures. When appropriate, use the $\boxed{\pi}$ key on your calculator and round your answer to the nearest hundredths.

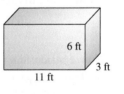

(a)

(b)

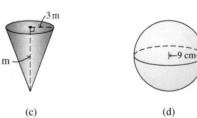

(c)                    (d)

**Solution**

a)  $V = lwh = 11 \cdot 3 \cdot 6 = 198 \text{ ft}^3$

$SA = 2lw + 2wh + 2lh = 2 \cdot 11 \cdot 3 + 2 \cdot 3 \cdot 6 + 2 \cdot 11 \cdot 6$

$= 66 + 36 + 132 = 234 \text{ ft}^2$

b)  $V = \pi r^2 h = \pi \cdot 4^2 \cdot 8 = 128\pi \approx 402.12 \text{ in}^3$

$SA = 2\pi rh + 2\pi r^2 = 2\pi \cdot 4 \cdot 8 + 2\pi \cdot 4^2$

$= 64\pi + 32\pi = 96\pi \approx 301.59 \text{ in}^2$

c)   $V = \frac{1}{3}\pi r^2 h = \frac{1}{3}\pi \cdot 3^2 \cdot 8 = \frac{1}{3}\pi \cdot 9 \cdot 8 = 24\pi \approx 75.40 \text{ m}^3$
  $SA = \pi r^2 + \pi r\sqrt{r^2 + h^2} = \pi \cdot 3^2 + \pi \cdot 3 \cdot \sqrt{3^2 + 8^2}$
  $= 9 \cdot \pi + 3 \cdot \pi \cdot \sqrt{73} \approx 108.80 \text{ m}^2$

d)   $V = \frac{4}{3}\pi r^3 = \frac{4}{3} \cdot \pi \cdot 9^3 = \frac{4}{3} \cdot \pi \cdot 729 = 972\pi \approx 3053.63 \text{ cm}^3$
  $SA = 4\pi r^2 = 4 \cdot \pi \cdot 9^2 = 4 \cdot \pi \cdot 81 = 324\pi \approx 1017.88 \text{ cm}^2$

## Example 2   *Replacing a Sand Volleyball Court*

Robin Ayers is the manager at the Colony Apartments and needs to replace the sand in the rectangular sand volleyball court. The court is 30 ft wide by 60 ft long, and the sand has a uniform depth of 18 in. (see figure below). Sand sells for $27 per cubic yard.

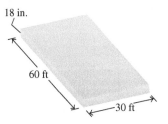

18 in.

60 ft

30 ft

a)  How many cubic yards of sand does Robin need?

b)  How much will the sand cost?

*Solution*

a)  Since we are asked to find the volume in cubic yards, we will convert each measurement to yards. There are 3 ft in a yard. Thus, 30 ft equals $\frac{30}{3}$, or 10 yd, and 60 ft equals $\frac{60}{3}$, or 20 yd. There are 36 in. in a yard, so 18 in. equals $\frac{18}{36}$, or $\frac{1}{2}$ yd. The amount of sand needed is determined using the formula for the volume of a rectangular solid, $V = l \cdot w \cdot h$. In this case, the height of the rectangular solid can be considered the depth of the sand.

$$V = l \cdot w \cdot h = 10 \cdot 20 \cdot \tfrac{1}{2} = 100 \text{ yd}^3$$

Note that since the measurements for length, width, and height are each in terms of yards, the answer is in terms of cubic yards.

b)  One cubic yard of sand costs $27, so 100 $\text{yd}^3$ will cost 100 $\times$ $27, or $2700.

## Example 3   *Homecoming Float*

The basketball team at Southwestern High School is building a float for the homecoming parade. On the float is a large papier-mâché basketball that has a radius of 4.5 ft. Team members need to know the surface area of the basketball so that they can determine how much paint they will need to buy to paint the basketball.

a)  Determine the surface area of the basketball.

b)  If 1 quart of paint covers approximately 100 sq. ft, how many quarts of paint will team members need to buy?

*Solution*

a)  The basketball has the shape of a sphere. We will use the formula for the surface area of a sphere: $SA = 4\pi r^2 = 4 \cdot \pi \cdot (4.5)^2 = 81\pi \approx 254.47$ sq. ft.

b)  Since each quart of paint will cover about 100 sq. ft, they will need about $\frac{254.47}{100} = 2.5447$ quarts. Since you cannot buy a portion of a quart of paint, the team will need to buy **3 quarts** of paint to paint the basketball.

Example **4** *Silage Storage*

Gordon Langeneger has three silos on his farm. The silos are each in the shape of a right circular cylinder (see Fig. 9.38). One silo has a 12-ft diameter and is 40 ft tall. The second silo has a 14-ft diameter and is 50 ft tall. The third silo has an 18-ft diameter and is 60 ft tall.

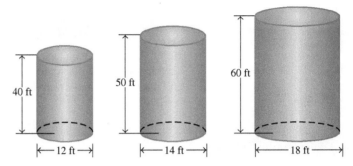

Figure 9.38

a) What is the total capacity of the three silos in cubic feet?

b) If Gordon fills all three of his silos and then feeds his cattle 150 ft³ of silage per day, in how many days will all three silos be empty?

**Solution**

a) The capacity of each silo can be determined using the formula for the volume of a right circular cylinder, $V = \pi r^2 h$. Since the radius is half the diameter, the radii for the three silos are 6 ft, 7 ft, and 9 ft, respectively. Now let's determine the volumes.

$$\text{Volume of the first silo} = \pi r^2 h = \pi \cdot 6^2 \cdot 40$$
$$= \pi \cdot 36 \cdot 40 = 1440\pi \approx 4523.89 \text{ ft}^3$$

$$\text{Volume of the second silo} = \pi r^2 h = \pi \cdot 7^2 \cdot 50$$
$$= \pi \cdot 49 \cdot 50 = 2450\pi \approx 7696.90 \text{ ft}^3$$

$$\text{Volume of the third silo} = \pi r^2 h = \pi \cdot 9^2 \cdot 60$$
$$= \pi \cdot 81 \cdot 60 = 4860\pi \approx 15{,}268.14 \text{ ft}^3$$

Therefore, the total capacity of all three silos is about

$$4523.89 + 7696.90 + 15{,}268.14 \approx 27{,}488.93 \text{ ft}^3$$

b) To find how long it takes to empty all three silos, we will divide the total capacity by 150 ft³, the amount fed to Gordon's cattle every day.

$$\frac{27{,}488.93}{150} \approx 183.26$$

Thus, the silos will be empty in about 183 days. ∎

## Polyhedra, Prisms, and Pyramids

A *polyhedron* (plural, *polyhedra*) is a closed surface formed by the union of polygonal regions. Figure 9.39 on page 517 illustrates some polyhedra.

Each polygonal region is called a *face* of the polyhedron. The line segment formed by the intersection of two faces is called an *edge*. The point at which two or more edges intersect is called a *vertex*. In Fig. 9.39(a), there are 6 faces, 12 edges, and 8 vertices.

**Polyhedra**

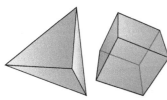

Vertex  Edge  Face

(a)  (b)  (c)  (d)

Figure 9.39

Note that:

$$\text{Number of vertices} - \text{number of edges} + \text{number of faces} = 2$$
$$8 \quad - \quad 12 \quad + \quad 6 \quad = 2$$

This formula, credited to Leonhard Euler, is true for any polyhedron.

## Euler's Polyhedron Formula

$$\text{Number of vertices} - \text{number of edges} + \text{number of faces} = 2$$

We suggest that you verify that this formula holds for Fig. 9.39(b), (c), and (d).

### Example 5  *Using Euler's Polyhedron Formula*

A certain polyhedron has 20 vertices and 12 faces. Determine the number of edges on the polyhedron.

**Solution**  Since we are seeking the number of edges, we will let $x$ represent the number of edges on the polyhedron. Next, we will use Euler's polyhedron formula to set up an equation:

$$\text{Number of vertices} - \text{number of edges} + \text{number of faces} = 2$$
$$20 \quad - \quad x \quad + \quad 12 \quad = 2$$
$$32 - x = 2$$
$$-x = -30$$
$$x = 30$$

Therefore, the polyhedron has 30 edges.  ∎

A *platonic solid*, also known as a *regular polyhedron*, is a polyhedron whose faces are all regular polygons of the same size and shape. There are exactly five platonic solids. All five platonic solids are illustrated in the *Did You Know?* at left.

A *prism* is a special type of polyhedron whose bases are congruent polygons and whose sides are parallelograms. These parallelogram regions are called the *lateral faces* of the prism. If all the lateral faces are rectangles, the prism is said to be a *right prism*. The prisms illustrated in Fig. 9.40 are all right prisms. When we use the word *prism* in this book, we are referring to a right prism.

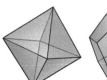

**Prisms**

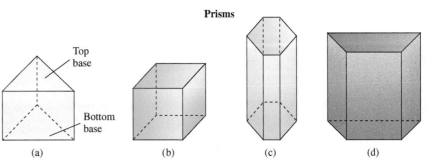

Top base

Bottom base

(a)  (b)  (c)  (d)

Figure 9.40

The volume of any prism can be found by multiplying the area of the base, $B$, by the height, $h$, of the prism.

### Volume of a Prism

$$V = Bh$$

where $B$ is the area of a base and $h$ is the height.

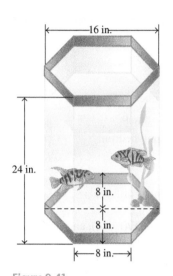

Figure 9.41

## Example 6  *Volume of a Hexagonal Prism Fish Tank*

Frank Nicolzaao's fish tank is in the shape of a hexagonal prism as shown in Fig. 9.41. Use the dimensions shown in the figure and the fact that 1 gal $= 231$ in$^3$ to

a) determine the volume of the fish tank in cubic inches.

b) determine the volume of the fish tank in gallons (round your answer to the nearest gallon).

*Solution*

a) First we will need to calculate the area of the hexagonal base of the fish tank. Notice from Fig. 9.41 that by drawing a diagonal as indicated, the base can be divided into two identical trapezoids. To find the area of the hexagonal base, we will calculate the area of one of these trapezoids and then multiply by 2.

$$\text{Area of one trapezoid} = \tfrac{1}{2}h(b_1 + b_2)$$
$$= \tfrac{1}{2}(8)(16 + 8) = 96 \text{ in}^2$$
$$\text{Area of the hexagonal base} = 2(96) = 192 \text{ in}^2$$

Now to determine the volume of the fish tank, we will use the formula for the volume of a prism, $V = Bh$. We already determined that the area of the base, $B$, is 192 in.$^2$.

$$V = B \cdot h = 192 \cdot 24 = 4608 \text{ in}^3$$

In the above calculation, the area of the base, $B$, was measured in square inches and the height was measured in inches. The product of square inches and inches is cubic inches, or in.$^3$.

b) To determine the volume of the fish tank in gallons, we will divide the volume of the fish tank in cubic inches by 231.

$$V = \frac{4608}{231} \approx 19.95 \text{ gal}$$

Thus, the volume of the fish tank is approximately 20 gal.    ■

## Example 7  *Volumes Involving Prisms*

Determine the volume of the remaining solid after the cylinder, triangular prism, and square prism have been cut from the solid (Fig. 9.42).

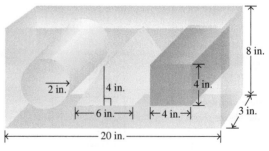

Figure 9.42

*Solution*   To determine the volume of the remaining solid, first determine the volume of the rectangular solid. Then subtract the volume of the two prisms and the cylinder that were cut out.

$$\text{Volume of rectangular solid} = l \cdot w \cdot h$$
$$= 20 \cdot 3 \cdot 8 = 480 \text{ in}^3$$
$$\text{Volume of circular cylinder} = \pi r^2 h$$
$$= \pi(2^2)(3)$$
$$= \pi(4)(3) = 12\pi \approx 37.70 \text{ in}^3$$
$$\text{Volume of triangular prism} = \text{area of the base} \cdot \text{height}$$
$$= \tfrac{1}{2}(6)(4)(3) = 36 \text{ in}^3$$
$$\text{Volume of square prism} = s^2 \cdot h$$
$$= 4^2 \cdot 3 = 48 \text{ in}^3$$
$$\text{Volume of solid} \approx 480 - 37.70 - 36 - 48$$
$$\approx 358.30 \text{ in}^3$$

Another special category of polyhedra is the *pyramid*. Unlike prisms, pyramids have only one base. The figures illustrated in Fig. 9.43 are pyramids. Note that all but one face of a pyramid intersect at a common vertex.

**Pyramids**

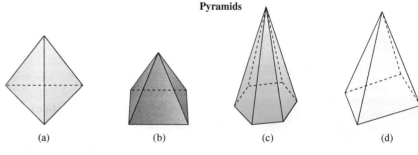

(a)          (b)          (c)          (d)

Figure 9.43

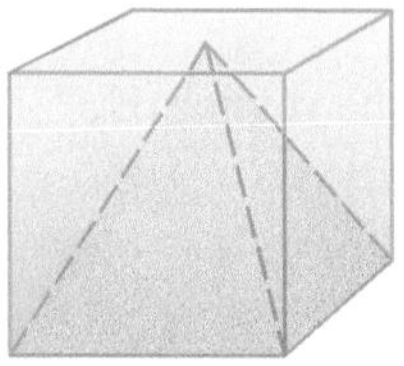

If a pyramid is drawn inside a prism, as shown in Fig. 9.44, the volume of the pyramid is less than that of the prism. In fact, the volume of the pyramid is one-third the volume of the prism.

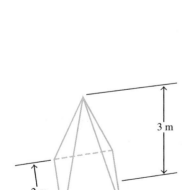

Figure 9.44

### Volume of a Pyramid

$$V = \tfrac{1}{3}Bh$$

where $B$ is the area of the base and $h$ is the height.

## Example 8  *Volume of a Pyramid*

Determine the volume of the pyramid shown in Fig. 9.45.

*Solution*   First find the area of the base of the pyramid. Since the base of the pyramid is a square,

$$\text{Area of base} = s^2 = 2^2 = 4 \text{ m}^2$$

Now use this information to find the volume of the pyramid.

$$V = \tfrac{1}{3} \cdot B \cdot h$$
$$= \tfrac{1}{3} \cdot 4 \cdot 3$$
$$= 4 \text{ m}^3$$

Thus, the volume of the pyramid is 4 m³.

Figure 9.45

## Cubic Unit Conversions

In certain situations, converting volume from one cubic unit to a different cubic unit might be necessary. For example, when purchasing topsoil you might have to change the amount of topsoil from cubic feet to cubic yards prior to placing your order. Example 9 shows how that may be done.

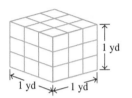

**Figure 9.46**

### Example 9 *Cubic Yards and Cubic Feet*

a) Convert 1 yd³ to cubic feet. (See Fig. 9.46.)

b) Convert 8.9 yd³ to cubic feet.

c) Convert 749.25 ft³ to cubic yards.

*Solution*

a) We know that 1 yd = 3 ft. Thus, 1 yd³ = 3 ft × 3 ft × 3 ft = 27 ft³.

b) In part (a), we learned that 1 yd³ = 27 ft³. Thus, 8.9 yd³ = 8.9 × 27 = 240.3 ft³.

c) In part (b), we converted from cubic yards to cubic feet by *multiplying* the number of cubic yards by 27. Now, to convert from cubic feet to cubic yards we will *divide* the number of cubic feet by 27. Therefore, 749.25 ft³ = $\frac{749.25}{27}$ yd³ = 27.75 yd³.

### Example 10 *Filling in a Swimming Pool*

Madeline Bates recently purchased a home with a rectangular swimming pool. The pool is 30 ft long and 15 ft wide, and it has a uniform depth of 4.5 ft. Madeline lives in a cold climate, so she plans to fill the pool in with dirt to make a flower garden. How many cubic yards of dirt will Madeline have to purchase to fill in the swimming pool?

*Solution* To find the amount of dirt, we will use the formula for the volume of a rectangular solid:

$$V = lwh$$
$$= (30)(15)(4.5)$$
$$= 2025 \text{ ft}^3$$

Now we must convert this volume from cubic feet to cubic yards. In Example 9, we learned that 1 yd³ = 27 ft³. Therefore, 2025 ft³ = $\frac{2025}{27}$ = 75 yd³. Thus, Madeline needs to purchase 75 yd³ of dirt to fill in her swimming pool.

## SECTION 9.4 *Exercises*

### Warm Up Exercises

*In Exercises 1–6, fill in the blanks with an appropriate word, phrase, or symbol(s).*

1. A measure of the capacity of a three-dimensional figure is called the figure's _____.

2. The sum of the areas of the surfaces of a three-dimensional figure is called the figure's _____ area.

3. A regular polyhedron, whose faces are all regular polygons of the same size and shape, is also called a _____ solid.

4. A polyhedron whose bases are congruent polygons and whose sides are parallelograms is called a _____.

5. A prism whose sides are rectangles is called a _____ prism.

6. Euler's polyhedron formula states that, for any polyhedron, the number of vertices minus the number of edges plus the number of faces equals_____.

## Practice the Skills

*In Exercises 7–16, determine (a) the volume and (b) the surface area of the three-dimensional figure. When appropriate, use the $\boxed{\pi}$ key on your calculator and round your answer to the nearest hundredth.*

**7.**

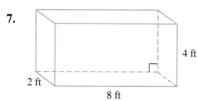

4 ft
2 ft
8 ft

**8.**

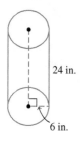

25 mm
6 mm
8 mm

**9.**

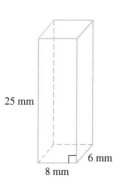

2 yd
2 yd
2 yd

**10.**

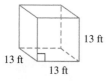

13 ft
13 ft
13 ft

**11.**

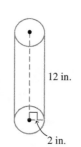

12 in.
2 in.

**12.**

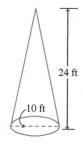

24 in.
6 in.

**13.**

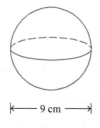

3 cm
14 cm

**14.**

24 ft
10 ft

**15.**

9 cm

**16.**

|←7 mi→|

*In Exercises 17–20, determine the volume of the three-dimensional figure. When appropriate, round your answer to the nearest hundredth.*

**17.**

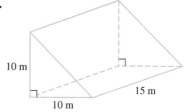

10 m
10 m
15 m

**18.**

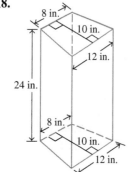

8 in.
10 in.
12 in.
24 in.
8 in.
10 in.
12 in.

**19.**

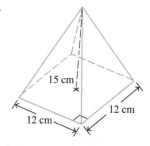

15 cm
12 cm
12 cm

**20.**

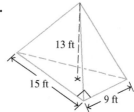

13 ft
15 ft
9 ft

## Problem Solving

*In Exercises 21–28, determine the volume of the shaded region. When appropriate, use the $\boxed{\pi}$ key on your calculator and round your answer to the nearest hundredth.*

**21.**

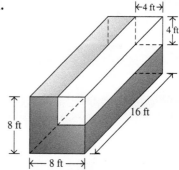

4 ft
4 ft
8 ft
16 ft
8 ft

**22.**

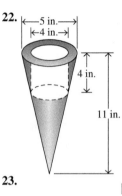

**23.**

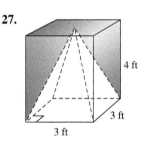

**24.**

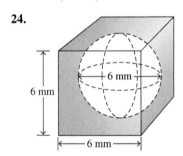

**25.**

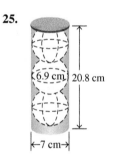

**26.**

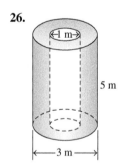

**27.**

**28.**

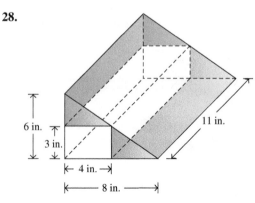

*In Exercises 29–32, use the fact that 1 yd³ equals 27 ft³ to make the conversion.*

**29.** 3 yd³ to cubic feet    **30.** 7.25 yd³ to cubic feet

**31.** 153 ft³ to cubic yards    **32.** 2457 ft³ to cubic yards

*In Exercises 33–36, use the fact that 1 m³ equals 1,000,000 cm³ to make the conversion.*

**33.** 0.56 m³ to cubic centimeters

**34.** 17.6 m³ to cubic centimeters

**35.** 7,500,000 cm³ to cubic meters

**36.** 7,300,000 cm³ to cubic meters

**37.** *Playground Mulch* Bob Malena is building a backyard playground for his grandchildren and wishes to put down rubber mulch to provide safety from falls. Bob wishes to put the mulch in a pit in the shape of a rectangular solid 20 ft long, 15 ft wide, and 9 in deep.

   **a)** Determine the volume, in cubic feet, of mulch Bob will need.

   **b)** If mulch costs $11 per cubic foot, what will the cost of the mulch be?

**38.** *Volume of a Freezer* The dimensions of the interior of an upright freezer are height 46 in., width 25 in., and depth 25 in. Determine the volume of the freezer

   **a)** in cubic inches.    **b)** in cubic feet.

**39.** *CD Case* A compact disc case is a rectangular solid that is 142 mm long, 125 mm wide, and 10 mm high. Determine its surface area.

**40.** *Globe Surface Area* The Everest model globe has a diameter of 20 in. Determine the surface area of this globe. Round your answer to the nearest hundredth.

**41.** *Volume of a Bread Pan* A bread pan is 12 in. × 4 in. × 3 in. How many quarts does it hold, if 1 in³ ≈ 0.01736 qt?

**42.** *Ice-Cream Comparison* The Louisburg Creamery packages its homemade ice cream in tubs and in boxes. The tubs are in the shape of a right cylinder with a radius of 3 in. and height of 5 in. The boxes are in the shape of a cube with each side measuring 5 in. Determine the volume of each container.

**43.** *A Fish Tank*

**a)** How many cubic centimeters of water will a rectangular fish tank hold if the tank is 80 cm long, 50 cm wide, and 30 cm high?

**b)** If 1 cm$^3$ holds 1 m$\ell$ of liquid, how many milliliters will the tank hold?

**c)** If 1 $\ell$ = 1000 m$\ell$, how many liters will the tank hold?

**44.** *The Pyramid of Cheops* The Pyramid of Cheops in Egypt has a square base measuring 720 ft on a side. Its height is 480 ft. What is its volume?

**45.** *Engine Capacity* The engine in a 1957 Chevrolet Corvette has eight cylinders. Each cylinder is a right cylinder with a bore (diameter) of 3.875 in. and a stroke (height) of 3 in. Determine the total displacement (volume) of this engine.

**46.** *Rose Garden Topsoil* Marisa Raffaele wishes to plant a rose garden in her backyard. The rose garden will be in the shape of a 9 ft by 18 ft rectangle. Marisa wishes to add a 4-in. layer of organic topsoil on top of the rectangular area. The topsoil sells for $42 per cubic yard. Determine

**a)** how many cubic yards of topsoil Marisa will need.

**b)** how much the topsoil will cost.

**47.** *Pool Toys* A Wacky Noodle Pool Toy, frequently referred to as a "noodle," is a cylindrical flotation device made from cell foam (see photo). One style of noodle is a cylinder that has a diameter of 2.5 in. and a length of 5.5 ft. Determine the volume of this style of noodle in

**a)** cubic inches. **b)** cubic feet.

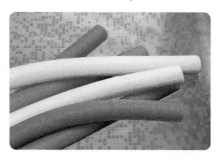

**48.** *Comparing Cake Pans* When baking a cake, you can choose between a round pan with a 9-in. diameter and a 7 in. × 9 in. rectangular pan.

**a)** Determine the area of the base of each pan.

**b)** If both pans are 2 in. deep, determine the volume of each pan.

**c)** Which pan has the larger volume?

**49.** *Cake Icing* A bag used to apply icing to a cake is in the shape of a cone with a diameter of 3 in. and a height of 6 in. How much icing will this bag hold when full?

**50.** *Flower Box* The flower box shown below is 4 ft long, and its ends are in the shape of a trapezoid. The upper and lower bases of the trapezoid measure 12 in. and 8 in., respectively, and the height is 9 in. Find the volume of the flower box

**a)** in cubic inches. **b)** in cubic feet.

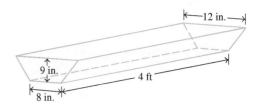

*In Exercises 51–56, find the missing value indicated by the question mark. Use the following formula.*

$$\left(\begin{array}{c}\text{Number of}\\\text{vertices}\end{array}\right) - \left(\begin{array}{c}\text{number of}\\\text{edges}\end{array}\right) + \left(\begin{array}{c}\text{number}\\\text{of faces}\end{array}\right) = 2$$

| | Number of Vertices | Number of Edges | Number of Faces |
|---|---|---|---|
| **51.** | 8 | ? | 4 |
| **52.** | 12 | 16 | ? |
| **53.** | ? | 8 | 4 |
| **54.** | 11 | ? | 5 |
| **55.** | 7 | 12 | ? |
| **56.** | ? | 10 | 4 |

## Challenge Problems/Group Activities

**57. *Earth and Moon Comparisons*** The diameter of Earth is approximately 12,756.3 km. The diameter of the moon is approximately 3474.8 km. Assume that both Earth and the moon are spheres.

**a)** Determine the surface area of Earth.

**b)** Determine the surface area of the moon.

**c)** How many times larger is the surface area of Earth than the surface area of the moon?

**d)** Determine the volume of Earth.

**e)** Determine the volume of the moon.

**f)** How many times larger is the volume of Earth than the volume of the moon?

**58. *Packing Orange Juice*** A box is packed with six cans of orange juice. The cans are touching each other and the sides of the box, as shown. What percent of the volume of the interior of the box is not occupied by the cans?

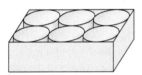

**59. *Doubling the Edges of a Cube*** In this exercise, we will explore what happens to the volume of a cube if we double the length of each edge of the cube.

**a)** Choose a number between 1 and 10 and call this number $s$.

**b)** Calculate the volume of a cube with the length of each edge equal to $s$.

**c)** Now double $s$ and call this number $t$.

**d)** Calculate the volume of a cube with the length of each edge equal to $t$.

**e)** Repeat parts (a) through (d) for a different value of $s$.

**f)** Compare the results from part (b) with the results from part (d) and explain what happens to the volume of a cube if we double the length of each edge.

**60. *Doubling the Radius of a Sphere*** In this exercise, we will explore what happens to the volume of a sphere if we double the radius of the sphere.

**a)** Choose a number between 1 and 10 and call this number $r$.

**b)** Calculate the volume of a sphere with radius $r$ (use the $\boxed{\pi}$ key on your calculator).

**c)** Now double $r$ and call this number $t$.

**d)** Calculate the volume of a sphere with radius $t$.

**e)** Repeat parts (a) through (d) for a different value of $r$.

**f)** Compare the results from part (b) with the results from part (d) and explain what happens to the volume of a sphere if we double the radius.

**61. a)** Explain how to demonstrate, using the cube shown below, that
$$(a + b)^3 = a^3 + 3a^2b + 3ab^2 + b^3$$

**b)** What is the volume in terms of $a$ and $b$ of each numbered piece in the figure?

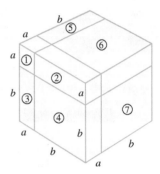

**c)** An eighth piece is not illustrated. What is its volume?

## Recreational Mathematics

**62. *More Pool Toys*** Wacky Noodle Pool Toys (see Exercise 47) come in many different shapes and sizes.

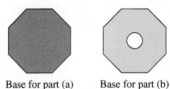

Base for part (a)     Base for part (b)

**a)** Determine the volume, in cubic inches, of a noodle that is in the shape of a 5.5-ft-long solid octagonal prism whose base has an area of 5 in². 

**b)** Determine the volume, in cubic inches, of a hollow noodle that has the same shape as the noodle described in part (a) except that a right circular cylinder of diameter 0.75 in. has been removed from the center.

## Internet/Research Activities

**63. *Air-Conditioner Selection*** Calculate the volume of the room in which you sleep or study. Go to a store that sells room air conditioners and find out how many cubic feet can be cooled by the different models available. Describe the model that would be the proper size for your room. What is the initial cost? How much does that model cost to operate? If you moved to a room that had twice the amount

of floor space and the same height, would the air conditioner you selected still be adequate? Explain.

**64.** Pappus of Alexandria (ca. A.D. 350) was the last of the
well-known ancient Greek mathematicians. Write a paper
on his life and his contributions to mathematics.

**65.** *Platonic Solids*  Construct cardboard models of one
or more of the platonic solids. Visit the Web site www.
mathsnet.net/geometry/solid/platonic.html or similar
Web sites for patterns to follow.

## SECTION 9.5 — Transformational Geometry, Symmetry, and Tessellations

Consider the capital letters of the alphabet. Now consider a kindergarten-age child
who is practicing to write capital letters. Usually, children will write some of the letters
"backwards." However, some letters cannot be made backwards. For example, the
capital letter A would look the same backwards as it does forwards, but the capital
letters B and C would look different backwards than they do forwards. The capital
letters that appear the same forwards as they do backwards have a property called
*symmetry* that we will define and study in this section. Symmetry is part of another
branch of geometry known as *transformational geometry*.

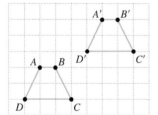

▲ *Capital letters can be used to display symmetry.*

**Why** *This is Important*  Transformational geometry can be used to describe many natural
phenomena in biology, physics, chemistry, and other scientific areas.

I n our study of geometry, we have thus far focused on definitions, axioms, and theorems that are used in the study of *Euclidean geometry*. We will now introduce a
second type of geometry called *transformational geometry*. In *transformational
geometry*, we study various ways to move a geometric figure without altering the
shape or size of the figure. When discussing transformational geometry, we often use
the term *rigid motion*.

### Definition:  **Rigid Motion or Transformation**
The act of moving a geometric figure from some starting position to some ending
position without altering its shape or size is called a **rigid motion** (or **transformation**).

**Figure 9.47**

Consider trapezoid *ABCD* in Fig. 9.47. If we move each point on this trapezoid
4 units to the right and 3 units up, the trapezoid is in the location specified by trapezoid
*A'B'C'D'*. This figure illustrates one type of rigid motion. When studying rigid motions, we are concerned only about the starting and ending positions of the figure and not
what happens in between. When discussing rigid motions of two-dimensional figures,
we note there are four basic types of rigid motions: reflections, rotations, translations,
and glide reflections. We call these four types of rigid motions the *basic rigid motions in
a plane*. After we discuss the four rigid motions, we will discuss symmetry of geometric
figures and tessellations.

## Reflections

The first rigid motion we will study is *reflection*. In our everyday life, we are
quite familiar with the concept of reflection. In transformational geometry, a reflection is an image of a geometric figure that appears on the opposite side of a
designated line.

Definition: **Reflection**

A **reflection** is a rigid motion that moves a geometric figure to a new position such that the figure in the new position is a mirror image of the figure in the starting position. In two dimensions, the figure and its mirror image are equidistant from a line called the **reflection line** or the **axis of reflection**.

Figure 9.48 shows trapezoid *ABCD*, a reflection line *l*, and the reflected trapezoid *A'B'C'D'*. Notice that vertex *A* is 6 units to the *left* of reflection line *l* and that vertex *A'* is 6 units to the *right* of reflection line *l*. Next notice that vertex *B* is 2 units to the *left* of *l* and that vertex *B'* is 2 units to the *right* of *l*. A similar relationship holds true for vertices *C* and *C'* and for vertices *D* and *D'*. It is important to see that the trapezoid is not simply *moved* to the other side of the reflection line, but instead it is *reflected*. Notice in the trapezoid *ABCD* that the longer base $\overline{BC}$ is on the *right* side of the trapezoid, but in the reflected trapezoid *A'B'C'D'* the longer base $\overline{B'C'}$ is on the *left* side of the trapezoid. Finally, notice the colors of the sides of the two trapezoids. Side $\overline{AB}$ in trapezoid *ABCD* and side $\overline{A'B'}$ in the reflected trapezoid are both blue. Side $\overline{BC}$ and side $\overline{B'C'}$ are both red, sides $\overline{CD}$ and $\overline{C'D'}$ are both gold, and sides $\overline{DA}$ and $\overline{D'A'}$ are both green. In this section, we will occasionally use such color coding to help you visualize the effect of a rigid transformation on a figure.

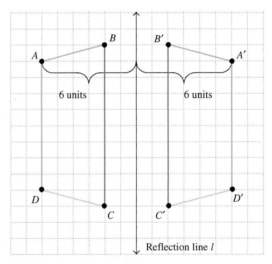

**Figure 9.48**

┌ Example **1** *Reflection of a Triangle*

Construct the reflection of triangle *ABC*, shown in Fig. 9.49, about reflection line *l*.

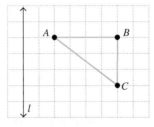

**Figure 9.49**

*Solution*    The reflection of triangle *ABC* will be called *A'B'C'*. To determine the position of the reflection, we first examine vertex *A* in Fig. 9.49. Notice that vertex *A* is 2 units to the *right* of line *l*. Thus, in the reflected triangle *A'B'C'*,

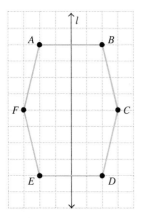

Figure 9.51

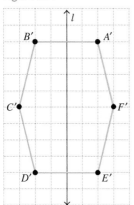

Figure 9.52

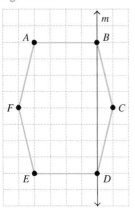

Figure 9.53

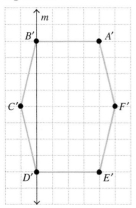

Figure 9.54

vertex $A'$ must also be 2 units away from, but to the *left* of, reflection line $l$ (see Fig 9.50 below). Next, notice that vertex $B$ is 6 units to the right of line $l$. Thus, in the reflected triangle $A'B'C'$, vertex $B'$ must also be 6 units away from, but to the *left* of, reflection line $l$. Next, notice that vertex $C$ is 6 units to the right of line $l$. Thus, in the reflected triangle $A'B'C'$, vertex $C'$ must also be 6 units away from, but to the *left* of, reflection line $l$. Figure 9.50 shows vertices $A'$, $B'$, and $C'$. Finally, we draw line segments between vertices $A'$ and $B'$, between $B'$, and $C'$, and between $A'$ and $C'$ to form the sides of the reflection triangle $A'B'C'$, as illustrated in Fig. 9.50.

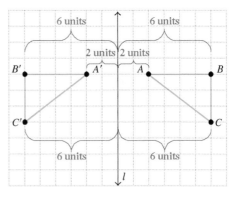

Figure 9.50

In Example 1, the reflection line did not intersect the figure being reflected. We will now study an example in which the reflection line goes directly through the figure to be reflected.

## Example 2  *Reflection of a Hexagon*

Construct the reflection of hexagon *ABCDEF*, shown in Fig. 9.51, about reflection line $l$.

*Solution*  From Fig. 9.51 (in the margin above), we see that vertex $A$ in hexagon *ABCDEF* is 2 units to the left of reflection line $l$. Thus, vertex $A'$ in the reflected hexagon will be 2 units to the right of $l$ (see Fig. 9.52). Notice that vertex $A'$ of the reflected hexagon is in the same location as vertex $B$ of hexagon *ABCDEF* in Fig. 9.51.

We next see that vertex $B$ in hexagon *ABCDEF* is 2 units to the right of $l$. Thus, vertex $B'$ in the reflected hexagon will be 2 units to the left of $l$. Notice that vertex $B'$ of the reflected hexagon is in the same location as vertex $A$ of hexagon *ABCDEF*. We continue this process to determine the locations of vertices $C'$, $D'$, $E'$, and $F'$ of the reflected hexagon. Notice once again that each vertex of the reflected hexagon is in the same location as a vertex of hexagon *ABCDEF*. Finally, we draw the line segments to complete the reflected hexagon $A'B'C'D'E'F'$ (see Fig. 9.52). For this example, we see that other than the vertex labels, the positions of the hexagon before and after the reflection are identical.

In Example 2, the reflection line was in the center of the hexagon in the original position. As a result, the reflection line was also in the center of the reflected hexagon. In this particular case the reflected hexagon lies directly on top of the hexagon in its original position. We will revisit reflections such as that in Example 2 again when we discuss *reflective symmetry* later in this section.

Now consider hexagon *ABCDEF* in Fig. 9.53 and its reflection about line $m$, hexagon $A'B'C'D'E'F'$ in Fig. 9.54. Notice that the positions of the hexagon before and after the reflection, relative to line $m$, are not the same. Furthermore, if we line up reflection line $m$ in Fig. 9.53 and Fig. 9.54, we would see that hexagon *ABCDEF* and hexagon $A'B'C'D'E'F'$ are in different positions.

## Translations

The next rigid motion we will discuss is the *translation*. In a translation, we simply move a figure along a straight line to a new position.

### Definition: **Translation or Glide**

A **translation** (or **glide**) is a rigid motion that moves a geometric figure by sliding it along a straight line segment in the plane. The direction and length of the line segment completely determine the translation.

After conducting a translation, we say the figure was *translated* to a new position.

A concise way to indicate the direction and the distance that a figure is moved during a translation is with a *translation vector*. In mathematics, vectors are typically represented with boldface letters. For example, in Fig. 9.55 we see trapezoid *ABCD* and a translation vector, **v**, which is pointing to the right and upward. This translation vector indicates a translation of 9 units to the right and 4 units upward. Notice that in Fig. 9.55 the translated vector appears on the right side of the polygon. The placement of the translation vector does not matter. Therefore, the translation vector could have been placed to the left, above, or below the polygon, and the translation would not change. When trapezoid *ABCD* is translated using **v**, every point on trapezoid *ABCD* is moved 9 units to the right and 4 units upward. This movement is demonstrated for vertex *A* in Fig. 9.56(a). Figure 9.56(b) shows trapezoid *ABCD* and the translated trapezoid *A'B'C'D'*. Notice in Fig. 9.56(b) that every point on trapezoid *A'B'C'D'* is 9 units to the right and 4 units up from its corresponding point on trapezoid *ABCD*.

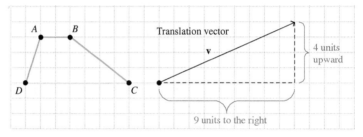

Figure 9.55

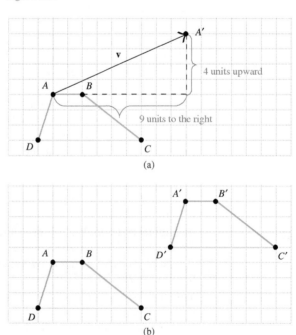

Figure 9.56

Example **3**   *A Translated Square*

Given square *ABCD* and translation vector **v**, shown in Fig. 9.57, construct the translated square *A'B'C'D'*.

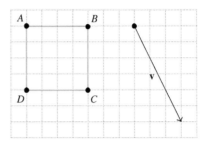

Figure 9.57

*Solution*   The translated figure will be a square of the same size and shape as square *ABCD*. We notice that the translation vector, **v**, points 6 units downward and 3 units to the right. To determine the location of vertex *A'* of the translated square, start at vertex *A* of square *ABCD* and move down 6 units and to the right 3 units. We label this vertex *A'* (see Fig. 9.58a). We determine vertices *B'*, *C'*, and *D'* in a similar manner by moving down 6 units and to the right 3 units from vertices *B*, *C*, and *D*, respectively. Figure 9.58(b) shows square *ABCD* and the translated square *A'B'C'D'*. Notice in Fig. 9.58(b) that every point on square *A'B'C'D'* is 6 units down and 3 units to the right of its corresponding point on square *ABCD*.

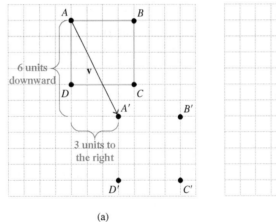
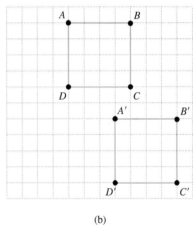

(a)                                        (b)

Figure 9.58

## Rotations

The next rigid motion we will discuss is *rotation*. To help visualize a rotation, examine Fig. 9.59, which shows right triangle *ABC* and point *P* about which right triangle *ABC* is to be rotated.

Imagine that this page was removed from this book and attached to a bulletin board with a single pin through point *P*. Next imagine rotating the page 90° in the *counterclockwise* direction. The triangle would now appear as triangle *A'B'C'* shown in Fig. 9.60 on page 530. Next, imagine rotating the original triangle 180° in a counterclockwise direction. The triangle would now appear as triangle *A"B"C"* shown in Fig. 9.61 on page 530.

Now that we have an intuitive idea of how to determine a rotation, we give the definition of rotation.

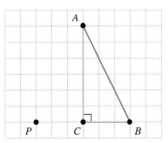

Figure 9.59

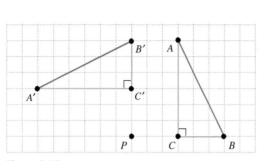

Figure 9.60

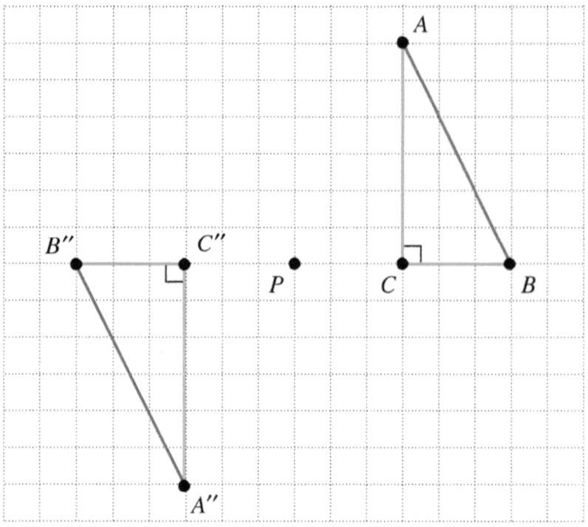

Figure 9.61

### Definition: Rotation

A **rotation** is a rigid motion performed by rotating a geometric figure in the plane about a specific point, called the **rotation point** or the **center of rotation**. The angle through which the object is rotated is called the **angle of rotation**.

We will measure angles of rotation using degrees. In mathematics, generally, *counterclockwise angles have positive degree measures and clockwise angles have negative degree measures.*

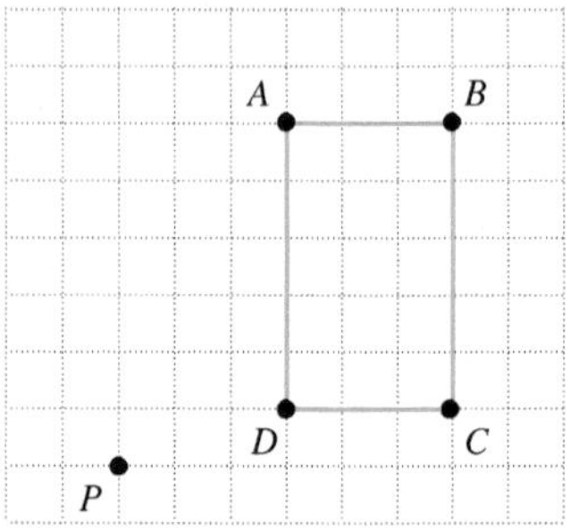

## Example 4    *A Rotated Rectangle*

Given rectangle *ABCD* and rotation point *P*, shown in Fig. 9.62, construct rectangles that result from rotations through

a) 90°.        b) 180°.        c) 270°.

*Solution*

a) First, since 90 is a *positive* number, we will rotate the figure in a counterclockwise direction. We also note that the rotated rectangle will be the same size and shape as rectangle *ABCD*. To get an idea of what the rotated rectangle will look like, pick up this book and rotate it counterclockwise 90°. Figure 9.63 shows rectangle *ABCD* and rectangle *A'B'C'D'* which is rectangle *ABCD* rotated 90° about point *P*. Notice how line segment *AB* in rectangle *ABCD* is horizontal, but in the rotated rectangle in Fig. 9.63 line segment *A'B'* is vertical. Also notice that in rectangle *ABCD* vertex *D* is 3 units to the *right* and 1 unit *above* rotation point *P*, but in the rotated rectangle, vertex *D'* is 3 units *above* and 1 unit to the *left* of rotation point *P*.

Figure 9.62

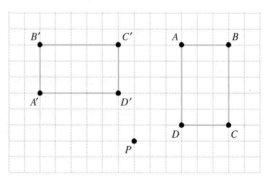

Figure 9.63

b) To gain some perspective on a 180° rotation, again pick up this book, but this time rotate the book 180° in the counterclockwise direction. The rotated rectangle $A''B''C''D''$ is shown along with the rectangle $ABCD$ in Fig. 9.64.

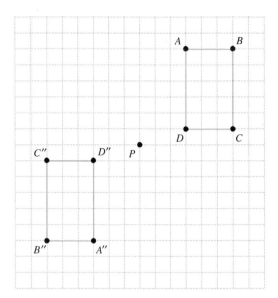

**Figure 9.64**

c) To gain some perspective on a 270° rotation, rotate this book 270° in the counterclockwise direction. The rotated rectangle $A'''B'''C'''D'''$ is shown along with rectangle $ABCD$ in Fig. 9.65.  ◼

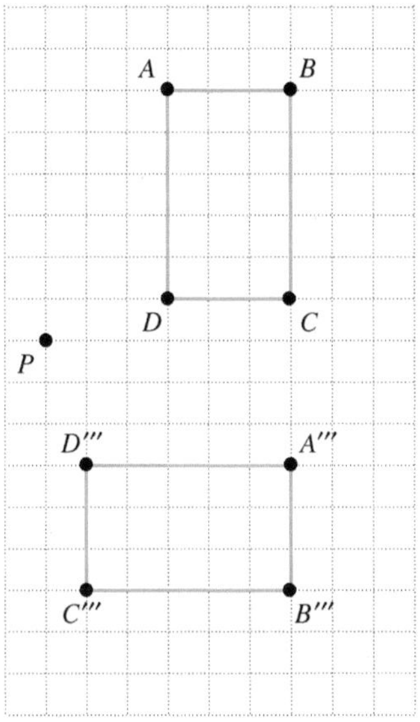

Thus far in our examples of rotations, the rotation point was outside the figure being rotated. We now will study an example where the rotation point is inside the figure to be rotated.

**Example 5**  *A Rotation Point Inside a Polygon*

Given polygon $ABCDEFGH$ and rotation point $P$, shown in Fig. 9.66, construct polygons that result from rotations through

a) 90°.          b) 180°.

*Solution*

a) We will rotate the polygon 90° in a counterclockwise direction. The resulting polygon will be the same size and shape as polygon $ABCDEFGH$. To visualize what the rotated polygon will look like, pick up this book and rotate it counterclockwise 90°. Figure 9.67 shows the polygon $ABCDEFGH$, in pale blue, and the rotated polygon $A'B'C'D'E'F'G'H'$, in deeper blue. Notice how line segments $\overline{AB}$, $\overline{CD}$, $\overline{EF}$, and $\overline{GH}$ in polygon $ABCDEFGH$ are *horizontal*, but in the rotated polygon $A'B'C'D'E'F'G'H'$, line segments $\overline{A'B'}$, $\overline{C'D'}$, $\overline{E'F'}$, and $\overline{G'H'}$ are *vertical*. Also notice in polygon $ABCDEFGH$ that line segment $\overline{GH}$ is 1 unit *above* rotation point $P$, but in the rotated polygon, line segment $\overline{G'H'}$ is 1 unit to the *left* of rotation point $P$.

b) To visualize the polygon obtained through a 180° rotation, we can pick up this book and rotate it 180° in the counterclockwise direction. Notice from Fig. 9.68 on page 532 that vertex $A''$ of the rotated polygon is in the same position as vertex $E$ of polygon $ABCDEFGH$. Also notice from Fig. 9.68 that vertex $B''$ of the rotated polygon is in the same position as vertex $F$ of polygon $ABCDEFGH$. In fact, each of the vertices in the rotated polygon is in the same position as a different vertex in polygon $ABCDEFGH$. From

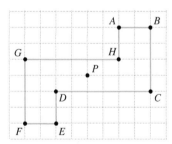

**Figure 9.65**

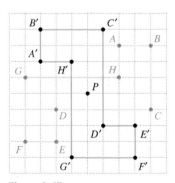

**Figure 9.66**

**Figure 9.67**

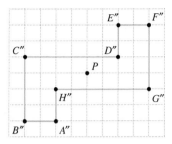

**Figure 9.68**

Fig. 9.68 we see that, other than vertex labels, the position of rotated polygon $A''B''C''D''E''F''G''H''$ is the same as the position of polygon $ABCDEFGH$. ∎

The polygon used in Example 5 will be discussed again later when we discuss *rotational symmetry*. The three rigid motions we have discussed thus far are reflection, translation, and rotation. Now we will discuss the fourth rigid motion, *glide reflection*.

## Glide Reflections

> **Definition: Glide Reflection**
> A **glide reflection** is a rigid motion formed by performing a *translation* (or *glide*) followed by a *reflection*.

A glide reflection, as its name suggests, is a translation (or glide) followed by a reflection. Both translations and reflections were discussed earlier in this section. Consider triangle $ABC$ (shown in blue), translation vector **v**, and reflection line $l$ in Fig. 9.69. The translation of triangle $ABC,$ obtained using translation vector **v**, is triangle $A'B'C'$ (shown in red). The reflection of triangle $A'B'C'$ about reflection line $l$ is triangle $A''B''C''$ (shown in green). Thus, triangle $A''B''C''$ is the glide reflection of triangle $ABC$ using translation vector **v** and reflection line $l$.

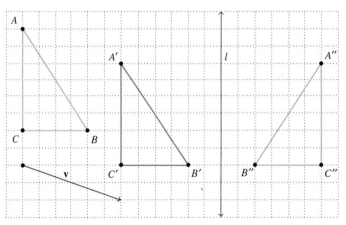

**Figure 9.69**

### Example 6  *A Glide Reflection of a Parallelogram*

Construct a glide reflection of parallelogram $ABCD$, shown in Fig. 9.70, using translation vector **v** and reflection line $l$.

*Solution*   To construct the glide reflection of parallelogram $ABCD$, first translate the parallelogram 2 units to the left and 5 units up, as indicated by translation vector **v**. This translated parallelogram is labeled $A'B'C'D'$, shown in red in Fig. 9.71(a) on page 533. Next, we will reflect parallelogram $A'B'C'D'$ about reflection line $l$. Parallelogram $A'B'C'D'$, shown in red, and the reflected parallelogram, labeled $A''B''C''D''$, shown in green, are shown in Fig. 9.71(b). The glide reflection of the parallelogram $ABCD$ is parallelogram $A''B''C''D''$. ∎

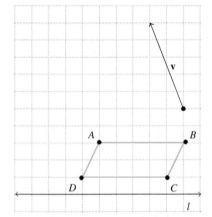

**Figure 9.70**

## Symmetry

We are now ready to discuss symmetry. Our discussion of symmetry involves a rigid motion of an object.

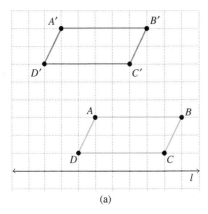

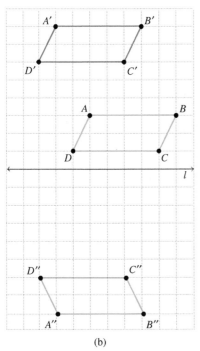

Figure 9.71

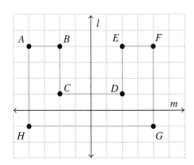

Figure 9.73

## Definition: Symmetry

A **symmetry** of a geometric figure is a rigid motion that moves the figure back onto itself. That is, the beginning position and ending position of the figure must be identical.

Suppose we start with a figure in a specific position and perform a rigid motion on this figure. If the position of the figure after the rigid motion is identical to the position of the figure before the rigid motion (if the beginning and ending positions of the figure coincide), then the rigid motion is a symmetry and we say that the figure has symmetry. For a two-dimensional figure, there are four types of symmetries: reflective symmetry, rotational symmetry, translational symmetry, and glide reflective symmetry. In this textbook, however, we will discuss only reflective symmetry and rotational symmetry.

Consider the polygon and reflection line *l* shown in Fig. 9.72(a). If we use the rigid motion of reflection and reflect the polygon *ABCDEFGH* about line *l*, we get polygon *A'B'C'D'E'F'G'H'*. Notice that the ending position of the polygon is identical to the starting position, as shown in Fig. 9.72(b). Compare Fig. 9.72(a) with Fig. 9.72(b). Although the vertex labels are different, the reflected polygon is in the same position as the polygon in the original position. Thus, we say that the polygon has *reflective symmetry* about line *l*. We refer to line *l* as a *line of symmetry*.

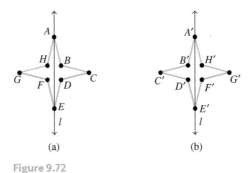

Figure 9.72

Recall Example 2 on page 527 in which hexagon *ABCDEF* was reflected about reflection line *l*. Examine the hexagon in the original position ( Fig. 9.51) and the hexagon in the final position after being reflected about line *l* ( Fig. 9.52). Other than the labels of the vertices, the beginning and ending positions of the hexagon are identical. Therefore, hexagon *ABCDEF* has reflective symmetry about line *l*.

## Example 7  *Reflective Symmetries of Polygons*

Determine whether the polygon shown in Fig. 9.73 has reflective symmetry about each of the following lines.

a) Line *l*      b) Line *m*

**Solution**

a) Examine the reflection of the polygon about line *l* as seen in Fig. 9.74(a) on page 534. Notice that other than the vertex labels, the beginning and ending positions of the polygon are identical. Thus, the polygon has reflective symmetry about line *l*.

b) Examine the reflection of the polygon about line *m* as seen in Fig. 9.74(b). Notice that the position of the reflected polygon is different from the original position of the polygon. Thus, the polygon does not have reflective symmetry about line *m*.

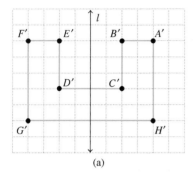

(a)

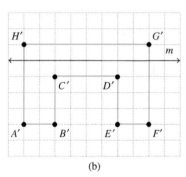

(b)

Figure 9.74

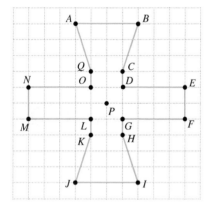

Figure 9.76

We will now discuss a second type of symmetry, rotational symmetry. Consider the polygon and rotation point $P$ shown in Fig. 9.75(a). The rigid motion of rotation of polygon $ABCDEFGH$ through a 90° angle about point $P$ gives polygon $A'B'C'D'E'F'G'H'$ shown in Fig. 9.75(b). Compare Fig. 9.75(a) with Fig. 9.75(b). Although the vertex labels are different, the position of the polygon before and after the rotation is identical. Thus, we say that the polygon has 90° *rotational symmetry* about point $P$. We refer to point $P$ as the *point of symmetry*.

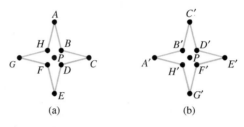

(a)                    (b)

Figure 9.75

Recall Example 5 on page 531, in which polygon $ABCDEFGH$ was rotated 90° about point $P$ in part (a) and 180° in part (b). First examine the polygon in the original position in Fig. 9.66 and the 90° rotated polygon in Fig. 9.67. Notice the position of the polygon after the 90° rotation is different from the original position of the polygon. Therefore, polygon $ABCDEFGH$ in Fig. 9.67 does not have 90° rotational symmetry about point $P$. Now examine the 180° rotated polygon in Fig. 9.68 on page 532. Notice that other than the vertex labels, the positions of the two polygons $ABCDEFGH$ and $A'B'C'D'E'F'G'H'$ are identical with respect to rotation about point $P$. Therefore, polygon $ABCDEFGH$ in Fig. 9.66 has 180° rotational symmetry about point $P$.

## Example 8 *Rotational Symmetries*

Determine whether the polygon shown in Fig. 9.76 on page 533 has rotational symmetry about point $P$ for rotations through each of the following angles.

a) 90°          b) 180°

*Solution*

a) To determine whether the polygon has 90° counterclockwise rotational symmetry about point $P$, we rotate the polygon 90° as shown in Fig. 9.77(a). Compare Fig. 9.77(a) with Fig. 9.76. Notice that the position of the polygon after the rotation in Fig. 9.77(a) is different than the original position of the polygon (Fig. 9.76). Therefore, the polygon does not have 90° rotational symmetry.

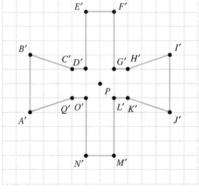

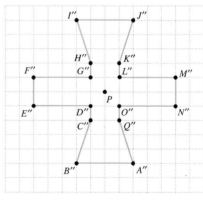

Figure 9.77          (a)                                        (b)

**Symmetry in Nature**

$S$ymmetry can be found every-where in nature. One type of symmetry in nature is reflective symmetry, or *bilateral* symmetry. For example, if you draw a line down the center of a maple leaf, you will often find that one half has the same shape as the other half.

Rotational symmetry, or *radial* symmetry, is also found in nature. Starfish, sand dollars, and many flowers all display rotational sym-metry. For example, if you rotate a daisy 90°,180°, or 270°, the rotated daisy will look identical to the origi-nal daisy. There are many other examples of symmetry in nature. In Exercise 63 on page 542 you are asked to find other examples of re-flective symmetry and rotational symmetry.

b) To determine whether the polygon has 180° counterclockwise rotational sym-metry about the point $P$, we rotate the polygon 180° as shown in Fig. 9.77(b) on page 534. Compare Fig. 9.77(b) with Fig. 9.76. Notice that other than vertex labels, the position of the polygon after the rotation in Fig. 9.77(b) is identical to the position of the polygon before the rotation (Fig. 9.76). Therefore, the poly-gon has 180° rotational symmetry.

## Tessellations

A fascinating application of transformational geometry is the creation of *tessellations*.

### Definition:  Tessellation or Tiling
A **tessellation** (or **tiling**) is a pattern consisting of the repeated use of the same geometric figures to entirely cover a plane, leaving no gaps. The geometric figures used are called the **tessellating shapes** of the tessellation.

Figure 9.78 shows an example of a tessellation from ancient Egypt. Perhaps the most famous person to incorporate tessellations into his work is M. C. Escher (see *Profiles in Mathematics* on page 536).

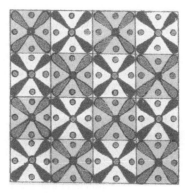

Figure 9.78

The simplest tessellations use one single regular polygon as the tessellating shape. Recall that a *regular polygon* is one whose sides are all the same length and whose interior angles all have the same measure. A tessellation that uses one single regular polygon as the tessellating shape is called a *regular tessellation*. It can be shown that only three regular tessellations exist: those that use an equilateral trian-gle, a square, or a regular hexagon as the tessellating shape. Figure 9.79 shows each of these regular tessellations. Notice that each tessellation can be obtained from a single tessellating shape through the use of reflections, translations, or rotations.

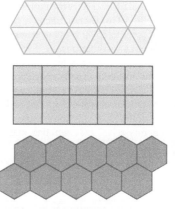

Figure 9.79

We will now learn how to create unique tessellations. We will do so by constructing a unique tessellating shape from a square. We could also construct other tessellating shapes, using an equilateral triangle or a regular hexagon. If you wish to follow along with our construction, you will need some lightweight cardboard, a ruler, cellophane tape, and a pair of scissors. We will start by measuring and cutting out a square 2 in. by 2 in. from the cardboard. We next cut the square into two parts by cutting it from top to bottom using any kind of cut. One example is shown in Fig. 9.80. We then rearrange the pieces and tape the two vertical edges together as shown in Fig. 9.81. Next we cut this new shape into two parts by cutting it from left to right using any kind of cut as shown in Fig. 9.82. We then rearrange the pieces and tape the two horizontal edges together as shown in Fig. 9.83. This completes our tessellating shape.

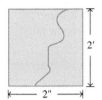

Figure 9.80

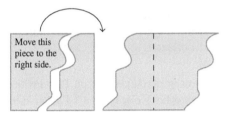

Figure 9.81

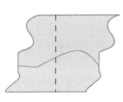

Figure 9.82

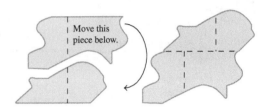

Figure 9.83

Figure 9.84

We now set the cardboard tessellating shape in the middle of a blank piece of paper (the tessellating shape can be rotated to any position as a starting point) and trace the outline of the shape onto the paper. Next move the tessellating shape so that it lines up with the figure already drawn and trace the outline again. Continue to do that until the page is completely covered. Once the page is covered with the tessellation, we can add some interesting colors or even some unique sketches to the tessellation. Figure 9.84 shows one tessellation created using the tessellation shape in Fig. 9.83. In Fig. 9.84, the tessellation shape was rotated about 45° counterclockwise.

An infinite number of different tessellations can be created using the method described by altering the cuts made. We could also create different tessellations using an equilateral triangle, a regular hexagon, or other types of polygons. There are also other, more complicated ways to create the tessellating shape. The Internet has many sites devoted to the creation of tessellations by hand. Many computer programs that generate tessellations are also available.

## *Profile In Mathematics*

### Maurits Cornelius Escher

In addition to being wonderfully engaging art, the work of M. C. Escher (1898–1972) also displays some of the more beautiful and intricate aspects of mathematics. Escher's work involves Euclidean, non-Euclidean (to be studied shortly), and transformational geometries. Amazingly, Escher had no formal training in mathematics.

In 1936, Escher became obsessed with tessellations, that is, with creating art that used objects to cover a plane so as to leave no gaps. Symmetry became a cornerstone of Escher's famous tessellations. In 1995, the mathematician Donald Coxeter published a paper in which he proved that the mathematics Escher displayed in the etching *Circle Limit III* (see page 557) was indeed perfectly consistent with mathematical theory.

Escher kept a notebook in which he kept background information for his artwork. In this notebook, Escher characterized all possible combinations of shapes, colors, and symmetrical properties of polygons in the plane. By doing so, Escher had unwittingly developed areas of a branch of mathematics known as *crystallography* years before any mathematician had done so!

Escher's *Self Portrait in Spherical Mirror*

**Exercises**

### Warm Up Exercises

*In Exercises 1–14, fill in the blanks with an appropriate word, phrase, or symbol(s).*

**1.** The act of moving a geometric figure from some starting position to some ending position without altering its shape or size is called a(n) _____ motion.

**2.** A rigid motion that moves a geometric figure to a new position such that the new position is a mirror image of the figure in the starting position is called a(n) _____.

**3.** In two dimensions, the geometric figure and its reflected image are equidistant from a line called the reflection line, or the _____ of reflection.

**4.** A rigid motion that moves a geometric figure by sliding it along a straight line segment in the plane is called a(n) _____.

**5.** A concise way to indicate the direction and the distance that a figure is moved during a translation is with a translation _____.

**6.** A rigid motion performed by rotating a geometric figure in the plane about a specific point is called a(n) _____.

**7.** The point about which a geometric figure is rotated during a rotation is called the rotation point, or the _____ of rotation.

**8.** The angle through which a geometric figure is rotated during a rotation is called the angle of _____.

**9.** A rigid motion formed by performing a translation followed by a reflection is called a(n) _____ reflection.

**10.** A rigid motion that moves the geometric figure back onto itself is called a(n) _____.

**11.** Rectangle *ABCD* shown below has _____ symmetry about line *l*.

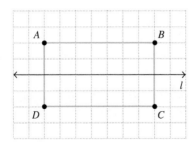

**12.** Rectangle *ABCD* shown below has 180° _____ symmetry about point *P*.

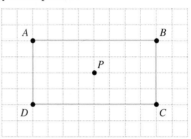

**13.** A pattern consisting of the repeated use of the same geometric figures to entirely cover a plane, leaving no gaps, is called a(n) _____.

**14.** The geometric figures used to cover a plane are called the _____ shapes of the tessellation.

### Practice the Skills/Problem Solving

*In Exercises 15–22, use the given figure and lines of reflection to construct the indicated reflections. Show the figure in the positions both before and after the reflection.*

*In Exercises 15 and 16, use the following figure. Construct*

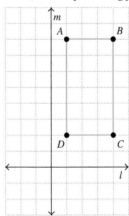

**15.** the reflection of rectangle *ABCD* about line *m*.

**16.** the reflection of rectangle *ABCD* about line *l*.

*In Exercises 17 and 18, use the following figure. Construct*

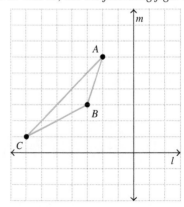

**17.** the reflection of triangle *ABC* about line *l*.

**18.** the reflection of triangle *ABC* about line *m*.

*In Exercises 19 and 20, use the following figure. Construct*

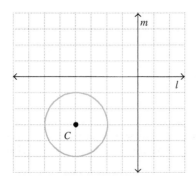

**19.** the reflection of circle *C* about line *l*.

**20.** the reflection of circle *C* about line *m*.

*In Exercises 21 and 22, use the following figure. Construct*

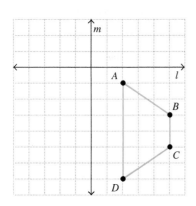

**21.** the reflection of trapezoid *ABCD* about line *m*.

**22.** the reflection of trapezoid *ABCD* about line *l*.

*In Exercises 23–30, use the translation vectors* **v** *and* **w**, *shown below, to construct the translations indicated in the exercises. Show the figure in the positions both before and after the translation.*

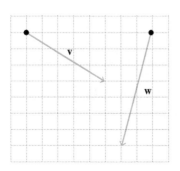

*In Exercises 23 and 24, use the following figure. Construct*

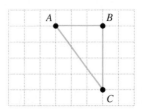

**23.** the translation of triangle *ABC* using translation vector **v**.

**24.** the translation of triangle *ABC* using translation vector **w**.

*In Exercises 25 and 26, use the following figure. Construct*

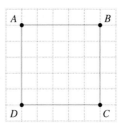

**25.** the translation of square *ABCD* using translation vector **w**.

**26.** the translation of square *ABCD* using translation vector **v**.

*In Exercises 27 and 28, use the following figure. Construct*

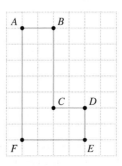

**27.** the translation of polygon *ABCDEF* using translation vector **v**.

**28.** the translation of polygon *ABCDEF* using translation vector **w**.

*In Exercises 29 and 30, use the following figure. Construct*

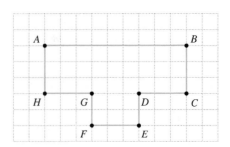

**29.** the translation of polygon *ABCDEFGH* using translation vector **w** (shown on page 538).

**30.** the translation of polygon *ABCDEFGH* using translation vector **v** (shown on page 538).

*In Exercises 31–38, use the given figure and rotation point P to construct the indicated rotations. Show the figure in the positions both before and after the rotation.*

*In Exercises 31 and 32, use the following figure. Construct*

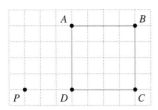

**31.** a 90° rotation of square *ABCD* about point *P*.

**32.** a 180° rotation of square *ABCD* about point *P*.

*In Exercises 33 and 34, use the following figure. Construct*

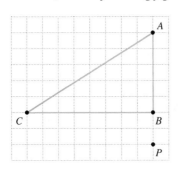

**33.** a 180° rotation of triangle *ABC* about point *P*.

**34.** a 270° rotation of triangle *ABC* about point *P*.

*In Exercises 35 and 36, use the following figure. Construct*

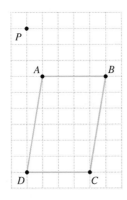

**35.** a 270° rotation of parallelogram *ABCD* about point *P*.

**36.** a 180° rotation of parallelogram *ABCD* about point *P*.

*In Exercises 37 and 38, use the following figure. Construct*

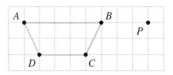

**37.** a 90° rotation of trapezoid *ABCD* about point *P*.

**38.** a 270° rotation of trapezoid *ABCD* about point *P*.

*In Exercises 39–46, use the given figure, translation vectors **v** and **w**, and reflection lines l and m to construct the indicated glide reflections. Show the figure in the positions before and after the glide reflection.*

*In Exercises 39 and 40, use the following figure. Construct*

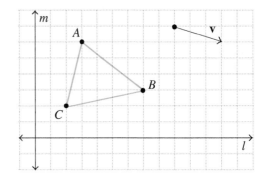

**39.** a glide reflection of triangle *ABC* using vector **v** and reflection line *l*.

**40.** a glide reflection of triangle *ABC* using vector **v** and reflection line *m*.

*In Exercises 41 and 42, use the following figure. Construct*

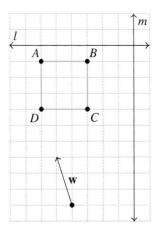

**41.** a glide reflection of square *ABCD* using vector **w** and reflection line *l*.

**42.** a glide reflection of square *ABCD* using vector **w** and reflection line *m*.

*In Exercises 43 and 44, use the following figure. Construct*

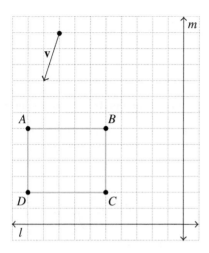

**43.** a glide reflection of rectangle *ABCD* using vector **v** and reflection line *l*.

**44.** a glide reflection of rectangle *ABCD* using vector **v** and reflection line *m*.

*In Exercises 45 and 46, use the following figure. Construct*

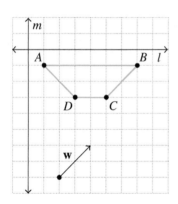

**45.** a glide reflection of trapezoid *ABCD* using vector **w** and reflection line *l*.

**46.** a glide reflection of trapezoid *ABCD* using vector **w** and reflection line *m*.

**47. a)** Reflect triangle *ABC*, shown below, about line *l*. Label the reflected triangle *A'B'C'*.

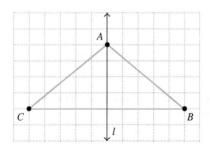

**b)** Other than vertex labels, is the position of triangle *A'B'C'* identical to the position of triangle *ABC*?

**c)** Does triangle *ABC* have reflective symmetry about line *l*?

**48. a)** Reflect rectangle *ABCD*, shown below, about line *l*. Label the reflected rectangle *A'B'C'D'*.

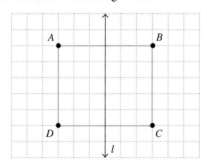

**b)** Other than vertex labels, is the position of rectangle *A'B'C'D'* identical to the position of rectangle *ABCD*?

**c)** Does rectangle *ABCD* have reflective symmetry about line *l*?

**49. a)** Reflect parallelogram *ABCD*, shown below, about line *l*. Label the reflected parallelogram *A'B'C'D'*.

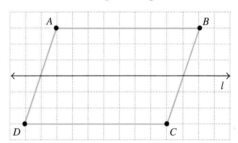

**b)** Other than vertex labels, is the position of parallelogram *A'B'C'D'* identical to the position of parallelogram *ABCD*?

**c)** Does parallelogram *ABCD* have reflective symmetry about line *l*?

**50. a)** Reflect triangle *ABC*, shown below, about line *l*. Label the reflected triangle *A'B'C'*.

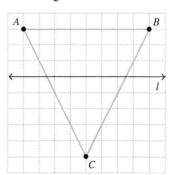

**b)** Other than vertex labels, is the position of triangle *A'B'C'* identical to the position of triangle *ABC*?

**c)** Does triangle *ABC* have reflective symmetry about line *l*?

**51. a)** Rotate rectangle *ABCD*, shown below, 90° about point *P*. Label the rotated rectangle *A'B'C'D'*.

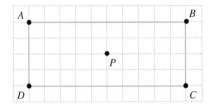

**b)** Other than vertex labels, is the position of rectangle *A'B'C'D'* identical to the position of rectangle *ABCD*?

**c)** Does rectangle *ABCD* have 90° rotational symmetry about point *P*?

**d)** Now rotate the rectangle in the original position, rectangle *ABCD*, 180° about point *P*. Label the rotated rectangle *A"B"C"D"*.

**e)** Other than vertex labels, is the position of rectangle *A"B"C"D"* identical to the position of rectangle *ABCD*?

**f)** Does rectangle *ABCD* have 180° rotational symmetry about point *P*?

**52. a)** Rotate parallelogram *ABCD*, shown below, 90° about point *P*. Label the rotated parallelogram *A'B'C'D'*.

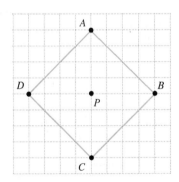

**b)** Other than vertex labels, is the position of parallelogram *A'B'C'D'* identical to the position of parallelogram *ABCD*?

**c)** Does parallelogram *ABCD* have 90° rotational symmetry about point *P*?

**d)** Now rotate the parallelogram in the original position, parallelogram *ABCD*, shown above, 180° about point *P*. Label the rotated parallelogram *A"B"C"D"*.

**e)** Other than vertex labels, is the position of parallelogram *A"B"C"D"* identical to the position of parallelogram *ABCD*?

**f)** Does parallelogram *ABCD* have 180° rotational symmetry about point *P*?

**53.** Consider the following figure.

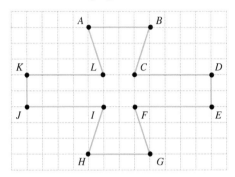

**a)** Insert a vertical line *m* through the figure so the figure has reflective symmetry about line *m*.

**b)** Insert a horizontal line *l* through the figure so the figure has reflective symmetry about line *l*.

**c)** Insert a point *P* within the figure so the figure has 180° rotational symmetry about point *P*.

**d)** Is it possible to insert a point *P* within the figure so the figure has 90° rotational symmetry about point *P*? Explain your answer.

**54.** Consider the following figure.

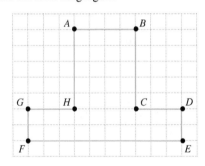

**a)** Insert a vertical line *m* through the figure so the figure has reflective symmetry about line *m*.

**b)** Is it possible to insert a horizontal line *l* through the figure so the figure has reflective symmetry about line *l*? Explain your answer.

**c)** Is it possible to insert a point *P* within the figure so the figure has 90° rotational symmetry about point *P*? Explain your answer.

**d)** Is it possible to insert a point *P* within the figure so the figure has 180° rotational symmetry about point *P*? Explain your answer.

## Challenge Problems/Group Activities

**55.** *Glide Reflection, Order* Examine the figure below and then do the following:

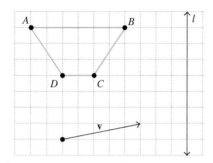

**a)** Determine a glide reflection of trapezoid *ABCD* by first applying translation vector **v** and then reflecting about the line *l*. Label the glide reflection *A′B′C′D′*.

**b)** In this step, we will reverse the order of the translation and the reflection. First reflect trapezoid *ABCD* about the line *l* and then translate the reflection using vector **v**. Label the resulting figure *A″B″C″D″*.

**c)** Is figure *A′B′C′D′* in the same position as figure *A″B″C″D″*?

**d)** What can be said about the order of the translation and the reflection used in a glide reflection? Is the figure obtained in part (a) or part (b) the glide reflection?

**56.** *Tessellation with a Square* Create a unique tessellation from a square piece of cardboard by using the method described on page 536. Be creative, using color and sketches to complete your tessellation.

**57.** *Tessellation with a Hexagon* Using the method described on page 536, create a unique tessellation using a regular hexagon like the one shown below. Be creative, using color and sketches to complete your tessellation.

**58.** *Tessellation with an Octagon?*

Trace the regular octagon, shown below, onto a separate piece of paper.

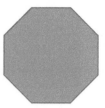

Try to create a regular tessellation by tracing this octagon repeatedly. Attempt to cover the entire piece of paper where no two octagons overlap each other. What conclusion can you draw about using a regular octagon as a tessellating shape?

**59.** *Tessellation with a Pentagon?* Repeat Exercise 58 using the regular pentagon below instead of a regular octagon.

## Recreational Mathematics

**60.** Examine each capital letter in the alphabet and determine which letters have reflective symmetry about a horizontal line through the center of the letter.

**61.** Examine each capital letter in the alphabet and determine which letters have reflective symmetry about a vertical line through the center of the letter.

**62.** Examine each capital letter in the alphabet and determine which letters have 180° rotational symmetry about a point in the center of the letter.

## Internet/Research Activities

**63.** In the study of biology, reflective symmetry is called *bilateral symmetry* and rotational symmetry is called *radial symmetry*. Do research and write a report on the role symmetry plays in the study of biology.

**64.** Write a paper on the mathematics displayed in the artwork of M. C. Escher. Include such topics as tessellations, optical illusions, perspective, and non-Euclidean geometry.

Topology

Examine the outline of the map of the continental United States shown below. Now suppose you were given four crayons, each of a different color. Could you color this map with the four crayons in a way so that no two bordering states have the same color? In this section, we will discuss this question and many other questions that are relevant to the branch of mathematics known as *topology*.

**Why** *This is Important* Topology is used in many applications in the fields of map making (cartography), computer science, robotics, and biology.

▲ *How many different colors are needed so that no two bordering states share the same color?*

The branch of mathematics called *topology* is sometimes referred to as "rubber sheet geometry" because it deals with bending and stretching of geometric figures.

One of the first pioneers of topology was the German astronomer and mathematician August Ferdinand Möbius (1790–1866). A student of Gauss, Möbius was the director of the University of Leipzig's observatory. He spent a great deal of time studying geometry and he played an essential part in the systematic development of projective geometry. He is best known for his studies of the properties of one-sided surfaces, including the one called the Möbius strip.

## Möbius Strip

If you place a pencil on one surface of a sheet of paper and do not remove it from the sheet, you must cross the edge to get to the other surface. Thus, a sheet of paper has one edge and two surfaces. The sheet retains these properties even when crumpled into a ball. The *Möbius strip*, also called a *Möbius band*, is a one-sided, one-edged surface. You can construct one, as shown in Fig. 9.85, by (a) taking a strip of paper, (b) giving one end a half twist, and (c) taping the ends together.

The Möbius strip has some very interesting properties. To better understand these properties, perform the following experiments.

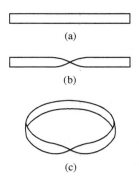

(a)

(b)

(c)

Figure 9.85

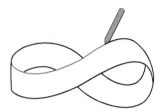

**Figure 9.86**

**Figure 9.87**

**Figure 9.88**

**Figure 9.89**

*Experiment 1* Make a Möbius strip using a strip of paper and tape as illustrated in Fig. 9.85. Place the point of a felt-tip pen on the edge of the strip (Fig. 9.86). Pull the strip slowly so that the pen marks the edge; do not remove the pen from the edge. Continue pulling the strip and observe what happens.

*Experiment 2* Make a Möbius strip. Place the tip of a felt-tip pen on the surface of the strip (Fig. 9.87). Pull the strip slowly so that the pen marks the surface. Continue and observe what happens.

*Experiment 3* Make a Möbius strip. Use scissors to make a small slit in the middle of the strip. Starting at the slit, cut along the strip, keeping the scissors in the middle of the strip (Fig. 9.88). Continue cutting and observe what happens.

*Experiment 4* Make a Möbius strip. Make a small slit at a point about one-third of the width of the strip. Cut along the strip, keeping the scissors the same distance from the edge (Fig. 9.89). Continue cutting and observe what happens.

If you give a strip of paper several twists, you get variations on the Möbius strip. To a topologist, the important distinction is between an odd number of twists, which leads to a one-sided surface, and an even number of twists, which leads to a two-sided surface. All strips with an odd number of twists are topologically the same as a Möbius strip, and all strips with an even number of twists are topologically the same as an ordinary cylinder, which has no twists.

## Klein Bottle

Another topological object is the punctured *Klein bottle*; see Fig. 9.90. This object, named after Felix Klein (1849–1925), resembles a bottle but only has one side.

A punctured Klein bottle can be made by stretching a hollow piece of glass tubing. The neck is then passed through a hole and joined to the base.

Look closely at the model of the Klein bottle shown in Fig. 9.90. The punctured Klein bottle has only one edge and no outside or inside because it has just one side. Figure 9.91 shows a Klein bottle blown in glass by Alan Bennett of Bedford, England.

Imagine trying to paint a Klein bottle. You start on the "outside" of the large part and work your way down the narrowing neck. When you cross the self-intersection, you have to pretend temporarily that it is not there, so you continue to

Limericks from unknown writers:

"A mathematician confided
That a Möbius band is one-sided,
And you'll get quite a laugh
If you cut one in half
For it stays in one piece when divided."

"A mathematician named Klein
Thought the Möbius band was divine.
He said, 'If you glue
the edges of two
You'll get a weird bottle like mine.' "

**Figure 9.90**

**Figure 9.91** *Klein bottle,* a one-sided surface, blown in glass by Alan Bennett.

follow the neck, which is now inside the bulb. As the neck opens up, to rejoin the bulb, you find that you are now painting the inside of the bulb! What appear to be the inside and outside of a Klein bottle connect together seamlessly since it is one-sided.

If a Klein bottle is cut along a curve, the results are two (one-twist) Möbius strips; see Fig. 9.92. Thus, a Klein bottle could also be made by gluing together two Möbius strips along the edges.

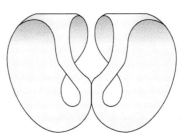

**Figure 9.92** Two Möbius strips result from cutting a Klein bottle along a curve.

## Maps

Mapmakers have known for a long time that regardless of the complexity of the map and whether it is drawn on a flat surface or a sphere, only four colors are needed to differentiate each country (or state) from its immediate neighbors. Thus, every map can be drawn by using only four colors, and no two countries with a common border will have the same color. Regions that meet at only one point (such as the states of Arizona, Colorado, Utah, and New Mexico) are not considered to have a common border. In Fig. 9.93(a), no two states with a common border are marked with the same color.

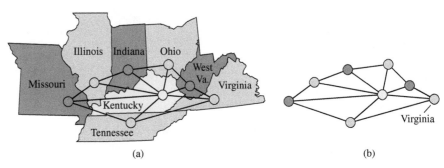

**Figure 9.93**

The "four-color" problem was first suggested by a student of Augustus DeMorgan in 1852. In 1976, Kenneth Appel and Wolfgang Haken of the University of Illinois—using their ingenuity, logic, and 1200 hours of computer time—succeeded in proving that only four colors are needed to draw a map. They solved the four-color map problem by reducing any map to a series of points and connecting line segments. They replaced each country with a point. They connected two countries having a common border with a straight line; see Fig. 9.93(b). They then showed that the points of any graph in the plane could be colored by using only four colors in such a way that no two points connected by the same line were the same color.

Mathematicians have shown that, on different surfaces, more than four colors may be needed to draw a map. For example, a map drawn on a Möbius strip requires

**Topological Paper Constructions**

In addition to the Möbius strip, many other interesting surfaces can be made using paper, scissors, and cellophane tape. Shown above is a surface that shares some of the same characteristics as a Möbius strip, but is not topologically equivalent to a Möbius strip. Notice that, like a Möbius strip, this surface has 1 side and 1 edge.

Construct the surface shown above using two strips of paper, scissors, and tape. Attempt to cut the surface "in half" by making a small slit along a dashed line in the middle of the paper surface. Then cut along the dashed line shown in the figure, keeping the scissors the same distance from the edge. What happens? Exercise 45 on page 549 describes another topological construction.

Many Internet Web sites are devoted to topological constructions. One such Web site is www.woollythoughts.com/mobius.html. This Web site demonstrates a Möbius strip made with a zipper. This process allows you to "cut" the Möbius strip and then put the two parts back together again.

a maximum of six colors, as in Fig. 9.94(a). A map drawn on a torus (the shape of a doughnut) requires a maximum of seven colors, as in Fig. 9.94(b).

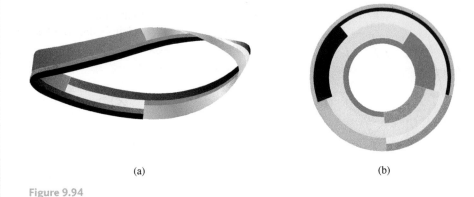

(a)                                   (b)

Figure 9.94

## Jordan Curves

A *Jordan curve* is a topological object that can be thought of as a circle twisted out of shape; see Fig. 9.95 (a)–(d). Like a circle, it has an inside and an outside. To get from one side to the other, at least one line must be crossed. Consider the Jordan curve in Fig. 9.95(d). Are points $A$ and $B$ inside or outside the curve?

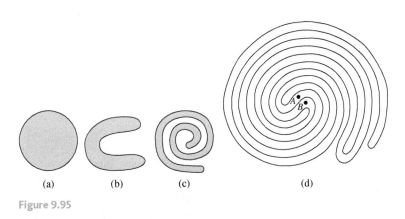

(a)          (b)          (c)                    (d)

Figure 9.95

A quick way to tell whether the two dots are inside or outside the curve is to draw a straight line from each dot to a point that is clearly outside the curve. If the straight line crosses the curve an even number of times, the dot is outside. If the straight line crosses the curve an odd number of times, the dot is inside the curve. Can you explain why this procedure works? Determine whether point $A$ and point $B$ are inside or outside the curve (see Exercises 17 and 18 at the end of this section).

## Topological Equivalence

Someone once said that a topologist is a person who does not know the difference between a doughnut and a coffee cup. Two geometric figures are said to be *topologically equivalent* if one figure can be elastically twisted, stretched, bent, or shrunk into the other figure without puncturing or ripping the original figure. If a doughnut is made of elastic material, it can be stretched, twisted, bent, shrunk, and distorted until it resembles a coffee cup with a handle, as shown in Fig. 9.96 on page 547. Thus, the doughnut and the coffee cup are topologically equivalent.

In topology, figures are classified according to their *genus*. The *genus* of an object is determined by the number of holes that go *through* the object. A cup and a doughnut each have one hole and are of genus 1 (and are therefore topologically equivalent). Notice that the cup's handle is considered a hole, whereas the opening at the rim of the cup is not considered a hole. For our purposes, we will consider an object's opening a hole if you could pour liquid *through* the opening. For example, a typical bowling ball has three openings in the surface into which you can put your fingers when preparing to roll the ball, but liquid cannot be poured *through* any of these openings. Therefore, a bowling ball has genus 0 and is topologically equivalent to a marble. Figure 9.97 illustrates the genus of several objects.

| Genus 0 | Genus 1 | Genus 2 | Genus 3 or more |
|---|---|---|---|
| Marble | Doughnut | Kettle | Strainer |
| Bowling Ball | Coffee Cup | Scissors | Grater |

**Figure 9.96**

**Figure 9.97**

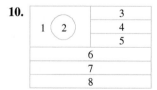
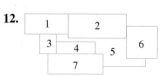

## SECTION 9.6
### *Exercises*

### Warm Up Exercises

*In Exercises 1–8, fill in the blanks with an appropriate word, phrase, or symbol(s).*

**1.** Because it deals with bending and stretching of geometric figures, topology is sometimes referred to as _____ sheet geometry.

**2.** A one-sided, one-edged surface is a(n) _____ strip.

**3.** A topological object that resembles a bottle but has only one side is a(n) _____ bottle.

**4.** If you color a map of the United States, the maximum number of colors needed so that no two states that share a common border have the same color is _____.

**5.** A topological object that can be thought of as a circle twisted out of shape is a(n) _____ curve.

**6.** The number of holes that go through an object determines the _____ of the object.

**7.** A compact disc is an example of an object that has a genus of _____.

**8.** A pair of scissors is an example of an object that has a genus of _____.

### Practice the Skills

*In Exercises 9–12, color the map by using a maximum of four colors so that no two regions with a common border have the same color.*

**9.**

**10.**

| 1 | 2 | 3 |
| | | 4 |
| | | 5 |
| | 6 | |
| | 7 | |
| | 8 | |

**11.**

**12.**

***Using the Four-Color Theorem*** *In Exercises 13–16, maps show certain areas of the United States, Canada, and Mexico. Shade in the states (or provinces) using a maximum of four colors so that no two states (or provinces) with a common border have the same color.*

**13.**

**14.**

**15.**

**16.**

**17.** Determine whether point *A* in Fig. 9.95(d) on page 546 is inside or outside the Jordan curve.

**18.** Determine whether point *B* in Fig. 9.95(d) is inside or outside the Jordan curve.

*At right is a Jordan curve. In Exercises 19–22, determine if the point is inside or outside the curve.*

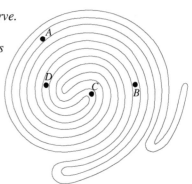

**19.** Point *A*

**20.** Point *B*

**21.** Point *C*

**22.** Point *D*

*In Exercises 23–34, give the genus of the object. If the object has a genus larger than 5, write "larger than 5."*

**23.**

**24.**

**25.**

**26.**

**27.**

**28.**

**29.**

**30.**

**31.**

**32.**

**33.**      **34.**

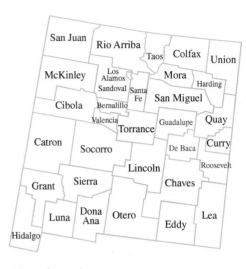

**35.** Name at least three objects not mentioned in this section that have

  **a)** genus 0.       **b)** genus 1.

  **c)** genus 2.       **d)** genus 3 or more.

**36.** Use the result of Experiment 1 on page 544 to find the number of edges on a Möbius strip.

**37.** Use the result of Experiment 2 on page 544 to find the number of surfaces on a Möbius strip.

**38.** How many separate strips are obtained in Experiment 3 on page 544?

**39.** How many separate strips are obtained in Experiment 4 on page 544?

**40.** Make a Möbius strip. Cut it one-third of the way from the edge, as in Experiment 4 on page 544. You should get two loops, one going through the other. Determine whether either (or both) of these loops is itself a Möbius strip.

**41. a)** Take a strip of paper, give it one full twist, and connect the ends. Is the result a Möbius strip with only one side? Explain.

  **b)** Determine the number of edges, as in Experiment 1.

  **c)** Determine the number of surfaces, as in Experiment 2.

  **d)** Cut the strip down the middle. What is the result?

**42.** Take a strip of paper, make one whole twist and another half twist, and then tape the ends together. Test by a method of your choice to determine whether this has the same properties as a Möbius strip.

## Challenge Problems/Group Activities

**43.** Using clay (or glazing compound), make a doughnut. Without puncturing or tearing the doughnut, reshape it into a topologically equivalent figure, a cup with a handle.

**44.** Using at most four colors, color the following map of the counties of New Mexico. Do not use the same color for any two counties that share a common border.

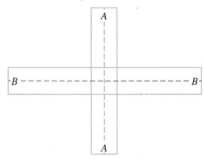

## Recreational Math

**45.** *Topological Paper Constructions* Using paper, scissors, and tape, perform the construction described in the *Recreational Mathematics* box on page 546. Once you have completed the construction, cut along the dashed line as instructed. Set the result aside.

  In this exercise we will construct another interesting surface. We begin by constructing a "cross" shape from two strips of paper, as shown below, using scissors and tape. Note the red dashed line and the green dashed line and the ends of the strips labeled *A* or *B*.

  Next, using tape connect the two ends labeled *A without* twisting the ends. Then, connect the two ends labeled *B* by giving one end a half twist. The strip that connects the *B* ends should resemble a Möbius strip. Finally, cut the object first along the green dashed line and then along the red dashed line. Compare the result with that from the construction on page 546. What do you notice?

## Internet/Research Activities

**46.** Use the Internet to find a map of your state that shows the outline of all the counties within your state. Print this map and, using at most four colors, color it. Do not use the same color for any two counties that share a common border.

**47.** The short story *Paul Bunyan versus the Conveyor Belt* (1947) by William Hazlett Upson focuses on a conveyor belt in the shape of a Möbius strip. The story can be found in several books that include mathematical essays. Read Upson's short story and write a 200-word description of what Paul Bunyan does to the conveyor belt. Confirm the outcome of the story by repeating Paul's actions with a paper Möbius strip.

# Non-Euclidean Geometry and Fractal Geometry

▲ *Many branches of geometry are needed to accurately represent space.*

Ponder the following question: Given a line *l* and a point *P* not on the line *l*, how many lines can you draw through *P* that are parallel to *l*?

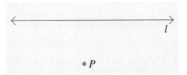

You may answer that only one line may be drawn through *P* parallel to *l*. This answer would be correct *provided* the setting of the problem is in a plane and not on the surface of a curved object. The study of this question led to the development of several new branches of geometry. It is now believed all of these branches of geometry, taken together, can be used to accurately represent space. In this section, we will study the geometry of surfaces other than the geometry of the plane.

**Why** *This is Important* Scientists now believe that space and time can best be represented using a combination of these different branches of geometry. In addition, many applications of the geometry described in this section are used in modern technology, such as cellular phones, computer memory, and medical imaging.

## Non-Euclidean Geometry

In Section 9.1, we stated that postulates or axioms are statements to be accepted as true. In his book *Elements*, Euclid's fifth postulate was, "If a straight line falling on two straight lines makes the interior angles on the same side less than two right angles, the two straight lines, if produced indefinitely, meet on that side on which the angles are less than the two right angles."

Euclid's fifth axiom may be better understood by observing Fig. 9.98. The sum of angles *A* and *B* is less than the sum of two right angles (180°). Therefore, the two lines will meet if extended.

John Playfair (1748–1819), a Scottish physicist and mathematician, wrote a geometry book that was published in 1795. In his book, Playfair gave a logically equivalent interpretation of Euclid's fifth postulate. This version is often referred to as Playfair's postulate or the Euclidean parallel postulate.

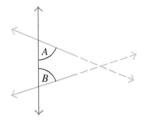

**Figure 9.98**

### The Euclidean Parallel Postulate
Given a line and a point not on the line, one and only one line can be drawn through the given point parallel to the given line ( Fig. 9.99).

The Euclidean parallel postulate may be better understood by looking at Fig. 9.99. Many mathematicians after Euclid believed that this postulate was not as self-evident as the other nine postulates given by Euclid. Others believed that this postulate could be proved from the other nine postulates and therefore was not needed at all. Of the many attempts to prove that the fifth postulate was not needed, the most noteworthy one was presented by Girolamo Saccheri (1667–1733), a Jesuit

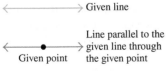

**Figure 9.99**

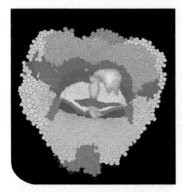
priest in Italy. In the course of his elaborate chain of deductions, Saccheri proved many of the theorems of what is now called hyperbolic geometry. However, Saccheri did not realize what he had done. He believed that Euclid's geometry was the only "true" geometry and concluded that his own work was in error. Thus, Saccheri narrowly missed receiving credit for a great achievement: the founding of *non-Euclidean geometry*.

Over time, geometers became more and more frustrated at their inability to prove Euclid's fifth postulate. One of them, a Hungarian named Farkos Bolyai, in a letter to his son, Janos Bolyai, wrote, "I entreat you leave the science of parallels alone.... I have traveled past all reefs of this infernal dead sea and have always come back with a broken mast and torn sail." The son, refusing to heed his father's advice, continued to think about parallels until, in 1823, he saw the whole truth and enthusiastically declared, "I have created a new universe from nothing." He recognized that geometry branches in two directions, depending on whether Euclid's fifth postulate is applied. He recognized two different geometries and published his discovery as a 24-page appendix to a textbook written by his father. The famous mathematician George Bruce Halsted called it "the most extraordinary two dozen pages in the whole history of thought." Farkos Bolyai proudly presented a copy of his son's work to his friend Carl Friedrich Gauss, then Germany's greatest mathematician, whose reply to the father had a devastating effect on the son. Gauss wrote, "I am unable to praise this work.... To praise it would be to praise myself. Indeed, the whole content of the work, the path taken by your son, the results to which he is led, coincides almost entirely with my meditations which occupied my mind partly for the last thirty or thirty-five years." We now know from his earlier correspondence that Gauss had indeed been familiar with *hyperbolic geometry* even before Janos was born. In his letter, Gauss also indicated that it was his intention not to let his theory be published during his lifetime, but to record it so that the theory would not perish with him. It is believed that the reason Gauss did not publish his work was that he feared being ridiculed by other prominent mathematicians of his time.

At about the same time as Bolyai's publication, Nikolay Ivanovich Lobachevsky, a Russian, published a paper that was remarkably like Bolyai's, although it was quite independent of it. Lobachevsky made a deeper investigation and wrote several books. In marked contrast to Bolyai, who received no recognition during his lifetime, Lobachevsky received great praise and became a professor at the University of Kazan.

After the initial discovery, little attention was paid to the subject until 1854, when G. F. Bernhard Riemann (1826–1866), a student of Gauss, suggested a second type of non-Euclidean geometry, which is now called *spherical, elliptical*, or *Riemannian geometry*. The hyperbolic geometry of his predecessors was synthetic; that is, it was not based on or related to any concrete model when it was developed. Riemann's geometry was closely related to the theory of surfaces. A *model* may be considered a physical interpretation of the undefined terms that satisfies the axioms. A model may be a picture or an actual physical object.

The two types of non-Euclidean geometries we have mentioned are elliptical geometry and hyperbolic geometry. The major difference among the three geometries lies in the fifth axiom. The fifth axiom of the three geometries is summarized here.

### The Fifth Axiom of Geometry

| Euclidean | Elliptical | Hyperbolic |
|---|---|---|
| Given a line and a point not on the line, one and only one line can be drawn parallel to the given line through the given point | Given a line and a point not on the line, no line can be drawn through the given point parallel to the given line. | Given a line and a point not on the line, two or more lines can be drawn through the given point parallel to the given line. |

To understand the fifth axiom of the two non-Euclidean geometries, remember that the term *line* is undefined. Thus, a line can be interpreted differently in different geometries. A model for Euclidean geometry is a plane, such as a blackboard (Fig. 9.100a). A model for elliptical geometry is a sphere (Fig. 9.100b). A model for hyperbolic geometry is a pseudosphere (Fig. 9.100c). A pseudosphere is similar to two trumpets placed bell to bell. Obviously, a line on a plane cannot be the same as a line on either of the other two figures.

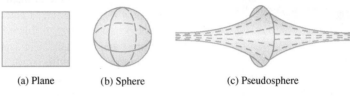

(a) Plane          (b) Sphere          (c) Pseudosphere

**Figure 9.100**

## Elliptical Geometry

A circle on the surface of a sphere is called a great circle if it divides the sphere into two equal parts. If we were to cut through a sphere along a great circle, we would have two identical pieces. If we interpret a line to be a great circle, then the two red curves in Fig. 9.101(a) are lines. Figure 9.101(a) shows that the fifth axiom of elliptical geometry is true. Two great circles on a sphere must intersect; hence, there can be no parallel lines ( Fig. 9.101a).

If we were to construct a triangle on a sphere, the sum of its angles would be greater than 180° (Fig. 9.101b). The theorem "The sum of the measures of the angles of a triangle is greater than 180°" has been proven by means of the axioms of elliptical geometry. The sum of the measures of the angles varies with the area of the triangle and gets closer to 180° as the area decreases.

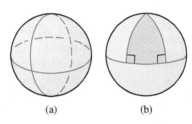

(a)          (b)

**Figure 9.101**

## Hyperbolic Geometry

Lines in hyperbolic geometry*are represented by geodesics on the surface of a pseudosphere. A *geodesic* is the shortest and least-curved arc between two points on a surface. Figure 9.102 shows two different lines represented by geodesics on the surface of a pseudosphere. For simplicity of the diagrams, we only show one of the "bells" of the pseudosphere.

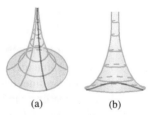

(a)          (b)

**Figure 9.102**

---

*A formal discussion of hyperbolic geometry is beyond the scope of this text.

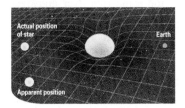
Albert Einstein's general theory of relativity, published in 1916, approached space and time differently from our everyday understanding of them. Einstein's theory unites the three dimensions of space with one of time in a four-dimensional space–time continuum. His theory dealt with the path that light and objects take while moving through space under the force of gravity. Einstein conjectured that mass (such as stars and planets) caused space to be curved. The greater the mass, the greater the curvature.

To prove his conjecture, Einstein exposed himself to Riemann's non-Euclidean geometry. Einstein believed that the trajectory of a particle in space represents not a straight line but the straightest curve possible, a geodesic. Einstein's theory was confirmed by the solar eclipses of 1919 and 1922.

Space–time is now thought to be a combination of three different types of curvature: spherical (described by Riemannian geometry), flat (described by Euclidean geometry), and saddle-shaped (described by hyperbolic geometry).

"The Great Architect of the universe now appears to be a great mathematician."
British physicist Sir James Jeans

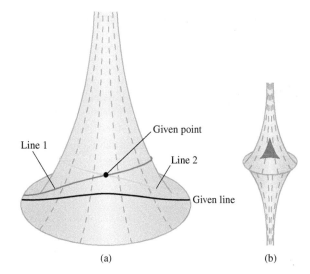

Figure 9.103

Figure 9.103(a) illustrates the fifth axiom of hyperbolic geometry. The diagram illustrates one way that, through the given point, two lines are drawn parallel to the given line. If we were to construct a triangle on a pseudosphere, the sum of the measures of the angles would be less than 180° (Fig. 9.103b). The theorem "The sum of the measures of the angles of a triangle is less than 180°" has been proven by means of the axioms of hyperbolic geometry.

We have stated that the sum of the measures of the angles of a triangle is 180°, is greater than 180°, and is less than 180°. Which statement is correct? Each statement is correct *in its own geometry.* Many theorems hold true for all three geometries; vertical angles still have the same measure, we can uniquely bisect a line segment with a straightedge and compass alone, and so on.

The many theorems based on the fifth postulate may differ in each geometry. It is important for you to realize that each theorem proved is true *in its own geometry* because each is logically deduced from the given set of axioms of the geometry. No one system is the "best" system. Euclidean geometry may appear to be the one to use in the classroom, where the blackboard is flat. In discussions involving Earth as a whole, however, elliptical geometry may be the most useful since Earth is a sphere. If the object under consideration has the shape of a saddle or pseudosphere, hyperbolic geometry may be the most useful.

## Fractal Geometry

We are familiar with one-, two-, and three-dimensional figures. Many objects, however, are difficult to categorize as one-, two-, or three-dimensional. For example, how would you classify the irregular shapes we see in nature, such as a coastline, or the bark on a tree, or a mountain, or a path followed by lightning? For a long time mathematicians assumed that making realistic geometric models of natural shapes and figures was almost impossible, but the development of *fractal geometry* now makes it possible. Both color photos on the next page were made by using fractal geometry. The discovery and study of fractal geometry has been one of the most popular mathematical topics in recent times.

The word *fractal* (from the Latin word *fractus,* "broken up, fragmented") was first used in the mid-1970s by mathematician Benoit Mandelbrot to describe shapes that had several common characteristics, including some form of "self-similarity," as will be seen shortly in the Koch snowflake.

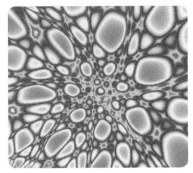

▲ *Fractal images*

Typical fractals are extremely irregular curves or surfaces that "wiggle" enough so that they are not considered one-dimensional. Fractals do not have integer dimensions; their dimensions are between 1 and 2. For example, a fractal may have a dimension of 1.26. Fractals are developed by applying the same rule over and over again, with the end point of each simple step becoming the starting point for the next step, in a process called *recursion*.

Using the recursive process, we will develop a famous fractal called the *Koch snowflake* named after Helga von Koch, a Swedish mathematician who first discovered its remarkable characteristics. The Koch snowflake illustrates a property of all fractals called *self-similarity*; that is, each smaller piece of the curve resembles the whole curve.

To develop the Koch snowflake:

1. Start with an equilateral triangle (Step 1, Fig. 9.104).

2. Whenever you see an edge —— replace it with ⁀⁀ (Steps 2–4).

What is the perimeter of the snowflake in Fig. 9.104, and what is its area? A portion of the boundary of the Koch snowflake known as the Koch curve, or the snowflake curve, is represented in Fig. 9.105.

The Koch curve consists of infinitely many pieces of the form ⁀⁀. Notice that after each step, the perimeter is $\frac{4}{3}$ times the perimeter of the previous step. Therefore, the Koch snowflake has an infinite perimeter. It can be shown that the area of the snowflake is 1.6 times the area of the starting equilateral triangle. Thus, the area of the snowflake is finite. The Koch snowflake has a finite area enclosed by an infinite boundary! This fact may seem difficult to accept, but it is true. However, the Koch snowflake, like other fractals, is not an everyday run-of-the-mill geometric shape.

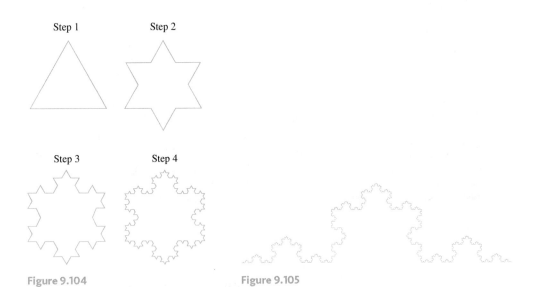

Figure 9.104                Figure 9.105

Let us look at a few more fractals made using the recursive process. We will now construct what is known as a *fractal tree.* Start with a tree trunk (Fig. 9.106a on page 555). Draw two branches, each one a bit smaller than the trunk (Fig. 9.106b). Draw two branches from each of those branches, and continue; see Fig. 9.106(c) and (d). Ideally, we continue the process forever.

If you take a little piece of any branch and zoom in on it, it will look exactly like the original tree. Fractals are *scale independent*, which means that you cannot really tell whether you are looking at something very big or something very small because the fractal looks the same whether you are close to it or far from it.

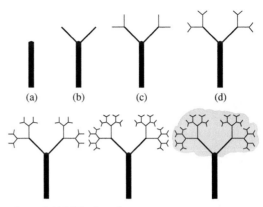

Figure 9.106 The fractal tree

In Figs. 9.107 and 9.108, we develop two other fractals through the process of recursion. Figure 9.107 shows a fractal called the Sierpinski triangle, and Fig. 9.108 shows a fractal called the Sierpinski carpet. Both fractals are named after Waclaw Sierpinski, a Polish mathematician who is best known for his work with fractals and space-filling curves.

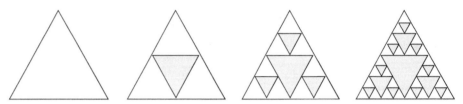

Figure 9.107 Sierpinski triangle

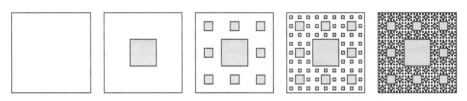

Figure 9.108 Sierpinski carpet

Fractals provide a way to study natural forms such as coastlines, trees, mountains, galaxies, polymers, rivers, weather patterns, brains, lungs, and blood supply. Fractals also help explain that which appears chaotic. The blood supply in the body is one example. The branching of arteries and veins appears chaotic, but closer inspection reveals that the same type of branching occurs for smaller and smaller blood vessels, down to the capillaries. Thus, fractal geometry provides a geometric structure for chaotic processes in nature. The study of chaotic processes is called *chaos theory*.

Fractals nowadays have a potentially important role to play in characterizing weather systems and in providing insight into various physical processes such as the occurrence of earthquakes or the formation of deposits that shorten battery life. Some scientists view fractal statistics as a doorway to unifying theories of medicine, offering a powerful glimpse of what it means to be healthy.

Fractals lie at the heart of current efforts to understand complex natural phenomena. Unraveling their intricacies could reveal the basic design principles at work in our world. Until recently, there was no way to describe fractals. Today, we are beginning to see such features everywhere. Tomorrow, we may look at the entire universe through a fractal lens.

## SECTION 9.7    *Exercises*

## Warm Up Exercises

*In Exercises 1–8, fill in the blanks with an appropriate word, phrase, or symbol(s).*

**1.** The fifth axiom of Euclidean geometry states that given a line and a point not on the line, one and only one line can be drawn through the given point _____ to the given line.

**2.** The fifth axiom of elliptical geometry states that given a line and a point not on the line, _____ line can be drawn through the given point parallel to the given line.

**3.** The fifth axiom of hyperbolic geometry states that given a line and a point not on the line, _____ or more lines can be drawn through the given point parallel to the given line.

**4.** A model for Euclidean geometry is a(n) _____.

**5.** A model for elliptical geometry is a(n) _____.

**6.** A model for hyperbolic geometry is a(n) _____.

**7.** The shortest and least-curved arc between two points on a surface is a(n) _____.

**8.** The study of chaotic processes is known as _____ theory.

## Practice the Skills

*In the following, we show a fractal-like figure made using a recursive process with the letter "M." In Exercises 9–12, use this fractal-like figure as a guide in constructing fractal-like figures with the letter given. Show three steps, as is done here.*

**9.** I        **10.** E        **11.** H        **12.** W

**13. a)** Develop a fractal by beginning with a square and replacing each side ——— with a ⌐⌐. Repeat this process twice.

   **b)** If you continue this process, will the fractal's perimeter be finite or infinite? Explain.

   **c)** Will the fractal's area be finite or infinite? Explain.

## Problem Solving/Group Activity

**14.** In forming the Koch snowflake in Figure 9.104 on page 554, the perimeter becomes greater at each step in the process. If each side of the original triangle is 1 unit, a general formula for the perimeter, $L$, of the snowflake at any step, $n$, may be found by the formula

$$L = 3\left(\frac{4}{3}\right)^{n-1}$$

For example, at the first step when $n = 1$, the perimeter is 3 units, which can be verified by the formula as follows:

$$L = 3\left(\frac{4}{3}\right)^{1-1} = 3\left(\frac{4}{3}\right)^{0} = 3 \cdot 1 = 3$$

At the second step, when $n = 2$, we find the perimeter as follows:

$$L = 3\left(\frac{4}{3}\right)^{2-1} = 3\left(\frac{4}{3}\right) = 4$$

Thus, at the second step the perimeter of the snowflake is 4 units.

**a)** Use the formula to complete the following table.

| Step | Perimeter |
|------|-----------|
| 1 | |
| 2 | |
| 3 | |
| 4 | |
| 5 | |
| 6 | |

**b)** Use the results of your calculations to explain why the perimeter of the Koch snowflake is infinite.

**c)** Explain how the Koch snowflake can have an infinite perimeter, but a finite area.

## Concept/Writing Exercises

**15.** What do we mean when we say that no one axiomatic system of geometry is "best"?

**16.** List the three types of curvature of space and the types of geometry that correspond to them.

**17.** List at least five natural forms that appear chaotic that we can study using fractals.

**18.** State the theorem concerning the sum of the measures of the angles of a triangle in

    **a)** Euclidean geometry.

    **b)** Hyperbolic geometry.

    **c)** Elliptical geometry.

*In Exercises 19–24 describe the accomplishments of the mathematician.*

**19.** Benoit Mandelbrot

**20.** G. F. Bernhard Riemann

**21.** Nikolay Ivanovich Lobachevsky

**22.** Carl Friedrich Gauss

**23.** Janos Bolyai

**24.** Girolamo Saccheri

## Internet/Research Activities

*In Exercises 25–27, references include the Internet, books on art, encyclopedias, and history of mathematics books.*

**25.** To complete his masterpiece *Circle Limit III*, M. C. Escher studied a model of hyperbolic geometry called the *Poincaré disk*. Write a paper on the Poincaré disk and how it was used in Escher's art. Include representations of *infinity* and the concepts of *point* and *line* in hyperbolic geometry.

▲ Escher's *Circle Limit III*

**26.** To transfer his two-dimensional tiling known as *Symmetry Work 45* to a sphere, M. C. Escher used the spherical geometry of Bernhard Riemann. Write a paper on Escher's use of geometry to complete this masterpiece.

**27.** Go to the Web site *Fantastic Fractals* at www.fantastic-fractals.com and study the information about fractals given there. Print copies, in color if a color printer is available, of the Mandlebrot set and the Julia set.

## CHAPTER 9   *Summary*

| Important Facts and Concepts | Examples and Discussion |
|---|---|
| **Section 9.1** | |
| **Point, line, plane, ray, half line, line segment, angle,** and related terms and definitions are discussed throughout Section 9.1. | Discussion, pages 480–482, Examples 1 and 2, pages 481–483 |
| Two angles are **complementary angles** if the sum of their measures is 90°. Two angles are **supplementary angles** if the sum of their measures is 180°. | Examples 3 and 4, pages 484 and 485 |
| **Vertical angles, alternate interior angles, alternate exterior angles,** and **corresponding angles** and related terms are discussed in Section 9.1 | Discussion, pages 485–486, Example 6, page 486 |
| **Section 9.2** | |
| The sum of the measures of the interior angles of an $n$-sided polygon is $(n-2)\,180°$. | Discussion, page 491, Example 1, page 491 |
| Two polygons are **similar** if their corresponding angles have the same measure and the lengths of their corresponding sides are in proportion. | Discussion, page 492, Examples 2–3, pages 493–494 |

Section 9.3
**Perimeter, P, and Area, A**

**TRIANGLE**

$$P = s_1 + s_2 + s_3 \quad (s_3 = b)$$
$$A = \tfrac{1}{2}bh$$

**SQUARE**

$$P = 4s$$
$$A = s^2$$

**RECTANGLE**

$$P = 2l + 2w$$
$$A = lw$$

**PARALLELOGRAM**

$$P = 2b + 2w$$
$$A = bh$$

**TRAPEZOID**

$$P = s_1 + s_2 + b_1 + b_2$$
$$A = \tfrac{1}{2}h(b_1 + b_2)$$

**Pythagorean Theorem**

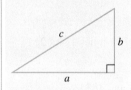

$$a^2 + b^2 = c^2$$

**Area, A, and Perimeter, P, of a Circle**

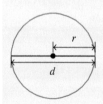

$$A = \pi r^2; \; C = 2\pi r \text{ or } C = \pi d$$

Discussion, pages 500–502, Example 1, page 502, Examples 3–5, pages 504–506

Example 2, page 503

Discussion, page 504, Examples 3–5, pages 504–506

## Section 9.4
### Volume, V, and Surface Area, SA

**CUBE**

$V = s^3$
$SA = 6s^2$

**RECTANGULAR SOLID**

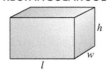

$V = lwh$
$SA = 2lw + 2wh + 2lh$

Discussion, pages 512–514,
Examples 1–8, pages 514–519

**CYLINDER**

$V = \pi r^2 h$
$SA = 2\pi rh + 2\pi r^2$

**CONE**

$V = \frac{1}{3}\pi r^2 h$
$SA = \pi r^2 + \pi r\sqrt{r^2 + h^2}$

**SPHERE**

$V = \frac{4}{3}\pi r^3$
$SA = 4\pi r^2$

**PYRAMID**

$V = \frac{1}{3}Bh$, where
$B$ is the area of the base

**PRISM**

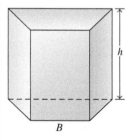

$V = Bh$, where $B$ is the area of the base

## Section 9.5
### Rigid Motions

The **rigid motions: Reflections, translations, rotations,** and **glide reflections** are defined and discussed throughout Section 9.5.

Discussion, pages 525–526, 528, 529, 532,
Examples 1–6, pages 526–532

**Reflective symmetry, rotational symmetry**, and **tessellations** are described in Section 9.5.

Discussion, pages 532–533, Examples 7–8,
pages 533–534

## Section 9.6
### Topology

**Möbius strip, Klein bottle, maps, Jordan curves,** and **topological equivalence** are described in Section 9.6.

Discussion, pages 543–547

## Section 9.7

**The Fifth Axiom**

**Fifth axiom in Euclidean geometry:** Given a line and a point not on the line, only one line can be drawn through the given point parallel to the given line.

**Fifth axiom in elliptical geometry:** Given a line and a point not on the line, no line can be drawn through the given point parallel to the given line.

**Fifth axiom in hyperbolic geometry:** Given a line and a point not on the line, two or more lines can be drawn through the given point parallel to the given line.

Discussion, pages 550–555

## CHAPTER 9  *Review Exercises*

### 9.1

*In Exercises 1–6, use the figure shown to determine the following.*

**1.** $\measuredangle ABF \cap \measuredangle DBI$

**2.** $\overrightarrow{AB} \cap \overrightarrow{DC}$

**3.** $\overline{BF} \cup \overline{FC} \cup \overline{BC}$

**4.** $\overrightarrow{BH} \cup \overrightarrow{HB}$

**5.** $\overleftrightarrow{HI} \cap \overleftrightarrow{EG}$

**6.** $\overrightarrow{CF} \cap \overrightarrow{CG}$

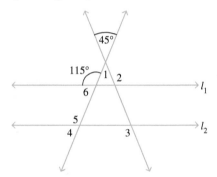

**7.** $m\measuredangle A = 35.4°$. Determine the measure of the complement of $\measuredangle A$.

**8.** $m\measuredangle B = 100.5°$. Determine the measure of the supplement $\measuredangle B$.

### 9.2

*In Exercises 9–12, use the similar triangles ABC and A′B′C shown to determine the following.*

**9.** The length of $\overline{BC}$

**10.** The length of $\overline{A'B'}$

**11.** $m\measuredangle BAC$

**12.** $m\measuredangle ABC$

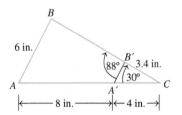

**13.** In the following figure, $l_1$ and $l_2$ are parallel lines. Determine $m\measuredangle 1$ through $m\measuredangle 6$.

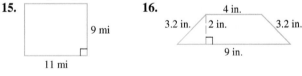

**14.** Determine the sum of the measures of the interior angles of an octagon.

### 9.3

*In Exercises 15–18, determine (a) the area and (b) the perimeter of the figure.*

**15.**

**16.**

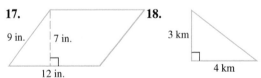

**17.**

**18.**

**19.** Determine (a) the area and (b) the circumference of the circle. Use the $\boxed{\pi}$ key on a calculator and round your answer to the nearest hundredth.

*In Exercises 20 and 21, determine the shaded area. When appropriate, use the $\boxed{\pi}$ key on your calculator and round your answer to the nearest hundredth.*

**20.**

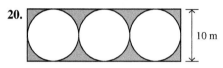

10 m

**21.**

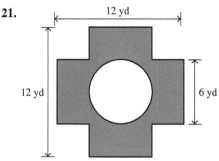

12 yd

12 yd                    6 yd

**22.** *Cost of Kitchen Tile* Determine the total cost of covering a 14-ft by 16-ft kitchen floor with ceramic tile. The cost of the tile selected is $5.25 per square foot.

## 9.4

*In Exercises 23–26, determine (a) the volume and (b) the surface area of the figure. When appropriate, use the $\boxed{\pi}$ key on your calculator and round your answer to the nearest hundredth.*

**23.**                                    **24.**

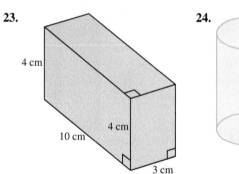

4 cm

4 cm
10 cm
3 cm

9 ft

3 ft

**25.**                                    **26.**

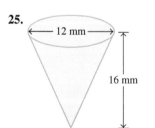

12 mm

16 mm

7 yd

*In Exercises 27 and 28, determine the volume of the figure.*

**27.**                                    **28.**

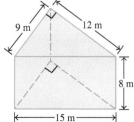

9 m        12 m

8 m

15 m

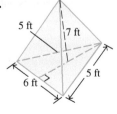

5 ft    7 ft

5 ft
6 ft

*In Exercises 29 and 30, determine the volume of the shaded area. When appropriate, use the $\boxed{\pi}$ key and round your answer to the nearest hundredth.*

**29.**                                    **30.**

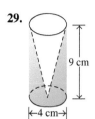

9 cm

4 cm

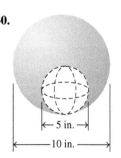

5 in.

10 in.

**31.** *Water Trough* Steven Dale has a water trough whose ends are trapezoids and whose sides are rectangles, as illustrated. He is afraid that the base it is sitting on will not support the weight of the trough when it is filled with water. He knows that the base will support 4800 lb.

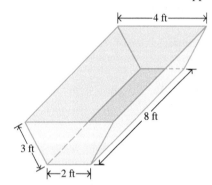

4 ft

8 ft

3 ft

2 ft

**a)** If the trough is filled with water, determine the number of cubic feet of water contained in the trough.

**b)** Determine the total weight, assuming that the trough weighs 375 lb and the water weighs 62.4 lb per cubic foot. Is the base strong enough to support the trough filled with water?

**c)** If 1 gal of water weighs 8.3 lb, how many gallons of water will the trough hold?

## 9.5

*In Exercises 32 and 33, use the given triangle and reflection lines to construct the indicated reflections. Show the triangle in the positions both before and after the reflection.*

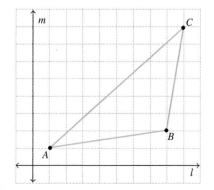

m

C

B

A

l

**32.** Construct the reflection of triangle *ABC* (see p. 561) about line *l*.

**33.** Construct the reflection of triangle *ABC* (see p. 561) about line *m*.

*In Exercises 34 and 35, use translation vectors **v** and **w** to construct the indicated translations. Show the rectangle in the positions both before and after the translation.*

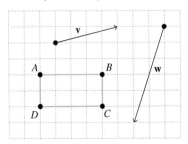

**34.** Construct the translation of rectangle *ABCD* using translation vector **v**.

**35.** Construct the translation of rectangle *ABCD* using translation vector **w**.

*In Exercises 36–38, use the given figure and rotation point P to construct the indicated rotations. Show the trapezoid in the positions both before and after the rotation.*

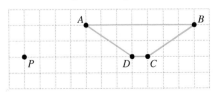

**36.** Construct a 90° rotation of trapezoid *ABCD* about point *P*.

**37.** Construct a 180° rotation of trapezoid *ABCD* about point *P*.

**38.** Construct a 270° rotation of trapezoid *ABCD* about point *P* .

*In Exercises 39 and 40, use the given figure, translation vector **v**, and reflection lines l and m to construct the indicated glide reflections. Show the triangle in the positions both before and after the glide reflection.*

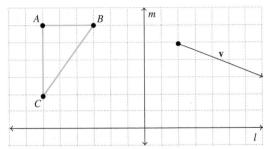

**39.** Construct a glide reflection of triangle *ABC* using vector **v** and reflection line *l*.

**40.** Construct a glide reflection of triangle *ABC* using vector **v** and reflection line *m*.

*In Exercises 41 and 42, use the following figure to answer the following questions.*

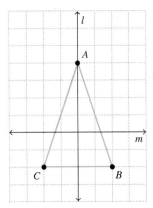

**41.** Does triangle *ABC* have reflective symmetry about line *l*? Explain.

**42.** Does triangle *ABC* have reflective symmetry about line *m*? Explain.

*In Exercises 43 and 44, use the following figure to answer the following questions.*

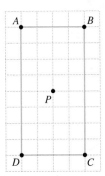

**43.** Does rectangle *ABCD* have 90° rotational symmetry about point *P*? Explain.

**44.** Does rectangle *ABCD* have 180° rotational symmetry about point *P*? Explain.

## 9.6

**45.** Give an example of an object that has

    **a)** genus 0.        **b)** genus 1.

    **c)** genus 2.        **d)** genus 3 or more.

**46.** Color the map by using a maximum of four colors so that no two regions with a common border have the same color.

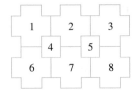

**47.** Determine whether point *A* is inside or outside the Jordan curve.

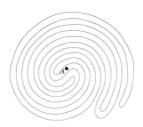

**48.** State the fifth axiom of Euclidean, elliptical, and hyperbolic geometry.

**49.** Develop a fractal by beginning with a square and replacing each side —— with a ⌐ㄴ. Repeat this process twice.

**50.** Construct a Koch snowflake by beginning with an equilateral triangle and replacing each side with a ⌃. Repeat this process twice.

## CHAPTER 9 ) Test

*In Exercises 1–4, use the figure to describe the following sets of points.*

**1.** $\overleftrightarrow{AF} \cap \overleftrightarrow{EF}$

**2.** $\overline{BC} \cup \overline{CD} \cup \overline{BD}$

**3.** $\angle EDF \cap \angle BDC$

**4.** $\overrightarrow{AC} \cup \overrightarrow{BA}$

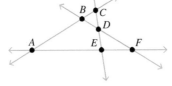

**5.** $m\angle A = 74.9°$. Determine the measure of the complement of $\angle A$.

**6.** $m\angle B = 10.4°$. Determine the measure of the supplement of $\angle B$.

**7.** In the figure, determine the measure of $\angle x$.

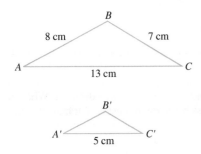

**8.** Determine the sum of the measures of the interior angles of a pentagon.

**9.** Triangles *ABC* and *A'B'C'* are similar figures. Determine the length of side $\overline{B'C'}$.

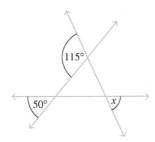

**10.** Right triangle *ABC* (see below) has one leg of length 12 in. and a hypotenuse of length 13 in.

a) Determine the length of the other leg.

b) Determine the perimeter of the triangle.

c) Determine the area of the triangle.

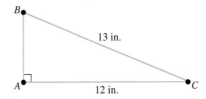

**11.** Determine (a) the volume and (b) the surface area of a sphere of diameter 14 cm.

**12.** Determine the volume of the shaded area. Use the $\boxed{\pi}$ key on your calculator and round your answer to the nearest hundredth.

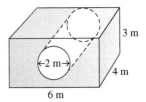

**13.** Determine the volume of the pyramid.

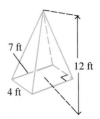

**14.** Construct a reflection of rectangle *ABCD*, shown below, about line *l*. Show the rectangle in the positions both before and after the reflection.

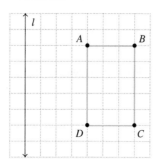

**15.** Construct a translation of quadrilateral *ABCD*, shown below, using translation vector **v**. Show the quadrilateral in the positions both before and after the translation.

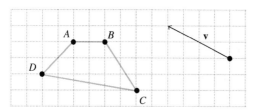

**16.** Construct a 180° rotation of triangle *ABC*, shown below, about rotation point *P*. Show the triangle in the positions both before and after the rotation.

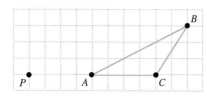

**17.** Construct a glide reflection of rectangle *ABCD*, shown below, using translation vector **v** and reflection line *l*. Show the rectangle in the positions both before and after the glide reflection.

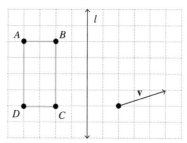

**18.** Use the figure below to answer the following questions.

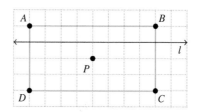

**a)** Does rectangle *ABCD* have reflective symmetry about line *l*? Explain.

**b)** Does rectangle *ABCD* have 180° rotational symmetry about point *P*? Explain.

**19.** What is a Möbius strip?

**20. a)** Sketch an object of genus 1.

**b)** Sketch an object of genus 2.

## GROUP PROJECTS

### Supporting a Hot Tub

**1.** Samantha Saraniti is thinking of buying a circular hot tub 12 ft in diameter, 4 ft deep, and weighing 475 lb. She wants to place the hot tub on a deck built to support 30,000 lb.

**a)** Determine the volume of the water in the hot tub in cubic feet.

**b)** Determine the number of gallons of water the hot tub will hold. (*Note:* 1 ft$^3$ ≈ 7.5 gal.)

**c)** Determine the weight of the water in the hot tub. (*Hint:* Fresh water weighs about 62.4 lb/ft$^3$.)

**d)** Will the deck support the weight of the hot tub and water?

**e)** Will the deck support the weight of the hot tub, water, and four people, whose average weight is 115 lb?

### Designing a Ramp

**2.** David and Sandra Jessee are planning to build a ramp so that the front entrance of their home is wheelchair accessible. The ramp will be 3 feet wide. It will rise 2 in. for each foot of length of horizontal distance. Where the ramp meets the porch, the ramp must be 2 ft high. To provide stability for the ramp, the Jessees will install a slab of concrete 4 in. thick and 6 in. longer and wider than the ramp (see accompanying figure on page 565). The top of the slab will be level with the ground. The ramp may be constructed of concrete or pressure-treated lumber. You are to estimate the cost of materials for constructing the slab, the ramp of concrete, and the ramp of pressure-treated lumber.

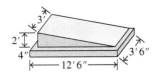

### Slab

a) Determine the length of the base of the ramp.

b) Determine the dimensions of the concrete slab on which the ramp will be set.

c) Determine the volume of the concrete in cubic yards needed to construct the slab.

d) If ready-mix concrete costs $45 per cubic yard, determine the cost of the concrete needed to construct the slab.

### Concrete Ramp

e) To build the ramp of concrete, a form in the shape of the ramp must be framed. The two sides of the form are triangular, and the shape of the end, which is against the porch, is rectangular. The form will be framed from $\frac{3}{4}$-in. plywood, which comes in 4 ft $\times$ 8 ft sheets. Determine the number of sheets of plywood needed. Assume that the entire sheet(s) will be used to make the sides and the end of the form and that there is no waste.

f) If the plywood costs $18.95 for a 4 ft $\times$ 8 ft sheet, determine the cost of the plywood.

g) To brace the form, the Jessees will need two boards 2 in. $\times$ 4 in. $\times$ 8 ft (referred to as 8-ft 2 $\times$ 4's) and six pieces of lumber 2 in. $\times$ 4 in. $\times$ 3 ft. These six pieces of lumber will be cut from 8-ft 2 $\times$ 4 boards. Determine the number of 8-ft 2 $\times$ 4 boards needed.

h) Determine the cost of the 8-ft 2 $\times$ 4 boards needed in part (g) if one board costs $2.14.

i) Determine the volume, in cubic yards, of concrete needed to fill the form.

j) Determine the cost of the concrete needed to fill the form.

k) Determine the total cost of materials for building the ramp of concrete by adding the results in parts (d), (f), (h), and (j).

### Wooden Ramp

l) Determine the length of the top of the ramp.

m) The top of the ramp will be constructed of $\frac{5}{4}$-in. $\times$ 6 in. $\times$ 10 ft pressure-treated lumber. The boards will be butted end to end to make the necessary length and will be supported from underneath by a wooden frame. Determine the number of boards needed to cover the top of the ramp. The boards are laid lengthwise on the ramp.

n) Determine the cost of the boards to cover the top of the ramp if the price of a 10-ft length is $6.47.

o) To support the top of the ramp, the Jessees will need 10 pieces of 8-ft 2 $\times$ 4's. The price of a pressure-treated 8-ft 2 $\times$ 4 is $2.44. Determine the cost of the supports.

p) Determine the cost of the materials for building a wooden ramp by adding the amounts from parts (d), (n), and (o).

q) Are the materials for constructing a concrete ramp or a wooden ramp less expensive?

# 12
# Probability

◄ *Probability is involved in all games of chance, determining the cost of car insurance, and weather forecasting.*

## What You Will Learn

- Empirical probability and theoretical probability
- Compound probability, conditional probability, and binomial probability
- Odds against an event and odds in favor of an event
- Expected value
- Tree diagrams
- Mutually exclusive events and independent events
- The counting principle, permutations, and combinations

## Why This is Important

Each year, millions of Americans play lotteries. If you play a lottery, your hope is to beat the odds and be the person with the winning numbers. Not satisfied with leaving things to chance, mathematicians of the sixteenth, seventeenth, and eighteenth centuries invented the study of probability to determine the likelihood of an event such as winning the lottery.

Although the rules of probability were first applied to gaming, they have many other applications. The cost of your car insurance, the weather forecast, the expected number of people who will attend an outdoor concert if it is raining all involve probability. In this chapter, we will learn many of the important concepts of probability that can help us make informed decisions in our lives.

**SECTION 12.1** The Nature of Probability

▲ *We can determine the probability of an event, such as the probability that a particular auto part will fail before the warranty expires, based on actual observations.*

How do researchers determine if a new potential drug is superior to a standard drug? How do automobile manufacturers determine the chance that a particular part will fail before the warranty expires? These and many other similar questions are answered through experimentation and observation of the results. Determining the chance of something happening in the future by observing past results is called empirical probability.

**Why** *This is Important* Understanding how to calculate probabilities based on past experience is essential to our daily lives. Empirical probability is used to determine insurance premiums and the length of a warranty. It is also used in medical and genetics research, as well as many other areas.

I n this section we introduce some basic concepts of probability including the Law of Large Numbers.

## History

Probability is used in many areas, including public finance, medicine, insurance, elections, manufacturing, educational tests and measurements, genetics, weather forecasting, investments, opinion polls, the natural sciences, and games of chance. The study of probability originated from the study of games of chance. Archaeologists have found artifacts used in games of chance in Egypt dating from about 3000 B.C.

Mathematical problems relating to games of chance were studied by a number of mathematicians of the Renaissance. Italy's Girolamo Cardano (1501–1576) in his *Liber de Ludo Aleae* (book on the games of chance) presents one of the first systematic computations of probabilities. Although it is basically a gambler's manual, many consider it the first book ever written on probability. A short time later, two French mathematicians, Blaise Pascal (1623–1662) and Pierre de Fermat (1601–1665), worked together studying "the geometry of the die." In 1657, Dutch mathematician Christian Huygens (1629–1695) published *De Ratiociniis in Luno Aleae* (on ratiocination in dice games), which contained the first documented reference to the concept of mathematical expectation (see Section 12.4). Swiss mathematician Jacob Bernoulli (1654–1705), whom many consider the founder of probability theory, is said to have fused pure mathematics with the empirical methods used in statistical experiments. The works of Pierre-Simon de Laplace (1749–1827) dominated probability throughout the nineteenth century.

## The Nature of Probability

Before we discuss the meaning of the word *probability* and learn how to calculate probabilities, we must introduce a few definitions.

### Definition: **Experiment**
An **experiment** is a controlled operation that yields a set of results.

The process by which medical researchers administer experimental drugs to patients to determine their reaction is one type of experiment.

### Definition: **Outcomes**
The possible results of an experiment are called its **outcomes**.

## Profile In Mathematics

### Jacob Bernoulli (1654–1705)

Swiss mathematician Jacob Bernoulli was considered a pioneer of probability theory. He was part of a famous family of mathematicians and scientists. In *Ars Conjectand,* published posthumously in 1713, he proposed that an increased degree of accuracy can be obtained by increasing the number of trials of an experiment. This theorem, called Bernoulli's theorem (of probability), is also known as the law of large numbers. Bernoulli's theorem of fluid dynamics, used in aircraft wing design, was developed by Daniel Bernoulli (1700–1782). Daniel was one of Jacob's younger brother Johann's three sons.

▲ *A die (one of a pair of dice) contains six surfaces, called faces. Each face contains a unique number of dots, from 1 to 6. The sum of the dots on opposite surfaces is 7.*

For example, the possible outcomes from administering an experimental drug may be a favorable reaction, no reaction, or an adverse reaction.

> Definition: **Event**
> An **event** is a subcollection of the outcomes of an experiment.

For example, when a die is rolled, the event of rolling a number greater than 2 can be satisfied by any one of four outcomes: 3, 4, 5, or 6. The event of rolling a 5 can be satisfied by only one outcome, the 5 itself. The event of rolling an even number can be satisfied by any of three outcomes: 2, 4, or 6.

Probability is classified as either *empirical* (experimental) or *theoretical* (mathematical). *Empirical probability* is the relative frequency of occurrence of an event and is determined by actual observations of an experiment. *Theoretical probability* is determined through a study of the possible *outcomes* that can occur for the given experiment. We will indicate the probability of an event $E$ by $P(E)$, which is read "*P* of *E*."

## Empirical Probability

In this section, we will briefly discuss empirical probability. The emphasis in the remaining sections is on theoretical probability. Following is the formula for computing empirical probability, or relative frequency.

### Empirical Probability (Relative Frequency)
The empirical probability of an event, $P(E)$, can be determined by the following formula.

$$P(E) = \frac{\text{number of times event } E \text{ has occurred}}{\text{total number of times the experiment has been performed}}$$

The probability of an event, whether empirical or theoretical, is always a number between 0 and 1, inclusive, and may be expressed as a decimal number or a fraction. An empirical probability of 0 indicates that the event has never occurred. An empirical probability of 1 indicates that the event has always occurred.

┌ Example **1** *Heads Up!*

In 100 tosses of a fair coin, 44 landed heads up. Determine the empirical probability of the coin landing heads up.

Solution  Let $E$ be the event that the coin lands heads up. Then

$$P(E) = \frac{44}{100} = 0.44$$

┌ Example **2** *Blood Pressure Reduction*

A pharmaceutical company is testing a drug that is supposed to help reduce high blood pressure. The drug is given to 500 individuals with the following outcomes.

| Blood pressure reduced | Blood pressure unchanged | Blood pressure increased |
|---|---|---|
| 379 | 62 | 59 |

If this drug is given to an individual, determine the empirical probability that the person's blood pressure is (a) reduced, (b) unchanged, (c) increased.

*Solution*

a) Let $E$ be the event that the blood pressure is reduced.

$$P(E) = \frac{379}{500} = 0.758$$

b) Let $E$ be the event that the blood pressure is unchanged.

$$P(E) = \frac{62}{500} = 0.124$$

c) Let $E$ be the event that the blood pressure is increased.

$$P(E) = \frac{59}{500} = 0.118$$

*Empirical probability is used when probabilities cannot be theoretically calculated.* For example, life insurance companies use empirical probabilities to determine the chance of an individual in a certain profession, with certain risk factors, living to age 65.

## Empirical Probability in Genetics

Using empirical probability, Gregor Mendel (1822–1884) developed the laws of heredity by crossbreeding different types of "pure" pea plants and observing the relative frequencies of the resulting offspring. These laws became the foundation for the study of genetics. For example, when he crossbred a pure yellow pea plant and a pure green pea plant, the resulting offspring (the first generation) were always yellow; see Fig. 12.1(a). When he crossbred a pure round-seeded pea plant and a pure wrinkled-seeded pea plant, the resulting offspring (the first generation) were always round; see Fig. 12.1(b).

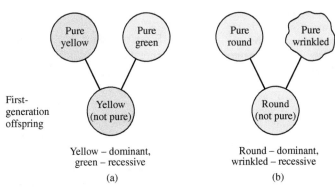

Figure 12.1

Mendel called traits such as yellow color and round seeds *dominant* because they overcame or "dominated" the other trait. He labeled the green color and the wrinkled traits *recessive*.

Mendel then crossbred the offspring of the first generation. The resulting second-generation offspring had both the dominant and the recessive traits of their grandparents; see Fig. 12.2(a) and 12.2(b) on page 678. What's more, these traits always appeared in approximately a 3 to 1 ratio of dominant to recessive.

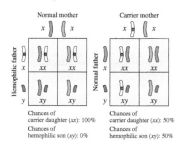
"The laws of probability, so true in general, so fallacious in particular."
Edward Gibbon, 1796

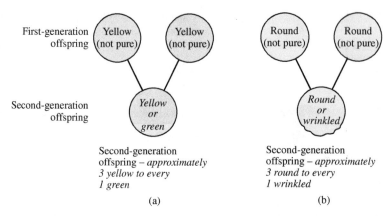

First-generation offspring: Yellow (not pure), Yellow (not pure) → Second-generation offspring: *Yellow or green*

Second-generation offspring – *approximately 3 yellow to every 1 green*

(a)

Round (not pure), Round (not pure) → *Round or wrinkled*

Second-generation offspring – *approximately 3 round to every 1 wrinkled*

(b)

Figure 12.2

Table 12.1 lists some of the actual results of Mendel's experiments with pea plants. Note that the ratio of dominant trait to recessive trait in the second-generation offspring is about 3 to 1 for each experiment. The empirical probability of the dominant trait has also been calculated. How would you find the empirical probability of the recessive trait?

Table 12.1 Second-Generation Offspring

| Dominant Trait | Number with Dominant Trait | Recessive Trait | Number with Recessive Trait | Ratio of Dominant to Recessive | P (Dominant Trait) |
|---|---|---|---|---|---|
| Yellow seeds | 6022 | Green seeds | 2001 | 3.01 to 1 | $\frac{6022}{8023} \approx 0.75$ |
| Round seeds | 5474 | Wrinkled seeds | 1850 | 2.96 to 1 | $\frac{5474}{7324} \approx 0.75$ |

From his work, Mendel concluded that the sex cells (now called gametes) of the pure yellow (dominant) pea plant carried some factor that caused the offspring to be yellow and that the gametes of the green variety had a variant factor that "induced the development of green plants." In 1909, Danish geneticist W. Johannsen called these factors "genes." Mendel's work led to the understanding that each pea plant contains two genes for color, one that comes from the mother and the other from the father. If the two genes are alike—for instance, both for yellow plants or both for green plants—the plant will be that color. If the genes for color are different, the plant will grow the color of the dominant gene. Thus, if one parent contributes a gene for the plant to be yellow (dominant) and the other parent contributes a gene for the plant to be green (recessive), the plant will be yellow.

## The Law of Large Numbers

Most of us accept that if a "fair coin" is tossed many, many times, it will land heads up approximately half of the time. Intuitively, we can guess that the probability that a fair coin will land heads up is $\frac{1}{2}$. Does that mean that if a coin is tossed twice, it will land heads up exactly once? If a fair coin is tossed 10 times, will there necessarily be five heads? The answer is clearly no. What, then, does it mean when we state that the

**Did You Know?**

**Batting Averages**

▲ Josh Hamilton

If Josh Hamilton of the the Texas Rangers gets three hits in his first three at bats of the season, he is batting a thousand (1.000). Over the course of the 162 games of the season (with three or four at bats per game), however, his batting average will fall closer to 0.359 (his 2010 major league leading batting average). In 2010, out of 518 at bats, Hamilton had 186 hits, an average above all other players' but much less than 1.000. His batting average is a relative frequency (or empirical probability) of hits to at bats. It is only the long-term average that we take seriously because it is based on the law of large numbers.

probability that a fair coin will land heads up is $\frac{1}{2}$? To answer this question, let's examine Table 12.2, which shows what may occur when a fair coin is tossed a given number of times.

Table 12.2

| Number of Tosses | Expected Number of Heads | Actual Number of Heads Observed | Relative Frequency of Heads |
|---|---|---|---|
| 10 | 5 | 4 | $\frac{4}{10} = 0.4$ |
| 100 | 50 | 45 | $\frac{45}{100} = 0.45$ |
| 1000 | 500 | 546 | $\frac{546}{1000} = 0.546$ |
| 10,000 | 5000 | 4852 | $\frac{4852}{10,000} = 0.4852$ |
| 100,000 | 50,000 | 49,770 | $\frac{49,770}{100,000} = 0.49770$ |

The far right column of Table 12.2, the relative frequency of heads, is a ratio of the number of heads observed to the total number of tosses of the coin. The relative frequency is the empirical probability, as defined earlier. Note that as the number of tosses increases, the relative frequency of heads gets closer and closer to $\frac{1}{2}$, or 0.5, which is what we expect.

The nature of probability is summarized by the law of large numbers.

## Definition:  Law of Large Numbers
The **law of large numbers** states that probability statements apply in practice to a large number of trials, not to a single trial. It is the relative frequency over the long run that is accurately predictable, not individual events or precise totals.

What does it mean to say that the probability of rolling a 2 on a die is $\frac{1}{6}$? It means that over the long run, on the average, one of every six rolls will result in a 2.

## SECTION 12.1  *Exercises*

### Warm Up Exercises

*In Exercises 1–6, fill in the blank with an appropriate word, phrase, or symbol(s).*

1. A controlled operation that yields a set of results is called a(n) _____.

2. The possible results of an experiment are called its _____.

3. A subcollection of the outcomes of an experiment is called a(n) _____.

4. Probability is classified as either theoretical probability or _____ probability.

5. Probability determined by the relative frequency of occurrence of an event, or actual observations of an experiment is called _____ probability.

6. Probability determined through a study of the possible outcomes that can occur for a given experiment is called _____ probability.

## Practice the Skills

**7. *Flip a Coin*** Flip a coin 50 times and record the results. Determine the empirical probability of flipping

**a)** a head.            **b)** a tail.

**c)** Does the probability of flipping a head appear to be the same as flipping a tail?

**8. *Pair of Dice*** Roll a pair of dice 60 times and record the sums. Determine the empirical probability of rolling a sum of

**a)** 2.            **b)** 7.

**c)** Does the probability of rolling a sum of 2 appear to be the same as the probability of rolling a sum of 7?

**9. *Roll a Die*** Roll a die 50 times and record the results. Determine the empirical probability of rolling

**a)** a 1.            **b)** a 4.

**c)** Does the probability of rolling a 1 appear to be the same as the probability of rolling a 4? Explain.

**10. *Two Coins*** Flip two coins 50 times and record the number of times exactly one head was obtained. Determine the empirical probability of flipping exactly one head.

## Problem Solving

**11. *Boat Rentals*** The last 30 boat rentals at Green Lakes Boat Rentals were 14 sunfish, 10 kayaks, and 6 rowboats. Use this information to determine the empirical probability that the next boat rental is a

**a)** sunfish.        **b)** kayak.        **c)** rowboat.

**12. *Music Purchases*** At the Virgin Music store in Times Square, 60 people entering the store were selected at random and were asked to choose their favorite type of music. Of the 60, 12 chose rock, 16 chose country, 8 chose classical, and 24 chose something other than rock, country, or classical. Determine the empirical probability that the next person entering the store favors

**a)** rock music.        **b)** country music.

**c)** something other than rock, country, or classical music.

**13. *Veterinarian*** In a given week, a veterinarian treated the following animals.

| Animal | Number Treated |
|--------|----------------|
| Dog    | 45             |
| Cat    | 40             |
| Bird   | 15             |
| Rabbit | 5              |

Determine the empirical probability that the next animal she treats is

**a)** a dog.        **b)** a cat.        **c)** a rabbit.

**14. *Prader–Willi Syndrome*** In a sample of 50,000 first-born babies, 5 were found to have Prader–Willi syndrome. Find the empirical probability that a family's first child will be born with this syndrome.

**15. *Studying Abroad*** The table below shows the 10 most popular destinations for U.S. college students studying abroad for the 2008–2009 school year.

| Destination | Number of Students |
|-------------|--------------------|
| United Kingdom | 31,342 |
| Italy | 27,362 |
| Spain | 24,169 |
| France | 16,910 |
| China | 13,674 |
| Australia | 11,140 |
| Germany | 8330 |
| Mexico | 7320 |
| Ireland | 6858 |
| Costa Rica | 6363 |
| Total | 153,468 |

Source: *Institute of International Education*

If a student were selected at random from those who studied abroad in 2008–2009 at one of the destinations in the table, determine the empirical probability that the student studied in

**a)** China.     **b)** Italy.     **c)** Australia.

**16.** *Travel Web Sites* The following table shows the number of visitors to the five most frequently visited travel Web sites in October 2010.

| Web Site | Number of Visitors |
|---|---|
| Trip Advisor | 24,000,000 |
| Yahoo! Travel | 23,250,000 |
| Expedia | 23,000,000 |
| Travelocity | 16,000,000 |
| Priceline | 15,000,000 |
| Total | 101,250,000 |

Source: ebizmba.com

Assuming this trend continues, if a person chooses to visit only one of the listed Web sites, determine the empirical probability the person will visit

**a)** Priceline.     **b)** Expedia.     **c)** Trip Advisor.

**17.** *Top-Selling Video Games* The following table shows the number of video games sold worldwide for the five highest-selling video games in 2010.

▲ *Wii Fit Plus*

| Title | Units Sold |
|---|---|
| Call of Duty: Black Ops | 18,880,000 |
| Wii Sports | 16,600,000 |
| Super Mario Bros.Wii | 11,310,000 |
| Wii Sports Resort | 11,290,000 |
| Wii Fit Plus | 8,870,000 |
| Total | 66,950,000 |

Source: vgchartz.com

Assuming this trend continues, if a person chooses to purchase a video game, determine the empirical probability that the person will purchase

**a)** Wii Sports.     **b)** Wii Fit Plus.

**c)** Call of Duty: Black Ops.

**18.** *Grade Distribution* Mr. Doole's grade distribution over the past 3 years for a course in college algebra is shown in the chart below.

| Grade | Number |
|---|---|
| A | 43 |
| B | 182 |
| C | 260 |
| D | 90 |
| F | 62 |
| I | 8 |

If Sue Gilligan plans to take college algebra with Mr. Doole, determine the empirical probability that she receives a grade of

**a)** A.     **b)** C.     **c)** D or higher.

**19.** *Election* In an election for student council president at Russell Sage College, 80 students were polled and asked for whom they planned to vote. The table shows the results of the poll.

| Candidate | Votes |
|---|---|
| Allison | 22 |
| Emily | 18 |
| Kimberly | 20 |
| Johanna | 14 |
| Other | 6 |

If one student from Russell Sage College is selected at random, determine the empirical probability that the person planned to vote for

**a)** Allison.     **b)** Emily.

**c)** Kimberly.     **d)** Johanna.

**e)** Someone other than the four people-listed above.

**20.** *Volunteer Hours* The graph below shows the average number of hours volunteered per week by Americans in 2009.

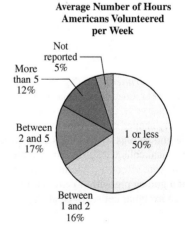

Source: CNCS (www.serve.gov)

If one American who participated in volunteer work is selected at random, determine the empirical probability the person volunteered

**a)** between 1 and 2 hours per week.

**b)** more than 5 hours per week.

**c)** between 2 and 5 hours per week.

**21.** *Hitting a Bull's-Eye* The pattern of hits shown on the target resulted from a marksman firing 20 rounds. For a single shot,

    **a)** determine the empirical probability that the marksman hits the 50-point bull's-eye (the center of the target).

    **b)** determine the empirical probability that the marksman does not hit the bull's-eye.

    **c)** determine the empirical probability that the marksman scores at least 20 points.

    **d)** determine the empirical probability that the marksman does not score any points (the area outside the large circle).

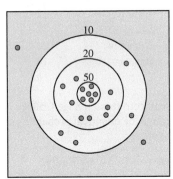

**22.** *Rock Toss* Jim Handy finds an irregularly shaped five-sided rock. He labels each side and tosses the rock 100 times. The results of his tosses are shown in the table. Determine the empirical probability that the rock will land on side 4 if tossed again.

| Side | 1 | 2 | 3 | 4 | 5 |
|------|----|----|----|----|----|
| Frequency | 32 | 18 | 15 | 13 | 22 |

**23.** *Cell Biology Experiment* An experimental serum was injected into 500 guinea pigs. Initially, 150 of the guinea pigs had circular cells, 250 had elliptical cells, and 100 had irregularly shaped cells. After the serum was injected, none of the guinea pigs with circular cells were affected, 50 with elliptical cells were affected, and all those with irregular cells were affected. Determine the empirical probability that a guinea pig with (a) circular cells, (b) elliptical cells, and (c) irregular cells will be affected by injection of the serum.

**24.** *Gender* In a large lecture hall there are 325 students of which 160 are male and 165 are female. If one student is

selected at random, determine the empirical probability the individual selected is

**a)** male.         **b)** female.

**25.** *Mendel's Experiment* In one of his experiments (see pages 677–678), Mendel crossbred nonpure purple flower pea plants. These purple pea plants had two traits for flowers, purple (dominant) and white (recessive). The result of this crossbreeding was 705 second-generation plants with purple flowers and 224 second-generation plants with white flowers. Determine the empirical probability of a second-generation plant having

**a)** white flowers.         **b)** purple flowers.

**26.** *Second-Generation Offspring* In another experiment, Mendel crossbred nonpure tall pea plants. As a result, the second-generation offspring were 787 tall plants and 277 short plants. Determine the empirical probability of a second-generation plant being

**a)** tall.         **b)** short.

## Concept/Writing Exercises

**27.** The theoretical probability of a coin landing heads up is $\frac{1}{2}$. Does this probability mean that if a coin is flipped two times, one flip will land heads up? If not, what does it mean?

**28.** To determine premiums, life insurance companies must compute the probable date of death. On the basis of a great deal of research, Mr. Duncan, age 36, is expected to live another 43.21 years. Does this determination mean that Mr. Duncan will live until he is 79.21 years old? If not, what does it mean?

**29. a)** Explain how you would find the empirical probability of rolling a 5 on a die.

    **b)** What do you believe is the empirical probability of rolling a 5?

    **c)** Determine the empirical probability of rolling a 5 by rolling a die 40 times.

**30.** The theoretical probability of rolling a 4 on a die is $\frac{1}{6}$. Does this probability mean that if a die is rolled six times one 4 will appear? If not, what does it mean?

## Challenge Problem/Group Activity

**31. a)** *Design an Experiment* Which do you believe is used more frequently in a magazine or newspaper article, the word *a* or the word *the*?

b) Design an experiment to determine the empirical probabilities (or relative frequencies) of the words *a* and *the* appearing in a magazine or newspaper article.

c) Perform the experiment in part (b) and determine the empirical probabilities.

d) Which word, *a* or *the*, appears to occur more frequently?

### Recreational Mathematics

**32.** *Cola Preference*  Can people selected at random distinguish Coke from Pepsi? Which do they prefer?

a) Design an experiment to determine the empirical probability that a person selected at random can select Coke when given samples of both Coke and Pepsi.

b) Perform the experiment in part (a) and determine the empirical probability.

c) Determine the empirical probability that a person selected at random will prefer Coke over Pepsi.

### Internet/Research Activities

**33.** Write a paper on how insurance companies use empirical probabilities in determining insurance premiums. An insurance agent may be able to direct you to a source of information.

**34.** Write a paper on how Gregor Mendel's use of empirical probability led to the development of the science of genetics. You may want to check with a biology professor to determine references to use.

---

## SECTION 12.2   Theoretical Probability

▲ *We can use probability to determine the likelihood of winning games of chance.*

Should you spend the money for a stamp to return a sweepstakes ticket? What are your chances of winning a lottery? If you go to a carnival, bazaar, or casino, which games provide the greatest chance of winning? These and similar questions can be answered once you have an understanding of theoretical probability that we will discuss in this section.

**Why** *This is Important*  Understanding how to calculate theoretical probability is essential to many real-life applications, including games of chance. Theoretical probability is also necessary to determine the odds of an event happening, and the expected gain or loss of business ventures.

---

$R$ecall from Section 12.1 that the results of an experiment are called outcomes. When you roll a die and observe the number of points that face up, the possible outcomes are 1, 2, 3, 4, 5, and 6. It is equally likely that you will roll any one of the possible numbers.

#### Definition: **Equally Likely Outcomes**
If each outcome of an experiment has the same chance of occurring as any other outcome, we say that the outcomes are **equally likely outcomes**.

Can you think of a second set of equally likely outcomes when a die is rolled? An odd number is as likely to be rolled as an even number. Therefore, odd and even numbers are another set of equally likely outcomes.

If an event $E$ has *equally likely outcomes*, the theoretical probability of event $E$, symbolized by $P(E)$, may be calculated with the following formula.

#### Probability
The **theoretical probability** of an event can be calculated using the following formula.

$$P(E) = \frac{\text{number of outcomes favorable to } E}{\text{total number of possible outcomes}}$$

*In the remainder of this chapter, the word* **probability** *will refer to* **theoretical probability**.

**TIMELY TIP**

To be able to do the problems in this section and the remainder of the chapter, you must have a thorough understanding of fractions. If you have forgotten how to work with fractions, we strongly suggest that you review Section 5.3 before beginning this section.

Example 1 illustrates how to use this formula.

## Example 1 *Determining Probabilities*

A die is rolled. Determine the probability of rolling

a) a 5.              b) an even number.          c) a number greater than 3.

d) a 7.              e) a number less than 7.

*Solution*

a) There are six possible equally likely outcomes: 1, 2, 3, 4, 5, and 6. The event of rolling a 5 can occur in only one way.

$$P(5) = \frac{\text{number of outcomes that will result in a 5}}{\text{total number of possible outcomes}} = \frac{1}{6}$$

b) The event of rolling an even number can occur in three ways: 2, 4, or 6.

$$P(\text{even number}) = \frac{\text{number of outcomes that result in an even number}}{\text{total number of possible outcomes}}$$
$$= \frac{3}{6} = \frac{1}{2}$$

c) Three numbers are greater than 3, namely, 4, 5 and 6.

$$P(\text{number greater than 3}) = \frac{3}{6} = \frac{1}{2}$$

d) No outcomes will result in a 7. Thus, the event cannot occur and the probability is 0.

$$P(7) = \frac{0}{6} = 0$$

e) All the outcomes 1 through 6 are less than 7. Thus, the event must occur and the probability is 1.

$$P(\text{number less than 7}) = \frac{6}{6} = 1$$

Four important facts about probability follow.

## Important Probability Facts

1. The probability of an event that cannot occur is 0.
2. The probability of an event that must occur is 1.
3. Every probability is a number between 0 and 1 inclusive; that is, $0 \le P(E) \le 1$.
4. The sum of the probabilities of all possible outcomes of an experiment is 1.

## Example 2 *Choosing One Bird from a List*

The names of 15 birds and their food preferences are listed in Table 12.3 on page 685. Each of the 15 birds' names is listed on a slip of paper, and the 15 slips are placed in a bag. One slip is to be selected at random from the bag. Determine the probability that the slip contains the name of

a) a finch (any type listed).

b) a bird that has a high attractiveness to cracked corn.

c) a bird that has a low attractiveness to peanut kernels, *and* a low attractiveness to cracked corn, *and* a high attractiveness to black-striped sunflower seeds.

d) a bird that has a high attractiveness to either peanut kernels *or* cracked corn (or both).

Table 12.3   Birds and Their Food Preferences

| Bird | Peanut Kernels | Cracked Corn | Black-Striped Sunflower Seeds |
|---|---|---|---|
| American goldfinch | L | L | H |
| Blue jay | H | M | H |
| Chickadee | M | L | H |
| Common grackle | M | H | H |
| Evening grosbeak | L | L | H |
| House finch | M | L | H |
| House sparrow | L | M | M |
| Mourning dove | L | M | M |
| Northern cardinal | L | L | H |
| Purple finch | L | L | H |
| Scrub jay | H | L | H |
| Song sparrow | L | L | M |
| Tufted titmouse | H | L | H |
| White-crowned sparrow | H | M | H |
| White-throated sparrow | H | H | H |

Source: *How to Attract Birds* (Ortho Books)

Note: H = high attractiveness; M = medium attractiveness; L = low attractiveness.

Solution

a) Three of the 15 birds listed are finches (American goldfinch, house finch, and purple finch).

$$P(\text{finch}) = \frac{3}{15} = \frac{1}{5}$$

b) Two of the 15 birds listed have a high attractiveness to cracked corn (common grackle and white-throated sparrow).

$$P(\text{high attractiveness to cracked corn}) = \frac{2}{15}$$

c) Reading across the rows reveals that 4 birds have a low attractiveness to peanut kernels, a low attractiveness to cracked corn, and a high attractiveness to black-striped sunflower seeds (American goldfinch, evening grosbeak, northern cardinal, and purple finch).

$$P\left(\begin{array}{c}\text{low attractiveness to peanuts, and low to}\\\text{corn, and high to black-striped sunflower sweeds}\end{array}\right) = \frac{4}{15}$$

d) Six birds have a high attractiveness to either peanut kernels or to cracked corn (or both). They are the blue jay, common grackle, scrub jay, tufted titmouse, white-crowned sparrow, and white-throated sparrow.

$$P(\text{high attractiveness to peanut kernels or cracked corn}) = \frac{6}{15} = \frac{2}{5}$$

In any experiment, an event must either occur or not occur. *The sum of the probability that an event will occur and the probability that it will not occur is 1.* Thus, for any event *A* we conclude that

### The Sum of the Probabilities Equals 1

$$P(A) + P(\text{not } A) = 1$$

or

$$P(\text{not } A) = 1 - P(A)$$

For example, if the probability that event *A* will occur is $\frac{5}{12}$, the probability that event *A* will not occur is $1 - \frac{5}{12}$, or $\frac{7}{12}$. Similarly, if the probability that event *A* will not occur is 0.3, the probability that event *A* will occur is $1 - 0.3 = 0.7$, or $\frac{7}{10}$. We make use of this concept in Example 3.

### Example 3 *Selecting One Card from a Deck*

A standard deck of 52 playing cards is shown in Fig. 12.3. The deck consists of four suits: hearts, clubs, diamonds, and spades. Each suit has 13 cards, including numbered cards ace (1) through 10 and three picture (or face) cards, the jack, the queen, and the king. Hearts and diamonds are red cards; clubs and spades are black cards. There are 12 picture cards, consisting of 4 jacks, 4 queens, and 4 kings. One card is to be selected at random from the deck of cards. Determine the probability that the card selected is

a) a 7.

b) not a 7.

c) a diamond.

d) a jack *or* queen *or* king (a picture card).

e) a heart *and* a spade.

f) a card greater than 6 *and* less than 9.

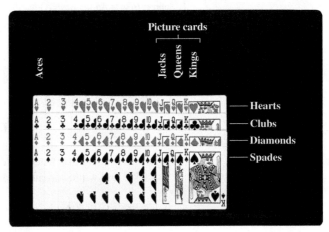

**Figure 12.3**

a) There are four 7's in a deck of 52 cards.

$$P(7) = \frac{4}{52} = \frac{1}{13}$$

b) $P(\text{not a } 7) = 1 - P(7) = 1 - \frac{1}{13} = \frac{12}{13}$

This probability could also have been found by noting that there are 48 cards that are not 7's in a deck of 52 cards.

$$P(\text{not a } 7) = \frac{48}{52} = \frac{12}{13}$$

c) There are 13 diamonds in the deck.

$$P(\text{diamond}) = \frac{13}{52} = \frac{1}{4}$$

d) There are 4 jacks, 4 queens, and 4 kings, or a total of 12 picture cards.

$$P(\text{jack } or \text{ queen } or \text{ king}) = \frac{12}{52} = \frac{3}{13}$$

e) The word *and* means that *both* events must occur. Since it is not possible to select one card that is both a heart and a spade the probability is 0.

$$P(\text{heart and spade}) = \frac{0}{52} = 0$$

f) The cards that are both greater than 6 and less than 9 are 7's and 8's. There are four 7's and four 8's, or a total of eight cards.

$$P(\text{greater than } 6 \text{ } and \text{ less than } 9) = \frac{8}{52} = \frac{2}{13}$$

---

## SECTION 12.2 *Exercises*

### Warm Up Exercises

*In Exercises 1–10, fill in the blank with an appropriate word, phrase, or symbol(s).*

**1.** If each outcome of an experiment has the same chance of occurring as any other outcome, the outcomes are _____ likely outcomes.

**2.** The probability of an event that cannot occur is _____.

**3.** The probability of an event that must occur is _____.

**4.** Every probability is a number between _____ and _____ inclusive.

**5.** The sum of the probabilities of all possible outcomes of an experiment is _____.

**6.** For any event A, $P(A) + P(\text{not } A) = $ _____.

**7.** If the probability that an event occurs is $\frac{3}{7}$, the probability that the event does not occur is _____.

**8.** If the probability that an event occurs is 0.2, the probability that the event does not occur is _____.

**9.** If the probability that an event does not occur is 0.9, the probability that the event occurs is _____.

**10.** If the probability that an event does not occur is $\frac{4}{9}$, the probability that the event occurs is _____.

### Practice the Skills

**11.** *Multiple-Choice Test* A multiple-choice test has five possible choices for each question.

a) If you randomly select one of the choices, what is the probability that you select the correct answer for one particular question?

b) If you eliminate one of the five possible choices and guess from the remaining choices, what is the probability that you select the correct answer to that question?

**12.** *Remote Control* A TV remote control has keys for channels 0 through 9. If you select one key at random,

a) what is the probability that you press channel 6?

b) what is the probability that you press a key for an even number?

c) what is the probability that you press a key for a number less than 7?

**13.** *Raffle* In a raffle where one number is chosen, determine the probability that you would win if you have a choice of 40 numbers to choose from.

**14.** *Raffle* In a raffle where one number is chosen, determine the probability that you would win if you have a choice of 52 numbers to choose from.

*Select a Card* In Exercises 15–24, one card is selected at random from a deck of cards. Determine the probability that the card selected is

**15.** a 5.

**16.** a 5 or a 10.

**17.** not a 5.

**18.** the five of diamonds.

**19.** a black card.

**20.** a diamond.

**21.** a red card or a black card.

**22.** a red card and a black card.

**23.** a card greater than 3 and less than 8.

**24.** a king and a club.

*Spin the Spinner* In Exercises 25–28, assume that the spinner cannot land on a line. Determine the probability that the spinner lands on (a) red, (b) green, (c) yellow, (d) blue.

**25.**    **26.**

**27.**    **28.**

*Picnic* In Exercises 29–32, a cooler at a picnic contains 100 cans of soda covered by ice. There are 30 cans of cola, 40 cans of orange soda, 10 cans of ginger ale, and 20 cans of root beer. The cans are all the same size and shape. If one can is selected at random from the cooler, determine the probability that the soda selected is

**29.** root beer.

**30.** cola or orange soda.

**31.** cola, root beer, or orange soda.

**32.** ginger ale.

*Wheel of Fortune* In Exercises 33–36, use the small replica of the Wheel of Fortune.

If the wheel is spun at random, determine the probability that the indicated sector will stop under the pointer.

**33.** $600

**34.** A number greater than $700

**35.** Lose a turn or Bankrupt

**36.** $2500 or Surprise

*Basketballs* In Exercises 37–40, 30 basketballs, including 15 Spalding, 10 Wilson, and 5 other brand-name balls, are on a basketball court. Barry Wood closes his eyes and arbitrarily picks up a ball from the court. Determine the probability that the ball selected is

**37.** a Spalding.

**38.** a Wilson.

**39.** not a Wilson.

**40.** a Wilson or a Spalding.

*Traffic Light* In Exercises 41–44, a traffic light is red for 25 sec, yellow for 5 sec, and green for 55 sec. What is the probability that when you reach the light,

**41.** the light is green.

**42.** the light is yellow.

**43.** the light is not red.

**44.** the light is not green.

*TALLAHASSEE* In Exercises 45–50, each individual letter of the word *TALLAHASSEE* is placed on a piece of paper and all 11 pieces of paper are placed in a hat. If one letter is selected at random from the hat, determine the probability that

**45.** the letter *S* is selected.

**46.** the letter *S* is not selected.

**47.** a consonant is selected.

**48.** the letter *T* or *E* is selected.

**49.** the letter *W* is selected.

**50.** the letter *V* is not selected.

*National Parks* In Exercises 51–54, use the list below which shows the 10 U.S. National Parks with the most visitors in 2010.

| Park | Location | Visits |
|------|----------|--------|
| Great Smokey Mountains National Park | North Carolina/ Tennessee | 9,463,538 |
| Grand Canyon National Park | Arizona | 4,388,386 |
| Yosemite National Park | California | 3,901,408 |
| Yellowstone National Park | Wyoming | 3,640,185 |
| Rocky Mountain National Park | Colorado | 2,955,821 |
| Olympic National Park | Washington | 2,844,563 |
| Grand Teton National Park | Wyoming | 2,669,374 |
| Zion National Park | Utah | 2,665,972 |
| Acadia National Park | Maine | 2,504,208 |
| Cuyahoga Valley National Park | Ohio | 2,492,670 |

Source: *National Park Service*

▲ *Grand Teton National Park, Jackson, WY*

If one of the parks in the list is selected at random, determine the probability the park

**51.** is located in California.

**52.** is located in Wyoming.

**53.** had more than 4 million visitors.

**54.** had fewer than 3 million visitors.

*Dart Board* In Exercises 55–58, a dart is thrown randomly and sticks on the circular dart board with 26 partitions, as shown.

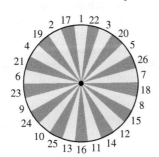

Assuming the dart cannot land on the black area or on a border between colors, determine the probability that the dart lands on

**55.** the area marked 15.      **56.** an orange area.

**57.** an area marked with a number greater than or equal to 22.

**58.** an area marked with a number greater than 6 and less than or equal to 9.

*Car Dealership* In Exercises 59–64, refer to the following table, which shows the type and manufacturer of vehicles at a specific car dealership.

|  | General Motors | Toyota | Total |
|------|----------------|--------|-------|
| **Car** | 55 | 30 | 85 |
| **SUV** | 28 | 17 | 45 |
| **Total** | 83 | 47 | 130 |

If one person selects a vehicle at random from the dealership, determine the probability that the person selects

**59.** a car.                 **60.** an SUV.

**61.** a vehicle manufactured by General Motors.

**62.** a vehicle manufactured by Toyota.

**63.** a car manufactured by General Motors.

**64.** an SUV manufactured by General Motors.

*Stocking Taco Sauce* In Exercises 65–70, refer to the following table, which contains information about a shopping cart full of jars of taco sauce that must be stocked on a shelf. Assume all jars are the same size and shape.

| Brand | Mild | Medium | Hot | Total |
|-------|------|--------|-----|-------|
| Taco Bell | 5 | 8 | 4 | 17 |
| Ortega | 2 | 5 | 3 | 10 |
| Old El Paso | 3 | 6 | 2 | 11 |
| Other | 1 | 2 | 1 | 4 |
| Total | 11 | 21 | 10 | 42 |

If a stock clerk selects one jar at random to place on the shelf, determine the probability he selects a jar of

**65.** Ortega.              **66.** Old El Paso.

**67.** a mild taco sauce.    **68.** a hot taco sauce.

**69.** Taco Bell medium taco sauce.

**70.** Old El Paso hot taco sauce.

*Bean Bag Toss* In Exercises 71–76, a bean bag is randomly thrown onto the square table top shown below and does not touch a line.

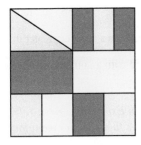

*Determine the probability that the bean bag lands on*

**71.** a red area.

**72.** a green area.

**73.** a yellow area.

**74.** a red or green area.

**75.** a yellow or green area.

**76.** a red or yellow area.

## Challenge Problems/Group Activities

*Before working Exercises 77 and 78, reread the material on genetics in Section 12.1.*

**77. *Genetics*** Cystic fibrosis is an inherited disease that occurs in about 1 in every 2500 Caucasian births in North America and in about 1 in every 250,000 non-Caucasian births in North America. Let's denote the cystic fibrosis gene as $c$ and a disease-free gene as $C$. Since the disease-free gene is dominant, only a person with $cc$ genes will have the disease. A person who has $Cc$ genes is a carrier of cystic fibrosis but does not actually have the disease. If one parent has $CC$ genes and the other parent has $cc$ genes, determine the probability that

**a)** an offspring will inherit cystic fibrosis, that is, $cc$ genes.

**b)** an offspring will be a carrier of cystic fibrosis but not contract the disease.

**78. *Genetics*** Sickle-cell anemia is an inherited disease that occurs in about 1 in every 500 African-American births and about 1 in every 160,000 non–African-American births. Unlike cystic fibrosis, in which the cystic fibrosis gene is recessive, sickle-cell anemia is *codominant*. In other words, a person inheriting two sickle-cell genes will have sickle-cell anemia, whereas a person inheriting only one of the sickle-cell genes will have a mild version of sickle-cell anemia, called *sickle-cell trait.* Let's call the disease-free genes $s_1$ and the sickle cell gene $s_2$. If both parents have $s_1 s_2$ genes, determine the probability that

**a)** an offspring will have sickle-cell anemia.

**b)** an offspring will have the sickle-cell trait.

**c)** an offspring will have neither sickle-cell anemia nor the sickle-cell trait.

In Exercises 79 and 80, the solutions involve material that we will discuss in later sections of the chapter. Try to solve them before reading ahead.

**79. *Marbles*** A bottle contains two red and two green marbles, and a second bottle also contains two red and two green marbles. If you select one marble at random from each bottle, determine the probability (to be discussed in Section 12.6) that you obtain

**a)** two red marbles.          **b)** two green marbles.

**c)** a red marble from the first bottle and a green marble from the second bottle.

**80. *Birds*** Consider Table 12.3 on page 685. Suppose you are told that one bird's name was selected at random from the birds listed and the bird selected has a low attractiveness to peanut kernels. Determine the probability (to be discussed in Section 12.7) that

**a)** the bird is a sparrow.

**b)** the bird has a high attractiveness to cracked corn.

**c)** the bird has a high attractiveness to black-striped sunflower seeds.

## Recreational Mathematics

**81. *Dice*** On a die, the sum of the dots on the opposite faces is seven. Two six-sided dice are placed together on top of one another, on a table, as shown in the figure below. The top and bottom faces of the bottom die and the bottom face of the top die cannot be seen. If you walk around the table, what is the sum of all the dots on all the visible faces of the dice?

## Internet/Research Activity

**82.** On page 675, we briefly discuss Jacob Bernoulli. The Bernoulli family produced several prominent mathematicians, including Jacob I, Johann I, and Daniel. Write a paper on the Bernoulli family, indicating some of the accomplishments of each of the three Bernoullis named and their relationship to one another. Indicate which Bernoulli the Bernoulli numbers are named after, which Bernoulli the Bernoulli theorem in statistics is named after, and which Bernoulli the Bernoulli theorem of fluid dynamics is named after.

Odds

The odds against winning the Fabulous Fortune lottery are about 2.6 million to 1. The odds against being audited by the IRS this year are about 47 to 1. The odds against the San Francisco Giants winning the World Series this year may be 6 to 1. We see the word *odds* daily in newspapers and magazines and often use it ourselves. Yet there is widespread misunderstanding of its meaning. In this section, we will explain the meaning of odds. We will also discuss how to determine odds against an event and how to determine odds in favor of an event.

▲ *What are the odds against the San Francisco Giants winning the World Series this year?*

**Why** *This is Important* Many real-life applications involve odds, including sporting events and games of chance.

## Odds Against an Event

The odds given at horse races, at craps, and at all gambling games in Las Vegas and other casinos throughout the world are always *odds against* unless they are otherwise specified. The *odds against* an event is a ratio of the probability that the event will fail to occur (failure) to the probability that the event will occur (success). Thus, *to find odds you must first know or determine the probability of success and the probability of failure.*

### Odds Against an Event
The following formula may be used to determine the odds against an event.

$$\text{Odds against event} = \frac{P(\text{event fails to occur})}{P(\text{event occurs})} = \frac{P(\text{failure})}{P(\text{success})}$$

### Did You Know?

**Gambling in Ancient Times**

Archaeologists have found evidence of gambling in all cultures, from the Stone Age Australian aborigines to the ancient Egyptians, and across cultures touched by the Roman Empire. There is an equally long history of moral and legal opposition to gambling.

### Example 1 *Rolling a 4*

Determine the odds against rolling a 4 on one roll of a die.

**Solution** Before we can determine the odds, we must first determine the probability of rolling a 4 (success) and the probability of not rolling a 4 (failure). When a die is rolled there are six possible outcomes: 1, 2, 3, 4, 5, and 6.

$$P(\text{rolling a 4}) = \frac{1}{6} \qquad P(\text{failure to roll a 4}) = \frac{5}{6}$$

Now that we know the probabilities of success and failure, we can determine the odds against rolling a 4.

$$\text{Odds against rolling a 4} = \frac{P(\text{failure to roll a 4})}{P(\text{rolling a 4})}$$

$$= \frac{\frac{5}{6}}{\frac{1}{6}} = \frac{5}{\cancel{6}} \cdot \frac{\cancel{6}}{1} = \frac{5}{1}$$

**TIMELY TIP**
The denominators of the probabilities in an odds problem will always divide out, as was shown in Example 1.

The ratio $\frac{5}{1}$ is commonly written as 5:1 and is read "5 to 1." Thus, the odds against rolling a 4 are 5 to 1.

In Example 1, we considered the possible outcomes of the die: 1, 2, 3, 4, 5, 6. Over the long run, one of every six rolls will result in a 4, and five of every six rolls will result in a number other than 4. Therefore, if a person is gambling, for each dollar bet in favor of the rolling of a 4, $5 should be bet against the rolling of a 4 if the person is to break even. The person betting in favor of the rolling of a 4 will either lose $1 (if a number other than a 4 is rolled) or win $5 (if a 4 is rolled). The person betting against the rolling of a 4 will either win $1 (if a number other than a 4 is rolled) or lose $5 (if a 4 is rolled). If this game is played for a long enough period, each player theoretically will break even.

Example 2 involves a circle graph that contains percents; see Fig. 12.4. Before we discuss Example 2, let us briefly discuss percents. Recall that probabilities are numbers between 0 and 1, inclusive. We can change a percent between 0% and 100% to a probability by writing the percent as a fraction or a decimal number. In Fig. 12.4, we see 36% in one of the sectors (or areas) of the circle. To change 36% to a probability, we can write $\frac{36}{100}$ or 0.36. Note that both the fraction and the decimal number are numbers between 0 and 1, inclusive.

┌ Example **2**  *Occupations*

The circle graph in Fig. 12.4 shows the percent of U.S. workers employed in professional, service, sales, construction, and production occupations. If one U.S. worker is selected at random, use the graph to determine the odds against the person being employed in a sales occupation.

**Occupation of U.S. Workers**

Source: *Bureau of Labor Statistics*

**Figure 12.4**

*Solution*  From the graph, we can determine that 25%, or $\frac{25}{100}$, of U.S. workers are employed in sales occupations. Therefore, the probability that a U.S. worker is employed in a sales occupation is $\frac{25}{100}$. The probability that a U.S. worker is *not* employed in a sales occupation is $1 - \frac{25}{100} = \frac{75}{100}$.

Odds against the person being employed in a sales occupation $= \dfrac{P(\text{person is not employed in a sales occupation})}{P(\text{person is employed in a sales occupation})}$

$$= \frac{\dfrac{75}{100}}{\dfrac{25}{100}} = \frac{75}{100} \cdot \frac{\cancel{100}}{25} = \frac{75}{25} = \frac{3}{1}, \text{ or } 3{:}1$$

Thus, the odds against the person being employed in a sales occupation are 3:1.  ■

## Odds in Favor of an Event

Although odds are generally given against an event, at times they may be given in favor of an event. The *odds in favor of* an event are expressed as a ratio of the probability that the event will occur to the probability that the event will fail to occur.

## Odds in Favor of an Event

The following formula may be used to determine the odds in favor of an event.

$$\text{Odds in favor of event} = \frac{P(\text{event occurs})}{P(\text{event fails to occur})} = \frac{P(\text{success})}{P(\text{failure})}$$

If the odds *against* an event are $a:b$, the odds *in favor of* the event are $b:a$.

### Example 3  *Smartphones*

The circle graph in Fig. 12.5 shows the U.S. market share for the operating systems used in smartphones, as of December 2010. If an individual who owns a smartphone is selected at random, use the graph to determine

a) the odds against the individual owning a Google phone.

b) the odds in favor of the individual owning a Google phone.

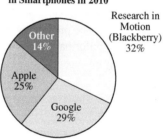

**U.S. Market Share of Operating Systems Used in Smartphones in 2010**

Source: ComScore

Figure 12.5

**Solution**

a) The graph shows that 29%, or $\frac{29}{100}$, of individuals who owned a smartphone owned a Google phone. Thus, the probability that an individual owned a Google phone is $\frac{29}{100}$. Therefore, the probability that an individual did not own a Google phone is $1 - \frac{29}{100} = \frac{71}{100}$

$$\begin{aligned}\text{Odds against an individual} \\ \text{owning a Google phone}\end{aligned} = \frac{P(\text{an individual did not own a Google phone})}{P(\text{an individual owned a Google phone})}$$

$$= \frac{\dfrac{71}{100}}{\dfrac{29}{100}} = \frac{71}{\cancel{100}} \cdot \frac{\cancel{100}}{29} = \frac{71}{29} \quad \text{or} \quad 71:29$$

Thus, the odds against the individual owning a Google phone are $71:29$.

b) The odds in favor of the individual owning a Google phone are $29:71$. ∎

## Finding Probabilities from Odds

When odds are given, either in favor of or against a particular event, it is possible to determine the probability that the event occurs and the probability that the event does not occur. The denominators of the probabilities are found by adding the numbers in the odds statement. The numerators of the probabilities are the numbers given in the odds statements.

Example 4 *Determining Probabilities from Odds*

The odds against Robin Murphy being admitted to the college of her choice are 9:2. Determine the probability that (a) Robin is admitted and (b) Robin is not admitted.

Solution

a) We have been given odds against and have been asked to find probabilities.

$$\text{Odds against being admitted} = \frac{P(\text{fails to be admitted})}{P(\text{is admitted})}$$

Since the odds statement is 9:2, the denominators of both the probability of success and the probability of failure must be 9 + 2 or 11. To get the odds ratio of 9:2, the probabilities must be $\frac{9}{11}$ and $\frac{2}{11}$. Since odds against is a ratio of failure to success, the $\frac{9}{11}$ and $\frac{2}{11}$ represent the probabilities of failure and success, respectively. Thus, the probability that Robin is admitted (success) is $\frac{2}{11}$.

b) The probability that Robin is not admitted (failure) is $\frac{9}{11}$.

Odds and probability statements are sometimes stated incorrectly. For example, consider the statement, "The odds of being selected to represent the district are 1 in 5." Odds are given using the word *to*, not *in*. Thus, there is a mistake in this statement. The correct statement might be, "The odds of being selected to represent the district are 1 to 5" or "The probability of being selected to represent the district is 1 in 5." Without additional information, it is not possible to tell which statement is the correct interpretation.

## SECTION 12.3  *Exercises*

### Warm Up Exercises

*In Exercises 1–8, fill in the blank with an appropriate word, phrase, or symbol(s).*

1. The ratio of the probability that an event will fail to occur to the probability that the event will occur is called the odds _____ an event.

2. The ratio of the probability that the event will occur to the probability that the event will fail to occur is called the odds _____ an event.

3. If the odds in favor of *Just in Time* winning a horse race are 1:3, then the odds against *Just in Time* winning the race are _____.

4. If the odds against winning at Monopoly are 4:1, then the odds in favor of winning at Monopoly are _____.

5. If the probability that an event will occur is $\frac{2}{3}$ then the probability that the event will not occur is $\frac{1}{3}$, and the odds in favor of the event occurring are _____.

6. If the probability that an event will fail to occur is $\frac{1}{4}$ then the probability that the event will occur is $\frac{3}{4}$ and the odds against the event occurring are _____.

7. If the odds against an event are 1:3, the probability that the event will fail to occur is _____.

8. If the odds against an event are *a* to *b*, then the probability that the event occurs is _____.

### Practice the Skills/Problem Solving

9. *Dressing Up* Lila Jaquez is going to wear a blue dress and is trying to decide which pair of shoes she should wear with it. In her closet, she has 12 pairs of shoes, 5 of which go well with the dress. If Lila selects one pair of shoes at random, determine

   a) the probability that the shoes go well with the dress.

   b) the probability that the shoes do not go well with the dress.

   c) the odds against the shoes going well with the dress.

   d) the odds in favor of the shoes going well with the dress.

10. *Making a Donation* In her wallet, Anne Kelly has 12 bills. Six are $1 bills, two are $5 bills, three are $10 bills, and one is a $20 bill. She passes a volunteer seeking donations for the Salvation Army and decides to select one bill at random from her wallet and give it to the Salvation Army. Determine

   a) the probability that she selects a $5 bill.

   b) the probability that she does not select a $5 bill.

   c) the odds in favor of her selecting a $5 bill.

   d) the odds against her selecting a $5 bill.

***Deal or No Deal*** *In Exercises 11 and 12, consider the TV show Deal or No Deal. (See the Mathematics Today on page 693.) In the game show, there are 26 numbered cases, each indicating a cash prize ranging from 1 cent to $1,000,000. Contestants on the show have a series of choices to make, and each time they can either accept the cash offer made by the banker or select a case from the remaining cases. Assume that one of the remaining cases contains a $1,000,000 cash prize. Determine the odds against and the odds in favor of selecting the case containing the $1,000,000 cash prize if there are*

**11.** seven cases remaining.

**12.** four cases remaining.

***Toss a Die*** *In Exercises 13–16, a die is tossed. Determine the odds against rolling*

**13.** a 2.

**14.** an odd number.

**15.** a number less than 3.

**16.** a number greater than 4.

***Deck of Cards*** *In Exercises 17–20, a card is picked from a standard deck of cards. Determine the odds against and the odds in favor of selecting*

**17.** a king.

**18.** a heart.

**19.** a picture card.

**20.** a card greater than 5 (ace is low).

***Spin the Spinner*** *In Exercises 21–24, assume that the spinner cannot land on a line. Determine the odds against the spinner landing on the color red.*

**21.**     **22.**

**23.**     **24.**

**25.** ***Students*** One person is selected at random from a class of 16 men and 14 women. Determine the odds against selecting

    **a)** a woman.    **b)** a man.

**26.** ***Lottery*** One million tickets are sold for a lottery in which a single prize will be awarded.

**a)** If you purchase a ticket, determine your odds against winning.

**b)** If you purchase 10 tickets, determine your odds against winning.

***Billiard Balls*** *In Exercises 27–32, use the rack of 15 billiard balls shown.*

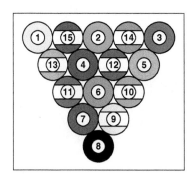

**27.** If one ball is selected at random, determine the odds against it containing a stripe. (Balls numbered 9 through 15 contain stripes.)

**28.** If one ball is selected at random, determine the odds in favor of it being a ball other than the 8 ball.

**29.** If one ball is selected at random, determine the odds in favor of it being an even-numbered ball.

**30.** If one ball is selected at random, determine the odds against it containing any red coloring (solid or striped).

**31.** If one ball is selected at random, determine the odds against it containing a number greater than or equal to 9.

**32.** If one ball is selected at random, determine the odds in favor of it containing two digits.

**33.** ***LPGA Winnings*** The chart below shows the winnings, in dollars, for the 10 golfers with the highest total LPGA winnings for the 2010 season.

| Golfer | 2010 Winnings |
|---|---|
| Na Yeon Choi | $1,871,166 |
| Jiyai Shin | $1,783,127 |
| Cristie Kerr | $1,601,552 |
| Yani Tseng | $1,573,529 |
| Suzann Pettersen | $1,557,175 |
| Ai Miyazato | $1,457,384 |
| In-Kyung Kim | $1,210,068 |
| Song-Hee Kim | $1,208,698 |
| Michelle Wie | $888,017 |
| Paula Creamer | $883,870 |

Source: *LPGA.com*

If one of the golfers listed in the chart is selected at random, determine

a) the probability the golfer earned more than $1 million in 2010.

b) the odds against the golfer earning more than $1 million in 2010.

▲ Paula Creamer

**34. Rolling a Special Die** A special die used in a game contains one dot on one side, two dots on two sides, and three dots on three sides. If the die is rolled, determine

a) the probability of rolling two dots.

b) the odds against rolling two dots.

**35. Medical Tests** The results of a medical test show that of 85 people selected at random who were given the test, 80 tested negative and 5 tested positive. Determine the odds against a person selected at random testing negative on the test.

**36. A Red Marble** A box contains 9 red and 2 blue marbles. If you select one marble at random from the box, determine the odds against selecting a blue marble.

**37. Scholarship Award** The odds in favor of Wendy White winning a scholarship are 7:4. Determine the probability that

a) Wendy wins.

b) Wendy does not win.

**38. Selling a Car** The odds in favor of Sam Riveria selling his car are 3:8. Determine the probability that Sam will

a) sell his car.

b) not sell his car.

**39. College Acceptance** The odds against Jason Judd getting accepted into the college his choice are 4:11. Determine the probability that Jason gets accepted into the college of his choice.

**40. Winning a Race** The odds against Paul Phillips winning the 100 yard dash are 7:2. Determine the probability that

a) Paul wins.          b) Paul does not win.

**Playing Bingo** When playing bingo, 75 balls are placed in a bin and balls are selected at random. Each ball is marked with a letter and number as indicated in the following chart.

| B | I | N | G | O |
|---|---|---|---|---|
| 1–15 | 16–30 | 31–45 | 46–60 | 61–75 |

For example, there are balls marked B1, B2, up to B15; I16, I17, up to I30; and so on (see photo). In Exercises 41–46, assuming one bingo ball is selected at random, determine

**41.** the probability that it contains the letter G.

**42.** the probability that it does not contain the letter G.

**43.** the odds in favor of it containing the letter G.

**44.** the odds against it containing the letter G.

**45.** the odds against it being B9.

**46.** the odds in favor of it being B9.

**Blood Types** In Exercises 47–52, the following circle graph shows the percent of Americans with the various types of blood.

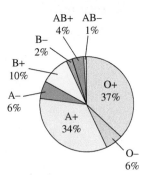

**Blood Types of Americans**

Source: Red Cross

If one American is selected at random, use the graph to determine

**47.** the probability that the person has A+ blood.

**48.** the probability that the person has B− blood.

**49.** the odds against the person having A+ blood.

**50.** the odds in favor of the person having B− blood.

**51.** the odds in favor of the person having either O+ or O− blood.

**52.** the odds against the person having either A+ or O+ blood.

**53.** *Fixing a Car* Suppose that the probability that a mechanic fixes a car correctly is 0.9. Determine the odds against the mechanic fixing a car correctly.

**54.** *Diabetes* According to the Centers for Disease Control, 8% of Americans have diabetes. If an American is selected at random, determine the odds in favor of this person having diabetes.

**55.** *Bookcase Assembly* Suppose that the probability that all the parts needed to assemble a bookcase are included in the carton is $\frac{7}{8}$. Determine the odds in favor of the carton including all the needed parts.

**56.** *Flight Delays* Of 899,000 flights in May 2010, five were delayed on the tarmac by more than three hours. If one of these 899,000 flights was selected at random, determine

  **a)** the probability that the flight was delayed more than three hours.

  **b)** the odds against the flight being delayed more than three hours.

**57.** *Birth Defects* Birth defects affect 1 in 33 babies born in the United States each year.

  **a)** What is the probability that a baby born in the United States will have a birth defect?

  **b)** What are the odds against a baby born in the United States having a birth defect?

## Challenge Problems/Group Activities

**58.** *Odds Against* Determine the odds against an even number or a number greater than 3 being rolled on a die.

**59.** *Horse Racing* Racetracks quote the approximate odds against each horse winning on a large board called a *tote*

*board.* The odds quoted on a tote board for a race with five horses is as follows.

| Horse Number | Odds |
|:---:|:---:|
| 2 | 7:2 |
| 3 | 2:1 |
| 4 | 15:1 |
| 5 | 7:5 |
| 6 | 1:1 |

Determine the probability of each horse winning the race. (Do not be concerned that the sum of the probabilities is not 1.)

**60.** *Roulette* Turn to the roulette wheel illustrated on page 707. If the wheel is spun, determine

  **a)** the probability that the ball lands on red.

  **b)** the odds against the ball landing on red.

  **c)** the probability that the ball lands on 0 or 00.

  **d)** the odds in favor of the ball landing on 0 or 00.

## Recreational Mathematics

**61.** *Multiple Births* Multiple births make up about 3% of births per year in the United States. The following illustrates the number and type of multiple births in 2008.

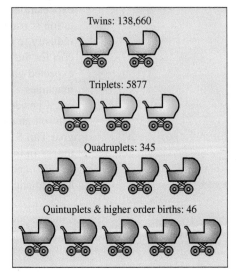

**Multiple Births in the United States in 2008**

Source: *National Center for Health Services*

Using the above information, determine an estimate for the odds against a birth being a multiple birth in 2008.

## Internet/Research Activities

**62.** *State Lottery* Determine whether your state has a lottery. If so, do research and write a paper indicating

a) the probability of winning the grand prize.

b) the odds against winning the grand prize.

c) Explain, using real objects such as pennies or table tennis balls, what these odds actually mean.

**63.** *Casino Advantages* There are many types of games of chance to choose from at casinos. The house has the advantage in each game, but the advantages differ according to the game.

a) List the games available at a typical casino.

b) List those for which the house has the smallest advantage of winning.

c) List those for which the house has the greatest advantage of winning.

---

## SECTION 12.4    Expected Value (Expectation)

▲ *Expected value can be used to estimate the future profits of a new product.*

When a construction company estimates the number of days it will take to complete the resurfacing of a road, it will consider many things including the probability of rain, which can slow down the completion. In trying to decide whether to make a new product, such as a new cereal or new model car, a company will estimate its potential profit (or loss). When companies estimate how long it will take them to complete a task, or their expected profit, they often use expected value, or expectation, which we will discuss in this section.

**Why** *This is Important* Expectation is used to make important decisions in many areas, including insurance and business ventures, and in games of chance.

---

Expected value, also called *expectation*, is often used to determine the expected results of an experiment or business venture *over the long term*. People use expectation to make important decisions in many different areas. For example, expectation is used in business to predict future profits of a new product. In the insurance industry, expectation is used to determine how much each insurance policy should cost for the company to make an overall profit. Expectation is also used to predict the expected gain or loss in games of chance such as the lottery, roulette, craps, and slot machines.

Consider the following situation. Tim tells Barbara that he will give her $1 if she can roll an even number on a single die. If she fails to roll an even number, she must give Tim $1. Who would win money in the long run if this game were played many times? In this situation, we would expect in the long run that half the time Tim would win $1 and half the time he would lose $1; therefore, Tim would break even. Mathematically, we could find Tim's expected gain or loss by the following procedure:

$$\text{Tim's expected gain or loss} = P\left(\begin{array}{c}\text{Tim}\\\text{wins}\end{array}\right) \cdot \left(\begin{array}{c}\text{amount}\\\text{Tim wins}\end{array}\right) + P\left(\begin{array}{c}\text{Tim}\\\text{loses}\end{array}\right) \cdot \left(\begin{array}{c}\text{amount}\\\text{Tim loses}\end{array}\right)$$

$$= \frac{1}{2}(\$1) + \frac{1}{2}(-\$1) = \$0$$

Note that the loss is written as a negative number. This procedure indicates that Tim has an expected gain or loss (or expected value) of $0. The expected value of zero indicates that he would indeed break even, as we had anticipated. Thus, the game is a *fair game*. If Tim's expected value were positive, it would indicate a gain; if negative, a loss.

The expected value, *E*, is calculated by multiplying the probability of an event occurring by the *net* amount gained or lost if the event occurs. If there are a number of different events and amounts to be considered, we use the following formula.

## Expected Value

$$E = P_1 \cdot A_1 + P_2 \cdot A_2 + P_3 \cdot A_3 + \ldots + P_n \cdot A_n$$

The symbol $P_1$ represents the probability that the first event will occur, and $A_1$ represents the net amount won or lost if the first event occurs. $P_2$ is the probability of the second event, and $A_2$ is the net amount won or lost if the second event occurs, and so on. The sum of these products of the probabilities and their respective amounts is the expected value. The expected value is the average (or mean) result that would be obtained if the experiment were performed a great many times.

### Example 1   *A Building Contract*

The Rich Walker Construction Company has just received a building contract. From past experience, Rich estimates there is a 60% chance of making a $500,000 profit, a 10% chance of breaking even, and a 30% chance of losing $200,000, depending on weather conditions and other factors. What is the expected value of the company's contract?

*Solution*   Three amounts are to be considered: a gain of $500,000, breaking even at $0, and a loss of $200,000. The probability of gaining $500,000 is 0.6, the probability of breaking even is 0.1, and the probability of losing $200,000 is 0.3.

$$\begin{aligned}
\text{Rich's expectation} &= P_1 A_1 + P_2 A_2 + P_3 A_3 \\
&= (0.6)(\$500,000) + (0.1)(\$0) + (0.3)(-\$200,000) \\
&= \$240,000
\end{aligned}$$

Rich has an expectation, or expected average gain, of $240,000 for this contract. Thus, if the company receives similar contracts like this one, with these particular probabilities and amounts, in the long run the company would have an average gain of $240,000 per contract. However, you must remember that there is a 30% chance the company will lose $200,000 on this *particular* contract or any particular contract with these probabilities and amounts.   ∎

### Example 2   *Test-Taking Strategy*

Maria is taking a multiple-choice exam in which there are five possible answers for each question. The instructions indicate that she will be awarded 2 points for each correct response, that she will lose $\frac{1}{2}$ point for each incorrect response, and that no points will be added or subtracted for answers left blank.

a) If Maria does not know the correct answer to a question, is it to her advantage or disadvantage to guess at an answer?

b) If she can eliminate one of the possible choices, is it to her advantage or disadvantage to guess at the answer?

*Solution*

a) Let's determine the expected value if Maria guesses at an answer. Only one of five possible answers is correct.

$$P(\text{guesses correctly}) = \frac{1}{5} \qquad P(\text{guesses incorrectly}) = \frac{4}{5}$$

$$\text{Maria's expectation} = \overbrace{P_1 \cdot A_1}^{\substack{\text{Guesses} \\ \text{correctly}}} + \overbrace{P_2 \cdot A_2}^{\substack{\text{Guesses} \\ \text{incorrectly}}}$$

$$= \frac{1}{5}(2) + \frac{4}{5}\left(-\frac{1}{2}\right)$$

$$= \frac{2}{5} - \frac{2}{5} = 0$$

Thus, Maria's expectation is zero when she guesses. Therefore, over the long run she will neither gain nor lose points by guessing.

b) If Maria can eliminate one possible choice, one of four answers will be correct.

$$P(\text{guesses correctly}) = \frac{1}{4} \qquad P(\text{guesses incorrectly}) = \frac{3}{4}$$

$$\text{Maria's expectation} = \overbrace{P_1 \cdot A_1}^{\substack{\text{Guesses} \\ \text{correctly}}} + \overbrace{P_2 \cdot A_2}^{\substack{\text{Guesses} \\ \text{incorrectly}}}$$

$$= \frac{1}{4}(2) + \frac{3}{4}\left(-\frac{1}{2}\right)$$

$$= \frac{2}{4} - \frac{3}{8} = \frac{4}{8} - \frac{3}{8} = \frac{1}{8}$$

Since the expectation is a positive $\frac{1}{8}$, Maria will, on average, gain $\frac{1}{8}$ point each time she guesses when she can eliminate one possible choice.

## Example 3  *Selling Hot Dogs*

An outdoor hot dog vendor sells an average of 50 hot dogs per day in dry weather and an average of 15 per day in wet weather. If the weather in this area is wet 20% of the time, determine the expected (average) number of hot dogs sold per day.

*Solution*   The amounts in this example are the number of hot dogs sold. Since the weather is wet 20% of the time, it will be dry $100\% - 20\% = 80\%$ of the time. When written as probabilities, 20% and 80% are 0.2 and 0.8, respectively.

$$E = P(\text{dry}) \cdot (\text{number sold}) + P(\text{wet}) \cdot (\text{number sold})$$

$$= 0.8(50) + 0.2(15)$$

$$= 40 + 3 = 43$$

Thus, the average, or expected, number of hot dogs sold per day is 43.

When we gave the expectation formula, we indicated that the amounts were the **net amounts**, which are the actual amounts gained or lost. Examples 4 and 5 illustrate how net amounts are used in two applications of expected value.

## Example 4  *Winning a Door Prize*

When Josh Rosenberg attends a charity event, he is given a free ticket for the $50 door prize. A total of 100 tickets will be given out. Determine his expectation of winning the door prize.

*Solution*   The probability of winning the door prize is $\frac{1}{100}$ since Josh has 1 of 100 tickets. If he wins, his net or actual winnings will be $50 since he did not pay for the ticket. The probability that Josh loses is $\frac{99}{100}$. If Josh loses, the amount he loses is $0 because he did not pay for the ticket.

**It Pays to Be Original**

Commonly Selected Numbers
7–14–21–28–35–42
1–2–3–4–5–6
5–10–15–20–25–30
3–8–13–18–23–28

The numbers you select when picking lottery numbers have no effect on your probability of winning. However, your expectation (expected winnings) varies greatly with the numbers you select. Because the jackpot is divided among all the winners, the fewer the number of winners the more each winner receives. Some groups of numbers are commonly selected. Some are illustrated above. In a lottery with a large jackpot, there may be as many as 10,000 people who select the numbers 7-14-21-28-35-42. If the jackpot was $40 million and these numbers were selected, each winner would receive about $4000. That is quite a difference from the $40 million a single winner would receive. Many people use birthdays or other dates when selecting lottery numbers. Therefore, there may be fewer people selecting numbers greater than 31.

Expectation $= P(\text{Josh wins}) \cdot (\text{amount won}) + P(\text{Josh loses}) \cdot (\text{amount lost})$

$$= \frac{1}{100}(50) + \frac{99}{100}(0) = \frac{50}{100} = 0.50$$

Thus, Josh's expectation is $0.50, or 50 cents.   ∎

Now we will consider a problem similar to Example 4, but this time we will assume that Josh must purchase the ticket for the door prize.

## Example 5   *Winning a Door Prize*

When Josh Rosenberg attends a charity event, he is given the opportunity to purchase a ticket for the $50 door prize. The cost of the ticket is $2, and 100 tickets will be sold. Determine Josh's expectation if he purchases one ticket.

*Solution*  As in Example 4, Josh's probability of winning is $\frac{1}{100}$. However, if he does win, his actual or net winnings will be $48. The $48 is obtained by subtracting the cost of the ticket, $2, from the amount of the door prize, $50. There is also a probability of $\frac{99}{100}$ that Josh will not win the door prize. If he does not win the door prize, he has lost the $2 that he paid for the ticket. Therefore, we must consider two amounts when we determine Josh's expectation, winning $48 and losing $2.

Expectation $= P(\text{Josh wins}) \cdot (\text{amount won}) + P(\text{Josh loses}) \cdot (\text{amount lost})$

$$= \frac{1}{100}(48) + \frac{99}{100}(-2)$$

$$= \frac{48}{100} - \frac{198}{100} = -\frac{150}{100} = -1.50$$

Josh's expectation is $−1.50 when he purchases one ticket.   ∎

In Example 5, we determined that Josh's expectation was −$1.50 when he purchased one ticket. If he purchased two tickets, his expectation would be 2(−$1.50), or −$3.00. We could also compute Josh's expectation if he purchased two tickets as follows:

$$E = \frac{2}{100}(46) + \frac{98}{100}(-4) = -3.00$$

This answer, −$3.00, checks with the answer obtained by multiplying the expectation for a single ticket by 2.

Let's look at one more example in which a person must pay for a chance to win a prize. In the following example, there will be more than two amounts to consider.

## Example 6   *Raffle Tickets*

One thousand raffle tickets are sold for $1 each. One grand prize of $500 and two consolation prizes of $100 will be awarded. The tickets are placed in a bin. The winning tickets will be selected from the bin. Assuming that the probability that any given ticket selected for the grand prize is $\frac{1}{1000}$ and the probability that any given ticket selected for a consolation prize is $\frac{2}{1000}$, determine

a) Irene Drew's expectation if she purchases one ticket.

b) Irene's expectation if she purchases five tickets.

*Solution*

a) Three amounts are to be considered: the net gain in winning the grand prize, the net gain in winning one of the consolation prizes, and the loss of the cost of the ticket. If Irene wins the grand prize, her net gain is $499 ($500 minus $1 spent for the ticket). If Irene wins one of the consolation prizes, her net gain is $99 ($100 minus $1). The probability that Irene wins the grand prize is $\frac{1}{1000}$ and the probability that she wins a consolation prize is $\frac{2}{1000}$. The probability that she does not win a prize is $1 - \frac{1}{1000} - \frac{2}{1000} = \frac{997}{1000}$.

$$E = P_1 \cdot A_1 + P_2 \cdot A_2 + P_3 \cdot A_3$$

$$= \frac{1}{1000}(\$499) + \frac{2}{1000}(\$99) + \frac{997}{1000}(-\$1)$$

$$= \frac{499}{1000} + \frac{198}{1000} - \frac{997}{1000} = -\frac{300}{1000} = -0.30$$

Thus, Irene's expectation is −$0.30 per ticket purchased.

b) On average, Irene loses 30 cents on each ticket purchased. On five tickets, her expectation is (−$0.30)(5), or −$1.50.  ∎

## Fair Price

In Example 5, we determined that Josh's expectation was −$1.50. Now let's determine how to find out how much should have been charged for a ticket so that his expectation would be $0. If Josh's expectation were to be $0, he could be expected to break even over the long run. Suppose that Josh paid 50 cents, or $0.50, for the ticket. His expectation, if paying $0.50 for the ticket, would be calculated as follows.

$$\text{Expectation} = P(\text{Josh wins}) \cdot (\text{amount won}) + P(\text{Josh loses}) \cdot (\text{amount lost})$$

$$= \frac{1}{100}(49.50) + \frac{99}{100}(-\$0.50)$$

$$= \frac{49.50}{100} - \frac{49.50}{100} = 0$$

Thus, if Josh paid 50 cents per ticket, his expectation would be $0. The 50 cents, in this case, is called the fair price of the ticket. The *fair price* is the amount to be paid that will result in an expected value of $0. The fair price may be found by adding the *cost to play* to the *expected value*.

**Fair Price**

To determine the fair price, use the following formula.

**Fair price** = expected value + cost to play

In Example 5, the cost to play was $2 and the expected value was determined to be −$1.50. The fair price for a ticket in Example 5 may be found as follows.

Fair price = expected value + cost to play
= −1.50 + 2.00 = 0.50

We obtained a fair price of $0.50. If the tickets were sold for the fair price of $0.50 each, Josh's expectation would be $0, as shown above. Can you now find the fair price that Irene should pay for a raffle ticket in Example 6? In Example 6, the cost of a ticket was $1 and we determined that the expected value was −$0.30.

Fair price = expected value + cost to play
= −$0.30 + $1.00 = $0.70

Thus, the fair price for a ticket in Example 6 is $0.70, or 70 cents. Verify for yourself now that if the tickets were sold for $0.70, the expectation would be $0.00.

Example **7** *Expectation and Fair Price*

At a game of chance, the expected value is found to be −$1.50, and the cost to play the game is $4.00. Determine the fair price to play the game.

*Solution*   We use the formula

$$\text{Fair price} = \text{expected value} + \text{cost to play}$$
$$= -1.50 + 4.00$$
$$= 2.50$$

Thus, the fair price to play this game would be $2.50. If the cost to play was $2.50 instead of $4.00, the expected value would be $0.

---

**SECTION 12.4**   *Exercises*

## Warm Up Exercises

*In Exercises 1–4, fill in the blank with an appropriate word, phrase, or symbol(s).*

**1.** The expected gain or loss of an experiment over the long run is called the _____ value.

**2.** In an experiment, if an individual expects to have a loss in the long run, the expected value is _____.

**3.** In an experiment, if an individual expects to have a gain in the long run, the expected value is _____.

**4.** In an experiment, if an individual expects to break even in the long run, the expected value is _____.

## Practice the Skills/Problem Solving

**5.** *Expected Attendance*   For an outdoor art and craft show, event organizers estimate that 60,000 people will attend if it is not raining. If it is raining, event organizers estimate that 21,000 people will attend. On the day of the show, meteorologists predict a 70% chance of rain. Determine the expected number of people who will attend this show.

**6.** *A New Business*   In a proposed business venture, Stephanie Morrison estimates that there is a 60% chance she will make $80,000 and a 40% chance she will lose $20,000. Determine Stephanie's expected value.

**7.** *Basketball*   Shenise Johnson is a star player for the University of Miami Hurricanes women's basketball team. She has injured her ankle, and it is doubtful that she will be able to play in an upcoming game. If Shenise can play, the coach estimates that the Hurricanes will score 78 points. If Shenise is not able to play, the coach estimates that they will score 62 points. The team doctor estimates that there is a 50% chance Shenise will play. Determine the number of points the team can expect to score.

▲ *Shenise Johnson (left)*

**8.** *Career Fair Attendance*   For a Nursing and Allied Health Care Career Fair, organizers estimate that 50 people will attend if it does not rain and 65 will attend if it rains. The weather forecast indicates that there is a 40% chance it will not rain and a 60% chance it will rain on the day of the career fair. Determine the expected number of people who will attend the fair.

**9.** *TV Shows*   The Fox television network is scheduling its fall lineup of shows. For the Tuesday night 8 P.M. slot, Fox has selected the show *Glee*. If its rival network CBS schedules the show *NCIS* during the same time slot, Fox estimates that *Glee* will get 1.2 million viewers. However, if CBS schedules the show *Survivor* during that time slot, Fox estimates that *Glee* will get 1.6 million viewers. Fox believes that the probability that CBS will show *NCIS* is 0.4 and the probability that CBS will show *Survivor* is 0.6. Determine the expected number of viewers for the show *Glee*.

10. *Seattle Greenery*  In July in Seattle, the grass grows $\frac{1}{2}$ in. a day on a sunny day and $\frac{1}{4}$ in. a day on a cloudy day. In Seattle in July, 75% of the days are sunny and 25% are cloudy.

   a) Determine the expected amount of grass growth on a typical day in July in Seattle.

   b) Determine the expected total grass growth in the month of July in Seattle.

11. *Investment Club*  The Triple L investment club is considering purchasing a certain stock. After considerable research, the club members determine that there is a 70% chance of making $10,000, a 10% chance of breaking even, and a 20% chance of losing $7500. Determine the expectation of this purchase.

12. *Clothing Sale*  At a special clothing sale at the Crescent Oaks Country Club, after the cashier rings up your purchase, you select a slip of paper from a box. The slip of paper indicates the dollar amount, either $5 or $10, that is deducted from your purchase price. The probability of selecting a slip indicating $5 is $\frac{7}{10}$, and the probability of selecting a slip indicating $10 is $\frac{3}{10}$. If your original purchase before you select the slip of paper is $200, determine

   a) the expected dollar amount to be deducted from your purchase.

   b) the expected dollar amount you will pay for your purchase.

13. *Fortune Cookies*  At the Royal Dragon Chinese restaurant, a slip in the fortune cookies indicates a dollar amount that will be subtracted from your total bill. A bag of 10 fortune cookies is given to you from which you will select one. If seven fortune cookies contain "$1 off," two contain "$2 off," and one contains "$5 off," determine the expectation of a selection.

14. *Pick a Card*  Mike and Dave play the following game. Mike picks a card from a deck of cards. If he selects a club, Dave gives him $4. If not, he gives Dave $2.

   a) Determine Mike's expectation.

   b) Determine Dave's expectation.

15. *Roll a Die*  Alyssa and Gabriel play the following game. Alyssa rolls a die. If she rolls a 1, 2, or 3, Gabriel gives Alyssa $3. If Alyssa rolls a 4 or 5, Gabriel gives Alyssa $2. However, if Alyssa rolls a 6, she gives Gabriel $14.

   a) Determine Alyssa's expectation.

   b) Determine Gabriel's expectation.

16. *Blue Chips and Red Chips*  A bag contains 4 blue chips and 6 red chips. Chi and Dolly play the following game. Chi selects one chip at random from the bag. If Chi selects

a blue chip, Dolly gives Chi $6. If Chi selects a red chip, Chi gives Dolly $5.

   a) Determine Chi's expectation.

   b) Determine Dolly's expectation.

17. *Multiple-Choice Test*  A multiple-choice exam has five possible answers for each question. For each correct answer, you are awarded 5 points. For each incorrect answer, 1 point is subtracted from your score. For answers left blank, no points are added or subtracted.

   a) If you do not know the correct answer to a particular question, is it to your advantage to guess? Explain.

   b) If you do not know the correct answer but can eliminate one possible choice, is it to your advantage to guess? Explain.

18. *Multiple-Choice Test*  A multiple-choice exam has four possible answers for each question. For each correct answer, you are awarded 5 points. For each incorrect answer, 2 points are subtracted from your score. For answers left blank, no points are added or subtracted.

   a) If you do not know the correct answer to a particular question, is it to your advantage to guess? Explain.

   b) If you do not know the correct answer but can eliminate one possible choice, is it to your advantage to guess? Explain.

19. *Fair Price*  The expected value when you purchase a lottery ticket is −$2.00, and the cost of the ticket is $5.00. Determine the fair price of the lottery ticket.

20. *Fair Price*  The expected value of a carnival game is −$6.50, and the cost to play the game is $10.00. Determine the fair price to play the game.

21. *Raffle Tickets*  Five hundred raffle tickets are sold for $3 each. One prize of $500 is to be awarded. Raul Mondesi purchases one ticket.

   a) Determine his expected value.

   b) Determine the fair price of a ticket.

**22. Raffle Tickets**   One thousand raffle tickets are sold for $1 each. One prize of $800 is to be awarded. Rena Condos purchases one ticket.

   **a)** Determine her expected value.

   **b)** Determine the fair price of a ticket.

**23. Raffle Tickets**   Two thousand raffle tickets are sold for $3 each. Three prizes will be awarded: one for $1000 and two for $500. Assume that the probability that any given ticket is selected for the $1000 prize is $\frac{1}{2000}$ and the probability that any given ticket is selected for the $500 prize is $\frac{2}{2000}$. Jeremy Sharp purchases one of these tickets.

   **a)** Determine his expected value.

   **b)** Determine the fair price of a ticket.

**24. Raffle Tickets**   Ten thousand raffle tickets are sold for $5 each. Four prizes will be awarded: one for $5000, one for $2500, and two for $1000. Assume that the probability that any given ticket is selected for the $5000 prize is $\frac{1}{10,000}$, the probability that any given ticket is selected for the $2500 prize is $\frac{1}{10,000}$, and the probability that any given ticket is selected for a $1000 prize is $\frac{2}{10,000}$. Sidhardt purchases one of these tickets.

   **a)** Determine his expected value.

   **b)** Determine the fair price of a ticket.

**Spinners**   In Exercises 25 and 26, assume that a person spins the pointer and is awarded the amount indicated by the pointer. Determine the person's expectation.

**25.**

**26.**

**Spinners**   In Exercises 27 and 28, assume that a person spins the pointer and is awarded the amount indicated if the pointer points to a positive number but must pay the amount indicated if the pointer points to a negative number. Determine the person's expectation if the person plays the game.

**27.**

**28.**

**Selecting an Envelope**   In Exercises 29–32, a person randomly selects one of the six envelopes shown below. Each envelope contains a check that the person gets to keep. Determine the person's expectation if the checks in the envelopes are as follows.

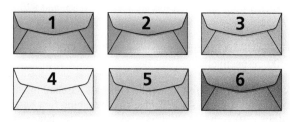

**29.** Three envelopes contain a $500 check, and three envelopes contain a $1000 check.

**30.** Four envelopes contain a $1000 check, and two envelopes contain a $5000 check.

**31.** The six envelopes contain checks for $100, $200, $300, $400, $500, and $1000, respectively.

**32.** Two envelopes contain a check for $600, two envelopes contain a check for $2000, and two envelopes contain a check for $5000.

**Spinners**   In Exercises 33–36, assume that a person spins the pointer and is awarded the amount indicated by the pointer. If it costs $2 to play the game, determine

   **a)** the expectation of a person who plays the game.

   **b)** the fair price to play the game.

**33.**                                          **34.**

**35.**                                          **36.**

**Selecting an Envelope**   In Exercises 37–40 on page 706, a person randomly selects one of the four envelopes shown below. Each envelope contains a check that the person gets to keep. However, before the person can select an envelope, he or she must pay $15 to play. For the value of the checks indicated in the exercises, determine the expectation for a person who plays.

**37.** Two envelopes contain a $10 check, and two envelopes contain a $25 check.

**38.** Three envelopes contain a $20 check, and one envelope contains a $0 check.

**39.** The checks in the envelopes are for $0, $2, $5, and $20, respectively.

**40.** The checks in the envelopes are for $2, $2, $100, and $400, respectively.

**41.** *Reaching Base Safely*  Based on his past baseball history, Jim Devias has a 17% chance of reaching first base safely, a 10% chance of hitting a double, a 2% chance of hitting a triple, an 8% chance of hitting a home run, and a 63% chance of making an out at his next at bat. Determine Jim's expected number of bases for his next at bat.

**42.** *Life Insurance*  According to Bristol Mutual Life Insurance's mortality table, the probability that a 20-year-old woman will survive 1 year is 0.994 and the probability that she will die within 1 year is 0.006. If a 20-year-old woman buys a $10,000 1-year policy for $100, what is Bristol Mutual's expected gain or loss?

**43.** *Choosing a Colored Chip*  In a box, there are a total of 10 chips. The chips are orange, green, and yellow, as shown below.

If you select an orange chip, you get 4 points, a green chip 3 points, and a yellow chip 1 point. If you select one chip at random, determine the expected number of points you will get.

**44.** *Choosing a Colored Chip*  Repeat Exercise 43 but assume that an orange chip is worth 5 points, a green chip 2 points, and a yellow chip −3 points (3 points are taken away).

**45.** *Employee Hiring*  The academic vice president at Brookdale Community College has requested that new academic programs be added to the college curriculum. If the college's Board of Trustees approves the new programs, the college will hire 75 new employees. If the new programs are not approved, the college will hire only 20 new employees. If the probability that the new programs will be approved is 0.65, what is the expected number of new employees to be hired by Brookdale Community College? Round your answer to the nearest whole number of employees.

**46.** *Completing a Project*  A mechanical contractor is preparing for a construction project. He determines that if he completes the project on schedule, his net profit will be $450,000. If he completes the project between 0 and 3 months late, his net profit decreases to $120,000. If he completes the project more

than 3 months late, his net loss is $275,000. The probability that he completes the project on schedule is 0.6, the probability that he completes the project between 0 and 3 months late is 0.3, and the probability that he completes the project more than 3 months late is 0.1. Determine his expected gain or loss for this project.

**47.** *New Store*  Dunkin' Donuts is opening a new store. The company estimates that there is a 75% chance the store will have a profit of $20,000, a 10% chance the store will break even, and a 15% chance the store will lose $3000. Determine the expected gain or loss for this store.

**48.** *China Cabinet*  The owner of an antique store estimates that there is a 40% chance she will make $2000 when she sells an antique china cabinet, a 50% chance she will make $750 when she sells the cabinet, and a 10% chance she will break even when she sells the cabinet. Determine the expected amount she will make when she sells the cabinet.

**49.** *Rolling a Die*  A die is rolled many times, and the points facing up are recorded. Determine the expected (average) number of points facing up over the long run.

**50.** *Lawsuit*  Don Vello is considering bringing a lawsuit against the Dummote Chemical Company. His lawyer estimates that there is a 70% chance Don will make $60,000, a 10% chance Don will break even, and a 20% chance they will lose the case and Don will need to pay $30,000 in legal fees. Estimate Don's expected gain or loss if he proceeds with the lawsuit.

**51.** *Road Service*  On a clear day in Boston, the Automobile Association of American (AAA) makes an average of 110 service calls for motorist assistance, on a rainy day it makes an average of 160 service calls, and on a snowy day it makes an average of 210 service calls. If the weather in Boston is clear 200 days of the year, rainy 100 days of the year, and snowy 65 days of the year, determine the expected number of service calls made by the AAA in a given day.

**52.** *Real Estate*  The expenses for Jorge Estrada, a real estate agent, to list, advertise, and attempt to sell a house are $1400. If Jorge succeeds in selling the house, he will receive a commission of 6% of the sales price. If an agent with a different company sells the house, Jorge still receives 3% of the sales price. If the house is unsold after 3 months, Jorge loses the listing and receives nothing. Suppose that the probability that he sells a $150,000 house is 0.2, the probability that another agent sells the house is 0.5, and the probability that the house is unsold after 3 months is 0.3. Determine Jorge's expectation if he accepts this house for listing. Should Jorge list the house?

**Dart Board** *In Exercises 53 and 54, assume that you are blindfolded and throw a dart at the dart board shown below. Assume that your dart sticks in the dart board, and not on a line.*

**a)** *Determine the probabilities that the dart lands on $1, $10, $20, and $100, respectively.*

**b)** *If you win the amount of money indicated by the section of the board where the dart lands, determine your expectation when you throw the dart.*

**53.**

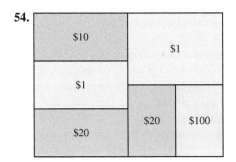

**54.**

## Challenge Problems/Group Activities

**55.** *Term Life Insurance* An insurance company will pay the face value of a term life insurance policy if the insured person dies during the term of the policy. For how much should an insurance company sell a 10-year term policy with a face value of $40,000 to a 30-year-old man for the company to make a profit? The probability of a 30-year-old man living to age 40 is 0.97. Explain your answer. Remember that the customer pays for the insurance before the policy becomes effective.

**56.** *Lottery Ticket* Is it possible to determine your expectation when you purchase a lottery ticket? Explain.

**Roulette** *In Exercises 57 and 58, use the roulette wheel illustrated. A roulette wheel typically contains slots with numbers 1–36 and slots marked 0 and 00. A ball is spun on the wheel and comes to rest in one of the 38 slots. Eighteen numbers are colored red, and 18 numbers are colored black. The 0 and 00 are colored green. If you bet on one particular number and the ball lands on that number, the house pays off odds of 35 to 1. If you bet on a red number or black number and win, the house pays 1 to 1 (even money).*

**57.** Determine the expected value of betting $1 on a particular number.

**58.** Determine the expected value of betting $1 on red.

## Recreational Mathematics

**59.** *Wheel of Fortune* The following is a miniature version of the Wheel of Fortune. When Dave Salem spins the wheel, he is awarded the amount on the wheel indicated by the pointer. If the wheel points to Bankrupt, he loses the total amount he has accumulated and also loses his turn. Assume that the wheel stops on a position at random and that each position is equally likely to occur.

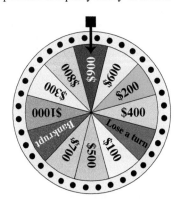

**a)** Determine Mr. Salem's expectation when he spins the wheel at the start of the game (he has no money to lose if he lands on Bankrupt).

**b)** If Mr. Salem presently has a balance of $1800, determine his expectation when he spins the wheel.

# SECTION 12.5     Tree Diagrams

Suppose a deli offers a lunch special consisting of a sandwich, a beverage, and a dessert. The sandwich choices are roast beef, ham, or turkey. The beverage choices are soda, coffee, or tea. The dessert choices are a brownie or a chocolate chip cookie. If a customer purchases a lunch special and makes selections at random, what is the probability the customer selects a roast beef sandwich and a chocolate chip cookie? In this section, we will illustrate how the counting principle and tree diagrams can be used to determine the answers to questions like the one posed above. We will also illustrate how tree diagrams can be used to determine all the possible outcomes of an experiment.

▲ We can use a tree diagram to illustrate the possible lunch specials at a deli.

**Why** *This is Important*  Being able to determine the number of possible outcomes in an experiment is essential to solving many probability problems.

N ow we will introduce the counting principle. The counting principle will be used again in Section 12.8.

### Counting Principle
If a first experiment can be performed in $M$ distinct ways and a second experiment can be performed in $N$ distinct ways, then the two experiments in that specific order can be performed in $M \cdot N$ distinct ways.

If we wanted to find the number of possible outcomes when a coin is tossed and a die is rolled, we could reason that the coin has two possible outcomes, heads and tails. The die has six possible outcomes: 1, 2, 3, 4, 5, and 6. Thus, the two experiments together have $2 \cdot 6$, or 12, possible outcomes.

A list of all the possible outcomes of an experiment is called a *sample space*. Each individual outcome in the sample space is called a *sample point. Tree diagrams* are helpful in determining sample spaces.

A tree diagram illustrating all the possible outcomes when a coin is tossed and a die is rolled (see Fig. 12.6) has two initial branches, one for each possible outcome of the coin. Each of these branches will have six branches emerging from them, one for each possible outcome of the die. That will give a total of 12 branches, the same number of possible outcomes found by using the counting principle. We can obtain the sample space by listing all the possible combinations of branches. Note that this sample space consists of 12 sample points.

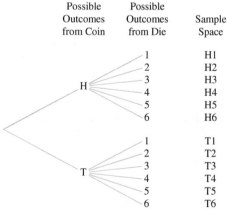

| Possible Outcomes from Coin | Possible Outcomes from Die | Sample Space |
|---|---|---|
| H | 1 | H1 |
|   | 2 | H2 |
|   | 3 | H3 |
|   | 4 | H4 |
|   | 5 | H5 |
|   | 6 | H6 |
| T | 1 | T1 |
|   | 2 | T2 |
|   | 3 | T3 |
|   | 4 | T4 |
|   | 5 | T5 |
|   | 6 | T6 |

Figure 12.6

Example 1 uses the phrase "without replacement." This phrase tells us that once an item is selected, it cannot be selected again, making it impossible to select the same item twice.

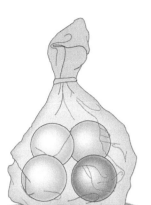

Figure 12.7

## Example 1  *Selecting Balls without Replacement*

Two balls are to be selected *without replacement* from a bag that contains one red, one blue, one green, and one orange ball (see Fig. 12.7).

a) Use the counting principle to determine the number of points in the sample space.
b) Construct a tree diagram and list the sample space.
c) Determine the probability that one orange ball is selected.
d) Determine the probability that a green ball followed by a red ball is selected.

### Solution

a) The first selection may be any one of the four balls. Once the first ball is selected, only three balls remain for the second selection. Thus, there are $4 \cdot 3$, or 12, sample points in the sample space.

b) The first ball selected can be red, blue, green, or orange. Since this experiment is done without replacement, the same colored ball cannot be selected twice. For example, if the first ball selected is red, the second ball selected must be either blue, green, or orange. The tree diagram and sample space are shown in Fig. 12.8. The sample space contains 12 points. That result checks with the answer obtained in part (a) using the counting principle.

| First Selection | Second Selection | Sample Space |
|---|---|---|
| R | B | RB |
|   | G | RG |
|   | O | RO |
| B | R | BR |
|   | G | BG |
|   | O | BO |
| G | R | GR |
|   | B | GB |
|   | O | GO |
| O | R | OR |
|   | B | OB |
|   | G | OG |

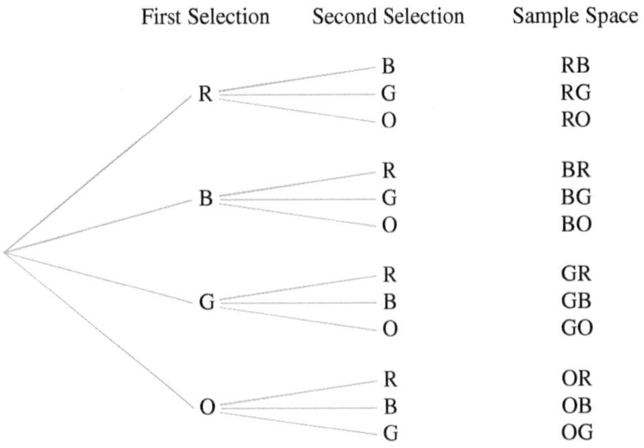

Figure 12.8

c) If we know the sample space, we can compute probabilities using the formula

$$P(E) = \frac{\text{number of outcomes favorable to } E}{\text{total number of outcomes}}$$

The total number of outcomes will be the number of points in the sample space. From Fig. 12.8, we determine that there are 12 possible outcomes. Six outcomes have one orange ball: RO, BO, GO, OR, OB, and OG.

$$P(\text{one orange ball is selected}) = \frac{6}{12} = \frac{1}{2}$$

d) One possible outcome meets the criteria of a green ball followed by a red ball: GR.

$$P(\text{green followed by red}) = \frac{1}{12}$$

The counting principle can be extended to any number of experiments, as illustrated in Example 2.

## Example 2  *Lunch Choices*

At Finlay's Restaurant, each lunch special consists of a sandwich, a salad, and a beverage. The sandwich choices are roast beef (R), ham (H), or turkey (T). The salad choices are macaroni (M) or potato (P). The beverage choices are coffee (C) or soda (S).

a) Use the counting principle to determine the number of different lunch specials offered by this restaurant.

b) Construct a tree diagram and list the sample space.

c) If a customer randomly selects one of the lunch specials, determine the probability that a roast beef sandwich and soda are selected.

d) If a customer randomly selects one of the lunch specials, determine the probability that neither macaroni salad nor coffee is selected.

### Solution

a) There are 3 choices for a sandwich, 2 choices for a salad, and 2 choices for a beverage. Using the counting principle, we can determine that there are $3 \cdot 2 \cdot 2$, or 12, different lunch specials.

b) The tree diagram illustrating the 12 lunch specials is given in Fig. 12.9.

| Sandwich | Salad | Beverage | Sample Space |
|----------|-------|----------|--------------|
| R | M | C | RMC |
|   |   | S | RMS |
|   | P | C | RPC |
|   |   | S | RPS |
| H | M | C | HMC |
|   |   | S | HMS |
|   | P | C | HPC |
|   |   | S | HPS |
| T | M | C | TMC |
|   |   | S | TMS |
|   | P | C | TPC |
|   |   | S | TPS |

**Figure 12.9**

c) Of the 12 lunch specials, 2 contain both a roast beef sandwich and soda (RMS, RPS).

$$P(\text{roast beef sandwich and soda are selected}) = \frac{2}{12} = \frac{1}{6}$$

d) Of the 12 lunch specials, 3 contain neither macaroni salad nor coffee (RPS, HPS, TPS).

$$P(\text{neither macaroni salad nor coffee are selected}) = \frac{3}{12} = \frac{1}{4}$$

▲ Bon Jovi

## Example 3  *Selecting Ticket Winners*

A radio station has two tickets to give away to a Bon Jovi concert. It held a contest and narrowed the possible recipients down to four people: Christine (C), Mike Hammer (MH), Mike Levine (ML), and Phyllis (P). The names of two of these four people will be selected at random from a hat, and the two people selected will be awarded the tickets.

a) Use the counting principle to determine the number of points in the sample space.

b) Construct a tree diagram and list the sample space.

c) Determine the probability that Christine is selected.

d) Determine the probability that neither Mike Hammer nor Mike Levine is selected.

e) Determine the probability that at least one Mike is selected.

**Solution**

a) The first selection may be any one of the four people; see Fig. 12.10. Once the first person is selected, only three people remain for the second selection. Thus, there are 4 · 3, or 12, sample points in the sample space.

b)

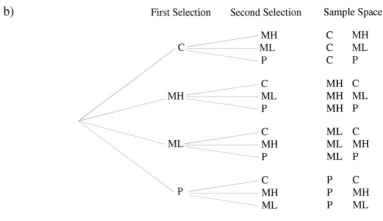

Figure 12.10

c) Of the 12 points in the sample space, 6 have Christine. They are C MH, C ML, C P, MH C, ML C, and P C.

$$P(\text{Christine is selected}) = \frac{6}{12} = \frac{1}{2}$$

d) Of the 12 points in the sample space, two have neither Mike. They are C P and P C.

$$P(\text{neither Mike selected}) = \frac{2}{12} = \frac{1}{6}$$

e) At least one Mike means that one or more Mikes are selected. There are 10 points in the sample space with at least one Mike (all those except C P and P C).

$$P(\text{at least one Mike is selected}) = \frac{10}{12} = \frac{5}{6}$$

In Example 3, if you add the probability of no Mike being selected with the probability of at least one Mike being selected, you get $\frac{1}{6} + \frac{5}{6}$, or 1. In any probability problem, if $E$ is a specific event, then either $E$ happens at least one time or it does not happen at all. Thus, $P(E \text{ happening at least once}) + P(E \text{ does not happen}) = 1$, which leads to the following rule.

### Probability of an Event Happening At Least Once
The probability of an event happening at least once can be determined by the following formula.

$$P(\text{event happening at least once}) = 1 - P(\text{event does not happen})$$

For example, suppose that the probability of not getting any red flowers from the seeds that are planted is $\frac{2}{7}$. Then the probability of getting at least one red flower from the seeds that are planted is $1 - \frac{2}{7} = \frac{5}{7}$. We will use this rule in later sections.

In all the tree diagrams in this section, the outcomes were always equally likely; that is, each outcome had the same probability of occurrence. Consider a rock that has 4 faces such that each face has a different surface area and the rock is not

Figure 12.11

uniform in density (see Fig. 12.11). When the rock is dropped, the probability that the rock lands on face 1 will not be the same as the probability that the rock lands on face 2. In fact, the probabilities that the rock lands on face 1, face 2, face 3, and face 4 may all be different. Therefore, the outcomes of the rock landing on face 1, face 2, face 3, and face 4 are not equally likely outcomes. Because the outcomes are not equally likely and we are not given additional information, we cannot determine the theoretical probability of the rock landing on each individual face. However, we can still determine the sample space indicating the faces that the rock may land on when the rock is dropped twice. The tree diagram and sample space are shown in Fig. 12.12.

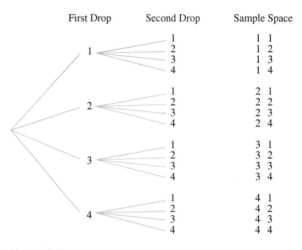

Figure 12.12

Since the outcomes are not equally likely, the probability of each of the 16 sample points in the sample space occurring cannot be determined. If the outcomes were equally likely, then each of the 16 points in the sample space would have a probability of $\frac{1}{16}$. See Exercises 27 and 28, which deal with outcomes that are not equally likely.

## Exercises

### Warm Up Exercises

*In Exercises 1–4, fill in the blank with an appropriate word, phrase, or symbol(s).*

1. A list of all possible outcomes of an experiment is called a(n) _____ space.

2. Each individual outcome in a sample space is called a sample _____.

3. If a first experiment can be performed in two distinct ways and a second experiment can be performed in seven distinct ways, the two experiments together can be performed in _____ distinct ways.

4. A helpful method to determine a sample space is to construct a(n) _____ diagram.

### Practice the Skills

5. **Selecting States** If two states are selected at random from the 50 U.S. states, use the counting principle to determine the number of possible outcomes if the states are selected

   a) with replacement.

   b) without replacement.

6. **Selecting Dates** If two dates are selected at random from the 365 days of the year, use the counting principle to determine the number of possible outcomes if the dates are selected

   a) with replacement.

   b) without replacement.

7. *Selecting Golfballs* A bag contains six golfballs, all the same size and equally likely to be selected. Each golfball is a different brand. If you select three golfballs at random, use the counting principle to determine how many points will be in the sample space if the golfballs are selected

a) with replacement.

b) without replacement.

8. *Remote Control* Your television remote control has buttons for digits 0–9. If you press two buttons, how many numbers are possible if

a) the same button may be pressed twice.

b) the same button may not be pressed twice.

## Problem Solving

*In Exercises 9–26, use the counting principle to determine the answer to part (a). Assume that each event is equally likely to occur.*

9. *Coin Toss* Two coins are tossed.

a) Determine the number of points in the sample space.

b) Construct a tree diagram and list the sample space.

Determine the probability that

c) no heads are tossed.

d) exactly one head is tossed.

e) two heads are tossed.

10. *Boys and Girls* A couple plans to have two children.

a) Determine the number of points in the sample space of the possible arrangements of boys and girls.

b) Construct a tree diagram and list the sample space.

Assuming that boys and girls are equally likely, determine the probability that the couple has

c) two girls.

d) at least one girl.

e) a girl and then a boy.

11. *Cards* A box contains three cards. On one card there is a sun, on another card there is a question mark, and on the third card there is an apple.

Two cards are to be selected at random with replacement.

a) Determine the number of points in the sample space.

b) Construct a tree diagram and list the sample space.

Determine the probability that

c) two apples are selected.

d) a sun and then a question mark are selected.

e) at least one apple is selected.

12. *Cards* Repeat Exercise 11 but assume that the cards are drawn without replacement.

13. *Marble Selection* A hat contains four marbles: 1 yellow, 1 red, 1 blue, and 1 green. Two marbles are to be selected at random without replacement from the hat.

a) Determine the number of points in the sample space.

b) Construct a tree diagram and list the sample space.

Determine the probability of selecting

c) exactly 1 red marble.

d) at least 1 marble that is not red.

e) no green marbles.

14. *Three Coins* Three coins are tossed.

a) Determine the number of points in the sample space.

b) Construct a tree diagram and list the sample space.

Determine the probability that

c) no heads are tossed.

d) exactly one head is tossed.

e) three heads are tossed.

15. *Paint Choices* The Flotterons plan to purchase paint for the walls and paint for the trim in their living room. They will select one color for the walls and one color for the trim from the following colors.

| Walls | Trim |
| --- | --- |
| Sable | Alabaster |
| Java | White |
| Chocolate | Oyster |

a) Determine the number of points in the sample space.

b) Construct a tree diagram and list the sample space.

Determine the probability that they select

c) Java.

d) Java and Oyster.

e) paint other than Java.

16. *Pet Shop*  A pet shop is selling a calico cat, a Siamese cat, a Persian cat, and a Himalayan cat. The Chens are going to select two cats to bring home as pets.

a) Determine the number of points in the sample space.

b) Construct a tree diagram and list the sample space.

Determine the probability that they select

c) the Persian cat.

d) the Persian cat and the calico cat.

e) cats other than the Persian cat.

17. *Rolling Dice*  Two dice are rolled.

a) Determine the number of points in the sample space.

b) Construct a tree diagram and list the sample space.

Determine the probability that

c) a double (a 1, 1 or 2, 2, etc.) is rolled.

d) a sum of 8 is rolled.

e) a sum of 2 is rolled.

f) Are you as likely to roll a sum of 2 as you are of rolling a sum of 8?

18. *Voting*  At a homeowners' association meeting, a board member can vote yes, vote no, or abstain on a motion. There are three motions on which a board member must vote.

a) Determine the number of points in the sample space.

b) Construct a tree diagram and determine the sample space.

Determine the probability that a board member votes

c) no, yes, no in that order.

d) yes on exactly two of the motions.

e) yes on at least one motion.

19. *Dinner Specials*  At Brio Restaurant, each dinner special consists of an appetizer, a salad, and an entrée. The choices of appetizer, salad, and entrée are listed below.

| Appetizer | Salad | Entrée |
|---|---|---|
| Bruschetta | Caesar | Ravioli |
| Antipasto | Greens | Salmon |
| | | Lasagna |

a) Determine the number of points in the sample space.

b) Construct a tree diagram and determine the sample space.

If a customer randomly selects one of the dinner specials, determine the probability the customer selects

c) bruschetta for the appetizer.

d) greens and lasagna.

e) an entrée other than ravioli.

20. *Gift Cards*  Three different people are to be selected at random, and each will be given one gift card. There is one card from Home Depot, one from Best Buy, and one from Red Lobster. The first person selected gets to choose one of the cards. The second person selected gets to choose between the two remaining cards. The third person selected gets the third card.

a) Determine the number of points in the sample space.

b) Construct a tree diagram and determine the sample space.

Determine the probability that

c) the Best Buy card is selected first.

d) the Home Depot card is selected first and the Red Lobster card is selected last.

e) The cards are selected in this order: Best Buy, Red Lobster, Home Depot.

21. *Apartment Options*  Don Cater plans to rent an apartment from Rustic Village Apartments. The following chart displays information regarding the possible number of bedrooms, bathrooms, and other features from which he can choose. For his apartment, Don will select the number of bedrooms, number of bathrooms, and one other feature.

| Bedrooms | Bathrooms | Other Features |
|---|---|---|
| 1 | 1 | Fireplace |
| 2 | 2 | Hardwood floors |
| 3 | | Balcony |

a) Determine the number of points in the sample space.

b) Construct a tree diagram and determine the sample space.

Determine the probability that Don selects

c) a two-bedroom apartment.

d) a two-bedroom apartment with a fireplace.

e) an apartment without a balcony.

**22.** *A New Home Theater System* You visit Best Buy to purchase a new home theater system. You are going to purchase a Blu-ray player, a receiver, and a speaker system from among the following brands.

| Blu-ray Player | Receiver | Speaker System |
|---|---|---|
| LG | Yamaha | Bose |
| Toshiba | Onkyo | JBL |
| Sony | Pioneer | |
| Insignia | | |

a) Determine the number of points in the sample space.

b) Construct a tree diagram and determine the sample space.

Determine the probability of selecting

c) a Sony Blu-ray player.

d) Bose speakers.

e) a Sony Blu-ray player and Bose speakers.

**23.** *Landscaping* Mr. and Mrs. Frank just moved into a new home and need to do some landscaping. They are going to purchase one tree, one shrub, and one lilac bush from the list below.

| Trees | Shrubs | Lilac Bushes |
|---|---|---|
| Dogwood | Forsythia | Common |
| Maple | Holly | Sensation |
| Birch | Juniper | Primrose |

a) Determine the number of points in the sample space.

b) Construct a tree diagram and determine the sample space.

Determine the probability that the Franks select

c) a maple tree.

d) a dogwood tree and a holly shrub.

e) a lilac bush other than Sensation.

▲ *Lilacs*

**24.** *Literature Choices* You decide to take a literature course. A requirement for the course is that you must read one classic book, one nonfiction book, and one science fiction book from the list below.

| Classic | Nonfiction | Science Fiction |
|---|---|---|
| *A Farewell to Arms* (*F*) | *John Adams* (*J*) | *Dune* (*D*) |
| *The Grapes of Wrath* (*G*) | *Angela's Ashes* (*A*) | *Ender's Game* (*E*) |
| *Tom Sawyer* (*T*) | | |
| *Moby-Dick* (*M*) | | |

a) Determine the number of points in the sample space.

b) Construct a tree diagram and determine the sample space.

Determine the probability that

c) *John Adams* is selected.

d) either *A Farewell to Arms* or *Tom Sawyer* is selected.

e) *Moby Dick* is not selected.

**25.** *Personal Characteristics* An individual can be classified as male or female with red, brown, black, or blond hair and with brown, blue, or green eyes.

a) How many different classifications are possible (for example, male, red-headed, blue-eyed)?

b) Construct a tree diagram to determine the sample space.

**c)** If each outcome is equally likely, determine the probability that the individual will be a male with black hair and blue eyes.

**d)** Determine the probability that the individual will be a female with blond hair.

**26. *Mendel Revisited*** A pea plant must have exactly one of each of the following pairs of traits: short (*s*) or tall (*t*); round (*r*) or wrinkled (*w*) seeds; yellow (*y*) or green (*g*) peas; and white (*wh*) or purple (*p*) flowers (for example, short, wrinkled, green pea with white flowers).

**a)** How many different classifications of pea plants are possible?

**b)** Use a tree diagram to determine all the classifications possible.

**c)** If each characteristic is equally likely, find the probability that the pea plant will have round peas.

**d)** Determine the probability that the pea plant will be short, have wrinkled seeds, have yellow seeds, and have purple flowers.

## Challenge Problems/Group Activities

**27. *Three Chips*** Suppose that a bag contains one white chip and two red chips. Two chips are going to be selected at random from the bag *with replacement*.

**a)** What is the probability of selecting a white chip from the bag on the first selection?

**b)** What is the probability of selecting a red chip from the bag on the first selection?

**c)** Are the outcomes of selecting a white chip and selecting a red chip on the first selection equally likely? Explain.

**d)** The sample space when two chips are selected from the bag with replacement is ww, wr, rw, rr. Do you believe that the probability of selecting ww is greater than, equal to, or less than the probability of selecting rr? Explain.

**28. *Thumbtacks*** A thumbtack is dropped on a concrete floor. Assume that the thumbtack can land only point up (u) or point down (d), as shown in the figure below.

If two thumbtacks are dropped, one after the other, the tree diagram below can be used to show the possible outcomes.

| First Thumbtack | Second Thumbtack | Sample Space |
|---|---|---|
| u | u | u u |
|   | d | u d |
| d | u | d u |
|   | d | d d |

**a)** Do you believe that the outcomes of the thumbtack landing point up and the thumbtack landing point down are equally likely? Explain.

**b)** List the sample points in the sample space of this experiment.

**c)** Do you believe that the probability that both thumbtacks land point up (*uu*) is the same as the probability that both thumbtacks land point down (*dd*)? Explain.

**d)** Can you compute the theoretical probability of a thumbtack landing point up and the theoretical probability of a thumbtack landing point down? Explain.

**e)** Obtain a box of thumbtacks and drop the thumbtacks out of the box with care. Determine the empirical probability of a thumbtack landing point up when dropped and the empirical probability of a thumbtack landing point down when dropped.

## Recreational Mathematics

**29. *Ties*** All my ties are red except two. All my ties are blue except two. All my ties are brown except two. How many ties do I have?

**30. *Rock Faces*** An experiment consists of 3 parts: flipping a coin, tossing a rock, and rolling a die. If the sample space consists of 60 sample points, determine the number of faces on the rock.

***Jumble*** *For Exercises 31–32, refer to the Recreational Math box on page 711. Determine*

**a)** *the number of possible arrangements of the letters given.*

**b)** *the word when the letters are placed in the proper order.*

**31.** RAHIC

**32.** STEABK

## OR and AND Problems

▲ *Selecting items from a restaurant menu often requires an understanding of the words* or *and* and.

Every day we see and interpret the words **or** and **and**. For example, in a court case a judge may sentence a person to five years in prison *and* payment of a $100,000 fine. Or a judge may sentence a person to either 1 night in jail *or* payment of a $100 fine. When you go into a restaurant, the menu may indicate that you should select soup *or* salad, *and* an entrée, *and* a dessert. In this section, we will learn to solve probability problems involving the words *or* and *and*.

**Why** *This is Important* Many real-life situations involve the words *or* and *and*. For example, what is the probability that a family planning to have 3 children has 3 boys (a boy *and* a boy *and* a boy)?

In Section 12.5, we showed how to work probability problems by constructing sample spaces. Often it is inconvenient or too time consuming to solve a problem by first constructing a sample space. For example, if an experiment consists of selecting two cards with replacement from a deck of 52 cards, there would be 52 · 52 or 2704 points in the sample space. Trying to list all these sample points could take hours. In this section, we learn how to solve *compound probability* problems that contain the words *and* or *or* without constructing a sample space.

### Or Problems

The *or probability problem* requires obtaining a "successful" outcome for *at least one* of the given events. For example, suppose that we roll one die and we are interested in finding the probability of rolling an even number *or* a number greater than 4. For this situation, rolling either a 2, 4, or 6 (an even number) or a 5 or 6 (a number greater than 4) would be considered successful. Note that the number 6 satisfies both criteria. Since 4 of the 6 numbers meet the criteria (the 2, 4, 5, and 6), the probability of rolling an even number *or* a number greater than 4 is $\frac{4}{6}$ or $\frac{2}{3}$.

A formula for finding the probability of event $A$ or event $B$, symbolized $P(A \text{ or } B)$, follows.

**Probability of A or B**

To determine the probability of $A$ or $B$, use the following formula.

$$P(A \text{ or } B) = P(A) + P(B) - P(A \text{ and } B)$$

Since we add (and subtract) probabilities to find $P(A \text{ or } B)$, this formula is sometimes referred to as the *addition formula*. We explain the use of the *or* formula in Example 1.

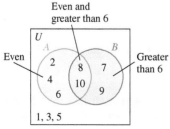

**Figure 12.13**

⌐Example **1** *Using the Addition Formula*

Each of the numbers 1, 2, 3, 4, 5, 6, 7, 8, 9, and 10 is written on a separate piece of paper. The 10 pieces of paper are then placed in a hat, and one piece is randomly selected. Determine the probability that the piece of paper selected contains an even number or a number greater than 6.

*Solution* We are asked to find the probability that the number selected is *even* or is *greater than 6*. Let's use set $A$ to represent the statement "the number is even" and set $B$ to represent the statement "the number is greater than 6." Figure 12.13 is a

Venn diagram, as introduced in Chapter 2, with sets $A$ (even) and $B$ (greater than 6). There are a total of 10 numbers, of which five are even (2, 4, 6, 8, and 10). Thus, the probability of selecting an even number is $\frac{5}{10}$. Four numbers are greater than 6: the 7, 8, 9, and 10. Thus, the probability of selecting a number greater than 6 is $\frac{4}{10}$. Two numbers are both even and greater than 6: the 8 and 10. Thus, the probability of selecting a number that is both even and greater than 6 is $\frac{2}{10}$.

If we substitute the appropriate statements for $A$ and $B$ in the formula, we obtain

$$P(A \text{ or } B) = P(A) + P(B) - P(A \text{ and } B)$$

$$P\begin{pmatrix} \text{even or} \\ \text{greater than 6} \end{pmatrix} = P(\text{even}) + P\begin{pmatrix} \text{greater} \\ \text{than 6} \end{pmatrix} - P\begin{pmatrix} \text{even and} \\ \text{greater than 6} \end{pmatrix}$$

$$= \frac{5}{10} + \frac{4}{10} - \frac{2}{10}$$

$$= \frac{7}{10}$$

Thus, the probability of selecting an even number or a number greater than 6 is $\frac{7}{10}$. The seven numbers that are even or greater than 6 are 2, 4, 6, 7, 8, 9, and 10.    ∎

Example 1 illustrates that when finding the probability of $A$ or $B$, we add the probabilities of events $A$ and $B$ and then subtract the probability of both events occurring simultaneously.

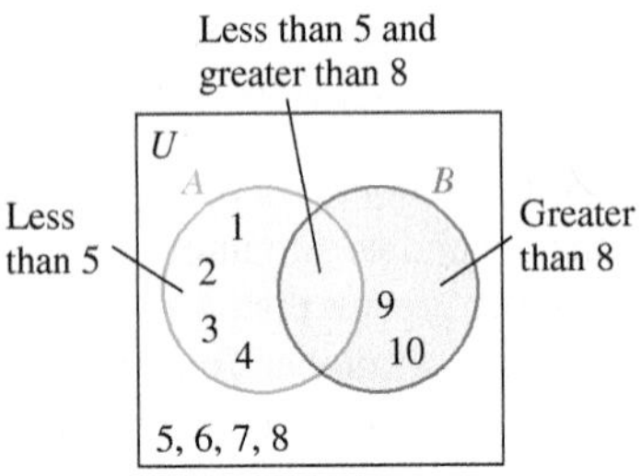

## Example 2    *Using the Addition Formula*

Consider the same sample space, the numbers 1 through 10, as in Example 1. If one piece of paper is selected, determine the probability that it contains a number less than 5 or a number greater than 8.

*Solution*    Let $A$ represent the statement "the number is less than 5" and $B$ represent the statement "the number is greater than 8." A Venn diagram illustrating these statements is shown in Figure 12.14.

$$P(\text{number is less than 5}) = \frac{4}{10}$$

$$P(\text{number is greater than 8}) = \frac{2}{10}$$

Since there are no numbers that are *both* less than 5 and greater than 8, $P(\text{number is less than 5 and greater than 8}) = 0$. Therefore,

$$P\begin{pmatrix} \text{number is} \\ \text{less than 5} \\ \text{or greater} \\ \text{than 8} \end{pmatrix} = P\begin{pmatrix} \text{number is} \\ \text{less than 5} \end{pmatrix} + P\begin{pmatrix} \text{number is} \\ \text{greater than 8} \end{pmatrix} - P\begin{pmatrix} \text{number is} \\ \text{less than 5} \\ \text{and greater} \\ \text{than 8} \end{pmatrix}$$

$$= \frac{4}{10} + \frac{2}{10} - 0 = \frac{6}{10} = \frac{3}{5}$$

Thus, the probability of selecting a number less than 5 or greater than 8 is $\frac{3}{5}$. The six numbers that are less than 5 or greater than 8 are 1, 2, 3, 4, 9, and 10.    ∎

In Example 2, it is impossible to select a number that is both less than 5 *and* greater than 8 when only one number is to be selected. Events such as these are said to be *mutually exclusive*.

Figure 12.14

Definition: **Mutually Exclusive**

Two events $A$ and $B$ are **mutually exclusive** if it is impossible for both events to occur simultaneously.

If events $A$ and $B$ are mutually exclusive, then $P(A \text{ and } B) = 0$ and the addition formula simplifies to $P(A \text{ or } B) = P(A) + P(B)$.

## Example 3  *Probability of A or B*

One card is selected from a standard deck of playing cards. Determine whether the following pairs of events are mutually exclusive and determine $P(A \text{ or } B)$.

a)  $A$ = an ace, $B$ = a 9
b)  $A$ = an ace, $B$ = a heart
c)  $A$ = a red card, $B$ = a black card
d)  $A$ = a picture card, $B$ = a red card

The ace of hearts is both an ace and a heart.

Solution

a)  There are four aces and four 9's in a standard deck of 52 cards. It is impossible to select both an ace and a 9 when only one card is selected. Therefore, these events are mutually exclusive.

$$P(\text{ace or } 9) = P(\text{ace}) + P(9) = \frac{4}{52} + \frac{4}{52} = \frac{8}{52} = \frac{2}{13}$$

b)  There are 4 aces and 13 hearts in a standard deck of 52 cards. One card, the ace of hearts, is both an ace and a heart. Therefore, these events are not mutually exclusive.

$$P(\text{ace}) = \frac{4}{52} \qquad P(\text{heart}) = \frac{13}{52} \qquad P(\text{ace and heart}) = \frac{1}{52}$$

$$P(\text{ace or heart}) = P(\text{ace}) + P(\text{heart}) - P(\text{ace and heart})$$

$$= \frac{4}{52} + \frac{13}{52} - \frac{1}{52}$$

$$= \frac{16}{52} = \frac{4}{13}$$

c)  There are 26 red cards and 26 black cards in a standard deck of 52 cards. It is impossible to select one card that is both a red card and a black card. Therefore, the events are mutually exclusive.

$$P(\text{red or black}) = P(\text{red}) + P(\text{black})$$

$$= \frac{26}{52} + \frac{26}{52} = \frac{52}{52} = 1$$

Since $P(\text{red or black}) = 1$, a red card or a black card must be selected.

d)  There are 12 picture cards in a standard deck of 52 cards. Six of the 12 picture cards are red (the jacks, queens, and kings of hearts and diamonds). Thus, selecting a picture card and a red card are not mutually exclusive.

$$P\left(\begin{array}{c}\text{picture card}\\\text{or red card}\end{array}\right) = P\left(\begin{array}{c}\text{picture}\\\text{card}\end{array}\right) + P\left(\begin{array}{c}\text{red}\\\text{card}\end{array}\right) - P\left(\begin{array}{c}\text{picture card}\\\text{and red card}\end{array}\right)$$

$$= \frac{12}{52} + \frac{26}{52} - \frac{6}{52}$$

$$= \frac{32}{52} = \frac{8}{13}$$

The probability that a husband and wife have nine children of which all are girls is $\left(\frac{1}{2}\right)^9$, or $\frac{1}{512}$.

The odds against a family having nine girls in a row is 511 to 1. Thus, for every 512 families with nine children, on average, one family will have all girls and 511 will not. However, should another child be born to that one family, the probability of the tenth child being a girl is still $\frac{1}{2}$.

## *And* Problems

A second type of probability problem is the *and probability problem*, which requires obtaining a favorable outcome in *each* of the given events. For example, suppose that *two* cards are to be selected from a deck of cards and we are interested in the probability of selecting two aces (one ace *and* then a second ace). Only if *both* cards selected are aces would this experiment be considered successful. A formula for finding the probability of events *A* and *B*, symbolized *P*(*A* and *B*), follows.

### Probability of *A* and *B*

To determine the probability of *A* and *B*, use the following formula.

$$P(A \text{ and } B) = P(A) \cdot P(B)$$

Since we multiply to find $P(A \text{ and } B)$, this formula is sometimes referred to as the *multiplication formula*. When using the multiplication formula, we **always assume that event A has occurred when calculating $P(B)$** because we are determining the probability of obtaining a favorable outcome in both of the given events.*

Unless we specify otherwise, $P(A \text{ and } B)$ indicates that we are determining the probability that event *A* occurs *and then* event *B* occurs (in that order). Consider a bag that contains three chips: 1 red chip, 1 blue chip, and 1 green chip. Suppose that two chips are selected from the bag with replacement. The tree diagram and sample space for the experiment are shown in Fig. 12.15. There are nine possible outcomes for the two selections, as indicated in the sample space.

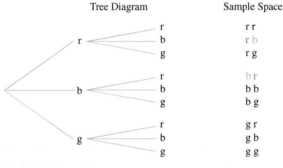

**Figure 12.15**

Note that the probability of selecting a red chip followed by a blue chip (rb), indicated by $P$(red and blue), is $\frac{1}{9}$. The probability of selecting a red chip and a blue chip, in any order (rb or br), is $\frac{2}{9}$. In this section, when we ask for $P(A \text{ and } B)$, it means the probability of event *A* occurring *and then* event *B* occurring, in that order.

### Example 4    *An Experiment with Replacement*

Two cards are to be selected *with replacement* from a deck of cards. Determine the probability that two spades will be selected.

**Solution**  Since the deck of 52 cards contains thirteen spades, the probability of selecting a spade on the first draw is $\frac{13}{52}$. The card selected is then returned to the deck. Therefore, the probability of selecting a spade on the second draw remains $\frac{13}{52}$.

---

*$P(B)$, assuming that event *A* has occurred, may be denoted $P(B|A)$, which is read "the probability of *B*, given *A*." We will discuss this type of probability (conditional probability) further in section 12.7

## Did You Know?

### The Birthday Problem

Among 24 people chosen at random, what would you guess is the probability that at least 2 of them have the same birthday? It might surprise you to learn that it is greater than 0.5. There are 365 days on which the first person selected can have a birthday. That person has a 365/365 chance of having a birthday on one of those days. The probability that the second person's birthday is on any other day is 364/365. The probability that the third person's birthday is on a day different from the first two is 363/365, and so on. The probability that the 24th person has a birthday on any other day than the first 23 people is 342/365. Thus, the probability, P, that of 24 people, no 2 have the same birthday is (365/365)×(364/365)×(363/365)× ... × (342/365) = 0.462. Then the probability of at least 2 people of 24 having the same birthday is $1 - P = 1 - 0.462 = 0.538$, or slightly larger than $\frac{1}{2}$.

If we let $A$ represent the selection of the first spade and $B$ represent the selection of the second spade, the formula may be written as follows.

$$P(A \text{ and } B) = P(A) \cdot P(B)$$

$$P(2 \text{ spades}) = P(\text{spade 1 } and \text{ spade 2}) = P(\text{spade 1}) \cdot P(\text{spade 2})$$

$$= \frac{13}{52} \cdot \frac{13}{52}$$

$$= \frac{1}{4} \cdot \frac{1}{4} = \frac{1}{16}$$

### Example 5  *An Experiment without Replacement*

Two cards are to be selected *without replacement* from a deck of cards. Determine the probability that two spades will be selected.

**Solution**  This example is similar to Example 4. However, this time we are doing the experiment without replacing the first card selected to the deck before selecting the second card.

The probability of selecting a spade on the first draw is $\frac{13}{52}$. When calculating the probability of selecting the second spade, we must assume that the first spade has been selected. Once this first spade has been selected, only 51 cards, including 12 spades, remain in the deck. The probability of selecting a spade on the second draw becomes $\frac{12}{51}$. The probability of selecting two spades without replacement is

$$P(2 \text{ spades}) = P(\text{spade 1}) \cdot P(\text{spade 2})$$

$$= \frac{13}{52} \cdot \frac{12}{51}$$

$$= \frac{1}{4} \cdot \frac{4}{17} = \frac{1}{17}$$

Now we introduce *independent events*.

### Definition:  Independent Events

Event $A$ and event $B$ are **independent events** if the occurrence of either event in no way affects the probability of occurrence of the other event.

Rolling dice and tossing coins are examples of independent events. In Example 4, the events are independent since the first card was returned to the deck. The probability of selecting a spade on the second draw was not affected by the first selection. The events in Example 5 are not independent since the probability of the selection of the second spade was affected by removing the first spade selected from the deck. Such events are called *dependent events*. *Experiments done with replacement will result in independent events, and those done without replacement will result in dependent events.*

### Example 6  *Independent or Dependent Events?*

One hundred people attended a charity benefit to raise money for cancer research. Three people in attendance will be selected at random without replacement, and each will be awarded one door prize. Are the events of selecting the three people who will be awarded the door prize independent or dependent events?

**Solution**   The events are dependent since each time one person is selected, it changes the probability of the next person being selected. In the first selection, the probability that a specific individual is selected is $\frac{1}{100}$. If that person is not selected first, the probability that the specific person is selected second changes to $\frac{1}{99}$. In general, in any experiment in which two or more items are selected *without replacement*, the events will be dependent.   ∎

The multiplication formula may be extended to more than two events, as illustrated in Example 7.

### Example 7   *Drug Reaction*

A new medicine was given to a sample of 25 of Dr. Cleary's patients with flu symptoms. Of the total, 19 patients reacted favorably, 2 reacted unfavorably, and 4 were unaffected. Three of these patients are selected at random. Determine the probability of each of the following.

a)  All three reacted favorably.

b)  The first patient reacted favorably, the second patient reacted unfavorably, and the third patient was unaffected.

c)  No patient reacted favorably.

d)  At least one patient reacted favorably.

**Solution**   Each time a patient is selected, the number of patients remaining decreases by one.

a)  The probability that the first patient reacted favorably is $\frac{19}{25}$. If the first patient reacted favorably, of the 24 remaining patients only 18 patients are left who reacted favorably. The probability of selecting a second patient who reacted favorably is $\frac{18}{24}$. If the second patient reacted favorably, only 17 patients are left who reacted favorably. The probability of selecting a third patient who reacted favorably is $\frac{17}{23}$.

$$P\begin{pmatrix}\text{three patients}\\\text{reacted}\\\text{favorably}\end{pmatrix} = P\begin{pmatrix}\text{first patient}\\\text{reacted}\\\text{favorably}\end{pmatrix} \cdot P\begin{pmatrix}\text{second patient}\\\text{reacted}\\\text{favorably}\end{pmatrix} \cdot P\begin{pmatrix}\text{third patient}\\\text{reacted}\\\text{favorably}\end{pmatrix}$$

$$= \frac{19}{25} \cdot \frac{18}{24} \cdot \frac{17}{23} = \frac{969}{2300}$$

b)  The probability that the first patient reacted favorably is $\frac{19}{25}$. Once a patient is selected, there are only 24 patients remaining. Two of the remaining 24 patients reacted unfavorably. Thus, the probability that the second patient reacted unfavorably is $\frac{2}{24}$. After the second patient is selected, there are 23 remaining patients, of which 4 were unaffected. The probability that the third patient was unaffected is therefore $\frac{4}{23}$.

$$P\begin{pmatrix}\text{first patient reacted favorably, the}\\\text{second patient reacted unfavorably, and}\\\text{the third patient was unaffected}\end{pmatrix}$$

$$= P\begin{pmatrix}\text{first patient}\\\text{reacted}\\\text{favorably}\end{pmatrix} \cdot P\begin{pmatrix}\text{second patient}\\\text{reacted}\\\text{unfavorably}\end{pmatrix} \cdot P\begin{pmatrix}\text{third patient}\\\text{was}\\\text{unaffected}\end{pmatrix}$$

$$= \frac{19}{25} \cdot \frac{2}{24} \cdot \frac{4}{23} = \frac{19}{1725}$$

**Which formula to use**

It is sometimes difficult to determine when to use the *or* formula and when to use the *and* formula. The following information may be helpful in deciding which formula to use.

**Or formula**

*Or* problems will almost always contain the word *or* in the statement of the problem. For example, determine the probability of selecting a heart *or* a 6. *Or* problems in this book generally involve only *one* selection. For example, "one card is selected" or "one die is rolled."

**And formula**

*And* problems often do *not* use the word *and* in the statement of the problem. For example, "determine the probability that both cards selected are red" or "determine the probability that none of those selected is a banana" are both *and*-type problems. *And* problems in this book will generally involve *more than one* selection. For example, the problem may read "two cards are selected" or "three coins are flipped."

c) If none of the patients reacted favorably, the patients either reacted unfavorably or were unaffected. Six patients did not react favorably (2 reacted unfavorably and 4 were unaffected). The probability that the first patient selected did not react favorably is $\frac{6}{25}$. After the first patient is selected, 5 of the remaining 24 patients did not react favorably. After the second patient is selected, 4 of the remaining 23 patients did not react favorably.

$$P\begin{pmatrix} \text{none} \\ \text{reacted} \\ \text{favorably} \end{pmatrix} = P\begin{pmatrix} \text{first patient} \\ \text{did not react} \\ \text{favorably} \end{pmatrix} \cdot P\begin{pmatrix} \text{second patient} \\ \text{did not react} \\ \text{favorably} \end{pmatrix} \cdot P\begin{pmatrix} \text{third patient} \\ \text{did not react} \\ \text{favorably} \end{pmatrix}$$

$$= \frac{6}{25} \cdot \frac{5}{24} \cdot \frac{4}{23} = \frac{1}{115}$$

d) In Section 12.5, we learned that

$$P(\text{event happening at least once}) = 1 - P(\text{event does not happen})$$

In part (c), we found that the probability of selecting three patients none of whom reacted favorably was $\frac{1}{115}$. Therefore, the probability that at least one of the patients selected reacted favorably can be found as follows.

$$P\begin{pmatrix} \text{at least one of the three} \\ \text{patients reacted favorably} \end{pmatrix} = 1 - P\begin{pmatrix} \text{none of the three} \\ \text{patients reacted favorably} \end{pmatrix}$$

$$= 1 - \frac{1}{115} = \frac{115}{115} - \frac{1}{115} = \frac{114}{115}$$

**SECTION 12.6**   *Exercises*

## Warm Up Exercises

*In Exercises 1–10, fill in the blank with an appropriate ward, phrase, or symbol(s).*

1. Probability problems that contain the words *and* or *or* are considered _____ probability problems.

2. Probability problems that require obtaining a successful outcome for at least one of the given events are _____ probability problems.

3. Probability problems that require obtaining a favorable outcome in each of the given events are _____ probability problems.

4. If it is impossible for two events *A* and *B* to occur simultaneously, then the events are considered to be _____ exclusive.

5. For two events *A* and *B*, if the occurrence of either event in no way affects the probability of the occurrence of

the other event, then the two events are considered to be _____ events.

6. For two events *A* and *B*, if the occurrence of either event has an effect on the probability of the occurrence of the other event, then the two events are considered to be _____ events.

7. Experiments done with replacement will result in _____ events.

8. Experiments done without replacement will result in _____ events.

9. The formula for finding the probability of event *A* or event *B* is $P(A \text{ or } B) =$ _____.

10. The formula for finding the probability of event *A* and event *B* is $P(A \text{ and } B) =$ _____.

## Practice the Skills

*In Exercises 11–14, determine the indicated probability.*

**11.** If $P(A) = 0.8$, $P(B) = 0.4$, and $P(A \text{ and } B) = 0.5$, determine $P(A \text{ or } B)$.

**12.** If $P(A \text{ or } B) = 0.9$, $P(A) = 0.8$, and $P(B) = 0.3$, determine $P(A \text{ and } B)$.

**13.** If $P(A \text{ or } B) = 0.7$, $P(A) = 0.6$, and $P(A \text{ and } B) = 0.3$, determine $P(B)$.

**14.** If $P(A \text{ or } B) = 0.6$, $P(B) = 0.3$, and $P(A \text{ and } B) = 0.1$, determine $P(A)$.

**15.** *Exam Preparation* Professor Connell is in charge of a program to prepare students for a high school equivalency exam. Records show that the probability that a student in the program needs help in mathematics is 0.7, the probability that a student needs help in English is 0.6, and the probability that a student needs help in both mathematics and English is 0.55. Determine the probability that a student in the program needs help in mathematics or English.

**16.** *Car Repair* The manager at Arango Automotive has found that the probability that a car brought into the shop requires an oil change is 0.6, the probability that a car brought into the shop requires brake repair is 0.2, and the probability that a car requires both an oil change and brake repair is 0.1. For a car brought into the shop, determine the probability that the car will require an oil change or brake repair.

*Roll a Die  In Exercises 17–20, a single die is rolled one time. Determine the probability of rolling*

**17.** a 2 or 6.

**18.** an odd number or a number greater than 4.

**19.** a number greater than 4 or less than 2.

**20.** a number greater than 3 or less than 5.

*Select One Card  In Exercises 21–26, one card is selected from a deck of playing cards. Determine the probability of selecting*

**21.** an ace or a 4.

**22.** a jack or a club.

**23.** a picture card or a black card.

**24.** a club or a red card.

**25.** a card less than 6 or a club. (*Note:* The ace is considered a low card.)

**26.** a card greater than 9 or a black card.

## Problem Solving

*Select Two Cards  In Exercises 27–34, a board game uses the deck of 20 cards shown.*

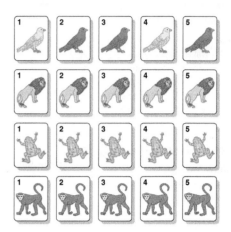

*Two cards are selected at random from this deck. Determine the probability of the following*

    **a)** *with replacement.*

    **b)** *without replacement.*

**27.** They both show lions.

**28.** They both show the number 3.

**29.** The first shows a monkey, and the second shows a bird.

**30.** The first shows a 2, and the second shows a 4.

**31.** The first shows a yellow bird, and the second shows a frog.

**32.** They both show even numbers.

**33.** Neither shows an even number.

**34.** The first shows a lion, and the second shows a red bird.

*Select One Card  In the deck of cards used in Exercises 27–34, if one card is drawn, determine the probability that the card shows*

**35.** a monkey or an even number.

**36.** a yellow bird or a number greater than 3.

**37.** a lion or a 2.

**38.** a red bird or an even number.

**Two Spins** In Exercises 39–48, assume that the pointer cannot land on the line and that each spin is independent. If the pointer in Fig. 12.16 is spun twice, determine the probability that the pointer lands on

**39.** red on both spins.   **40.** red and then yellow.

Figure 12.16

**Two Spins** If the pointer in Fig. 12.17 is spun twice, determine the probability that the pointer lands on

**41.** green and then red.   **42.** red on both spins.

Figure 12.17

**Two Spins** If the pointer in Fig. 12.18 is spun twice, determine the probability that the pointer lands on

**43.** red on both spins.

**44.** a color other than green on both spins.

Figure 12.18

**Two Spins** In Exercises 45–48, assume that the pointer in Fig. 12.16 is spun and then the pointer in Fig. 12.17 is spun. Determine the probability of the pointers landing on

**45.** red on both spins.

**46.** yellow on the first spin and red on the second spin.

**47.** a color other than red on both spins.

**48.** yellow on the first spin and a color other than yellow on the second spin.

**Selecting an Envelope** In Exercises 49–56, consider the colored envelopes shown below.

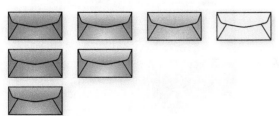

If one of the envelopes is selected at random, determine the probability that

**49.** a yellow or a blue envelope is selected.

**50.** an envelope other than a red envelope is selected.

If two envelopes are selected at random, with replacement, determine the probability that

**51.** both are red envelopes.

**52.** the first is a blue envelope and the second is a yellow envelope.

If three envelopes are selected at random, without replacement, determine the probability that

**53.** they are all red envelopes.

**54.** none is a red envelope.

**55.** the first is a red envelope, the second is a blue envelope, and the third is a blue envelope.

**56.** the first is a red envelope, the second is a green envelope, and the third is a red envelope.

**Having a Family** In Exercises 57–60, a couple has three children. Assuming independence and that the probability of a boy is $\frac{1}{2}$, determine the probability that

**57.** all three children are girls.

**58.** all three children are boys.

**59.** the youngest child is a boy and the two older children are girls.

**60.** the youngest child is a girl, the middle child is a boy, and the oldest child is a girl.

**61. a)** *Five Children* The Martinos plan to have five children. Determine the probability that all their children will be boys. (Assume that $P(\text{boy}) = \frac{1}{2}$ and assume independence.)

**b)** If their first four children are boys and Mrs. Martino is expecting another child, what is the probability that the fifth child will be a boy?

**62. a)** *The Probability of a Girl* The Bronsons plan to have eight children. Determine the probability that all their children will be girls. (Assume that $P(\text{girl}) = \frac{1}{2}$ and assume independence.)

**b)** If their first seven children are girls and Mrs. Bronson is expecting another child, what is the probability that the eighth child will be a girl?

*Books*  Angel Sanchez has seven books on a shelf: 4 mysteries, 2 science fiction books, and 1 biography. In Exercises 63–66, two books will be selected at random. Determine the probability of selecting each of the following

    **a)** *with replacement.*

    **b)** *without replacement.*

**63.** a mystery and then a biography

**64.** no science fiction books

**65.** at least one science fiction book

**66.** two biographies

*Health Insurance*  A sample of 75 people yielded the following information about their health insurance.

| Number of People | Type of Insurance |
|---|---|
| 33 | Managed care plan |
| 27 | Traditional insurance |
| 15 | No insurance |

*Two people who provided information for the table were selected at random, without replacement. Determine the probability that*

**67.** neither had traditional insurance.

**68.** they both had a managed care plan.

**69.** at least one had traditional insurance.

**70.** the first had traditional insurance and the second had a managed care plan.

*Hiring An Attorney*  A sample of 40 people who recently hired an attorney yielded the following information about their attorneys.

| Number of People | Would You Recommend Your Attorney to a Friend |
|---|---|
| 23 | Yes |
| 7 | No |
| 10 | Not sure |

*Three people who provided information for the table were selected at random. Determine the probability that*

**71.** they would all recommend their attorneys.

**72.** the first would not recommend the attorney, but the second and third would recommend their attorneys.

**73.** the first two would not recommend their attorneys, and the third is not sure if he or she would recommend the attorney.

**74.** the first would recommend the attorney, but the second and third would not recommend their attorneys.

*A New Medicine*  In Exercises 75–78, a new medicine was given to a sample of 100 hospital patients. Of the total, 70 patients reacted favorably, 10 reacted unfavorably, and 20 were unaffected by the drug. Assume that this sample is representative of the entire population. If this medicine is given to Mr. and Mrs. Rivera and their son Carlos, what is the probability of each of the following? (Assume independence.)

**75.** Mrs. Rivera reacts favorably.

**76.** Mr. and Mrs. Rivera react favorably, and Carlos is unaffected.

**77.** All three react favorably.

**78.** No one reacts favorably.

*Multiple-Choice Exam*  In Exercises 79–84, each question of a five-question multiple-choice exam has four possible answers. Gurshawn Salk picks an answer at random for each question. Determine the probability that he selects the correct answer on

**79.** any one question.

**80.** only the first question.

**81.** only the third and fourth questions.

**82.** all five questions.

**83.** none of the questions.

**84.** at least one of the questions.

*A Slot Machine*  In Exercises 85–88, consider a slot machine.

*Most people who play slot machines end up losing money because the machines are designed to favor the casino (the house). There are 22 positions on each reel. Assume that the following is a list of the number of symbols of each type on each of the three reels and each symbol has the same chance of occurring (which is not the case; see the Mathematics Today on page 722).*

| Pictures on Reels | Reels | | |
|---|---|---|---|
| | **1** | **2** | **3** |
| Cherries 🍒 | 2 | 5 | 4 |
| Oranges ◯ | 5 | 4 | 5 |
| Plums ◯ | 6 | 4 | 4 |
| Bells △ | 3 | 4 | 4 |
| Melons ◯ | 3 | 2 | 3 |
| Bars BAR | 2 | 2 | 1 |
| 7s 7 | 1 | 1 | 1 |

*For this slot machine, assuming that the wheels are independent, determine the probability of obtaining*

**85.** an orange on the first reel.

**86.** bells on all three reels.

**87.** no bars.

**88.** three 7's.

***Two Wheels*** *In Exercises 89–92, suppose that you spin the following double wheel.*

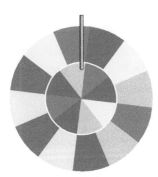

*Assuming that the wheels are independent and each outcome is equally likely, determine the probability that you get*

**89.** blue on both wheels.

**90.** red on the outer wheel and blue on the inner wheel.

**91.** red on neither wheel.

**92.** red on at least one wheel.

***Hitting a Target*** *In Exercises 93–96, the probability that a heat-seeking torpedo will hit its target is 0.4. If the first torpedo hits its target, the probability that the second torpedo will hit the target increases to 0.9 because of the extra heat generated by the first explosion. If two heat-seeking torpedoes are fired at a target, determine the probability that*

**93.** neither hits the target.

**94.** the first hits the target and the second misses the target.

**95.** both hit the target.

**96.** the first misses the target and the second hits the target.

**97.** ***Polygenetic Afflictions*** Certain birth defects and syndromes are *polygenetic* in nature. Typically, the chance that an offspring will be born with a polygenetic affliction is small. However, once an offspring is born with the affliction, the probability that future offspring of the same parents will be born with the same affliction increases. Let's assume that the probability of a child being born with affliction *A* is 0.001. If a child is born with this affliction, the probability of a future child being born with the same affliction becomes 0.04.

**a)** Are the events of the births of two children in the same family with affliction *A* independent?

**b)** A couple plans to have one child. Determine the probability that the child will be born with this affliction.

*A couple plans to have two children. Use the information provided to determine the probability that*

**c)** both children will be born with the affliction.

**d)** the first will be born with the affliction and the second will not.

**e)** the first will not be born with the affliction and the second will.

**f)** neither will be born with the affliction.

**98.** ***Lottery Ticket*** In a bin are an equal number of balls marked with the digits 0, 1, 2, 3, . . . , 9. Three balls are to be selected from the bin, one after the other, at random with replacement to make the winning three-digit lottery number. Ms. Jones has a lottery ticket with a three-digit number in the range 000 to 999. Determine the probability that Ms. Jones's number is the winning number.

***Chance of an Audit*** *In Exercises 99–102, assume that 36 in every 1000 people in the $34,000–$82,400 income bracket are audited yearly. Assuming that the returns to be audited are selected at random and each year's selections are independent of the previous year's selections, determine the probability that a person in this income bracket will be audited*

**99.** this year.

**100.** the next two years in succession.

**101.** this year but not next year.

**102.** neither this year nor next year.

## Challenge Problems/Group Activities

**103.** *Picking Chips* A bag contains five red chips, three blue chips, and two yellow chips. Two chips are selected from the bag without replacement. Determine the probability that two chips of the same color are selected.

**104.** *Peso Coins* Ron has ten coins from Mexico: three 1-peso coins, one 2-peso coin, two 5-peso coins, one 10-peso coin, and three 20-peso coins. He selects two coins at random without replacement. Assuming that each coin is equally likely to be selected, determine the probability that Ron selects at least one 1-peso coin.

**105.** *A Fair Game?* Two playing cards are dealt to you from a well-shuffled standard deck of 52 cards. If either card is a diamond or if both are diamonds, you win; otherwise, you lose. Determine whether this game favors you, is fair, or favors the dealer. Explain your answer.

**106.** *Picture Card Probability* You have three cards: an ace, a king, and a queen. A friend shuffles the cards, selects two of them at random, and discards the third. You ask your friend to show you a picture card, and she turns over the king. What is the probability that she also has the queen?

## Recreational Mathematics

*A Different Die* For exercises 107–110, consider a six-sided die that has 1 dot on one side, 2 dots on two sides, and 3 dots on three sides.

*If the die is rolled twice, determine the probability of rolling*

**107.** two 2's.          **108.** two 3's.

*If the die is rolled only once, determine the probability of rolling*

**109.** an even number or a number less than 3.

**110.** an odd number or a number greater than 1.

## Internet/Research Activity

**111.** Girolamo Cardano (1501–1576) wrote *Liber de Ludo Aleae*, which is considered to be the first book on probability. Cardano had a number of different vocations. Do research and write a paper on the life and accomplishments of Girolamo Cardano.

---

SECTION 12.7    Conditional Probability

▲ *Conditional probability may play a role in a candidate's bid for re-election.*

Often the probability of an event occurring may depend on one or more other events that previously occurred. For example, the probability of a candidate being re-elected may depend on the candidate's voting record or the current state of the economy. Or the probability that a salesperson is successful in selling a particular item may depend on whether the customer is a male or female. Probability problems like these, where the outcome of a previous event affects the probability of a later event, are called conditional probability problems.

**Why** *This is Important* We consider and use conditional probabilities all the time without realizing it, as you will see from the examples in this section.

---

In Section 12.6, we learned when two events are *dependent*, the occurrence of the first event, $A$, affected the probability of the second event, $B$, occurring. When we calculated $P(A \text{ and } B)$, when we determined the probability of event $B$, we assumed that event $A$ occurred. That is, we calculated the probability of event $B$, given event $A$. The probability of event $B$, given event $A$, is called a *conditional probability*. The definition of conditional probability follows.

### Definition: Conditional Probability

In general, the probability of event $E_2$ occurring, given that an event $E_1$ has happened (or will happen; the time relationship does not matter), is called a **conditional probability** and is written $P(E_2 | E_1)$.

The symbol $P(E_2 | E_1)$, read "the probability of $E_2$, given $E_1$," represents the probability of $E_2$ occurring, assuming that $E_1$ has already occurred (or will occur).

## Example 1 *Using Conditional Probability*

A single card is selected from a deck of cards. Determine the probability it is a club, given that it is black.

*Solution* We are told that the card is black. Thus, only 26 cards are possible, of which 13 are clubs. Therefore,

$$P(\text{club} | \text{black}) \text{ or } P(\text{C} | \text{B}) = \frac{13}{26} = \frac{1}{2}$$

## Example 2 *Girls in a Family*

A family has two children. Assuming that boys and girls are equally likely, determine the probability that the family has

a) two girls.

b) two girls if you know that at least one of the children is a girl.

c) two girls given that the older child is a girl.

*Solution*

a) To determine the probability that the family has two girls, we can determine the sample space of a family with two children. Then, from the sample space we can determine the probability that both children are girls. The sample space of two children can be determined by a tree diagram (see Fig. 12.19).

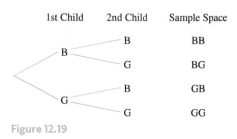

Figure 12.19

There are four possible equally likely outcomes: BB, BG, GB, and GG. Only one of the outcomes has two girls, GG. Thus,

$$P(2 \text{ girls}) = \frac{1}{4}$$

b) We are given that at least one of the children is a girl. Therefore, for this example the sample space is BG, GB, GG. Since there are three possibilities, of which only one has two girls, GG,

$$P(\text{both girls} | \text{at least one is a girl}) = \frac{1}{3}$$

c) If the older child is a girl, the sample space reduces to GB, GG. Thus,

$$P(\text{both girls} | \text{older child is a girl}) = \frac{1}{2}$$

A number of formulas can be used to find conditional probabilities. The one we will use follows on page 730.

The one we will use follows on page 730.

## Conditional Probability

For any two events, $E_1$ and $E_2$, the conditional probability, $P(E_2|E_1)$, is determined as follows.

$$P(E_2|E_1) = \frac{n(E_1 \text{ and } E_2)}{n(E_1)}$$

In the formula, $n(E_1 \text{ and } E_2)$ represents the number of sample points common to both event 1 and event 2, and $n(E_1)$ is the number of sample points in event $E_1$, the given event. Since the intersection of $E_1$ and $E_2$, symbolized $E_1 \cap E_2$, represents the sample points common to both $E_1$ and $E_2$, the formula can also be expressed as

$$P(E_2|E_1) = \frac{n(E_1 \cap E_2)}{n(E_1)}$$

Figure 12.20

Figure 12.20 is helpful in explaining conditional probability.

Here, the number of elements in $E_1$ is five, the number of elements in $E_2$ is six, and the number of elements in both $E_1$ and $E_2$, or $E_1 \cap E_2$, is two.

$$P(E_2|E_1) = \frac{n(E_1 \text{ and } E_2)}{n(E_1)} = \frac{2}{5}$$

Thus, for this situation, the probability of selecting an element from $E_2$, given that the element is in $E_1$, is $\frac{2}{5}$.

### Example 3  Using the Conditional Probability Formula

Two hundred and fifty patients who had knee, hip, or heart surgery were asked whether they were satisfied, dissatisfied, or neutral regarding the results of their surgery. The responses are given in the table below.

| Surgery | Satisfied | Dissatisfied | Total |
|---------|-----------|--------------|-------|
| Knee | 70 | 25 | 95 |
| Hip | 90 | 15 | 105 |
| Heart | 45 | 5 | 50 |
| Total | 205 | 45 | 250 |

If one person from the 250 patients surveyed is selected at random, determine the probability that the person

a) was satisfied with the results of the surgery.
b) was satisfied with the results of the surgery, given that the person had knee surgery.
c) was dissatisfied with the results of the surgery, given that the person had hip surgery.
d) had heart surgery, given that the person was dissatisfied with the results of the surgery.

Solution

a) The total number of patients is 250, of which 205 were satisfied with the results of the surgery.

$$P(\text{satisfied with the results of the surgery}) = \frac{205}{250} = \frac{41}{50}$$

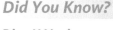

b) We are given that the person had knee surgery. Thus, we have a conditional probability problem. Let $E_1$ be the given information "the person had knee surgery." Let $E_2$ be "the person was satisfied with the results of the surgery." We are being asked to determine $P(E_2 | E_1)$. The number of people who had knee surgery, $n(E_1)$, is 95. The number of people who had knee surgery and were satisfied with the results of the surgery, $n(E_1 \text{ and } E_2)$, is 70. Thus,

$$P(E_2 | E_1) = \frac{n(E_1 \text{ and } E_2)}{n(E_1)} = \frac{70}{95} = \frac{14}{19}$$

c) We are given that the person had hip surgery. Thus, we have a conditional probability problem. Let $E_1$ be the given information "the person had hip surgery." Let $E_2$ be "the person was dissatisfied with the results of the surgery." We are asked to find $P(E_2 | E_1)$. The number of people who had hip surgery, $n(E_1)$, is 105. The number of people who had hip surgery and were dissatisfied with the results of the surgery, $n(E_1 \text{ and } E_2)$, is 15. Thus,

$$P(E_2 | E_1) = \frac{n(E_1 \text{ and } E_2)}{n(E_1)} = \frac{15}{105} = \frac{1}{7}$$

d) We are given that the person was dissatisfied with the results of the surgery. Thus, we have a conditional probability problem. Let $E_1$ be the given information "the person was dissatisfied with the results of the surgery." Let $E_2$ be "the person had heart surgery." We are asked to determine $P(E_2 | E_1)$. The number of people who were dissatisfied with the results of the surgery, $n(E_1)$, is 45. The number of people who were dissatisfied with the results of the surgery and had heart surgery, $n(E_1 \text{ and } E_2)$, is 5. Thus,

$$P(E_2 | E_1) = \frac{n(E_1 \text{ and } E_2)}{n(E_1)} = \frac{5}{45} = \frac{1}{9}$$

In many of the examples, we used the words *given that*. Other words may be used instead. For example, in Example 3(b), the question could have been worded "was satisfied with their surgery *if* the person had knee surgery."

## SECTION 12.7  *Exercises*

### Warm Up Exercises

*In Exercises 1–4, fill in the blank with an appropriate word, phrase, or symbol(s).*

**1.** The probability of event $E_2$ occurring, given that event $E_1$ has happened, is called a(n) _____ probability.

**2.** The notation for the probability of $E_2$, given $E_1$, is _____.

**3.** If $n(E_1 \text{ and } E_2) = 4$ and $n(E_1) = 12$, then $P(E_2 | E_1) =$ _____.

**4.** If $n(E_1 \text{ and } E_2) = 5$ and $n(E_1) = 22$, then $P(E_2 | E_1) =$ _____.

### Practice the Skills

*Select a Circle  In Exercises 5–10, consider the circles shown.*

*Assume that one circle is selected at random and each circle is equally likely to be selected. Determine the probability of selecting*

**5.** a 3, given that the circle is orange.

**6.** a 5, given that the circle is yellow.

**7.** an even number, given that the circle is not orange.

8. a number less than 2, given that the number is less than 5.

9. a red number, given that the circle is orange.

10. a number greater than 4, given that the circle is yellow.

*Select a Number*  *In Exercises 11–16, consider the following figures.*

*Assume that one number from 1 to 7 is equally likely to be selected at random. Each number corresponds to one of the seven figures shown. Determine the probability of selecting*

11. a triangle, given that an even number is selected.

12. a triangle, given that a number greater than or equal to 5 is selected.

13. a red figure, given that an even number is selected.

14. a red or a blue figure, given that an even number is selected.

15. a circle or square, given that a number less than 4 is selected.

16. a triangle, given that an odd number is selected.

*Spin the Wheel*  *In Exercises 17–24, consider the following wheel.*

*If the wheel is spun and each section is equally likely to stop under the pointer, determine the probability that the pointer lands on*

17. a two, given that the color is purple.

18. an odd number, given that the color is red.

19. purple, given that the number is odd.

20. a number greater than 6, given that the color is red.

21. a number greater than 4, given that the color is purple.

22. an even number, given that the color is red or purple.

23. gold, given that the number is greater than 5.

24. gold, given that the number is greater than 10.

*Money from a Hat*  *In Exercises 25–28, assume that a hat contains four bills: a $1 bill, a $5 bill, a $10 bill, and a $20 bill. Two bills are to be selected at random with replacement. Construct a sample space as was done in Example 2 and determine the probability that*

25. both bills are $1 bills.

26. both bills are $1 bills if the first selected is a $1 bill.

27. both bills are $5 bills if at least one of the bills is a $5 bill.

28. both bills have a value greater than a $5 bill if the second bill is a $10 bill.

*Two Dice*  *In Exercises 29–34, two dice are rolled one after the other. Construct a sample space and determine the probability that the sum of the dots on the dice total*

29. 7.

30. 7 if the first die is a 1.

31. 7 if the first die is a 3.

32. an even number if the second die is a 2.

33. a number greater than 7 if the second die is a 5.

34. a 7 or 11 if the first die is a 5.

## Problem Solving

*Costliest Hurricanes*  *In Exercises 35–40, use the following information concerning the nine costliest hurricanes to strike the U.S. mainland as of January 1, 2010.*

| Hurricane | Category | Damage (billions of dollars) |
|---|---|---|
| Katrina (2005) | 3 | 81.0 |
| Andrew (1992) | 5 | 35.0 |
| Wilma (2005) | 3 | 20.6 |
| Ike (2008) | 2 | 18.0 |
| Charley (2004) | 4 | 14.0 |
| Ivan (2004) | 3 | 13.0 |
| Rita (2005) | 3 | 10.0 |
| Hugo (1989) | 4 | 9.7 |
| Frances (2004) | 2 | 8.9 |

Source: *National Oceanic and Atmospheric Administration*

*If one hurricane from the list is selected at random, determine the probability that it*

**35.** was a category 4.

**36.** had damages of at least $16 billion.

**37.** had damages of at least $20 billion, given that it was a category 3.

**38.** had damages of at least $15 billion, given that it was a category 2.

**39.** was a category 5, given that it had damages of at least $25 billion.

**40.** was a category 3, given that it had damages of at least $10 billion.

***E-Z Pass*** *In Exercises 41–46, use the following table, which shows the number of cars and trucks that used the Pennsylvania Turnpike on a particular day. The number of cars and trucks that used, and did not use, the E-Z Pass on that same day was also recorded.*

| E-Z Pass | Cars | Trucks | Total |
|----------|------|--------|-------|
| Used | 527 | 316 | 843 |
| Did not use | 935 | 683 | 1618 |
| Total | 1462 | 999 | 2461 |

*If one of these vehicles is selected at random, determine the probability (as a decimal number rounded to four decimal places) that the*

**41.** vehicle was a car.

**42.** vehicle used the E-Z Pass.

**43.** vehicle used the E-Z Pass, given that the vehicle was a car.

**44.** vehicle used the E-Z Pass, given that the vehicle was a truck.

**45.** vehicle was a car, given that the vehicle used the E-Z Pass.

**46.** vehicle was a truck, given that the vehicle used the E-Z Pass.

▲ *A sign on the Pennsylvania Turnpike.*

***Sales Effectiveness*** *In Exercises 47–52, use the following information. Sales representatives at a car dealership were split into two groups. One group used an aggressive approach to sell a customer a new automobile. The other group used a passive approach. The following table summarizes the records for 650 customers.*

| Approach | Sale | No Sale | Total |
|----------|------|---------|-------|
| Aggressive | 100 | 250 | 350 |
| Passive | 220 | 80 | 300 |
| Total | 320 | 330 | 650 |

*If one of these customers is selected at random, determine the probability*

**47.** that the aggressive approach was used.

**48.** of a sale.

**49.** of no sale, given that the passive approach was used.

**50.** of a sale, given that the aggressive approach was used.

**51.** of a sale, given that the passive approach was used.

**52.** of no sale, given that the aggressive approach was used.

***New Residence*** *For Exercises 53–58, use the following information, which shows the educational attainment and the location of their new residence for people who moved in 2008. The data are rounded to the nearest thousand people.*

| Educational Attainment | Same County | Different County, Same State | Different State | Abroad | Total |
|------------------------|-------------|------------------------------|-----------------|--------|-------|
| Not a high school graduate | 2247 | 470 | 254 | 98 | 3069 |
| High school graduate | 3842 | 1074 | 712 | 145 | 5773 |
| Some college | 3319 | 1020 | 707 | 112 | 5158 |
| Bachelor's degree | 2072 | 760 | 667 | 182 | 3681 |
| Graduate degree | 913 | 383 | 461 | 118 | 1875 |
| Total | 12,393 | 3707 | 2801 | 655 | 19,556 |

Source: *U.S. Census Bureau*

*If one of these individuals is selected at random, determine the probability (as a decimal number rounded to four decimal places) that the individual*

**53.** moved within the same county.

**54.** moved within the same county, given the individual has a bachelor's degree.

**55.** moved to a different state, given the individual has a graduate degree.

**56.** has a graduate degree, given the individual moved abroad.

**57.** is a high school graduate, given the individual moved within the same state but different county.

**58.** moved to a different state or abroad, given the individual has a bachelor's degree.

*Quality Control* In Exercises 59–64, Sally Horsefall, a quality control inspector, is checking a sample of lightbulbs for defects. The following table summarizes her findings.

| Wattage | Good | Defective | Total |
|---------|------|-----------|-------|
| 20 | 80 | 15 | 95 |
| 50 | 100 | 5 | 105 |
| 100 | 120 | 10 | 130 |
| Total | 300 | 30 | 330 |

*If one of these lightbulbs is selected at random, determine the probability that the lightbulb is*

**59.** good.

**60.** good, given that it is 50 watts.

**61.** defective, given that it is 20 watts.

**62.** good, given that it is 100 watts.

**63.** good, given that it is 50 or 100 watts.

**64.** defective, given that it is not 50 watts.

*News Survey* In Exercises 65–70, 270 individuals are asked which evening news they watch most often. The results are summarized as follows.

| Viewers | ABC | NBC | CBS | Other | Total |
|---------|-----|-----|-----|-------|-------|
| Men | 30 | 20 | 40 | 55 | 145 |
| Women | 50 | 10 | 20 | 45 | 125 |
| Total | 80 | 30 | 60 | 100 | 270 |

*If one of these individuals is selected at random, determine the probability that the person watches*

**65.** ABC or NBC.

**66.** ABC, given that the individual is a woman.

**67.** ABC or NBC, given that the individual is a man.

**68.** a station other than CBS, given that the individual is a woman.

**69.** a station other than ABC, NBC, or CBS, given that the individual is a man.

**70.** NBC or CBS, given that the individual is a woman.

▲ *Diane Sawyer*, ABC Evening News

## Challenge Problems/Group Activities

*Mutual Fund Holdings* Use the following information in Exercises 71–74. Mutual funds often hold many stocks. Each stock may be classified as a value stock, a growth stock, or a blend of the two. The stock may also be categorized by how large the company is. It may be classified as a large company stock, medium company stock, or small company stock. A selected mutual fund contains 200 stocks as illustrated in the following chart.

| Value | Blend | Growth | |
|-------|-------|--------|--------|
| 28 | 23 | 42 | Large |
| 19 | 15 | 18 | Medium |
| 26 | 12 | 17 | Small |

Equity Investment Style

*If one stock is selected at random from the mutual fund, determine the probability that it is*

**71.** a large company stock.

**72.** a value stock.

**73.** a blend, given that it is a medium company stock.

**74.** a large company stock, given that it is a blend stock.

**75.** Consider the Venn diagram below. The numbers in the regions of the circle indicate the number of items that belong to that region. For example, 60 items are in set $A$ but not in set $B$.

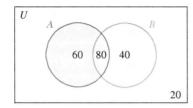

Determine **a)** $n(A)$ **b)** $n(B)$ **c)** $P(A)$ **d)** $P(B)$

Use the formula on page 730 to determine

**e)** $P(A|B)$. **f)** $P(B|A)$.

**g)** Explain why $P(A|B) \neq P(A) \cdot P(B)$.

**76.** A formula we gave for conditional probability is

$$P(E_2|E_1) = \frac{n(E_1 \text{ and } E_2)}{n(E_1)}$$

This formula may be derived from the formula

$$P(E_2|E_1) = \frac{P(E_1 \text{ and } E_2)}{P(E_1)}$$

Can you explain why? [*Hint:* Consider what happens to the denominators of $P(E_1 \text{ and } E_2)$ and $P(E_1,)$ when they are expressed as fractions and the fractions are divided out.]

**77.** Given that $P(A) = 0.3$, $P(B) = 0.5$, and $P(A \text{ and } B) = 0.15$, use the formula

$$P(E_2|E_1) = \frac{P(E_1 \text{ and } E_2)}{P(E_1)}$$

to determine

**a)** $P(A|B)$. **b)** $P(B|A)$.

**c)** Are $A$ and $B$ independent? Explain.

## Recreational Mathematics

*In Exercises 78–83, suppose that each circle is equally likely to be selected. One circle is selected at random.*

*Determine the probability indicated.*

**78.** $P(\text{green circle} \,|\, + \text{ obtained})$

**79.** $P(+| \text{ orange circle obtained})$

**80.** $P(\text{yellow circle} \,|\, - \text{ obtained})$

**81.** $P(\text{green} \, + \,|\, + \text{ obtained})$

**82.** $P(\text{green or orange circle} \,|\, \text{green} \, + \text{ obtained})$

**83.** $P(\text{orange circle with green} \, + \,|\, + \text{ obtained})$

---

▲ *In how many different ways can movie posters be displayed?*

You are the manager of a movie theater and want to display a poster for each of the eight different movies showing at your theater. In how many different ways can you display the eight posters? In this section, we will learn how to determine the number of different ordered arrangements of a set of objects.

**Why** *This is Important* There are many real-life situations in which we need to determine the number of different ordered arrangements of a set of objects, such as the number of 5-digit zip codes or the number of 7-digit telephone numbers.

## The Counting Principle

In Section 12.5, we introduced the counting principle, which is repeated here for your convenience.

### Definition: **Counting Principle**

If a first experiment can be performed in $M$ distinct ways and a second experiment can be performed in $N$ distinct ways, then the two experiments in that specific order can be performed in $M \cdot N$ distinct ways.

The counting principle is illustrated in Examples 1 and 2.

## Example 1 *Counting Principle: Passwords*

A password used to gain access to a computer account is to consist of two lowercase letters followed by four digits. Determine how many different passwords are possible if
a) repetition of letters and digits is permitted.
b) repetition of letters and digits is not permitted.
c) the first letter must be a vowel (*a, e, i, o, u*) and the first digit cannot be a 0, and repetition of letters and digits is not permitted.

**Solution**  There are 26 letters and 10 digits (0–9). We have six positions to fill, as indicated.

$$\overline{L}\ \overline{L}\ \overline{D}\ \overline{D}\ \overline{D}\ \overline{D}$$

a) Since repetition is permitted, there are 26 possible choices for both the first and second positions. There are 10 possible choices for the third, fourth, fifth, and sixth positions.

$$\frac{26}{L}\ \frac{26}{L}\ \frac{10}{D}\ \frac{10}{D}\ \frac{10}{D}\ \frac{10}{D}$$

Since $26 \cdot 26 \cdot 10 \cdot 10 \cdot 10 \cdot 10 = 6{,}760{,}000$, there are 6,760,000 different possible arrangements.

b) There are 26 possibilities for the first position. Since repetition of letters is not permitted, there are only 25 possibilities for the second position. The same reasoning is used when determining the number of digits for positions 3 through 6.

$$\frac{26}{L}\ \frac{25}{L}\ \frac{10}{D}\ \frac{9}{D}\ \frac{8}{D}\ \frac{7}{D}$$

Since $26 \cdot 25 \cdot 10 \cdot 9 \cdot 8 \cdot 7 = 3{,}276{,}000$, there are 3,276,000 different possible arrangements.

c) Since the first letter must be an *a, e, i, o,* or *u,* there are five possible choices for the first position. The second position can be filled by any of the letters except for the vowel selected for the first position. Therefore, there are 25 possibilities for the second position.

   Since the first digit cannot be a 0, there are nine possibilities for the third position. The fourth position can be filled by any digit except the one selected for the third position. Thus, there are nine possibilities for the fourth position. Since the fifth position cannot be filled by any of the two digits previously used, there are eight possibilities for the fifth position. The last position can be filled by any of the seven remaining digits.

$$\frac{5}{L}\ \frac{25}{L}\ \frac{9}{D}\ \frac{9}{D}\ \frac{8}{D}\ \frac{7}{D}$$

Since $5 \cdot 25 \cdot 9 \cdot 9 \cdot 8 \cdot 7 = 567{,}000$, there are 567,000 different arrangements that meet the conditions specified.    ∎

## Example 2 *Counting Principle: T-Shirt Colors*

At Old Navy, a supply of solid-colored T-shirts has just been received. The T-shirts come in the following colors: green, blue, white, yellow, and red. Billy Bragg, the floor manager, decides to display one of each color T-shirt in a row on a shelf.

a) In how many different ways can he display the five different color T-shirts on a shelf?

b) If he wants to place the blue T-shirt in the middle, in how many different ways can he arrange the T-shirts?

c) If Billy wants the white T-shirt to be the first T-shirt and the blue T-shirt to be the last T-shirt, in how many different ways can he arrange the T-shirts?

**Solution**

a) There are five positions to fill, using the five colors. In the first position, on the left, he can use any one of the five colors. In the second position, he can use any of the four remaining colors. In the third position, he can use any of the three remaining colors, and so on. The number of distinct possible arrangements is

$$\underline{5} \cdot \underline{4} \cdot \underline{3} \cdot \underline{2} \cdot \underline{1} = 120$$

b) We begin by satisfying the specified requirements stated. In this case, the blue T-shirt must be placed in the middle. Therefore, there is only one possibility for the middle position.

$$\underline{\phantom{1}}\;\underline{\phantom{1}}\;\underline{1}\;\underline{\phantom{1}}\;\underline{\phantom{1}}$$

For the first position, there are now four possibilities. For the second position, there will be three possibilities. For the fourth position, there will be two possibilities. Finally, in the last position, there is only one possibility.

$$\underline{4} \cdot \underline{3} \cdot \underline{1} \cdot \underline{2} \cdot \underline{1} = 24$$

Thus, under the condition stated, there are 24 different possible arrangements.

c) For the first T-shirt, there is only one possibility, the white T-shirt. For the last T-shirt, there is only one possibility, the blue T-shirt.

$$\underline{1}\;\underline{\phantom{1}}\;\underline{\phantom{1}}\;\underline{\phantom{1}}\;\underline{1}$$

The second position can be filled by any of the three remaining T-shirts. The third position can be filled by any of the two remaining T-shirts. There is only one T-shirt left for the fourth position. Thus, the number of possible arrangements is

$$\underline{1} \cdot \underline{3} \cdot \underline{2} \cdot \underline{1} \cdot \underline{1} = 6$$

There are only six possible arrangements that satisfy the given conditions. ■

## Permutations

Now we introduce the definition of a permutation.

### Definition: **Permutations**

A **permutation** is any *ordered arrangement* of a given set of objects.

"Larry, Shemp, Moe" and "Shemp, Moe, Larry" represent two different ordered arrangements or two different permutations of the same three names. In Example 2(a), there are 120 different ordered arrangements, or permutations, of the five colored T-shirts. In Example 2(b), there are 24 different ordered arrangements, or permutations possible, if the blue T-shirt must be displayed in the middle.

▲ *Shemp    Moe    Larry*

*When determining the number of permutations possible, we assume that repetition of an item is not permitted.* To help you understand and visualize permutations, we illustrate the various permutations possible when a triangle, rectangle, and circle are to be placed in a line; see Fig. 12.21.

Figure 12.21

For this set of three shapes, six different arrangements, or six permutations, are possible. We can obtain the number of permutations by using the counting principle. For the first position, there are three choices. There are then two choices for the second position, and only one choice is left for the third position.

$$\text{Number of permutations} = 3 \cdot 2 \cdot 1 = 6$$

The product $3 \cdot 2 \cdot 1$ is referred to as 3 factorial, and is written 3!. Thus,

$$3! = 3 \cdot 2 \cdot 1 = 6$$

### Number of Permutations

The number of permutations of $n$ distinct items is $n$ factorial, symbolized $n!$, where

$$n! = n(n-1)(n-2) \cdots (3)(2)(1)$$

It is important to note that 0! is defined to be 1. Many calculators have the ability to determine factorials. Often to determine factorials you need to press the $\boxed{\text{2nd}}$ or $\boxed{\text{INV}}$ key. Read your calculator manual to determine how to find factorials on your calculator.

┌ Example **3** *Cell Phones*

In how many different ways can six different cell phones be arranged on top of one another?

**Solution** Since there are six different cell phones, the number of permutations is 6!.

$$6! = 6 \cdot 5 \cdot 4 \cdot 3 \cdot 2 \cdot 1 = 720$$

The six cell phones can be arranged in 720 different ways. ∎

Example 4 illustrates how to use the counting principle to determine the number of permutations possible when only a part of the total number of items is to be selected and arranged.

Some of the many
permutations
of 3 of the 5 letters

Figure 12.22

┌ Example **4** *Permutations of Three Out of Five Letters*

Consider the five letters $a, b, c, d, e$. In how many distinct ways can three letters be selected and arranged if repetition is not allowed?

**Solution** We are asked to select and arrange only three of the five possible letters. Figure 12.22 shows some possibilities. Using the counting principle, we find that there are five possible letters for the first choice, four possible letters for the second choice, and three possible letters for the third choice:

$$5 \cdot 4 \cdot 3 = 60$$

Thus, there are 60 different possible ordered arrangements, or permutations. On the left, we show 5 of the 60 possible permutations. ∎

In Example 4, we determined the number of different ways in which we could select and arrange three of the five items. We can indicate that result by using the notation $_5P_3$. The notation $_5P_3$ is read "the number of permutations of five items taken three at a time." The notation $_nP_r$ is read "the number of permutations of $n$ items taken $r$ at a time."

We use the counting principle below to evaluate $_8P_4$, $_9P_3$, and $_{10}P_5$. Note the relationship between the number preceding the $P$, the number following the $P$, and the last number in the product.

$$_8P_4 = 8 \cdot 7 \cdot 6 \cdot \underset{\text{One more than } 8 - 4}{5}$$

$$_9P_3 = 9 \cdot 8 \cdot \underset{\text{One more than } 9 - 3}{7}$$

$$_{10}P_5 = 10 \cdot 9 \cdot 8 \cdot 7 \cdot \underset{\text{One more than } 10 - 5}{6}$$

To evaluate $_nP_r$, we begin with $n$ and form a product of $r$ consecutive descending factors. For example, to evaluate $_{10}P_5$, we start with 10 and form a product of five consecutive descending factors (see the preceding illustration).

In general, the number of permutations of $n$ items taken $r$ at a time, $_nP_r$, may be found by the formula

$$_nP_r = n(n-1)(n-2) \cdots \underset{\text{One more than } n - r}{(n-r+1)}$$

Therefore, when evaluating $_{20}P_{15}$, we would find the product of consecutive decreasing integers from 20 to $(20 - 15 + 1)$ or 6, which is written as $20 \cdot 19 \cdot 18 \cdot 17 \cdots \cdot 6$.

Now let's develop an alternative formula that we can use to find the number of permutations possible when $r$ objects are selected from $n$ objects:

$$_nP_r = n(n-1)(n-2) \cdots (n-r+1)$$

Now multiply the expression on the right side of the equals sign by $\dfrac{(n-r)!}{(n-r)!}$, which is equivalent to multiplying the expression by 1.

$$_nP_r = n(n-1)(n-2) \cdots (n-r+1) \times \frac{(n-r)!}{(n-r)!}$$

For example,

$$_{10}P_5 = 10 \cdot 9 \cdot \cdots \cdot 6 \times \frac{5!}{5!}$$

or

$$_{10}P_5 = \frac{10 \cdot 9 \cdot \cdots \cdot 6 \times 5!}{5!}$$

Since $(n-r)!$ means $(n-r)(n-r-1) \cdots (3)(2)(1)$, the expression for $_nP_r$ can be rewritten as

$$_nP_r = \frac{n(n-1)(n-2) \cdots (n-r+1)\overbrace{(n-r)(n-r-1) \cdots (3)(2)(1)}^{(n-r)!}}{(n-r)!}$$

Since the numerator of this expression is $n!$, we can write

$$_nP_r = \frac{n!}{(n-r)!}$$

For example,

$$_{10}P_5 = \frac{10!}{(10-5)!}$$

### Permutation Formula

The number of permutations possible when $r$ objects are selected from $n$ objects is found by the **permutation formula**

$$_nP_r = \frac{n!}{(n-r)!}$$

In Example 4, we found that when selecting three of five letters, there were 60 permutations. We can obtain the same result using the permutation formula:

$$_5P_3 = \frac{5!}{(5-3)!} = \frac{5!}{2!} = \frac{5 \cdot 4 \cdot 3 \cdot \cancel{2 \cdot 1}}{\cancel{2 \cdot 1}} = 60$$

### Example 5    *Using the Permutation Formula*

You are among eight people forming a skiing club. Collectively, you decide to put each person's name in a hat and to randomly select a president, a vice president, and a secretary. How many different arrangements or permutations of officers are possible?

*Solution*  There are eight people, $n = 8$, of which three are to be selected; thus, $r = 3$.

$$_8P_3 = \frac{8!}{(8-3)!} = \frac{8!}{5!} = \frac{8 \cdot 7 \cdot 6 \cdot \cancel{5 \cdot 4 \cdot 3 \cdot 2 \cdot 1}}{\cancel{5 \cdot 4 \cdot 3 \cdot 2 \cdot 1}} = 336$$

Thus, with eight people there can be 336 different arrangements for president, vice president, and secretary.    ∎

In Example 5, the fraction

$$\frac{8 \cdot 7 \cdot 6 \cdot \cancel{5 \cdot 4 \cdot 3 \cdot 2 \cdot 1}}{\cancel{5 \cdot 4 \cdot 3 \cdot 2 \cdot 1}} = 336$$

can be also expressed as

$$\frac{8 \cdot 7 \cdot 6 \cdot 5!}{5!} = 336$$

The solution to Example 5, like other permutation problems, can also be obtained using the counting principle.

### EXAMPLE 6

The Prince George County bicycle club has 10 different routes members wish to travel exactly once, but they have only 6 specific dates for their trips. In how many ways can the different routes be assigned to the dates scheduled for their trips?

Many scientific calculators and all graphing calculators have the ability to evaluate permutations. Read your calculator's instruction manual to determine the procedure to follow to evaluate permutations.

To evaluate $_{10}P_6$ on a TI-83 Plus or a TI-84 Plus calculator, enter the number 10. Then press the MATH key. Use the right arrow key to scroll over to PRB, which stands for probability. Then scroll down to $_nP_r$. Press the ENTER key. You should now see 10 $_nP_r$ on your screen. Next press 6. Press the ENTER key again. The answer will be 151,200, which agrees with our answer in Example 6.

## RECREATIONAL MATH

### Jumble

Read the material on Permutations of Duplicate Items on this page and the next page before working this Jumble.

In the *Recreational Mathematics* box on page 711 we introduced the JUMBLE puzzles. Sometimes the puzzles contain one or more letters multiple times. For each Jumble below, use the knowledge you have learned in this section to determine

a) the number of possible arrangements of the letters given.
b) the word that results when the letters are placed in their proper order (note that only one word is possible).

1. NOOZE
2. ZBEERE
3. LOCGEEL

The answers are listed upside down below. See Exercises 53–56, 70, 71 for more examples.

Answers:
1. a) 60  b) OZONE
2. a) 120  b) BREEZE
3. a) 1260  b) COLLEGE

*Solution* There are 10 possible routes but only 6 specific dates scheduled for the trips. Since traveling route A on day 1 and traveling route B on day 2 is different than traveling route B on day 1 and traveling route A on day 2, we have a permutation problem. There are 10 possible routes; thus, $n = 10$. There are 6 routes that are going to be selected and assigned to different days; thus, $r = 6$. Now we calculate the number of different permutations of selecting and arranging the dates for 6 out of 10 possible routes.

$$_{10}P_6 = \frac{10!}{(10-6)!} = \frac{10!}{4!} = \frac{10 \cdot 9 \cdot 8 \cdot 7 \cdot 6 \cdot 5 \cdot 4!}{4!} = 151{,}200$$

There are 151,200 different ways that 6 routes can be selected and scheduled from the 10 possible routes. ∎

Example 6 could also be worked using the counting principle because we are discussing an *ordered arrangement* (a permutation) that is done *without replacement*. For the first date scheduled, there are 10 possible outcomes. For the second date selected, there are 9 possible outcomes. By continuing this process we would determine that the number of possible outcomes for the 6 different trips is $10 \cdot 9 \cdot 8 \cdot 7 \cdot 6 \cdot 5 = 151{,}200$.

We have worked permutation problems (selecting and arranging, without replacement, $r$ items out of $n$ *distinct* items) by using the counting principle and using the permutation formula. When you are given a permutation problem, unless specified by your instructor, you may use either technique to determine its solution.

## Permutations of Duplicate Items

So far, all the examples we have discussed in this section have involved arrangements with distinct items. Now we will consider permutation problems in which some of the items to be arranged are duplicates. For example, the name BOB contains three letters, of which the two Bs are duplicates. How many permutations of the letters in the name BOB are possible? If the two Bs were distinguishable (one red and the other blue), there would be six permutations.

$$\begin{array}{ccc} \text{BOB} & \text{BBO} & \text{OBB} \\ \text{BOB} & \text{BBO} & \text{OBB} \end{array}$$

However, if the Bs are not distinguishable (replacing all colored Bs with black print), we see that there are only three permutations.

$$\begin{array}{ccc} \text{BOB} & \text{BBO} & \text{OBB} \end{array}$$

The number of permutations of the letters in BOB can be computed as

$$\frac{3!}{2!} = \frac{3 \cdot 2 \cdot 1}{2 \cdot 1} = 3$$

where 3! represents the number of permutations of three letters, assuming that none are duplicates, and 2! represents the number of ways the two items that are duplicates can be arranged (BB or BB). In general, we have the following rule.

## Permutations of Duplicate Items

The number of distinct permutations of $n$ objects where $n_1$ of the objects are identical, $n_2$ of the objects are identical, $\ldots$, $n_r$ of the objects are identical is found by using

$$\frac{n!}{n_1! n_2! \cdots n_r!}$$

┌─
EXAMPLE **7** *Duplicate Letters*

In how many different ways can the letters of the word "TALLAHASSEE" be arranged?

Solution  Of the 11 letters, three are A's, two are S's, two are L's, and two are E's. The number of possible arrangements is

$$\frac{11!}{3!2!2!2!} = \frac{11 \cdot 10 \cdot 9 \cdot 8 \cdot 7 \cdot 6 \cdot 5 \cdot 4 \cdot 3 \cdot 2 \cdot 1}{3 \cdot 2 \cdot 1 \cdot 2 \cdot 1 \cdot 2 \cdot 1 \cdot 2 \cdot 1} = 11 \cdot 10 \cdot 9 \cdot 7 \cdot 6 \cdot 5 \cdot 4 = 831,600$$

There are 831,600 different possible arrangements of the letters in the word "TALLAHASSEE."
└─

## SECTION 12.8    *Exercises*

### Warm Up Exercises

*In Exercises 1–8, fill in the blank with an appropriate word, phrase, or symbol(s).*

1. To determine the number of distinct ways two or more experiments can be performed, the _____ principle can be used.

2. Any ordered arrangement of a given set of objects is called a(n) _____.

3. The symbol for $n$ factorial is _____.

4. The formula for the number of permutations of $n$ distinct items is $n! = $ _____

5. The formula for the number of permutations when $r$ objects are selected from $n$ objects is $_nP_r = $ _____.

6. The number of permutations of $n$ objects, where $n_1$ of the items are identical, $n_2$ of the items are identical, $\ldots$, $n_r$ are identical, is found by _____.

7. The notation used to express the number of permutations of five items taken three at a time is _____.

8. The notation used to express the number of permutations of seven items taken two at a time is _____.

### Practice the Skills

*In Exercises 9–20, evaluate the expression.*

9. $5!$        10. $6!$        11. $_4P_2$        12. $_5P_2$

13. $0!$        14. $_7P_3$        15. $_8P_0$        16. $_6P_0$

17. $_9P_5$        18. $_3P_3$        19. $_8P_3$        20. $_{10}P_6$

### Problem Solving

21. *ATM Codes*  To use an automated teller machine, you generally must enter a four-digit code, using the digits 0–9. How many four-digit codes are possible if repetition of digits is permitted?

22. *Routes*  There are three different routes that Cassidy Cole can walk from home to the post office and two different routes that she can walk from the post office to the bank. How many different routes can Cassidy walk from home to the post office and then to the bank?

23. *Outfits*  Juan Rivera has three ties, four shirts, and two pairs of pants. How many different outfits can he wear if he chooses one tie, one shirt, and one pair of pants for each outfit?

24. *Passwords*  Assume that a password to log onto a computer account is to consist of any four digits or letters (repetition is permitted). Determine the number of passwords possible if

   a) the letters are not case sensitive (that is, a lowercase letter is treated the same as an uppercase letter).

   b) the letters are case sensitive (that is, an uppercase letter is considered different than the same lowercase letter).

**25.** *Car Door Locks* Some doors on cars can be opened by pressing a correct sequence of buttons. A display of the five buttons by the door handle of a car follows.*

The correct sequence of five buttons must be pressed to unlock the door.

**a)** How many different sequences of five buttons are possible (repetition is permitted)?

**b)** If a sequence of five buttons is pressed at random, determine the probability that the sequence unlocks the door.

**26.** *Social Security Numbers* A social security number consists of nine digits. How many different social security numbers are possible if repetition of digits is permitted?

**27.** *License Plate* In Italy, most car and motorcycle license plates consist of 2 letters, followed by 3 digits, followed by 2 letters. (See photo.) Determine the number of license plates possible if

▲ An Italian license plate

**a)** repetition is permitted (as it is in Italy).

**b)** repetition is not permitted.

**28.** *Winning the Trifecta* The trifecta at most racetracks consists of selecting the first-, second-, and third-place finishers in a particular race in their proper order. If there are seven entries in the trifecta race, how many tickets must you purchase to guarantee a win?

**29.** *Choosing Classes* Kai Lu plans to enroll in four classes: sociology, chemistry, economics, and humanities. There

are seven sociology classes, four chemistry classes, three economics classes, and four humanities classes that fit his schedule. How many different ways can he select his four classes?

**30.** *Geometric Shapes* Consider the five figures shown.

In how many different ways can the figures be arranged

**a)** from left to right?

**b)** from top to bottom if placed one under the other?

**c)** from left to right if the triangle is to be placed on the far right?

**d)** from left to right if the circle is to be placed on the far left and the triangle is to be placed on the far right?

**31.** *Arranging Pictures* The six pictures shown are to be placed side by side along a wall.

In how many ways can they be arranged from left to right if

**a)** they can be arranged in any order?

**b)** the bird must be on the far left?

**c)** the bird must be on the far left and the giraffe must be next to the bird?

**d)** a four-legged animal must be on the far right?

**32.** *Club Officers* If a club consists of 10 members, how many different arrangements of president, vice-president, and secretary are possible?

**33.** *Restaurant Positions* There are 10 candidates for three positions at Johnny Rockets. One position is for a cook. The second position is for a food server. The third position is for a cashier. If all 10 candidates are equally qualified for the three positions, in how many different ways can the three positions be filled?

**34.** *ISBN Codes* Each book registered in the Library of Congress must have an ISBN code number. For an ISBN number of the form D-DD-DDDDDD-D, where D represents a digit from 0–9, how many different ISBN numbers are possible if repetition of digits is allowed? (See research activity Exercise 72 on page 746.)

*On most cars, although each key lists two numbers, the key acts as a single number. Therefore, if your code is 1, 6, 8, 5, 3, the code 2, 5, 7, 6, 4 will also open the lock.

**35.** *Wedding Reception* At the reception line of a wedding, the bride, the groom, the best man, the maid of honor, the four ushers, and the four bridesmaids must line up to receive the guests.

   **a)** If these individuals can line up in any order, how many arrangements are possible?

   **b)** If the groom must be the last in line and the bride must be next to the groom, and the others can line up in any order, how many arrangements are possible?

   **c)** If the groom is to be last in line, the bride next to the groom, and males and females are to alternate, how many arrangements are possible?

**36.** *DJ* A disc jockey (DJ) has 9 songs to play. Five are slow songs, and 4 are fast songs. Each song is to be played only once. In how many ways can the DJ play the 9 songs if

   **a)** the songs can be played in any order?

   **b)** the first song must be a slow song and the last song must be a slow song?

   **c)** the first two songs must be fast songs?

*Letter Codes In Exercises 37–40, an identification code is to consist of three letters followed by four digits. How many different codes are possible if*

**37.** repetition is not permitted?

**38.** repetition is permitted?

**39.** repetition of letters is permitted, repetition of numbers is not permitted, and the first three entries must all be the same letter?

**40.** the first letter must be an *A, B, C,* or *D* and repetition is not permitted?

*License Plates In Exercises 41–44, a license plate is to consist of three digits followed by two uppercase letters. Determine the number of different license plates possible if*

**41.** repetition of numbers and letters is permitted.

**42.** repetition of numbers and letters is not permitted.

**43.** the first and second digits must be odd, and repetition is not permitted.

**44.** the first digit cannot be zero, and repetition is not permitted.

**45.** *Possible Phone Numbers* A telephone number consists of seven digits with the restriction that the first digit cannot be 0 or 1.

   **a)** How many distinct telephone numbers are possible?

   **b)** How many distinct telephone numbers are possible with three-digit area codes preceding the seven-digit number, where the first digit of the area code is not 0 or 1?

   **c)** With the increasing use of cell phones and paging systems, our society is beginning to run out of usable phone numbers. Various phone companies are developing phone numbers that use 8 digits instead of 7. How many distinct phone numbers can be made using a three digit area code followed by an eight digit phone number, where the first digit of the area code and the phone number cannot be 0 or 1?

**46.** *Fruit Juice Selection* Mrs. Hernandez and her three children go shopping at a local grocery store. Each of the children will be allowed to select one bottle of fruit juice. On the store's shelf there are 12 bottles of fruit juice, and each bottle contains a different type of juice. In how many ways can the selections be made?

**47.** *Skiing Event* A skiing event has 16 participants for the slalom. The 5 participants with the fastest speeds will be listed, in the order of their speed, on the leader board. How many different ways are there for the names to be listed?

**48.** *History Test* In one question on a history test, a student is asked to match 10 dates with 10 events; each date can only be matched with 1 event. In how many different ways can this question be answered?

**49.** *Color Permutations* Determine the number of permutations of the colors in the spectrum that follows.

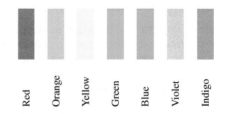

**50.** *Drive-Through at a Bank* A bank has three drive-through stations. Assuming that each is equally likely to be selected by customers, in how many different ways can the next six drivers select a station?

**51.** *Computer Systems* At a computer store, a customer is considering 5 different computers, 4 different monitors, 7 different printers, and 2 different scanners. Assuming that each of the components is compatible with one another and that one of each is to be selected, determine the number of different computer systems possible.

**52.** *Selecting Furniture* The Johnsons just moved into their new home and are selecting furniture for the family room. They are considering 5 different sofas, 2 different chairs, and 6 different tables. They plan to select one item from each category. Determine the number of different ways they can select the furniture.

**53.** Determine the number of permutations of the letters of the word "EDUCATION."

**54.** Determine the number of permutations of the letters of the word "EFFECTIVE."

**55.** In how many ways can the letters in the word "TENNESSEE" be arranged?

**56.** In how many ways can the letters in the word "COMMUNICATION" be arranged?

**57.** In how many ways can the digits in the number 4,568,865 be arranged?

**58.** In how many ways can the digits of the number 2,142,332 be arranged?

**59.** *Flag Messages* Five different colored flags will be placed on a pole, one beneath another. The arrangement of the colors indicates the message. How many messages are possible if five flags are to be selected from nine different colored flags?

**60.** *Multiple-Choice Test* Keri Kershaw is taking a 12-question multiple-choice exam. Each question has three possible answers, (a), (b), and (c). In how many possible ways can Keri answer the questions?

**61.** *Batting Order* In how many ways can the manager of a National League baseball team arrange his batting order of nine players if

**a)** the pitcher must bat last?

**b)** there are no restrictions?

**62.** *Painting Exhibit* Five Monet paintings are to be displayed in a museum.

**a)** In how many different ways can they be arranged if they must be next to one another?

**b)** In how many different ways can they be displayed if a specific one is to be in the middle?

▲ The Water Lily Pond, Pink Harmony, *1900 by Claude Monet*

## Challenge Problems/Group Activities

**63.** *Car Keys* Door keys for a certain automobile are made from a blank key on which five cuts are made. Each cut may be one of five different depths.

**a)** How many different keys can be made?

**b)** If 400,000 of these automobiles are made such that each of the keys determined in part (a) opens the same number of cars, determine how many cars can be opened by a specific key.

**c)** If one of these cars is selected at random, what is the probability that the key selected at random will unlock the door?

**64.** *Voting* On a ballot, each committee member is asked to rank three of eight candidates for recommendation for promotion, giving first, second, and third choices (no ties). What is the minimum number of ballots that must be cast to guarantee that at least two ballots are the same?

**65.** *Scrabble* Nancy Lin, who is playing Scrabble with Dale Grey, has seven different letters. She decides to test each five-letter permutation before her next move. If each permutation takes 5 sec, how long will it take Nancy to check all the permutations?

**66.** *Scrabble* In Exercise 65, assume, of Nancy's seven letters, that three are identical and two are identical. How long will it take Nancy to try all different permutations of her seven letters?

**67.** Does $_nP_r = {_nP_{(n-r)}}$ for all whole numbers, where $n \geq r$?

## Recreational Mathematics

**68.** *Stations* There are eight bus stations from town A to town B. How many different single tickets must be printed so that a passenger may purchase a ticket from any station to any other station?

A o o o o o o o o B
A                        B

**69. *Bus Loop*** How many tickets with different points of origin and destination can be sold on a bus line that travels a loop with 25 stops?

***Jumble*** *Many newspapers contain Jumble puzzles, where the letters of a word are given out of order. In Exercises 70 and 71, read the Recreational Math box on page 741 and determine*

**a)** *the number of possible arrangements of the letters given.*

**b)** *the word.*

**70.** HEICOC

**71.** ROSEGOC

## Internet/Research Activity

**72.** When a book is published, it is assigned a 10-digit code number called the International Standard Book Number (ISBN). Do research and write a report on how this coding system works.

---

## SECTION 12.9    Combinations

▲ *Combinations can be used to determine the number of different arrangements of toppings that can be placed on a hamburger.*

Zebb's Restaurant has 10 different toppings that can be added to a hamburger. Chase Weichman is going to select three of those toppings to add to his hamburger. How many different selections are possible? In this section, we will learn how to determine the number of selections when the order of selection of the items is not important to the final outcome.

**Why** **This is Important** There are many situations in which the order of the selections made is not important to the final outcome. For example, in determining the number of ways a committee can select 3 out of 8 candidates to receive a scholarship, the order in which the 3 are selected is not important.

---

When the order of the selection of the items is important to the final outcome, the problem is a permutation problem. When the order of the selection of the items is unimportant to the final outcome, the problem is a *combination* problem.

Recall from Section 12.8 that permutations are *ordered* arrangements. For example, *a, b, c* and *b, c, a* are two different permutations because the ordering of the three letters is different. The letters *a, b, c* and *b, c, a* represent the same combination of letters because the *same letters* are used in each set. However, the letters *a, b, c* and *a, b, d* represent two different combinations of letters because the letters contained in each set are different.

### Definition: **Combination**
A **combination** is a distinct group (or set) of objects without regard to their arrangement.

### Example 1 *Permutation or Combination*

Determine whether the situation represents a permutation or combination problem.

a) A group of five friends, Arline, Inez, Judy, Dan, and Eunice, are forming a club. The group will elect a president and a treasurer. In how many different ways can the president and treasurer be selected?

b) Of the five individuals named, two will be attending a meeting together. In how many different ways can they do so?

**Solution**

a) Since the president's position is different from the treasurer's position, we have a permutation problem. Judy as president with Dan as treasurer is different from Dan as president with Judy as treasurer. The order of the selection is important.

b) Since the order in which the two individuals selected to attend the meeting is not important, we have a combination problem. There is no difference if Judy is selected and then Dan is selected, or if Dan is selected and then Judy is selected.

In Section 12.8, you learned that $_nP_r$ represents the number of permutations when $r$ items are selected from $n$ distinct items. *Similarly, $_nC_r$ represents the number of combinations when $r$ items are selected from $n$ distinct items.*

Consider the set of elements $\{a, b, c, d, e\}$. The number of permutations of two letters from the set is represented as $_5P_2$, and the number of combinations of two letters from the set is represented as $_5C_2$. Twenty permutations of two letters and 10 combinations of two letters are possible from these five letters. Thus, $_5P_2 = 20$ and $_5C_2 = 10$, as shown.

| **Permutations** | **Combinations** |
|---|---|

$$\left.\begin{array}{l} ab,\ ba,\ ac,\ ca,\ ad,\ da,\ ae,\ ea,\ bc,\ cb, \\ bd,\ db,\ be,\ eb,\ cd,\ dc,\ ce,\ ec,\ de,\ ed \end{array}\right\} 20 \qquad \left.\begin{array}{l} ab,\ ac,\ ad,\ ae,\ bc, \\ bd,\ be,\ cd,\ ce,\ de \end{array}\right\} 10$$

*When discussing both combination and permutation problems, we always assume that the experiment is performed without replacement.* That is why duplicate letters such as *aa* or *bb* are not included in the preceding example.

Note that from one combination of two letters, two permutations can be formed. For example, the combination *ab* gives the permutations *ab* and *ba*, or twice as many permutations as combinations. Thus, for this example we may write

$$_5P_2 = 2 \cdot (_5C_2)$$

Since $2 = 2!$, we may write

$$_5P_2 = 2!\,(_5C_2)$$

If we repeated this same process for comparing the number of permutations in $_nP_r$ with the number of combinations in $_nC_r$, we would find that

$$_nP_r = r!\,(_nC_r)$$

Dividing both sides of the equation by $r!$ gives

$$_nC_r = \frac{_nP_r}{r!}$$

Since $_nP_r = \dfrac{n!}{(n-r)!}$, the combination formula may be expressed as

$$_nC_r = \frac{n!/(n-r)!}{r!} = \frac{n!}{(n-r)!\,r!}$$

## Did You Know?

**Poker versus Bridge**

A nice bridge hand

In popular card games, there is such a variety of possible combinations of cards that a player rarely gets the same hand twice. The total number of different 5-card poker hands using a standard deck of 52 cards is 2,598,960, and for 13-card bridge hands this number increases to 635,013,559,600.

## Combination Formula

The number of combinations possible when $r$ objects are selected from $n$ objects is found by the **combination formula**

$$_nC_r = \frac{n!}{(n-r)!r!}$$

### Example 2   *Museum Selection*

While visiting New York City, the Friedmans are interested in visiting 8 museums but have time to visit only 3. In how many ways can the Friedmans select 3 of the 8 museums to visit?

*Solution*   This problem is a combination problem because the order in which the three museums are selected does not matter.

$$_8C_3 = \frac{8!}{(8-3)!3!} = \frac{8!}{5!3!} = \frac{8 \cdot 7 \cdot 6 \cdot 5 \cdot 4 \cdot 3 \cdot 2 \cdot 1}{5 \cdot 4 \cdot 3 \cdot 2 \cdot 1 \cdot 3 \cdot 2 \cdot 1} = 56$$

There are 56 different ways that 3 of the 8 museums can be selected to visit. ∎

### Example 3   *Floral Arrangements*

Jan Funkhauser has 10 different cut flowers from which she will choose 6 to use in a floral arrangement. How many different ways can she do so?

*Solution*   This problem is a combination problem because the order in which the 6 flowers are selected is unimportant. There are a total of 10 different flowers, so $n = 10$. Six flowers are to be selected, so $r = 6$.

$$_{10}C_6 = \frac{10!}{(10-6)!6!} = \frac{10!}{4!6!} = \frac{10 \cdot \overset{3}{9} \cdot 8 \cdot 7 \cdot 6 \cdot 5 \cdot 4 \cdot 3 \cdot 2 \cdot 1}{4 \cdot 3 \cdot 2 \cdot 1 \cdot 6 \cdot 5 \cdot 4 \cdot 3 \cdot 2 \cdot 1} = 210$$

Thus, there are 210 different ways Jan can choose 6 cut flowers from a group of 10 cut flowers. ∎

### Example 4   *Dinner Combinations*

At the Royal Dynasty Chinese restaurant, dinner for eight people consists of 3 items from column A, 4 items from column B, and 3 items from column C. If columns A, B, and C have 5, 7, and 6 items, respectively, how many different dinner combinations are possible?

*Solution*   For column A, 3 of 5 items must be selected, which can be represented as $_5C_3$. For column B, 4 of 7 items must be selected, which can be represented as $_7C_4$. For column C, 3 of 6 items must be selected, or $_6C_3$.

$$_5C_3 = 10 \quad _7C_4 = 35 \quad \text{and} \quad _6C_3 = 20$$

Using the counting principle, we can determine the total number of dinner combinations by multiplying the number of choices from columns A, B, and C:

$$\text{Total number of dinner choices} = {_5C_3} \cdot {_7C_4} \cdot {_6C_3}$$
$$= 10 \cdot 35 \cdot 20 = 7000$$

Therefore, 7000 different combinations are possible under these conditions. ∎

We have presented various counting methods, including the counting principle, permutations, and combinations. You often need to decide which method to use to solve a problem. Table 12.4 may help you in selecting the procedure to use.

Table 12.4 **Summary of Counting Methods**

| **Counting Principle:** If a first experiment can be performed in $M$ distinct ways and a second experiment can be performed in $N$ distinct ways, then the two experiments in that specific order can be performed in $M \cdot N$ distinct ways.<br><br>The counting principle may be used with or without repetition of items. It is used when determining the number of different ways that two or more experiments can occur. It is also used when there are specific placement requirements, such as the first digit must be a 0 or 1. | **Determining the Number of Ways of Selecting $r$ Items from $n$ Items (Repetition is not Permitted)** | |
| | **Permutations** | **Combinations** |
| | Permutations are used when order is important.<br><br>For example, $a, b, c$ and $b, c, a$ are two different permutations of the same three letters.<br><br>$$_nP_r = \frac{n!}{(n-r)!}$$<br><br>Problems solved with the permutation formula may also be solved by using the counting principle. | Combinations are used when order is not important.<br><br>For example, $a, b, c$ and $b, c, a$ are the same combination of three letters. But $a, b, c,$ and $a, b, d$ are two different combinations of three letters.<br><br>$$_nC_r = \frac{n!}{(n-r)!\,r!}$$ |

## SECTION 12.9

### Exercises

## Warm Up Exercises

*In Exercises 1–6, fill in the blank with an appropriate word, phrase, or symbol(s).*

**1.** A distinct group of objects without regard to their arrangement is called a(n) _____.

**2.** The symbol for the number of combinations when $r$ items are selected from $n$ distinct items is _____.

**3.** If we want to select $r$ items from $n$ items, and the order of the arrangement is important, then _____ are used.

**4.** If we want to select $r$ items from $n$ items, and the order of the arrangement is not important, then _____ are used.

**5.** The notation used to express the number of combinations of 3 items selected from 7 distinct items is _____.

**6.** The notation used to express the number of combinations of 4 items selected from 10 distinct items is _____.

## Practice the Skills

*In Exercises 7–20, evaluate the expression.*

**7.** $_6C_2$

**8.** $_9C_3$

**9. a)** $_8C_4$    **b)** $_8P_4$

**10. a)** $_8C_2$    **b)** $_8P_2$

**11. a)** $_8C_0$    **b)** $_8P_0$

**12. a)** $_{12}C_8$    **b)** $_{12}P_8$

**13. a)** $_{10}C_3$    **b)** $_{10}P_3$

**14. a)** $_5C_5$    **b)** $_5P_5$

**15.** $\dfrac{_5C_3}{_5P_3}$

**16.** $\dfrac{_7C_2}{_7P_2}$

**17.** $\dfrac{_6C_4}{_6C_3}$

**18.** $\dfrac{_6C_6}{_8C_0}$

**19.** $\dfrac{_9P_4}{_{10}C_5}$

**20.** $\dfrac{_7P_0}{_7C_0}$

## Problem Solving

**21.** *Hiring* There are 12 qualified applicants for 4 nursing positions at a hospital. In how many ways can the positions be filled?

**22.** *Banana Split* An ice-cream parlor has 20 different flavors. Cynthia orders a banana split and has to select 3 different flavors. How many different selections are possible?

**23.** *Test Essays* Tina Campbell must select and answer four of five essay questions on a test. In how many ways can she do so?

24. *Software Packages* During a special promotion at CompUSA, a customer purchasing a computer and a printer is given the choice of 2 free software packages. If there are 9 different software packages from which to select, how many different ways can the 2 packages be selected?

25. *Scholarships* A scholarship committee has received 8 applications for a $500 scholarship. The committee has decided to select 3 of the 8 candidates for further consideration. In how many ways can the committee do so?

26. *Attending Plays* While visiting New York City, the Nygens want to attend 3 plays out of 10 plays they would like to see. In how many ways can they do so?

▲ Theater district, New York City

27. *Taxi Ride* A group of 7 people wants to use taxis to go to a local restaurant. When the first taxi arrives, the group decides that 4 people should get into the taxi. In how many ways can that be done?

28. *Plants* Mary Robinson purchased a package of 24 different plants, but she only needed 20 plants for planting. In how many ways can she select the 20 plants from the package to be planted?

29. *Entertainers* Ruth Eckerd Hall must select 8 of 12 possible entertainers for its summer schedule. In how many ways can that be done?

30. *CD Selection* James Ruiz has 7 CDs and wants to select 4 to play in his car CD player. In how many ways can he select 4 of 7 CDs?

31. *Trophies* Matthew Abbott has 10 shirts in his closet and must select 4 to take with him on vacation. In how many ways can Matthew select the shirts?

32. *Quinella Bet* A quinella bet consists of selecting the first- and second-place winners, in any order, in a particular event. For example, suppose you select a 2–5 quinella. If 2 wins and 5 finishes second, or if 5 wins and 2 finishes second, you win. Mr. Smith goes to a jai alai match. In the match, 8 jai alai teams compete. How many quinella tickets must Mr. Smith purchase to guarantee a win?

33. *Cameras and Lenses* Rowe Photography has nine different digital cameras and six different long-range lenses in stock. The manager wants to place three of the nine cameras and

two of the six lenses on sale. In how many ways can the manager select the items to be listed as sale items?

34. *Test Question* On an English test, Tito Ramirez must write an essay for three of the five questions in Part 1 and four of the six questions in Part 2. How many different combinations of questions can he answer?

35. *Plasma and LCD TVs* A television/stereo store has 12 different plasma televisions and 8 different LCD televisions in stock. The store's manager wishes to place 3 plasma televisions and 2 LCD televisions on sale. In how many ways can that be done?

36. *Newsletter* An animal shelter has 15 cats and 12 dogs available for adoption. The shelter wants to select 6 cats and 4 dogs to feature in the adoption newsletter. In how many ways can this be done?

37. *Dinner Party* Sue Less is having a dinner party. She has 10 different bottles of red wine and 8 different bottles of white wine on her wine rack. She wants to select 4 bottles of red wine and 2 bottles of white wine to serve at her party. In how many ways can she do so?

38. *Forming a Committee* The Webster Town Board is forming a committee to explore ways to improve public safety in the town. The committee will consist of 4 representatives from the town board and 3 representatives from a citizens advisory board. If there are 7 town board members and 5 citizens advisory board members from which to choose, how many different ways can the committee be formed?

39. *Selecting Soda* Angel Ramirez is sent to the store to get 5 different bottles of regular soda and 3 different bottles of diet soda. If there are 10 different types of regular sodas and 7 different types of diet sodas to choose from, how many different choices does Angel have?

40. *Constructing a Test* A teacher is constructing a mathematics test consisting of 10 questions. She has a pool of 28 questions, which are classified by level of difficulty as follows: 6 difficult questions, 10 average questions, and 12 easy questions. How many different 10-question tests can she construct from the pool of 28 questions if her test is to have 3 difficult, 4 average, and 3 easy questions?

41. *Selecting Mutual Funds* Joe Chang recently graduated from college and now has a job that provides a retirement investment plan. Joe wants to diversify his investments, so he wants to invest in four stock mutual funds and two bond mutual funds. If he has a choice of eight stock

mutual funds and five bond mutual funds, how many different selections of mutual funds does he have?

42. *Door Prize* As part of a door prize, Mary McCarty won three tickets to a baseball game and three tickets to a theater performance. She decided to give all the tickets to friends. For the baseball game she is considering six different friends, and for the theater she is considering eight different friends. In how many ways can she distribute the tickets?

43. *New Breakfast Cereals* General Mills is testing 4 oat cereals, 5 wheat cereals, and 6 rice cereals. If it plans to market 3 of the oat cereals, 2 of the wheat cereals, and 2 of the rice cereals, how many different combinations are possible?

44. *Catering Service* A catering service is making up trays of hors d'oeuvres. The hors d'oeuvres are categorized as inexpensive, average, and expensive. If the client must select three of the eight inexpensive, five of the nine average, and two of the four expensive hors d'oeuvres, how many different choices are possible?

## Challenge Problems/Group Activities

45. *Test Answers* Consider a 10-question test in which each question can be answered either correctly or incorrectly.

    **a)** How many different ways are there to answer the questions so that eight are correct and two are incorrect?

    **b)** How many different ways are there to answer the questions so that at least eight are correct?

46. **a)** *A Dinner Toast* Four people at dinner make a toast. If each person is to tap glasses with each other person one at a time, how many taps will take place?

    **b)** Repeat part (a) with five people.

    **c)** How many taps will there be if there are $n$ people at the dinner table?

47. *Pascal's Triangle* The notation $_nC_2$ may be written $\binom{n}{r}$.

    **a)** Use this notation to evaluate each of the combinations in the following array. Form a triangle of the results,

similar to the one given, by placing the answer to each combination in the same relative position in the triangle.

$$\binom{0}{0}$$
$$\binom{1}{0} \quad \binom{1}{1}$$
$$\binom{2}{0} \quad \binom{2}{1} \quad \binom{2}{2}$$
$$\binom{3}{0} \quad \binom{3}{1} \quad \binom{3}{2} \quad \binom{3}{3}$$
$$\binom{4}{0} \quad \binom{4}{1} \quad \binom{4}{2} \quad \binom{4}{3} \quad \binom{4}{4}$$

    **b)** Using the number pattern in part (a), find the next row of numbers of the triangle (known as *Pascal's triangle*).

48. *Lottery Combinations* Determine the number of combinations possible in a state lottery where you must select

    **a)** 6 of 46 numbers.

    **b)** 6 of 47 numbers.

    **c)** 6 of 48 numbers.

    **d)** 6 of 49 numbers.

    **e)** Does the number of combinations increase by the same amount going from part (a) to part (b) as from part (b) to part (c)?

49. **a)** *Table Seating Arrangements* How many distinct ways can four people be seated in a row?

    **b)** How many distinct ways can four people be seated at a circular table?

50. Show that $_nC_r = {_nC_{(n-r)}}$.

51. *Forming a Committee* A group of 15 people wants to form a committee consisting of a chair, vice chair, and three additional members. How many different committees can be formed?

## Recreational Mathematics

52. **a)** *Combination Lock* To open a combination lock, you must know the lock's three-number sequence in its proper order. Repetition of numbers is permitted. Why is this lock more like a permutation lock than a combination lock? Why is it not a true permutation problem?

    **b)** Assuming that a combination lock has 40 numbers, determine how many different three-number arrangements are possible if repetition of numbers is allowed.

c) Answer the question in part (b) if repetition is not allowed.

### Internet/Research Activity

53. The area of mathematics called combinatorics is the science of counting. Do research and write a paper on combinatorics and its many applications.

---

| SECTION 12.10 | Solving Probability Problems by Using Combinations |

▲ What is the probability of selecting two picture cards from a standard deck of 52 cards when the two cards are selected without replacement?

Suppose that we want to find the probability of selecting two picture cards (jacks, queens, or kings) when two cards are selected, without replacement, from a standard deck of cards. In Section 12.6, we used the *and* probability formula to solve this type of probability problem. In this section, we will learn another way to solve this type of probability problem by using combinations.

**Why** *This is Important* Combinations can be used in a variety of real-world probability applications.

---

Using the *and* formula for determining the probability of selecting two picture cards from a dark of 52 cards, we could reason as follows:

$$P(2 \text{ picture cards}) = P(\text{first picture card}) \cdot P(\text{second picture card})$$

$$= \frac{12}{52} \cdot \frac{11}{51} = \frac{132}{2652} \quad \text{or} \quad \frac{11}{221}$$

Since the order of the two picture cards selected is not important to the final answer, this problem can be considered a combination probability problem.

We can also find the probability of selecting two picture cards, using combinations, by finding the number of possible successful outcomes (selecting two picture cards) and dividing that answer by the total number of possible outcomes (selecting any two cards).

The number of ways in which two picture cards can be selected from the 12 picture cards in a deck is $_{12}C_2$, or

$$_{12}C_2 = \frac{12!}{(12-2)!2!} = \frac{\overset{6}{\cancel{12}} \cdot 11 \cdot \cancel{10!}}{\cancel{10!} \cdot \cancel{2} \cdot 1} = 66$$

The number of ways in which two cards can be selected from a deck of 52 cards is $_{52}C_2$, or

$$_{52}C_2 = \frac{52!}{(52-2)!2!} = \frac{\overset{26}{\cancel{52}} \cdot 51 \cdot \cancel{50!}}{\cancel{50!} \cdot \cancel{2} \cdot 1} = 1326$$

Thus,

$$P(\text{selecting 2 picture cards}) = \frac{_{12}C_2}{_{52}C_2} = \frac{66}{1326} = \frac{11}{221}$$

James Butler "Wild Bill" Hickok (1837–1876), known as "the fastest gun in the West," was a famous scout and federal marshal. Hickok was shot in the back and mortally wounded by Jack McCall while playing poker in a saloon in Deadwood, Dakota Territory (now South Dakota). McCall was hanged for his deed. The cards Hickok was holding when shot are shown here. Since that time, the two pairs, aces and eights, have become known as "the dead man's hand" (see Exercise 43 on page 757). Hickok is buried next to Martha Canary, better known as "Calamity Jane," in a cemetery overlooking the town of Deadwood.

Note that the same answer is obtained with either method. To give you more exposure to counting techniques, we will work the problems in this section using combinations.

### Example 1  *Committee of Three Women*

A club consists of four men and five women. Three members are to be selected at random to form a committee. What is the probability that the committee will consist of three women?

**Solution**  The order in which the three members are selected is not important. Therefore, we may work this problem using combinations.

$$P\left(\begin{array}{c}\text{committee consists}\\\text{of 3 women}\end{array}\right) = \frac{\text{number of possible committees with 3 women}}{\text{total number of possible 3-member committees}}$$

Since there is a total of 5 women, the number of possible committees with three women is $_5C_3 = 10$. Since there is a total of 9 people, the total number of possible three-member committees is $_9C_3 = 84$.

$$P(\text{committee consists of 3 women}) = \frac{10}{84} = \frac{5}{42}$$

The probability of randomly selecting a committee with three women is $\frac{5}{42}$. ∎

### Example 2  *A Heart Flush*

A flush in the game of poker is five cards of the same suit (5 hearts, 5 diamonds, 5 clubs, or 5 spades). If you are dealt a five-card hand, determine the probability that you will be dealt a heart flush.

**Solution**  The order in which the five hearts are dealt is not important. Therefore, we may work this problem using combinations.

$$P(\text{heart flush}) = \frac{\text{number of possible 5-card heart flushes}}{\text{total number of possible 5-card hands}}$$

Since there are 13 hearts in a deck of cards, the number of possible five-card heart flush hands is $_{13}C_5 = 1287$. The total number of possible five-card hands in a deck of 52 cards is $_{52}C_5 = 2{,}598{,}960$.

$$P(\text{heart flush}) = \frac{_{13}C_5}{_{52}C_5} = \frac{1287}{2{,}598{,}960} = \frac{33}{66{,}640}$$

The probability of being dealt a heart flush is $\frac{33}{66{,}640}$, or $\approx 0.000495$. ∎

### Example 3  *Employment Assignments*

A temporary employment agency has six men and five women who wish to be assigned for the day. One employer has requested four employees for security guard positions, and the second employer has requested three employees for moving furniture in an office building. If we assume that each of the potential employees has the same chance of being selected and being assigned at random and that only seven employees will be assigned, find the probability that

a)  three men will be selected for moving furniture.

b)  three men will be selected for moving furniture and four women will be selected for security guard positions.

Solution

a) $P\left(\begin{array}{c}\text{3 men selected}\\\text{for moving furniture}\end{array}\right) = \dfrac{\left(\begin{array}{c}\text{number of possible combinations}\\\text{of 3 men selected}\end{array}\right)}{\left(\begin{array}{c}\text{total number of possible combinations}\\\text{for selecting 3 people}\end{array}\right)}$

The number of possible combinations with 3 men is $_6C_3$. The total number of possible selections of 3 people is $_{11}C_3$.

$$P\left(\begin{array}{c}\text{3 men selected}\\\text{for moving furniture}\end{array}\right) = \dfrac{_6C_3}{_{11}C_3} = \dfrac{20}{165} = \dfrac{4}{33}$$

Thus, the probability that 3 men are selected is $\frac{4}{33}$.

b) The number of ways of selecting 3 men out of 6 is $_6C_3$, and the number of ways of selecting 4 women out of 5 is $_5C_4$. The total number of possible selections when 7 people are selected from 11 is $_{11}C_7$. Since both the 3 men *and* the 4 women must be selected, the probability is calculated as follows:

$$P\left(\begin{array}{c}\text{3 men and}\\\text{4 women selected}\end{array}\right) = \dfrac{\left(\begin{array}{c}\text{number of combinations}\\\text{of 3 men selected}\end{array}\right)\cdot\left(\begin{array}{c}\text{number of combinations}\\\text{of 4 women selected}\end{array}\right)}{\left(\begin{array}{c}\text{total number of possible combinations}\\\text{for selecting 7 people}\end{array}\right)}$$

$$= \dfrac{_6C_3 \cdot {}_5C_4}{_{11}C_7} = \dfrac{20 \cdot 5}{330} = \dfrac{100}{330} = \dfrac{10}{33}$$

Thus, the probability is $\frac{10}{33}$.

## Example 4  DVD Selection

Jennifer Alfredo has 4 *Scooby Doo* DVDs, 5 *Magic School Bus* DVDs, and 3 *Bob the Builder* DVDs. If Jennifer randomly selects 4 DVDs for her children to take on a road trip, determine the probability that

a) no *Scooby Doo* DVDs are selected.
b) at least 1 *Scooby Doo* DVD is selected.
c) 2 *Scooby Doo* DVDs and 2 *Magic School Bus* DVDs are selected.

Solution

a) If no *Scooby Doo* DVDs are to be selected, then only *Magic School Bus* and *Bob the Builder* DVDs must be selected. Eight DVDs are either *Magic School Bus* or *Bob the Builder*. Thus, the number of ways that 4 *Magic School Bus* or *Bob the Builder* DVDs may be selected from the possible 8 *Magic School Bus* or *Bob the Builder* DVDs is $_8C_4$. The total number of possible selections is $_{12}C_4$.

$$P(\text{no } \textit{Scooby Doo} \text{ DVDs}) = \dfrac{_8C_4}{_{12}C_4} = \dfrac{70}{495} = \dfrac{14}{99}$$

b) When 4 DVDs are selected, the choice must contain either no *Scooby Doo* DVDs or at least 1 *Scooby Doo* DVD. Since one of these outcomes must occur, the sum of the probabilities must be 1, or

$$P(\text{no } \textit{Scooby Doo} \text{ DVDs}) + P(\text{at least 1 } \textit{Scooby Doo} \text{ DVD}) = 1$$

Therefore,

$$P(\text{at least 1 } Scooby\ Doo \text{ DVD}) = 1 - P(\text{no } Scooby\ Doo \text{ DVDs})$$

$$= 1 - \frac{14}{99} = \frac{99}{99} - \frac{14}{99} = \frac{85}{99}$$

Note that the probability of selecting no *Scooby Doo* DVDs, $\frac{14}{99}$, was found in part (a).

c) The number of ways of selecting 2 *Scooby Doo* DVDs out of 4 *Scooby Doo* DVDs is $_4C_2$, which equals 6. The number of ways of selecting 2 *Magic School Bus* DVDs out of 5 *Magic School Bus* DVDs is $_5C_2$, which equals 10. The total number of possible selections when 4 DVDs are selected from the 12 choices is $_{12}C_4$, which equals 495. Since both the 2 *Scooby Doo* and 2 *Magic School Bus* DVDs must be selected, the probability is calculated as follows.

$$P(2\ Scooby\ Doo \text{ and } 2\ Magic\ School\ Bus) = \frac{_4C_2 \cdot {_5C_2}}{_{12}C_4} = \frac{6 \cdot 10}{495} = \frac{60}{495} = \frac{4}{33}$$ ∎

## Example 5  *Rare Coins*

Conner Shanahan's rare coin collection is made up of 8 silver dollars, 7 quarters, and 5 dimes. Conner plans to sell 8 of his 20 coins to finance part of his college education. If he selects the coins at random, what is the probability that 3 silver dollars, 2 quarters, and 3 dimes are selected?

**Solution**  The number of ways that Conner can select 3 out of 8 silver dollars is $_8C_3$. The number of ways he can select 2 out of 7 quarters is $_7C_2$. The number of ways he can select 3 out of 5 dimes is $_5C_3$. He will select 8 coins from a total of 20 coins. The number of ways he can do so is $_{20}C_8$. The probability that Conner selects 3 silver dollars, 2 quarters, and 3 dimes is calculated as follows.

$$P(3 \text{ silver dollars, 2 quarters, and 3 dimes}) = \frac{_8C_3 \cdot {_7C_2} \cdot {_5C_3}}{_{20}C_8}$$

$$= \frac{56 \cdot 21 \cdot 10}{125{,}970} = \frac{11{,}760}{125{,}970} = \frac{392}{4199}$$ ∎

## SECTION 12.10

### *Exercises*

### Practice the Skills

*In Exercises 1–8, set up the problem as if it were to be solved, but do not solve. Assume that each problem is to be done without replacement.*

1. Ten red balls and four blue balls are in a bag. If four balls from the bag are to be selected at random, determine the probability of selecting four red balls.

2. A class consists of 15 girls and 12 boys. If 8 of the students are to be selected at random, determine the probability that they are all girls.

3. Three letters are to be selected at random from the English alphabet of 26 letters. Determine the probability that 3 vowels (a, e, i, o, u) are selected.

4. Determine the probability of being dealt 3 aces from a standard deck of 52 cards when 3 cards are dealt.

5. A dog breeder has 15 puppies for sale, of which 8 are yellow Labrador retrievers. If 5 puppies are selected at random, determine the probability they are all yellow Labrador retrievers.

**6.** Of 80 people attending a dance, 28 have a college degree. If 4 people at the dance are selected at random, determine the probability that each of the 4 has a college degree.

**7.** Of 120 students attending a college orientation session, 23 are criminal justice majors. If 5 students at the orientation are selected at random, determine the probability that each of the 5 is a criminal justice major.

**8.** A class of 16 people contains 4 people whose birthday is in October. If 3 people from the class are selected at random, determine the probability that *none* of those selected has an October birthday.

## Problem Solving

*In Exercises 9–18, the problems are to be done without replacement. Use combinations to determine probabilities.*

**9.** *Selecting Lightbulbs* A box contains 3 defective and 7 good lightbulbs. If two lightbulbs are to be selected at random from the box, determine the probability that both lightbulbs are defective.

**10.** *Green and Red Balls* A bag contains four red balls and five green balls. You plan to select three balls at random. Determine the probability of selecting three green balls.

**11.** *Flu Vaccine* A doctor has five doses of flu protection vaccine left. He has six women and eight men who want the medication. If the names of five of these people are selected at random, determine the probability that five men's names are selected.

**12.** *Bills of Four Denominations* Duc Tran's wallet contains 8 bills of the following denominations: four $5 bills, two $10 bills, one $20 bill, and one $50 bill. If Duc selects two bills at random, determine the probability that he selects two $5 bills.

**13.** *Selecting Digits* Each of the digits 0–9 is written on a slip of paper, and the slips are placed in a hat. If three slips of paper are selected at random, determine the probability that the three numbers selected are greater than 5.

**14.** *Selecting Books* Barnes & Noble has 20 different books listed on its clearance list. Twelve books are listed as mystery, and 8 are listed as romance. If 4 books are selected at random from the list, determine the probability that they are all mystery books.

**15.** *Gift Certificates* The sales department at Atwell Studios consists of three people, the manufacturing department consists of six people, and the accounting department consists of two people. Three people will be selected at random from these people and will be given gift certificates to Sweet Tomatoes, a local restaurant. Determine the probability that two of those selected will be from the manufacturing department and one will be from the accounting department.

**16.** *Faculty-Student Committee* A committee of four is to be randomly selected from a group of seven teachers and eight students. Determine the probability that the committee will consist of two teachers and two students.

**17.** *Winning the Grand Prize* A lottery consists of 46 numbers. You select 6 numbers, and if they match the 6 numbers selected by the lottery commission, you win the grand prize. Determine the probability of winning the grand prize.

**18.** *Red Cards* You are dealt 5 cards from a standard deck of 52 cards. Determine the probability that you are dealt 5 red cards.

*TV Game Show In Exercises 19–22, a television game show has five doors, of which the contestant must pick two. Behind two of the doors are expensive cars, and behind the other three doors are consolation prizes. The contestant gets to keep the items behind the two doors she selects. Determine the probability that the contestant wins*

**19.** no cars.        **20.** both cars.

**21.** at least one car.        **22.** exactly one car.

*Baseball In Exercises 23–26, assume that a particular professional baseball team has 10 pitchers, 6 infielders, and 9 other players. If 3 players' names are selected at random, determine the probability that*

**23.** all 3 are infielders.

**24.** none of the three is a pitcher.

**25.** 2 are pitchers and 1 is an infielder.

**26.** 1 is a pitcher and 2 are players other than pitchers and infielders.

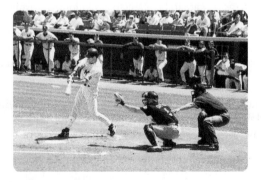

*Car Rental* In Exercises 27–30, a car rental agency has 10 midsized and 15 compact cars on its lot, from which 6 will be selected. Assuming that each car is equally likely to be selected and the cars are selected at random, determine the probability (as a decimal number rounded to four decimal places) that the cars selected consist of

**27.** all midsized cars.

**28.** 2 midsized cars and 4 compact cars.

**29.** 3 midsized cars and 3 compact cars.

**30.** at least 1 compact car.

*New Soup* In Exercises 31–34, Campbell's is testing 12 new soups for possible production. They are testing 3 Chunky soups, 4 Healthy Request soups, and 5 Select Harvest soups. If we assume each of the 12 soups has the same chance of being selected and 4 new soups will be produced, determine the probability that the four new soups selected will be as follows

**31.** 2 are Healthy Request soups and 2 are Chunky soups.

**32.** 3 are Select Harvest soups and 1 is a Healthy Request soup.

**33.** 1 is a Healthy Request soup, 1 is a Select Harvest soup, and 2 are Chunky soups.

**34.** at least one is a Chunky soup.

*Theater* In Exercises 35–38, five men and six women are going to be assigned to a specific row of seats in a theater. If the 11 tickets for the numbered seats are given out at random, determine the probability that

**35.** five women are given the first five seats next to the center aisle.

**36.** at least one woman is in one of the first five seats.

**37.** exactly one woman is in one of the first five seats.

**38.** three women are seated in the first three seats and two men are seated in the next two seats.

**39.** *Working Overtime* Of 24 employees at Lowe's home improvement store, 10 work as cashiers and 14 stock shelves. If 3 of the 24 employees are selected at random to work overtime, determine the probability that all 3 are cashiers.

**40.** *Poker Probability* A full house in poker consists of three of one kind and two of another kind in a five-card hand. For example, if a hand contains three kings and two 5's, it is a full house. If 5 cards are dealt at random from a standard deck of 52 cards, without replacement,

determine the probability of getting three kings and two 5's.

**41.** *A Royal Flush* A royal flush consists of an ace, king, queen, jack, and 10 all in the same suit. If 7 cards are dealt at random from a standard deck of 52 cards, determine the probability of getting a

**a)** royal flush in spades.

**b)** royal flush in any suit.

**42.** *Restaurant Staff* The staff of a restaurant consists of 25 people, including 8 waiters, 12 waitresses, and 5 cooks. For Mother's Day, a total of 9 people will need to be selected to work. If the selections are made at random, determine the probability that 3 waiters, 4 waitresses, and 2 cooks will be selected.

**43.** *"Dead Man's Hand"* A pair of aces and a pair of 8's is often known as a "dead man's hand." (See the *Did You Know?* on page 753.)

**a)** Determine the probability of being dealt a dead man's hand (any two aces, any two 8's, and one other card that is not an ace or an 8) when 5 cards are dealt, without replacement, from a standard deck of 52 cards.

**b)** The actual cards "Wild Bill" Hickok was holding when he was shot were the aces of spades and clubs, the 8's of spades and clubs, and the 9 of diamonds. If you are dealt five cards without replacement, determine the probability of being dealt this exact hand.

## Challenge Problems/Group Activities

**44.** *Alternate Seating* If three men and three women are to be assigned at random to six seats in a row at a theater, determine the probability that they will alternate by gender.

**45.** *Selecting Officers* A club consists of 15 people including Ali, Kendra, Ted, Alice, Marie, Dan, Linda, and Frank. From the 15 members, a president, vice president, and treasurer will be selected at random. An advisory committee of 5 other individuals will also be selected at random.

**a)** Determine the probability that Ali is selected president, Kendra is selected vice president, Ted is selected treasurer, and the other 5 individuals named form the advisory committee.

**b)** Determine the probability that 3 of the 8 individuals named are selected for the three officers' positions and the other 5 are selected for the advisory board.

**46.** *A Marked Deck* A number is written with a magic marker on each card of a deck of 52 cards. The number 1 is put on the first card, 2 on the second, and so on. The cards are then shuffled and cut. What is the probability that the top 4 cards will be in ascending order? (For example, the top card is 12, the second 22, the third 41, and the fourth 51.)

## Recreational Mathematics

**47.** *Hair* When the Isle of Flume took its most recent census, the population was 100,002 people. Nobody on the isle has more than 100,001 hairs on his or her head. Determine the probability that at least two people have exactly the same number of hairs on their head.

---

## SECTION 12.11    Binomial Probability Formula

▲ We can use the binomial formula to determine the probability that selected customers waited on will leave a tip.

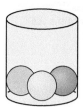

Figure 12.23

Suppose that you are a waiter at a restaurant and have learned from past experience that 80% of your customers leave a tip. If you wait on 6 customers, what is the probability that all 6 customers will leave a tip? If you wait on 8 customers, what is the probability that at least 5 of them will leave you a tip? In this section, we will learn how to use the binomial probability formula to answer these and similar questions.

**Why** *This is Important* Binomial probabilities have many applications in business and industry, as well as in the sciences and the pharmacological industry.

---

Suppose that a basket contains three identical balls, except for their color. One is red, one is blue, and one is yellow (Fig. 12.23). Suppose further that we are going to select three balls *with replacement* from the basket. We can determine specific probabilities by examining the tree diagram shown in Fig. 12.24. Note that 27 different selections are possible, as indicated in the sample space.

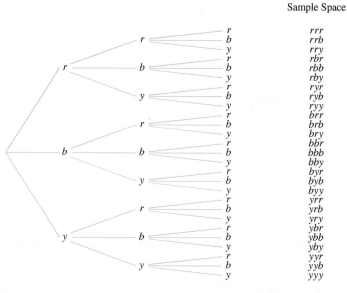

Figure 12.24

Our three selections may yield 0, 1, 2, or 3 red balls. We can determine the probability of selecting exactly 0, 1, 2, or 3 red balls by using the sample space. To determine the probability of selecting 0 red balls, we count those outcomes that do not contain a red ball. There are 8 of them (*bbb, bby, byb, byy, ybb, yby, yyb, yyy*). Thus, the probability of obtaining exactly 0 red balls is 8/27. We determine the probability of selecting exactly 1 red ball by counting the sample points that contain exactly 1 red ball. There are 12 of them. Thus, the probability is $\frac{12}{27}$, or $\frac{4}{9}$.

We can determine the probability of selecting exactly 2 red balls and exactly 3 red balls in a similar manner. The probabilities of selecting exactly 0, 1, 2, and 3 red balls are illustrated in Table 12.5.

Table 12.5 A Probability Distribution for Three Balls Selected with Replacement

| Number of Red Balls Selected, (x) | Probability of Selecting the Number of Red Balls, P(x) |
|---|---|
| 0 | $\frac{8}{27}$ |
| 1 | $\frac{12}{27}$ |
| 2 | $\frac{6}{27}$ |
| 3 | $\frac{1}{27}$ |
|  | Sum $= \frac{27}{27} = 1$ |

Note that the sum of the probabilities is 1. This table is an example of a *probability distribution*, which shows the probabilities associated with each specific outcome of an experiment. *In a probability distribution, every possible outcome must be listed and the sum of the probabilities must be 1.*

Let us specifically consider the probability of selecting 1 red ball in 3 selections. We see from Table 12.5 that this probability is $\frac{12}{27}$, or $\frac{4}{9}$. Can we determine this probability without developing a tree diagram? The answer is yes.

Suppose that we consider selecting a red ball success, S, and selecting a non–red ball failure, F. Furthermore, suppose that we let $p$ represent the probability of success and $q$ the probability of failure on any trial. Then $p = \frac{1}{3}$ and $q = \frac{2}{3}$. We can obtain 1 success in three selections in the following ways:

$$\text{SFF} \qquad \text{FSF} \qquad \text{FFS}$$

We can compute the probabilities of each of these outcomes using the multiplication formula because each of the selections is independent.

$$P(\text{SFF}) = P(\text{S}) \cdot P(\text{F}) \cdot P(\text{F}) = p \cdot q \cdot q = pq^2 = \frac{1}{3}\left(\frac{2}{3}\right)^2 = \frac{4}{27}$$

$$P(\text{FSF}) = P(\text{F}) \cdot P(\text{S}) \cdot P(\text{F}) = q \cdot p \cdot q = pq^2 = \frac{1}{3}\left(\frac{2}{3}\right)^2 = \frac{4}{27}$$

$$P(\text{FFS}) = P(\text{F}) \cdot P(\text{F}) \cdot P(\text{S}) = q \cdot q \cdot p = pq^2 = \frac{1}{3}\left(\frac{2}{3}\right)^2 = \frac{4}{27}$$

$$\text{Sum} = \frac{12}{27} = \frac{4}{9}$$

We obtained an answer of $\frac{4}{9}$, the same answer that was obtained using the tree diagram. Note that each of the 3 sets of outcomes above has 1 success and 2 failures.

Rather than listing all the possibilities containing 1 success and 2 failures, we can use the combination formula to determine the number of possible combinations of 1 success in 3 trials. To do so, evaluate $_3C_1$.

$$_3C_1 = \frac{3!}{(3-1)!1!} = \frac{3 \cdot 2 \cdot 1}{2 \cdot 1 \cdot 1} = 3$$

Number of trials    Number of successes

Thus, we see that there are 3 ways the 1 success could occur in 3 trials. To compute the probability of 1 success in 3 trials, we can multiply the probability of success in any one trial, $p \cdot q^2$, by the number of ways the 1 success can be arranged among the 3 trials, $_3C_1$. Thus, the probability of selecting 1 red ball, $P(1)$, in 3 trials may be found as follows.

$$P(1) = (_3C_1)p^1q^2 = 3\left(\frac{1}{3}\right)\left(\frac{2}{3}\right)^2 = \frac{12}{27} = \frac{4}{9}$$

The binomial probability formula, which we introduce shortly, explains how to obtain expressions like $P(1) = (_3C_1)p^1q^2$ and is very useful in finding certain types of probabilities.

To use the binomial probability formula, the following three conditions must hold.

### To Use The Binomial Probability Formula
1. There are $n$ repeated independent trials.
2. Each trial has two possible outcomes, *success* and *failure.*
3. For each trial, the probability of success (and failure) remains the same.

Before going further, let's discuss why we can use the binomial probability formula to find the probability of selecting a specific number of red balls when three balls are selected with replacement. First, since each trial is performed *with replacement*, the three trials are independent of each other. Second, we may consider selecting a red ball as success and selecting any ball of another color as failure. Third, for each selection, the probability of success (selecting a red ball) is $\frac{1}{3}$ and the probability of failure (selecting a ball of another color) is $\frac{2}{3}$. Now let's discuss the binomial probability formula.

### Binomial Probability Formula
The probability of obtaining exactly $x$ successes, $P(x)$, in $n$ independent trials is given by the binomial probability formula

$$P(x) = (_nC_x)p^xq^{n-x}$$

where $p$ is the probability of success on a single trial and $q$ is the probability of failure on a single trial.

In the formula, $p$ will be a number between 0 and 1, inclusive, and $q = 1 - p$. Therefore, if $p = 0.2$, then $q = 1 - 0.2 = 0.8$. If $p = \frac{3}{5}$, then $q = 1 - \frac{3}{5} = \frac{2}{5}$. Note that $p + q = 1$ and the values of $p$ and $q$ remain the same for each independent trial. The combination $_nC_x$ is called the *binomial coefficient.*

In Example 1, we use the binomial probability formula to solve the same problem we recently solved by using a tree diagram.

### Example 1   *Selecting Colored Balls with Replacement*

A basket contains 3 balls: 1 red, 1 blue, and 1 yellow. Three balls are going to be selected with replacement from the basket. Find the probability that

a) no red balls are selected.

b) exactly 1 red ball is selected.

c) exactly 2 red balls are selected.

d) exactly 3 red balls are selected.

**Solution**

a) We will consider selecting a red ball a success and selecting a ball of any other color a failure. Since only 1 of the 3 balls is red, the probability of success on any single trial, $p$, is $\frac{1}{3}$. The probability of failure on any single trial, $q$, is $1 - \frac{1}{3} = \frac{2}{3}$. We are finding the probability of selecting 0 red balls, or 0 successes. Since $x$ represents the number of successes, we let $x = 0$. There are 3 independent selections (or trials), so $n = 3$. In our calculations, we will need to evaluate $\left(\frac{1}{3}\right)^0$. Note that any nonzero number raised to a power of 0 is 1. Thus, $\left(\frac{1}{3}\right)^0 = 1$. We determine the probability of 0 successes, or $P(0)$, as follows.

$$P(x) = (_nC_x)p^xq^{n-x}$$
$$P(0) = (_3C_0)\left(\frac{1}{3}\right)^0\left(\frac{2}{3}\right)^{3-0}$$
$$= (1)(1)\left(\frac{2}{3}\right)^3$$
$$= \left(\frac{2}{3}\right)^3 = \frac{8}{27}$$

b) We are finding the probability of obtaining exactly 1 red ball or exactly 1 success in 3 independent selections. Thus, $x = 1$ and $n = 3$. We find the probability of exactly 1 success, or $P(1)$, as follows.

$$P(x) = (_nC_x)p^xq^{n-x}$$
$$P(1) = (_3C_1)\left(\frac{1}{3}\right)^1\left(\frac{2}{3}\right)^{3-1}$$
$$= 3\left(\frac{1}{3}\right)\left(\frac{2}{3}\right)^2$$
$$= 3\left(\frac{1}{3}\right)\left(\frac{4}{9}\right) = \frac{4}{9}$$

c) We are finding the probability of selecting exactly 2 red balls in 3 independent trials. Thus, $x = 2$ and $n = 3$. We find $P(2)$ as follows.

$$P(x) = (_nC_x)p^xq^{n-x}$$
$$P(2) = {_3C_2}\left(\frac{1}{3}\right)^2\left(\frac{2}{3}\right)^{3-2}$$
$$= 3\left(\frac{1}{3}\right)^2\left(\frac{2}{3}\right)^1$$
$$= 3\left(\frac{1}{9}\right)\left(\frac{2}{3}\right) = \frac{2}{9}$$

d) We are finding the probability of selecting exactly 3 red balls in 3 independent trials. Thus, $x = 3$ and $n = 3$. We find $P(3)$ as follows.

$$P(x) = (_nC_x)p^xq^{n-x}$$

$$P(3) = (_3C_3)\left(\frac{1}{3}\right)^3\left(\frac{2}{3}\right)^{3-3}$$

$$= 1\left(\frac{1}{3}\right)^3\left(\frac{2}{3}\right)^0$$

$$= 1\left(\frac{1}{27}\right)(1) = \frac{1}{27}$$

All the probabilities obtained in Example 1 agree with the answers obtained by using the tree diagram. Whenever you obtain a value for $P(x)$, you should obtain a value between 0 and 1, inclusive. If you obtain a value greater than 1, you have made a mistake.

## Example 2   *Quality Control for Batteries*

A manufacturer of batteries knows that 0.4% of the batteries produced by the company are defective.

a) Write the binomial probability formula that would be used to determine the probability that exactly $x$ out of $n$ batteries produced are defective.

b) Write the binomial probability formula that would be used to find the probability that exactly 3 batteries of 75 produced will be defective. Do not evaluate.

*Solution*

a) We want to find the probability that exactly $x$ batteries are defective where selecting a defective battery is considered success. The probability, $p$, that an individual battery is defective is 0.4%, or 0.004 in decimal form. The probability that a battery is not defective, $q$, is $1 - 0.004$, or 0.996. The general formula for finding the probability that exactly $x$ out of $n$ batteries produced are defective is

$$P(x) = (_nC_x)p^xq^{n-x}$$

Substituting 0.004 for $p$ and 0.996 for $q$, we obtain the formula

$$P(x) = (_nC_x)(0.004)^x(0.996)^{n-x}$$

b) We want to determine the probability that exactly 3 batteries out of 75 produced are defective. Thus, $x = 3$ and $n = 75$. Substituting these values into the formula in part (a) gives

$$P(3) = (_{75}C_3)(0.004)^3(0.996)^{75-3}$$
$$= (_{75}C_3)(0.004)^3(0.996)^{72}$$

The answer may be obtained using a scientific calculator.

## Example 3   *Spring Break*

According to a survey conducted by OnCampus Research, 20% of college students reported they will work during spring break. Determine the probability that

a) exactly 3 of 5 college students selected at random will work during spring break.

b) exactly 4 of 4 college students selected at random will work during spring break.

*Solution*

a) We want to determine the probability that exactly 3 of 5 college students selected at random will work during spring break. Therefore a college student

working during spring break is considered a success. Thus, $x = 3$ and $n = 5$. The probability of success, $p$, is 20%, or 0.2. The probability of failure, $q$, is $1-0.2$, or 0.8. Substituting these values into the binomial formula yields

$$P(x) = (_nC_x)p^x q^{n-x}$$
$$P(3) = (_5C_3)(0.2)^3(0.8)^{5-3}$$
$$= 10(0.2)^3(0.8)^2$$
$$= 10(0.008)(0.64)$$
$$= 0.0512$$

Thus, the probability that exactly 3 of 5 randomly selected college students will work during spring break is 0.0512.

b) We want to find the probability that 4 of 4 college students selected at random will work during spring break. Thus, $x = 4$ and $n = 4$. We wish to find $P(4)$.

$$P(x) = (_nC_x)p^x q^{n-x}$$
$$P(4) = (_4C_4)(0.2)^4(0.8)^{4-4}$$
$$= 1(0.2)^4(0.8)^0$$
$$= 10(0.0016)(1)$$
$$= 0.016$$

Thus, the probability that exactly 4 of 4 randomly selected college students will work during spring break is 0.016. ∎

## Example 4 *Planting Trees*

The probability that a tree planted by a landscaping company will survive is 0.8. Determine the probability that

a) none of four trees planted will survive.

b) at least one of four trees planted will survive.

*Solution*

a) Success is a tree survives. Thus, $p = 0.8$ and $q = 1 - p = 1 - 0.8 = 0.2$. We want to find the probability of 0 successes in 4 trials. Thus, $x = 0$ and $n = 4$. We find the probability of 0 successes, or $P(0)$, as follows.

$$P(x) = (_nC_x)p^x q^{n-x}$$
$$P(0) = (_4C_0)(0.8)^0(0.2)^{4-0}$$
$$= 1(1)(0.2)^4$$
$$= 1(1)(0.0016)$$
$$= 0.0016$$

Thus, the probability that none of the four trees planted will survive is 0.0016.

b) The probability that at least one tree of the four trees planted will survive can be found by subtracting from 1 the probability that none of the four trees survives. We worked problems of this type in earlier sections of the chapter, including Sections 12.6 and 12.10.

In part (a), we determined the probability that none of the four trees planted survives is 0.0016. Thus,

$$P(\text{at least one tree planted will survive}) = 1 - P\left(\begin{array}{c}\text{none of the four trees}\\\text{planted will survive}\end{array}\right)$$
$$= 1 - 0.0016$$
$$= 0.9984$$

## SECTION 12.11 *Exercises*

### Warm Up Exercises

*In Exercises 1–4, fill in the blank with an appropriate word, phrase, or symbol(s).*

1. A distribution that shows the probabilities associated with each specific outcome of an experiment is called a(n) _____ distribution.

2. In a probability distribution, the sum of all the probabilities must be _____.

3. In the binomial probability formula, $p$ represents the probability of _____.

4. In the binomial probability formula, $q$ represents the probability of _____.

### Practice the Skills

*In Exercises 5–10, assume that each of the n trials is independent and that p is the probability of success on a given trial. Use the binomial probability formula to find P(x).*

5. $n = 4, x = 3, p = 0.1$

6. $n = 5, x = 2, p = 0.6$

7. $n = 5, x = 2, p = 0.4$

8. $n = 3, x = 3, p = 0.8$

9. $n = 6, x = 0, p = 0.5$

10. $n = 5, x = 3, p = 0.9$

### Problem Solving

11. **A Dozen Eggs** An egg distributor determines that the probability that any individual egg has a crack is 0.14.

    a) Write the binomial probability formula to determine the probability that exactly $x$ eggs of $n$ eggs are cracked.

    b) Write the binomial probability formula to determine the probability that exactly 2 eggs in a one-dozen egg carton are cracked. Do not evaluate.

12. **Facebook** According to *Social Media Today,* as of April 2010, 41.6% of Americans had a Facebook account.

    a) Write the binomial formula to determine the probability that exactly $x$ out of $n$ randomly selected Americans had a Facebook account.

    b) Write the binomial formula to determine the probability that exactly 5 out of 20 randomly selected Americans had a Facebook account. Do not evaluate.

*In Exercises 13–21, use the binomial probability formula to answer the question. Round answers to five decimal places.*

13. **Auto Insurance** An insurance company reported that 60% of all automobile damage claims were made by people under the age of 25. If eight automobile damage claims were selected at random, determine the probability that exactly five of them were made by someone under the age of 25.

14. **Leaving a Tip** Thomas Zellner works as a waiter at Outback Steakhouse. He has learned from experience that 80% of customers who dine alone leave a tip. If Thomas waits on 6 customers dining alone, determine the probability that exactly 4 of them leave a tip.

15. **Staying Connected** According to a survey conducted by American Express, 77% of adults stated they want access to their cell phones and laptops while on vacation. If ten adults are selected at random, determine the probability that exactly six of them want access to their cell phones and laptops while on vacation.

16. **Bank Loans** Records from a specific bank show that 70% of car loan applications are approved. If eight car loan applications from this bank are selected at random, determine the probability that exactly five of the applications are approved.

17. **Dolphin Drug Care** When treated with the antibiotic resonocyllin, 92% of all dolphins are cured of a particular bacterial infection. If six dolphins with the particular bacterial infection are treated with resonocyllin, determine the probability that exactly four are cured.

18. **Manufacturing Lightbulbs** A quality control engineer at a GE lightbulb plant finds that 1% of its bulbs are defective. Determine the probability that exactly two of the next six bulbs made are defective.

19. **Water Heaters** The probability that a specific brand of water heater produces the water temperature it is set to produce is $\frac{4}{5}$. Determine the probability that if five of these water heaters are selected at random, exactly four of them will produce the water temperature they are set to produce.

20. **TV Purchases** At a Circuit City store, $\frac{1}{4}$ of those purchasing color televisions purchase a large-screen TV. Determine the probability that

a) none of the next four people who purchase a color television at Circuit City purchases a large-screen TV.

b) at least one of the next four people who purchase a color television at Circuit City purchases a large-screen TV.

**21. *Multiple-Choice Quiz***  Edward Dunn has to take a five-question multiple-choice quiz in his sociology class. Each question has four choices for answers, of which only one is correct. Assuming that Edward guesses on all five questions, what is the probability that he will answer

a) all five questions correctly.

b) exactly three questions correctly.

c) at least three questions correctly.

## Challenge Problems/Group Activities

**22. *Transportation to Work***  In a random sample of 80 working mothers in Duluth, Minnesota, the following data indicating how they get to work were obtained.

| Mode of Transportation | Number of Mothers |
|---|---|
| Car | 40 |
| Bus | 20 |
| Bike | 16 |
| Other | 4 |

If this sample is representative of all working mothers in Duluth, determine the probability that exactly three of five working mothers selected at random

a) take a car to work.

b) take a bus to work.

**23. *Selecting 6 Cards***  Six cards are selected from a standard deck of playing cards with replacement. Determine the probability that

a) exactly three picture cards are obtained.

b) exactly two spades are obtained.

**24. *Office Visit***  The probability that a person visiting Dr. Guillermo Suarez's office is more than 60 years old is 0.7. Determine the probability that

a) exactly three of the next five people visiting the office are more than 60 years old.

b) at least three of the next five people visiting the office are more than 60 years old.

## Recreational Mathematics

**25. *Aruba***  The island of Aruba is well known for its beaches and predictable warm, sunny weather. In fact, Aruba's weather is so predictable that the daily newspapers don't even bother to print a forecast. Strangely enough, however, on New Year's Eve, as the islanders were counting down the last 10 sec of 2011, it began to rain. What is the probability, from 0 to 1, that 72 hr later the sun will be shining?

---

### CHAPTER 12 ) *Summary*

## Important Facts And Concepts

### Examples and Discussion

| Important Facts And Concepts | Examples and Discussion |
|---|---|
| **Section 12.1** | |
| **Empirical Probability** | |
| $$P(E) = \frac{\text{number of times event } E \text{ has occurred}}{\left(\begin{array}{c}\text{total number of times the}\\ \text{experiment has been performed}\end{array}\right)}$$ | Examples 1–2, pages 676–677 |
| **The Law of Large Numbers** | |
| Probability statements apply in practice to a large number of trials, not to a single trial. It is the relative frequency over the long run that is accurately predictable, not individual events or precise totals. | Discussion, pages 678–679 |
| **Section 12.2** | |
| **Theoretical Probability** | |
| $$P(E) = \frac{\text{number of outcomes favorable to } E}{\text{total number of possible outcomes}}$$ | Examples 1–3, pages 684–687 |

## Probability Facts

The probability of an event that cannot occur is 0. The probability of an event that must occur is 1. Every probability must be a number between 0 and 1 inclusively; that is

$$0 \le P(E) \le 1$$

The sum of the probabilities of all possible outcomes of an event is 1.

$$P(A) + P(\text{not } A) = 1$$

Discussion, page 684

Example 3, page 686

## Section 12.3
### Odds Against an Event

$$\text{Odds against} = \frac{P(\text{event fails to occur})}{P(\text{event occurs})} = \frac{P(\text{failure})}{P(\text{success})}$$

Examples 1–3, pages 691–693

### Odds in Favor of an Event

$$\text{Odds in favor} = \frac{P(\text{event occurs})}{P(\text{event fails to occur})} = \frac{P(\text{success})}{P(\text{failure})}$$

Example 3, page 693

## Section 12.4
### Expected Value

$$E = P_1 A_1 + P_2 A_2 + P_3 A_3 + \cdots + P_n A_n$$

Examples 1–6, pages 699–702

## Section 12.5
### Counting Principle

If a first experiment can be performed in $M$ distinct ways and a second experiment can be performed in $N$ distinct ways, then the two experiments in that specific order can be performed in $M \cdot N$ distinct ways.

Examples 1–3, pages 709–711

## Section 12.6
### OR and AND problems

$$P(A \text{ or } B) = P(A) + P(B) - P(A \text{ and } B)$$
$$P(A \text{ and } B) = P(A) \cdot P(B)$$

Examples 1–3, pages 717–719
Examples 4–7, pages 720–723

## Section 12.7
### Conditional Probability

$$P(E_2 | E_1) = \frac{n(E_1 \text{ and } E_2)}{n(E_1)}$$

Examples 1–3, pages 729–731

## Section 12.8

The **number of permutations** of $n$ items is $n!$.

$$n! = n(n-1)(n-2) \cdots (3)(2)(1)$$

Example 3, page 738

### Permutation Formula

$$_nP_r = \frac{n!}{(n-r)!}$$

Examples 4–6, pages 738–741

The number of different permutations of $n$ objects where $n_1, n_2, \ldots, n_r$ of the objects are identical is

$$\frac{n!}{n_1! n_2! \cdots n_r!}$$

Example 7, page 742

Section 12.9, 12.10
**Combination Formula**

$$_nC_r = \frac{n!}{(n-r)!\,r!}$$

Examples 2–4, page 748
Examples 1–5, pages 753–755

Section 12.11
**Binomial Probability Formula**

$$P(x) = (_nC_x)p^x q^{n-x}$$

Examples 1–4, pages 761–763

## CHAPTER 12   *Review Exercises*

**12.1–12.11**

1. In your own words, explain the law of large numbers.

2. Explain how empirical probability can be used to determine whether a die is "loaded" (not a fair die).

3. *Cars*  Of 45 people who purchase a vehicle at a car dealership, 9 purchased an SUV. Determine the empirical probability that the next person who purchases a vehicle from that car dealership purchases an SUV.

4. *Cards*  Select a card from a deck of cards 40 times with replacement and compute the empirical probability of selecting a heart.

5. *Television News*  In a small town, 250 people were asked whether they watched ABC, CBS, NBC, Fox, or MSNBC news. The results are indicated below.

| Network | Number of People |
|---------|------------------|
| ABC     | 80               |
| CBS     | 35               |
| NBC     | 60               |
| Fox     | 35               |
| MSNBC   | 40               |

Determine the empirical probability that the next person selected at random from the town watches ABC news.

*Digits  In Exercises 6–9, each of the digits 0, 1, 2, 3, 4, 5, 6, 7, 8, 9 is written on a piece of paper and all the pieces of paper are placed in a hat. One number is selected at random. Determine the probability that the number selected is*

6. even.

7. odd or greater than 3.

8. greater than 2 or less than 6.

9. even and greater than 4.

*Yogurt Preference  In Exercises 10–13, a taste test is given to 50 customers at a supermarket. The customers are asked to taste 4 types of yogurt and to list their favorite. The results are summarized below.*

| Type            | Number of People |
|-----------------|------------------|
| Strawberry      | 18               |
| Raspberry       | 14               |
| Blueberry       | 11               |
| Banana creme pie| 7                |

*If one person who participated in the taste test is selected at random, determine the probability that the person's favorite was*

10. strawberry

11. blueberry

12. either strawberry or raspberry.

13. a yogurt other than banana creme pie.

14. *Obesity*  According to the U.S. Centers for Disease Control and Prevention, 20% of children in the United States,

age 6–11, are obese. If a child age 6–11 was selected at random, determine the odds

a) against the child being obese.

b) in favor of the child being obese.

15. *Vegetable Mix-up* Nicholas Delaney, a mischievous little boy, has removed labels on the eight cans of vegetables in the cabinet. Nicholas's father knows that there are three cans of corn, three cans of beans, and two cans of carrots. If the father selects and opens one can at random, determine the odds against his selecting a can of corn.

16. *Horseracing* The odds against Buttermilk winning the Triple Crown in horse racing are 82:3. Determine the probability that Buttermilk wins the Triple Crown.

17. *Dry Cleaner Success* The probability that a new dry cleaner will succeed at a given location is 0.85. Determine the odds in favor of the dry cleaner succeeding.

18. *Raffle Tickets* One thousand raffle tickets are sold at $2 each. Three prizes of $200 and two prizes of $100 will be awarded. Assume that the probability that any given ticket is selected for a $200 prize is $\frac{3}{1000}$ and the probability that any given ticket is selected for a $100 prize is $\frac{2}{1000}$.

a) Determine the expectation of a person who purchases a ticket.

b) Determine the expectation of a person who purchases three tickets.

19. *Expectation of a Card* If Cameron selects a picture card from a standard deck of 52 cards, Lindsey will give him $9. If Cameron does not select a picture card, he must give Lindsey $3.

a) Determine Cameron's expectation.

b) Determine Lindsey's expectation.

c) If Cameron plays this game 100 times, how much can he expect to lose or gain?

20. *Expected Attendance* If the day is sunny, 1000 people will attend the baseball game. If the day is cloudy, only 500 people will attend. If it rains, only 100 people will attend. The local meteorologist states that the probability of a sunny day is 0.4, of a cloudy day is 0.5, and of a rainy day is 0.1. Determine the number of people that are expected to attend.

21. *Fair Price* At a game of chance, the expected value is found to be −$2.50, and the cost to play the game is $6.50. Determine the fair price to play the game.

22. *Fair Price* The expected value when you purchase a lottery ticket is −$1.50, and the cost to play the game is $5.00. Determine the fair price of the lottery ticket.

23. *Club Officers* Tina, Jake, Gina, and Carla form a club. They plan to select a president and a vice president.

a) Construct a tree diagram showing all the possible outcomes.

b) List the sample space.

c) Determine the probability that Gina is selected president and Jake is selected vice president.

24. *A Coin and a Number* A coin is flipped and then a number from 1 through 4 is selected at random from a bag.

a) Construct a tree diagram showing all the possible outcomes.

b) List the sample space.

c) Determine the probability that a head is flipped and an odd number is selected.

d) Determine the probability that a head is flipped or an odd number is selected.

*Spinning Two Wheels* In Exercises 25–30, the outer and inner wheels are spun.

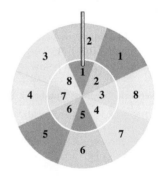

*Assuming that the wheels are independent and the outcomes are equally likely, determine the probability of obtaining*

25. even numbers on both wheels.

26. numbers greater than 5 on both wheels.

27. an odd number on the outer wheel and a number less than 6 on the inner wheel.

28. an even number or a number less than 6 on the outer wheel.

29. an even number or a color other than green on the inner wheel.

30. gold on the outer wheel and a color other than gold on the inner wheel.

***Sports Drink Selection*** *In Exercises 31–34, assume that Skip Bailey is going to purchase three bottles of sports drinks at a convenience store. The store has 12 different bottles of sports drinks, including 5 different bottles made by Gatorade, 4 different bottles made by Powerade, and 3 different bottles made by All Sport. If Skip selects 3 of these 12 bottles at random, determine the probability he selects*

**31.** 3 bottles of Gatorade.

**32.** no bottles of Powerade.

**33.** at least 1 bottle of Powerade.

**34.** a bottle of Gatorade, a bottle of Gatorade, and a bottle of All Sport, in that order.

***Spinner Probabilities*** *In Exercises 35–38, assume that the spinner cannot land on a line.*

*If spun once, determine*

**35.** the probability that the spinner lands on yellow.

**36.** the odds against and the odds in favor of the spinner landing on yellow.

**37.** You are awarded $5 if the spinner lands on red, $10 if it lands on yellow, and $20 if it lands on green. Determine your expected value.

**38.** If the spinner is spun twice, determine the probability that it lands on red and then green (assume independence).

***Spinner Probabilities*** *In Exercises 39–42, assume that the spinner cannot land on a line.*

*If spun once, determine*

**39.** the probability that the spinner does not land on green.

**40.** the odds in favor of and the odds against the spinner landing on green.

**41.** A person wins $10 if the spinner lands on green, wins $5 if the spinner lands on red, and loses $20 if the spinner lands on yellow. Find the expectation of a person who plays this game.

**42.** If the spinner is spun three times, determine the probability that at least one spin lands on red.

***Restaurant Service*** *In Exercises 43–46, use the results of a survey regarding the service at the Lake View Diner, which is summarized as follows.*

| Meal | Service Rated Good | Service Rated Poor | Total |
|---|---|---|---|
| Breakfast | 85 | 10 | 95 |
| Lunch | 65 | 10 | 75 |
| Total | 150 | 20 | 170 |

*If one person who completed the survey is selected at random, determine the probability that the person indicated that the*

**43.** service was rated good.

**44.** service was rated good, given that the meal was breakfast.

**45.** service was rated poor, given that the meal was lunch.

**46.** meal was breakfast, given that the service was rated poor.

***Neuroscience*** *In Exercises 47–50, assume that in a neuroscience course the students perform an experiment. Tests are given to determine if people are right brained, are left brained, or have no predominance. It is also recorded whether they are right handed or left handed. The following chart shows the results obtained.*

| | Right Brained | Left Brained | No Predominance | Total |
|---|---|---|---|---|
| Right handed | 40 | 130 | 60 | 230 |
| Left handed | 120 | 30 | 20 | 170 |
| Total | 160 | 160 | 80 | 400 |

*If one person who completed the survey is selected at random, determine the probability the person selected is*

**47.** right handed.

**48.** left brained, given that the person is left handed.

**49.** right handed, given that the person has no predominance.

**50.** right brained, given that the person is left handed.

**51.** ***Television Show*** Four contestants are on a television show. There are four different-colored rubber balls in a box, and each contestant gets to pick one from the box. Inside each ball is a slip of paper indicating the amount the contestant has won. The amounts are $10,000, $5000, $2000, and $1000.

 **a)** In how many different ways can the contestants select the balls?

 **b)** What is the expectation of a contestant?

**52.** *Spelling Bee* Five finalists remain in a high school spelling bee. Two will receive $50 each, two will receive $100 each, and one will receive $500. How many different arrangements of prizes are possible?

**53.** *Candy Selection* Mrs. Williams takes her 3 children shopping. Each of her children gets to select a different type of candy that only that child will eat. At the store, there are only 10 boxes of candy left and each is a different type. In how many ways can the 3 children select the candy?

**54.** *Astronaut Selection* Three of nine astronauts must be selected for a mission. One will be the captain, one will be the navigator, and one will perform scientific experiments. Assuming each of the nine astronauts can perform any of the tasks, in how many ways can a three-person crew be selected so that each person has a different assignment?

**55.** *Vaccine* Dr. Goldberg has three doses of vaccine for influenza type A. Six patients in the office require the vaccine. In how many different ways could Dr. Goldberg dispense the vaccine?

**56.** *Dogsled* Ten huskies are to be selected to pull a dogsled. How many different arrangements of the 10 huskies on a dogsled are possible?

**57.** *Mega Millions* To play the lottery game Mega Millions, you select 5 numbers from 1 through 56 and 1 Mega Ball number from 1 through 46. If you match all 6 numbers, you win the jackpot!

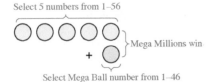

Select 5 numbers from 1–56

⟩ Mega Millions win

+

Select Mega Ball number from 1–46

**a)** What is the probability that you match the first 5 numbers?

**b)** What is the probability that you match the first 5 numbers and the Mega Ball?

**58.** *Parent-Teacher Committee* A committee of 7 is to be formed from 10 parents and 12 teachers. If the committee is to consist of 2 parents and 5 teachers, how many different committees are possible?

**59.** *Selecting Test Subjects* In a psychology research laboratory, one room contains eight men and another room contains five women. Three men and two women are to be selected at random to be given a psychological test. How many different combinations of these people are possible?

**60.** *Choosing Two Aces* Two cards are selected at random, without replacement, from a standard deck of 52 cards. Determine the probability that two aces are selected (use combinations).

*Color Chips* In Exercises 61–64, a bag contains five red chips, three white chips, and two blue chips. Three chips are to be selected at random, without replacement. Determine the probability that

**61.** all are red.

**62.** the first two are red and the third is blue.

**63.** the first is red, the second is white, and the third is blue.

**64.** at least one is red.

*Magazines* In Exercises 65–68, on a table in a doctor's office are five Newsweek magazines, six Parenting magazines, and three Sports Illustrated magazines. If Ramona Cleary randomly selects three magazines, determine the probability that

**65.** three *Newsweek* magazines were selected.

**66.** two *Parenting* magazines and one *Sports Illustrated* magazine were selected.

**67.** no *Parenting* magazine was selected.

**68.** at least one *Parenting* magazine was selected.

**69.** *New Homes* In the community of Spring Hill, 60% of the homes purchased cost more than $160,000.

    **a)** Write the binomial probability formula to determine the probability that exactly $x$ of the next $n$ homes purchased in Spring Hill cost more than $160,000

    **b)** Write the binomial probability formula to determine the probability that exactly 75 of the next 100 home purchases cost more than $160,000.

**70.** *Long-Stemmed Roses* At the Floyd's Flower Shop, $\frac{1}{5}$ of people ordering flowers select long-stemmed roses. Determine the probability that exactly 3 of the next 5 customers ordering flowers select long-stemmed roses.

**71.** *Taking a Math Course* During any semester at City College, 60% of the students are taking a mathematics course. Determine the probability that of five students selected at random,

    **a)** none is taking a mathematics course this semester.

    **b)** at least one is taking a mathematics course this semester.

## CHAPTER 12 ) TEST

**1.** *Flowers* Of the last 50 people who purchased flowers at Whistlestop Florist, 14 purchased roses. Determine the empirical probability that the next person who purchases flowers at Whistlestop Florist purchases roses.

*One Sheet of Paper* *In Exercises 2–4, each of the numbers 1–9 is written on a sheet of paper and the nine sheets of paper are placed in a hat. If one sheet of paper is selected at random from the hat, determine the probability that the number selected is*

**2.** greater than 4.

**3.** even.

**4.** even or greater than 5.

*Two Sheets of Paper* *In Exercises 5–7, if two of the same nine sheets of paper mentioned above are selected, without replacement, from the hat, determine the probability that*

**5.** both numbers are greater than 5.

**6.** the first number is odd and the second number is even.

**7.** neither of the numbers is greater than 6.

**8.** One card is selected at random from a standard deck of 52 cards. Determine the probability that the card selected is a red card or a picture card.

*One Chip and One Die* *In Exercises 9–13, one colored chip–red, blue, or green–is selected at random and a die is rolled.*

**9.** Use the counting principle to determine the number of sample points in the sample space.

**10.** Construct a tree diagram illustrating all the possible outcomes and list the sample space.

*In Exercises 11–13, by observing the sample space of the chips and die, determine the probability of obtaining*

**11.** the color green and the number 2.

**12.** the color red or the number 1.

**13.** a color other than red or an even number.

**14.** *Passwords* A personal password for an Internet brokerage account is to consist of a letter, followed by two digits, followed by two letters. Determine the number of personal codes possible if the first digit cannot be zero and repetition is permitted.

**15.** *Puppies* A litter of collie puppies consists of four males and five females. If one of the puppies is selected at random, determine the odds

**a)** against the puppy being male.

**b)** in favor of the puppy being female.

**16.** *Pick a Card* You get to select one card at random from a standard deck of 52 cards. If you pick a club, you win $8. If you pick a heart, you win $4. If you pick any other suit, you lose $6. Determine your expectation for this game.

**17.** *Cars and SUVs* The number of cars and the number of SUVs going through the toll gates of two bridges is recorded. The results are shown below.

| Bridge | Cars | SUVs | Total |
|---|---|---|---|
| George Washington | 120 | 106 | 226 |
| Golden Gate | 94 | 136 | 230 |
| Total | 214 | 242 | 456 |

▲ *A toll booth at the Golden Gate Bridge*

If one of these vehicles going over the bridges is selected at random, determine the probability that

**a)** it is a car.

**b)** it is going over the George Washington Bridge.

**c)** it is an SUV, given that it is going over the George Washington Bridge.

**d)** it is going over the Golden Gate Bridge, given that it is a car.

**18.** *Awarding Prizes* Three of six people are to be selected and given small prizes. One will be given a book, one will be given a calculator, and one will be given an iTunes card. In how many different ways can these prizes be awarded?

**19.** *Quality Control* A bin contains a total of 20 batteries, of which 6 are defective. If you select 2 at random, without replacement, determine the probability that

**a)** none of the batteries is good.

**b)** at least one battery is good.

**20.** *University Admission* The probability that a person is accepted for admission to a specific university is 0.6. Determine the probability that exactly two of the next five people who apply to the university get accepted.

## GROUP PROJECTS

### The Probability Of An Exact Measured Value

**1.** Your car's speedometer indicates that you are traveling at 65 mph. What is the probability that you are traveling at *exactly* 65 mph? Explain your answer.

### Taking An Exam

**2.** A 10-question multiple-choice exam is given, and each question has five possible answers. Pascal Gonyo takes this exam and guesses at every question. Use the binomial probability formula to determine the probability (to 5 decimal places) that

**a)** he gets exactly 2 questions correct.

**b)** he gets no questions correct.

**c)** he gets at least 1 question correct (use the information from part (b) to answer this part).

**d)** he gets at least 9 questions correct.

**e)** Without using the binomial probability formula, determine the probability that he gets exactly 2 questions correct.

**f)** Compare your answers to parts (a) and (e). If they are not the same, explain why.

### Keyless Entry

**3.** Many cars have keyless entry. To open the lock, you may press a 5-digit code on a set of buttons like that illustrated. The code may include repeated digits like 11433 or 55512.

**a)** How many different 5-digit codes can be made using the 10 digits if repetition is permitted?

**b)** How many different ways are there of pressing 5 buttons if repetition is allowed?

**c)** A burglar is going to press 5 buttons at random, with repetition allowed. What is the probability that the burglar hits the sequence to open the door?

**d)** Suppose that each button had only one number associated with it as illustrated below. How many different 5-digit codes can be made with the 5 digits if repetition is permitted?

**e)** Using the buttons labeled 1–5, how many different ways are there to press 5 buttons if repetition is allowed?

**f)** A burglar is going to press 5 buttons of those labeled 1–5 at random with repetition allowed. Determine the probability that the burglar hits the sequence to open the door.

**g)** Is a burglar more likely, is he or she less likely, or does he or she have the same likelihood of pressing 5 buttons and opening the car door if the buttons are labeled as in the first illustration or as in the second illustration? Explain your answer.

**h)** Can you see any advantages in labeling the buttons as in the first illustration? Explain.*

---

*In actuality, in most cars that have key pads like that shown on the bottom left, each key acts as if it contains a single digit. For example, if your code is 7, 9, 5, 1, 3, the code 8, 0, 6, 2, 4 will unlock the door. The extra numbers, in effect, give the owner a false sense of security.

# 13

# Statistics

## Why This is Important

Benjamin Disraeli (1804–1881), once prime minister of the United Kingdom, said that there are three kinds of lies: lies, damned lies, and statistics. Do numbers lie? Numbers are the foundation of all statistical information. The "lie" occurs when, either intentionally or carelessly, a number is used in such a way that leads us to an unjustified or incorrect conclusion. Numbers may not lie, but they can be manipulated and misinterpreted. This chapter will provide information that can help you recognize when statistical information is being manipulated and misinterpreted. It will also help you see the many valuable uses of statistics.

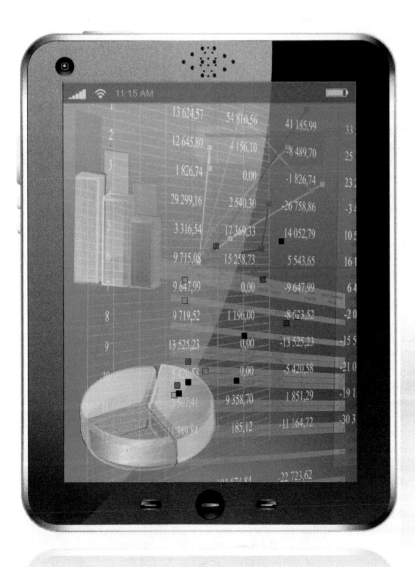

◀ *Numbers are the foundation of all statistical information.*

# SECTION 13.1    Sampling Techniques

▲ *Statisticians have several different techniques with which they can collect numerical information, such as how many Americans use an e-reader.*

According to Harris Interactive, 20% of Americans use an e-reader, an electronic reading device. It would be very expensive for Harris Interactive to ask every American if he or she uses an e-reader. Instead, to collect this information the polling company may ask a subset of Americans, called a *sample*. If it does not ask every American if he or she uses an e-reader, how do we know that Harris Interactive's results are accurate? In this section, we will discuss different techniques statisticians use to collect numerical information, and how they make accurate conclusions about an entire set of data from the sample collected.

**Why** *This is Important* Samples are used to determine a variety of information such as the percentage of college graduates in a city and the average credit card debt of an American family.

The study of statistics was originally used by governments to manage large amounts of numerical information. The use of statistics has grown significantly and today is applied in all walks of life. Governments use statistics to estimate the amount of unemployment and the cost of living. In psychology and education, the statistical theory of tests and measurements has been developed to compare achievements of individuals from diverse places and backgrounds. Newspapers and magazines carry the results of different polls on topics ranging from the president's popularity to the number of cans of soda consumed. Statistics is used in scores of other professions; in fact, it is difficult to find any profession that does not depend on some aspect of statistics.

Before we discuss different techniques used to collect numerical information, we will first introduce a few important definitions. *Statistics* is the art and science of gathering, analyzing, and making inferences (predictions) from numerical information obtained in an experiment. The numerical information so obtained is referred to as *data*. Statistics is divided into two main branches: descriptive and inferential. *Descriptive statistics* is concerned with the collection, organization, and analysis of data. *Inferential statistics* is concerned with making generalizations or predictions from the data collected.

Probability and statistics are closely related. Someone in the field of probability is interested in computing the chance of occurrence of a particular event when all the possible outcomes are known. A statistician's interest lies in drawing conclusions about possible outcomes through observations of only a few particular events.

If a probability expert and a statistician find identical boxes, the probability expert might open the box, observe the contents, replace the cover, and proceed to compute the probability of randomly selecting a specific object from the box. The statistician might select a few items from the box without looking at the contents and make a prediction as to the total contents of the box.

The entire contents of the box constitute the *population*. A population consists of all items or people of interest. The statistician often uses a subset of the population, called a *sample*, to make predictions concerning the population. It is important to understand the difference between a population and a sample. A population includes *all* items of interest. A sample includes *some* of the items in the population.

When a statistician draws a conclusion from a sample, there is always the possibility that the conclusion is incorrect. For example, suppose that a jar contains 90 blue marbles and 10 red marbles, as shown in Fig. 13.1 on page 775. If the statistician selects a random sample of five marbles from the jar and they are all blue, he or she may wrongly conclude that the jar contains all blue marbles. If the statistician takes a larger sample, say, 15 marbles, he or she is likely to select some red marbles. At that

Figure 13.1

point, the statistician may make a prediction about the contents of the jar based on the sample selected. Of course, the most accurate result would occur if every object in the jar, the entire population, were observed. However, in most statistical experiments, observing the entire population is not practical.

Statisticians use samples instead of the entire population for two reasons: (a) it is often impossible to obtain data on an entire population, and (b) sampling is less expensive because collecting the data takes less time and effort. For example, suppose that you wanted to determine the number of each species of all the fish in a lake. To do so would be almost impossible without using a sample. If you did try to obtain this information from the entire population, the cost would be astronomical. Or suppose that you wanted to test soup cans for spoilage. If every can produced by the company was opened and tested, the company wouldn't have any product left to sell. Instead of testing the entire population of soup cans, a sample is selected. The results obtained from the sample of soup cans selected are used to make conclusions about the entire population of soup cans.

Later in this chapter we will discuss statistical measures such as the *mean* and the *standard deviation*. When statisticians calculate the mean and the standard deviation of the entire population, they use different symbols and formulas than when they calculate the mean and standard deviation of a sample. The following chart shows the symbols used to represent the mean and standard deviation of a sample and of a population. Note that the mean and standard deviation of a population are symbolized by Greek letters.

| Measure | Sample | Population |
|---|---|---|
| Mean | $\bar{x}$ (read "x bar") | $\mu$ (mu) |
| Standard deviation | $s$ | $\sigma$ (sigma) |

*Unless otherwise indicated, in this book we will always assume that we are working with a sample and so we will use $\bar{x}$ and $s$.* If you take a course in statistics, you will use all four symbols and different formulas for a sample and for a population.

Consider the task of determining the political strength of a certain candidate running in a national election. It is not possible for pollsters to ask each of the approximately 213 million eligible voters his or her preference of a candidate. Thus, pollsters must select and use a sample of the population to obtain their information. How large a sample do you think they use to make predictions about an upcoming national election? You might be surprised to learn that pollsters use only about 1600 registered voters in their national sample. How can a pollster using such a small percentage of the population make an accurate prediction?

The answer is that when pollsters select a sample, they use sophisticated statistical techniques to obtain an unbiased sample. An *unbiased sample* is one that is a small replica of the entire population with regard to income, education, gender, race,

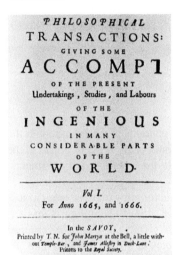
religion, political affiliation, age, and so on. The procedures statisticians use to obtain unbiased samples are quite complex. The following sampling techniques will give you a brief idea of how statisticians obtain unbiased samples.

## Random Sampling

If a sample is drawn in such a way that each time an item is selected each item in the population has an equal chance of being drawn, the sample is said to be a *random sample*. When using a random sample, one combination of a specified number of items has the same probability of being selected as any other combination. When all the items in the population are similar with regard to the specific characteristic we are interested in, a random sample can be expected to produce satisfactory results. For example, consider a large container holding 300 tennis balls that are identical except for color. One-third of the balls are yellow, one-third are white, and one-third are green. If the balls can be thoroughly mixed between each draw of a tennis ball so that each ball has an equally likely chance of being selected, randomness is not difficult to achieve. However, if the objects or items are not all the same size, shape, or texture, it might be impossible to obtain a random sample by reaching into a container and selecting an object.

The best procedure for selecting a random sample is to use a random number generator or a table of random numbers. A random number generator is a device, usually a calculator or computer program, that produces a list of random numbers. A random number table is a collection of random digits in which each digit has an equal chance of appearing. To select a random sample, first assign a number to each element in the population. Numbers are usually assigned in order. Then select the number of random numbers needed, which is determined by the sample size. Each numbered element from the population that corresponds to a selected random number becomes part of the sample.

## Systematic Sampling

When a sample is obtained by drawing every *n*th item on a list or production line, the sample is a *systematic sample*. The first item should be determined by using a random number.

It is important that the list from which a systematic sample is chosen includes the entire population being studied. See the *Did You Know?* called "Don't Count Your Votes Until They're Cast" on page 777. Another problem that must be avoided when this method of sampling is used is the constantly recurring characteristic. For example, on an assembly line, every 10th item could be the work of robot X. If only every 10th item is checked for defects, the work of other robots doing the same job may not be checked and may be defective.

## Cluster Sampling

A *cluster sample* is sometimes referred to as an *area sample* because it is frequently applied on a geographical basis. Essentially, the sampling consists of a random selection of groups of units. To select a cluster sample, we divide a geographic area into sections. Then we randomly select the sections or clusters. Either each member of the selected cluster is included in the sample or a random sample of the members of each cluster is used. For example, geographically we might randomly select city blocks to use as a sample unit. Then either every member of each selected city block would be used or a random sample from each selected city block would be used. Another example is to select *x* boxes of screws from a whole order, count the number of defective screws in the *x* boxes selected, and use this number to determine the expected number of defective screws in the whole order.

## Stratified Sampling

When a population is divided into parts, called strata, for the purpose of drawing a sample, the procedure is known as *stratified sampling*. Stratified sampling involves dividing the population by characteristics called *stratifying factors* such as gender, race, religion, or income. When a population has varied characteristics, it is desirable to separate the population into classes with similar characteristics and then take a random sample from each stratum (or class). For example, we could separate the population of undergraduate college students into strata called freshmen, sophomores, juniors, and seniors.

The use of stratified sampling requires some knowledge of the population. For example, to obtain a cross section of voters in a city, we must know where various groups are located and the approximate number of voters in each location.

## Convenience Sampling

A *convenience sample* uses data that are easily or readily obtained. Occasionally, data that are conveniently obtained may be all that is available. In some cases, some information is better than no information at all. Nevertheless, convenience sampling can be extremely biased. For example, suppose that a town wants to raise taxes to build a new elementary school. The local newspaper wants to obtain the opinion of some of the residents and sends a reporter to a senior citizens center. The first 10 people who exit the building are asked if they are in favor of raising taxes to build a new school. This sample could be biased against raising taxes for the new school. Most senior citizens would not have school-age children and may not be interested in paying increased taxes to build a new school. Although a convenience sample may be very easy to select, one must be very cautious when using the results obtained by this method.

### Example 1  *Identifying Sampling Techniques*

Identify the sampling technique used to obtain a sample in the following. Explain your answer.

a) Every 20th soup can coming off an assembly line is checked for defects.

b) A $50 gift certificate is given away at the Annual Bankers Convention. Tickets are placed in a bin, and the tickets are mixed up. Then the winning ticket is selected by a blindfolded person.

c) Children in a large city are classified based on the neighborhood school they attend. A random sample of five schools is selected. All the children from each selected school are included in the sample.

d) The first 50 people entering a zoo are asked if they support an increase in taxes to support a zoo expansion.

e) Viewers of the *USA Network* are classified according to age. Random samples from each age group are selected.

**Solution**

a) Systematic sampling. The sample is obtained by drawing every *n*th item. In this example, every 20th item on an assembly line is selected.

b) Random sampling. Every ticket has an equal chance of being selected.

c) Cluster sampling. A random sample of geographic areas is selected.

d) Convenience sampling. The sample is selected by picking data that are easily obtained.

e) Stratified sampling. The viewers are divided into strata based on their age. Then random samples are selected from each strata.

## SECTION 13.1    *Exercises*

### Warm Up Exercises

*In Exercises 1–12, fill in the blank with an appropriate word, phrase, or symbol(s).*

1. The art and science of gathering, analyzing, and making inferences (predictions) from numerical information obtained in an experiment is called _____.

2. Making generalizations or predictions from the data collected is called _____ statistics.

3. The collection, organization, and analysis of data is called _____ statistics.

4. All items or people of interest in an experiment is called a(n) _____.

5. A subset of a population used by statisticians to make predictions about a population is called a(n) _____.

6. When a sample is obtained by drawing every *n*th item, the sample is called a(n) _____ sample.

7. If a sample is drawn in such a way that each time an item is selected, each item in the population has an equal chance of being drawn, the sample is called a(n) _____ sample.

8. When a population is divided into parts, called strata, for the purpose of drawing a sample, the procedure is known as _____ sampling.

9. A sample that consists of a random selection of groups or units is called a(n) _____ sample.

10. A sample that uses data that are easily or readily obtained is called a(n) _____ sample.

11. A sample that is a small replica of the entire population is called a(n) _____ sample.

12. An area sample is another name for a(n) _____ sample.

### Practice the Skills

*Sampling Techniques In Exercises 13–22, identify the sampling technique used to obtain a sample. Explain your answer.*

13. All registered vehicles in the state of Georgia are classified according to type: subcompact, compact, mid-size, full-size, SUV, and truck. A random sample of vehicles from each category is selected.

14. Every 10th iPod coming off an assembly line is checked for defects.

▲ *See Exercise 14*

15. A state is divided into counties. A random sample of 12 counties is selected. A random sample from each of the 12 selected counties is selected.

16. A door prize is given away at a home improvement seminar. Tickets are placed in a bin, and the tickets are mixed up. Then a ticket is selected by a blindfolded person.

17. Every 17th person in line at a grocery store is asked his or her age.

18. The businesses in Iowa City are grouped according to type: medical, service, retail, manufacturing, financial, construction, restaurant, hotel, tourism, and other. A random sample of 10 businesses from each type is selected.

19. The first 25 adults leaving a grocery store are asked how much money they spend per week on entertainment.

20. The Food and Drug Administration randomly selects five stores from each of four randomly selected sections of a large city and checks food items for freshness. These stores are used as a representative sample of the entire city.

21. Bingo balls in a bin are shaken, and then balls are selected from the bin.

22. The Student Senate at the University of North Carolina is electing a new president. The first 25 people leaving the library are asked for whom they will vote.

### Challenge Problems/Group Activities

23. a) *Random Sampling* Select and indicate a topic and population of interest to which a random sampling technique can be applied to obtain data.

    b) Explain how you or your group would obtain a random sample for your population of interest.

    c) Actually obtain the sample by the procedure stated in part (b).

24. *Data from Questionnaire* Some subscribers of *Consumer Reports* respond to an annual questionnaire regarding their satisfaction with new appliances, cars, and other items. The information obtained from these questionnaires is then used as a sample from which frequency of repairs and other ratings are made by the magazine. Are the data obtained from these returned questionnaires representative of the entire population, or are they biased?

### Recreational Mathematics

**25.** Statistically speaking, what is the most dangerous job in the United States?

### Internet/Research Activity

**26.** We have briefly introduced sampling techniques. Using statistics books and Internet Web sites as references, select one type of sampling technique (it may be one that we have not discussed in this section) and write a report on how statisticians obtain that type of sample. Also indicate when that type of sampling technique may be preferred. List two examples of when the sampling technique may be used.

---

## SECTION 13.2   The Misuses of Statistics

▲ *It is important to examine statistical statements about products before accepting the statements as fact.*

Many of us may remember the advertisement stating, "Four out of five dentists recommend sugarless gum for their patients who chew gum." Seeing an advertisement like this one may cause some of us to be a bit skeptical. Should we believe that sugarless chewing gum will not harm our teeth? Or should we investigate a bit further before buying that next pack of chewing gum? In this section, we will learn how to examine statistical statements before accepting them as fact.

**Why** *This is Important* In order to be an educated consumer, it is important to be able to distinguish between misleading advertisements and actual facts.

---

Statistics, when used properly, is a valuable tool to society. However, many individuals, businesses, and advertising firms misuse statistics to their own advantage. You should examine statistical statements very carefully before accepting them as fact. You should ask yourself two questions: Was the sample used to gather the statistical data unbiased and of sufficient size? Is the statistical statement ambiguous; that is, can it be interpreted in more than one way?

Let's examine two advertisements. "Four out of five dentists recommend sugarless gum for their patients who chew gum." In this advertisement, we do not know the sample size and the number of times the experiment was performed to obtain the desired results. The advertisement does not mention that possibly only 1 out of 100 dentists recommended gum at all.

In a golf ball commercial, a "type A" ball is hit and a second ball is hit in the same manner. The type A ball travels farther. We are supposed to conclude that the type A is the better ball. The advertisement does not mention the number of times the experiment was previously performed or the results of the earlier experiments. Possible sources of bias include (1) wind speed and direction, (2) that no two swings are identical, and (3) that the ball may land on a rough or smooth surface.

Vague or ambiguous words also lead to statistical misuses or misinterpretations. The word *average* is one such culprit. There are at least four different "averages," some of which are discussed in Section 13.4. Each is calculated differently, and each may have a different value for the same sample. During contract negotiations, it is not uncommon for an employer to state publicly that the average salary of its employees is $45,000, whereas the employees' union states that the average is $40,000. Who is lying? Actually, both sides may be telling the truth. Each side will use the average that best suits its needs to present its case. Advertisers also use the average that most enhances their products. Consumers often misinterpret this average as the one with which they are most familiar.

Another vague word is *largest*. For example, ABC claims that it is the largest department store in the United States. Does that mean largest profit, largest sales, largest building, largest staff, largest acreage, or largest number of outlets?

**How Employers Make Workers Happy**

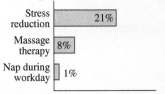

Stress reduction 21%
Massage therapy 8%
Nap during workday 1%

Visual graphics are often used to "dress up" what might otherwise be considered boring statistics. Although visually appealing, such creative displays of numerical data can be misleading. The graph above shows the percentage of employers that offer "perks" such as stress reduction, massage therapy, or a nap during the workday to make workers happy. This graph is misleading because the lengths of the bars are not proportional to one another as they should be to accurately reflect the percent of employers offering each of the named perks. For example, the bar for massage therapy should be eight times as long as the bar for nap during workday instead of being approximately four times as long, as the graph shows.

**Why This is Important** In order to correctly interpret data from a graph, it is important to be aware that a graph may be misleading.

Still another deceptive technique used in advertising is to state a claim from which the public may draw irrelevant conclusions. For example, a disinfectant manufacturer claims that its product killed 40,760 germs in a laboratory in 5 seconds. "To prevent colds, use disinfectant A." It may well be that the germs killed in the laboratory were not related to any type of cold germ. In another example, company C claims that its paper towels are heavier than its competition's towels. Therefore, they will hold more water. Is weight a measure of absorbency? A rock is heavier than a sponge, yet a sponge is more absorbent.

An insurance advertisement claims that in Duluth, Minnesota, 212 people switched to insurance company Z. One may conclude that this company is offering something special to attract these people. What may have been omitted from the advertisement is that 415 people in Duluth, Minnesota, dropped insurance company Z during the same period.

A foreign car manufacturer claims that 9 of every 10 of a popular-model car it sold in the United States during the previous 10 years were still on the road. From this statement, the public is to conclude that this foreign car is well manufactured and would last for many years. The commercial neglects to state that this model has been selling in the United States for only a few years. The manufacturer could just as well have stated that 9 of every 10 of these cars sold in the United States in the previous 100 years were still on the road.

Charts and graphs can also be misleading or deceptive. In Fig. 13.2, the two graphs show the performance of two stocks over a 6-month period. Based on the graphs, which stock would you purchase? Actually, the two graphs present identical information; the only difference is that the vertical scale of the graph for stock B has been exaggerated.

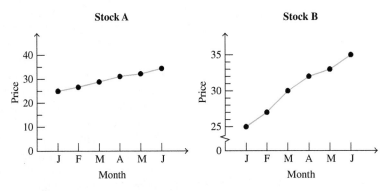

Figure 13.2

The two graphs in Fig. 13.3 show the same change. However, the graph in part (a) appears to show a greater increase than the graph in part (b), again because of a different scale.

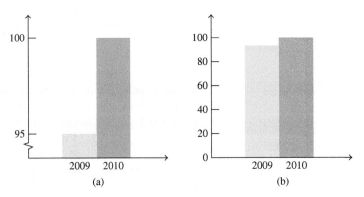

Figure 13.3

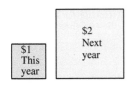

Figure 13.4

Consider a claim that if you invest $1, by next year you will have $2. This type of claim is sometimes misrepresented, as in Fig. 13.4. Actually, your investment has only doubled, but the area of the square on the right is four times that of the square on the left. By expressing the amounts as cubes (Fig. 13.5), you increase the volume eightfold.

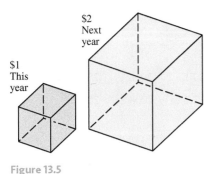

Figure 13.5

**Why People Surf the Web**

Top six reasons Americans say they use the Internet

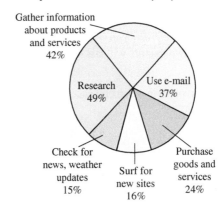

Figure 13.6

The graph in Fig. 13.6 is an example of a circle graph. We will discuss circle graphs in Section 13.3. In a circle graph, the total circle represents 100%. Therefore, the sum of the parts should add up to 100%. This graph is misleading since the sum of its parts is 183%. A graph other than a circle graph should have been used to display the top six reasons Americans say they use the Internet.

Despite the examples presented in this section, you should not be left with the impression that statistics is used solely for the purpose of misleading or cheating the consumer. As stated earlier, there are many important and necessary uses of statistics. Most statistical reports are accurate and useful. You should realize, however, the importance of being an aware consumer.

## SECTION 13.2    *Exercises*

### Practice the Skills

***Misinterpretations of Statistics*** *In Exercises 1–14, discuss the statement and tell what possible misuses or misinterpretations may exist.*

1. ***Cold Remedy*** In a study of patients with cold symptoms, each patient was found to have improved symptoms after taking honey. Therefore, honey cures the common cold.

2. In 2011, Liberty Travel received more requests for travel brochures to Hawaii than to Las Vegas. Therefore, in 2012, Liberty Travel sold more travel packages to Hawaii than to Las Vegas.

3. There are more empty spaces in the parking lot of Mama Mia's Italian restaurant than at Shanghai Chinese restaurant. Therefore, more people prefer Chinese food than Italian food.

4. Healthy Snacks cookies are fat free. So eat as many as you like and you will not gain weight.

5. Most accidents occur on Saturday night. That means that people do not drive carefully on Saturday night.

6. Morgan's is the largest department store in New York. So shop at Morgan's and save money.

7. Eighty percent of all automobile accidents occur within 10 miles of the driver's home. Therefore, it is safer to take long trips.

8. Arizona has the highest death rate for asthma in the United States. Therefore, it is unsafe to go to Arizona if you have asthma.

▲ *Sedona, Arizona*

9. Thirty students said that they would recommend Professor Malone to a friend. Twenty students said that they would recommend Professor Wagner to a friend. Therefore, Professor Malone is a better teacher than Professor Wagner.

10. A steak is more expensive at Dino's Steak House than at Rick's Prime Rib House. Therefore, the quality of a steak at Dino's Steak House is better than the quality of a steak at Rick's Prime Rib House.

11. John Deere lawn tractors cost more than Toro lawn tractors. Therefore, John Deere lawn tractors will last longer than Toro lawn tractors.

12. More men than women are involved in automobile accidents. Therefore, women are better drivers.

13. The average depth of the pond is only 3 ft, so it is safe to go wading.

14. In 2011, more men than women applied for sales positions at Dick's Sporting Goods. Therefore, in 2011, more men than women were hired for sales positions at Dick's Sporting Goods.

15. *Population of Honolulu* The following table shows the population, in thousands, in Honolulu, Hawaii, for selected years.

| Year | Population |
|------|-----------|
| 1980 | 365.0 |
| 1990 | 365.2 |
| 2000 | 371.7 |
| 2010 | 371.7 |

Source: U.S Census Bureau

Draw a line graph that makes the increase in the population of Honolulu for the years shown appear to be

**a)** small.                    **b)** large.

16. *Officers in the U.S. Marine Corps* The following table shows the number of officers, in thousands, on active duty in the U.S. Marine Corps for the years 2004–2009.

| Year | Number of Officers |
|------|--------------------|
| 2004 | 19.1 |
| 2005 | 19.1 |
| 2006 | 19.2 |
| 2007 | 19.5 |
| 2008 | 20.1 |
| 2009 | 21.0 |

Draw a line graph that makes the increase in the number of officers on active duty for the U.S. Marine Corps appear to be

**a)** small.                    **b)** large.

*First Marriage* In Exercises 17 and 18, use the following table.

Median Age at First Marriage

| Male | | Female | |
|------|-----|--------|-----|
| Year | Age | Year | Age |
| 2002 | 26.9 | 2002 | 25.3 |
| 2004 | 27.1 | 2004 | 25.3 |
| 2006 | 27.5 | 2006 | 25.5 |
| 2008 | 27.6 | 2008 | 25.9 |

Source: U.S. Census Bureau

17. **a)** Draw a bar graph that appears to show a small increase in the median age at first marriage for males.

**b)** Draw a bar graph that appears to show a large increase in the median age at first marriage for males.

18. **a)** Draw a bar graph that appears to show a small increase in the median age at first marriage for females.

**b)** Draw a bar graph that appears to show a large increase in the median age at first marriage for females.

19. *Price of a Movie Ticket* The following graph shows the average price of a movie ticket for the years 2009 and 2010.

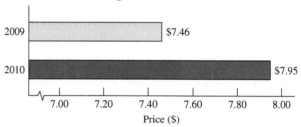

**Average Price of a Movie Ticket**

**a)** Draw a bar graph that shows the entire scale from $0 to $8.00.

**b)** Does the new graph give a different impression? Explain.

Concept/Writing Exercises

20. Find five advertisements or commercials that may be statistically misleading. Explain why each may be misleading.

**21.** The following circle graph shows the percentage of commuters who are frustrated by particular driving situations. Is the graph misleading? Explain.

**Driving Situations**
**Frustrating to Commuters**

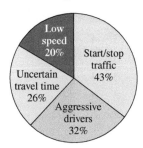

## Challenge Problem/Group Activity

**22.** Consider the following graph, which shows the U.S. population in 2000 and the projected U.S. population in 2050.

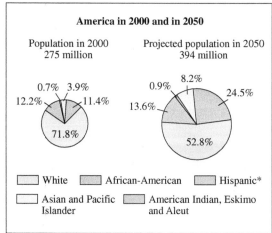

Source: U.S. Census Bureau

**a)** Compute the projected percent increase in population from 2000 to 2050 by using the formula given on page 603.

**b)** Measure the radius and then compute the area of the circle representing 2000. Use $A = \pi r^2$.

**c)** Repeat part (b) for the circle representing 2050.

**d)** Compute the percent increase in the size of the area of the circle from 2000 to 2050.

**e)** Are the circle graphs misleading?

## Recreational Mathematics

**23.** What mathematical symbol can you place between 1 and 2 to obtain a number greater than 1 but less than 2?

## Internet/Research Activity

**24.** Read the book *How to Lie with Statistics* by Darrell Huff and write a book report on it. Select three illustrations from the book that show how people manipulate statistics.

---

## SECTION 13.3 — Frequency Distributions and Statistical Graphs

Suppose you have a job as a waitress and decide to record the daily amount you make in tips. After keeping a list of your tips each day for several months, you realize that you have a large set of data and want to condense your data into a more manageable form. In this section we will learn a method to organize and summarize data. We will also introduce four types of graphs that can be used to display information in a meaningful way.

**Why This is Important** Organizing and summarizing data and using graphs to display information can make large sets of information more useful.

▲ *Organizing and summarizing data, such as a waitress's daily tips, can make large sets of information more useful.*

It is not uncommon for statisticians and others to have to analyze thousands of pieces of data. A *piece of data* is a single response to an experiment. When the amount of data is large, it is usually advantageous to construct a frequency distribution. A *frequency distribution* is a listing of the observed values and the corresponding frequency of occurrence of each value. Example 1 shows how we construct a frequency distribution.

Example **1**  *Frequency Distribution*

The number of children per family is recorded for 64 families surveyed. Construct a frequency distribution of the following data:

| | | | | | | | |
|---|---|---|---|---|---|---|---|
| 0 | 1 | 1 | 2 | 2 | 3 | 4 | 5 |
| 0 | 1 | 1 | 2 | 2 | 3 | 4 | 5 |
| 0 | 1 | 1 | 2 | 2 | 3 | 4 | 6 |
| 0 | 1 | 2 | 2 | 2 | 3 | 4 | 6 |
| 0 | 1 | 2 | 2 | 2 | 3 | 4 | 7 |
| 0 | 1 | 2 | 2 | 3 | 3 | 4 | 8 |
| 0 | 1 | 2 | 2 | 3 | 3 | 5 | 8 |
| 0 | 1 | 2 | 2 | 3 | 3 | 5 | 9 |

*Solution*  Listing the number of children (observed values) and the number of families (frequency) gives the following frequency distribution.

| Number of Children<br>(Observed Values) | Number of Families<br>(Frequency) |
|:---:|:---:|
| 0 | 8 |
| 1 | 11 |
| 2 | 18 |
| 3 | 11 |
| 4 | 6 |
| 5 | 4 |
| 6 | 2 |
| 7 | 1 |
| 8 | 2 |
| 9 | 1 |
| | 64 |

Eight families had no children, 11 families had one child, 18 families had two children, and so on. Note that the sum of the frequencies is equal to the original number of pieces of data, 64.                                                                               ∎

Often data are grouped in classes to provide information about the distribution that would be difficult to observe if the data were ungrouped. Graphs called *histograms* and *frequency polygons* can be made of grouped data, as will be explained later in this section. These graphs also provide a great deal of useful information.

When data are grouped in classes, certain rules should be followed.

---

**PROCEDURE**   RULES FOR DATA GROUPED BY CLASSES

1. The classes should be the same "width."
2. The classes should not overlap.
3. Each piece of data should belong to only one class.

---

In addition, it is often suggested that a frequency distribution should be constructed with 5 to 12 classes. If there are too few or too many classes, the distribution may become difficult to interpret. For example, if you use fewer than 5 classes, you risk losing too much information. If you use more than 12 classes, you may gain more detail but you risk losing clarity. Let the spread of the data be a guide in deciding the number of classes to use.

To understand these rules, let's consider a set of observed values that go from a low of 0 to a high of 26. Let's assume that the first class is arbitrarily selected to go from 0 through 4. Thus, any of the data with values of 0, 1, 2, 3, 4 would belong in this class. We say that the *class width* is 5 since there are five integral values that belong to the class. This first class ended with 4, so the second class must start with 5. If this class is to have a width of 5, at what value must it end? The answer is 9 (5, 6, 7, 8, 9). The second class is 5–9. Continuing in the same manner, we obtain the following set of classes.

Classes

Lower class limits $\begin{cases} 0–4 \\ 5–9 \\ 10–14 \\ 15–19 \\ 20–24 \\ 25–29 \end{cases}$ Upper class limits

We need not go beyond the 25–29 class because the largest value we are considering is 26. The classes meet our three criteria: They have the same width, there is no overlap among the classes, and each of the values from a low of 0 to a high of 26 belongs to one and only one class.

The choice of the first class, 0–4, was arbitrary. If we wanted to have more classes or fewer classes, we would make the class widths smaller or larger, respectively.

The numbers 0, 5, 10, 15, 20, 25 are called the *lower class limits*, and the numbers 4, 9, 14, 19, 24, 29 are called the *upper class limits*. Each class has a width of 5. Note that the class width, 5, can be obtained by subtracting the first lower class limit from the second lower class limit: $5 - 0 = 5$. The difference between any two consecutive lower class or upper class limits is also 5.

### Example 2   *A Frequency Distribution of Consumer Magazines*

Table 13.1 on page 786 shows the 2008 circulation for the 46 leading U.S. consumer magazines (excluding *AARP Magazine* and *AARP Bulletin*, which are far ahead of the other magazines). The circulation is rounded to the nearest ten thousand. Construct a frequency distribution of the data, letting the first class be 173–237.

**Solution**   Forty-six pieces of data are given in *descending order* from highest to lowest. We are given that the first class is 173–237. The second class must therefore start at 238. To find the class width, we subtract 173 (the lower class limit of the first class) from 238 (the lower class limit of the second class) to obtain a class width of 65. The upper class limit of the second class is found by adding the class width, 65, to the upper class limit of the first class, 237. Therefore, the upper class limit of the second class is $237 + 65 = 302$. Thus,

173–237   first class
238–302   second class

The other classes are found using a similar technique. They are 303–367, 368–432, 433–497, 498–562, 563–627, 628–692, 693–757, 758–822. Since the highest value in the data is 817, there is no need to go any further. Note that each two consecutive lower class limits differ by 65, as does each two consecutive upper class limits. There are 23 pieces of data in the 173–237 class. There are 8 pieces of data in the 238–302 class, 6 in the 303–367 class, 5 in the 368–432 class, 1 in the 433–497 class, 1 in the 498–562 class, 0 in the 563–627 class, 0 in the 628–692 class, 0 in the 693–757 class, and 2 in the 758–822 class. The complete frequency distribution of the 10 classes is given on page 786. The number of magazines totals 46, so we have included each piece of data.

Table 13.1

| Magazine | Circulation (ten thousands) |
|---|---|
| Reader's Digest | 817 |
| Better Homes and Gardens | 766 |
| National Geographic | 506 |
| Good Housekeeping | 468 |
| Woman's Day | 392 |
| Family Circle | 391 |
| AAA Westways | 384 |
| Ladies' Home Journal | 384 |
| People | 369 |
| Game Informer | 352 |
| Time | 336 |
| Prevention | 334 |
| TV Guide | 326 |
| Sports Illustrated | 322 |
| Taste of Home | 320 |
| Cosmopolitan | 293 |
| Southern Living | 283 |
| AAA | 281 |
| Newsweek | 270 |
| Playboy | 262 |
| AAA Going Places | 256 |
| Maxim | 252 |
| American Legion Magazine | 243 |
| O, The Oprah Magazine | 237 |
| Glamour | 229 |
| Redbook | 221 |
| Guideposts | 220 |
| AAA World | 213 |
| Parenting | 213 |
| Parents | 206 |
| ESPN The Magazine | 206 |
| Seventeen | 203 |
| Martha Stewart Living | 203 |
| Smithsonian | 203 |
| Real Simple | 198 |
| Remedy/Remedy MD | 196 |
| Money | 191 |
| Us Weekly | 190 |
| Family Fun | 188 |
| Men's Health | 186 |
| Entertainment Weekly | 180 |
| Endless Vacation | 179 |
| Cooking Light | 179 |
| Every Day with Rachael Ray | 178 |
| InStyle | 176 |
| Country Living | 173 |

Source: *Audit Bureau of Circulations*

| Circulation | Number of Magazines (ten thousands) |
|---|---|
| 173–237 | 23 |
| 238–302 | 8 |
| 303–367 | 6 |
| 368–432 | 5 |
| 433–497 | 1 |
| 498–562 | 1 |
| 563–627 | 0 |
| 628–692 | 0 |
| 693–757 | 0 |
| 758–822 | 2 |
| | 46 |

The *modal class* of a frequency distribution is the class with the greatest frequency. In Example 2, the modal class is 173–237. The *midpoint of a class*, also called the *class mark*, is found by adding the lower and upper class limits and dividing the sum by 2. The midpoint of the first class in Example 2 is

$$\frac{173 + 237}{2} = \frac{410}{2} = 205$$

Note that the difference between successive class marks is the class width. The class mark of the second class can therefore be obtained by adding the class width, 65, to the class mark of the first class, 205. The sum is $205 + 65 = 270$. Note that $\frac{238 + 302}{2} = 270$, which checks with the class mark obtained by adding the class width to the first class mark.

### Example 3   A Frequency Distribution of Family Income

The following set of data represents the family income (in thousands of dollars, rounded to the nearest hundred) of 15 randomly selected families.

| | | | | |
|---|---|---|---|---|
| 46.5 | 31.8 | 45.8 | 44.7 | 40.9 |
| 65.2 | 52.4 | 44.6 | 53.7 | 48.8 |
| 35.5 | 40.3 | 39.8 | 56.3 | 50.7 |

Construct a frequency distribution with a first class of 31.5–37.6.

**Solution**   First rearrange the data from lowest to highest so that the data will be easier to categorize.

| | | | | |
|---|---|---|---|---|
| 31.8 | 40.3 | 44.7 | 48.8 | 53.7 |
| 35.5 | 40.9 | 45.8 | 50.7 | 56.3 |
| 39.8 | 44.6 | 46.5 | 52.4 | 65.2 |

The first class goes from 31.5 to 37.6. Since the data are in tenths, the class limits will also be given in tenths. The first class ends with 37.6; therefore, the second class must start with 37.7. The class width of the first class is $37.7 - 31.5$, or 6.2. The upper class limit of the second class must therefore be $37.6 + 6.2$, or 43.8. The frequency distribution is given on page 787.

### MATHEMATICS TODAY

#### Cyberspace Is the Place to Be

Raleigh, North Carolina

Do you remember the days when you were only able to access the Internet from your office, school, or home? With wireless Internet access, we can now connect to the Internet to share information and enjoy entertainment while we are on the go. Today, wireless hotspots, locations offering wireless access to the Internet, show up in diverse places such as coffee shops, parks, gas stations, bowling alleys, airports, and golf courses in addition to more traditional places such as colleges and hotels. According to a survey conducted by *Forbes Magazine* in March 2010, Raleigh, North Carolina, was the most accessible wireless city in the United States. Many Web sites, such as www. wififreespot.com, list worldwide locations that offer free wireless Internet access.

*Why* **This is Important** More and more people are using wireless devices every day.

| Income ($1000) | Number of Families |
|---|---|
| 31.5–37.6 | 2 |
| 37.7–43.8 | 3 |
| 43.9–50.0 | 5 |
| 50.1–56.2 | 3 |
| 56.3–62.4 | 1 |
| 62.5–68.6 | 1 |
| | 15 |

Note in Example 3 that the class width is 6.2, the modal class is 43.9–50.0, and the class mark of the first class is $\frac{31.5 + 37.6}{2}$, or 34.55.

We have discussed how to organize and summarize data. Now we will introduce graphs that can be used to display information. We will consider four types of graphs: the histogram, the frequency polygon, the stem-and-leaf graph, and the circle graph.

## Histograms and Frequency Polygons

Histograms and frequency polygons are statistical graphs used to illustrate frequency distributions. A *histogram* is a graph with observed values on its horizontal scale and frequencies on its vertical scale. A bar is constructed above each observed value (or class when classes are used), indicating the frequency of that value (or class). The horizontal scale need not start at zero, and the calibrations on the horizontal and vertical scales do not have to be the same. The vertical scale must start at zero. To accommodate large frequencies on the vertical scale, it may be necessary to break the scale. Because histograms and other bar graphs are easy to interpret visually, they are used a great deal in newspapers and magazines.

### Example 4   *Construct a Histogram*

The frequency distribution developed in Example 1, on page 784, is repeated here. Construct a histogram of this frequency distribution.

| Number of Children (Observed Values) | Number of Families (Frequency) |
|---|---|
| 0 | 8 |
| 1 | 11 |
| 2 | 18 |
| 3 | 11 |
| 4 | 6 |
| 5 | 4 |
| 6 | 2 |
| 7 | 1 |
| 8 | 2 |
| 9 | 1 |

**Solution**   The vertical scale must extend at least to the number 18 since that is the greatest recorded frequency. The horizontal scale must include the numbers 0–9, the number of children observed. Eight families have no children. We indicate that by constructing a bar above the number 0, centered at 0, on the horizontal scale

## Profile in Mathematics

**Katherine K. Wallman— Chief U.S. Statistician**

Since 1992, Katherine Wallman has served as the chief statistician of the U.S. Office of Management and Budget. In this capacity, she oversees and coordinates U.S. federal statistical policies, standards, and programs; develops and advances long-term improvements in federal statistical activities; and represents the U.S. government in international statistics organizations, including the United Nations and the Organization for Economic Co-operation and Development.

In the United States, there are multiple agencies that actually produce statistics on which the country relies. For example, the Census Bureau provides population data; the Bureau of Economic Analysis provides national accounting data; and the National Center for Health Statistics provides data concerning health and well-being. In her capacity, Katherine Wallman sets standards for a federal statistical establishment that comprises more than 70 agencies spread across every cabinet department.

**TIMELY TIP**
When constructing a histogram or frequency polygon, be sure to label both scales of the graph.

extended up to 8 on the vertical scale (Fig. 13.7). Eleven families have one child, so we construct a bar extending to 11 above the number 1, centered at 1, on the horizontal scale. We continue this procedure for each observed value. Both the horizontal and vertical scales should be labeled, the bars should be the same width and centered at the observed value, and the histogram should have a title. In a histogram, the bars should always touch.

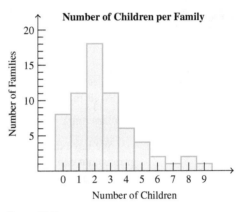

Figure 13.7

*Frequency polygons* are line graphs with scales the same as those of the histogram; that is, the horizontal scale indicates observed values and the vertical scale indicates frequency. To construct a frequency polygon, place a dot at the corresponding frequency above each of the observed values. Then connect the dots with straight-line segments. When constructing frequency polygons, always put in two additional class marks, one at the lower end and one at the upper end on the horizontal scale (values for these added class marks are not needed on the frequency polygon). Since the frequency at these added class marks is 0, the end points of the frequency polygon will always be on the horizontal scale.

### Example 5  *Construct a Frequency Polygon*

Construct a frequency polygon of the frequency distribution in Example 1 on page 784.

*Solution*  Since eight families have no children, place a mark above the 0 at 8 on the vertical scale, as shown in Fig. 13.8. Because there are 11 families with one child, place a mark above the 1 on the horizontal scale at the 11 on the vertical scale, and so on. Connect the dots with straight-line segments and bring the end points of the graph down to the horizontal scale, as shown.

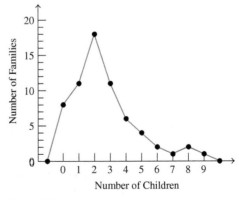

Figure 13.8

**Table 13.2**

| Distance (miles) | Number of Workers |
|---|---|
| 1–7 | 15 |
| 8–14 | 24 |
| 15–21 | 13 |
| 22–28 | 8 |
| 29–35 | 5 |
| 36–42 | 5 |

## Example 6 *Commuting Distances*

The frequency distribution of the one-way commuting distances for 70 workers is listed in Table 13.2. Construct a histogram and then construct a frequency polygon.

*Solution*  The histogram can be constructed with either class limits or class marks (class midpoints) on the horizontal scale. Frequency polygons are constructed with class marks on the horizontal scale. Since we will construct a frequency polygon on the histogram, we will use class marks. Recall that class marks are found by adding the lower class limit and upper class limit and dividing the sum by 2. For the first class, the class mark is $\frac{1 + 7}{2}$, or 4. Since the class widths are seven units, the class marks will also differ by seven units (see Fig. 13.9).

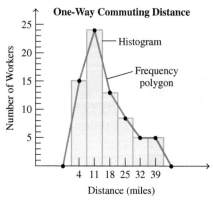

**Figure 13.9**

## Example 7 *Carry-on Luggage Weights*

The histogram in Fig. 13.10 shows the weights of selected pieces of carry-on luggage at an airport. Construct the frequency distribution from the histogram in Fig. 13.10.

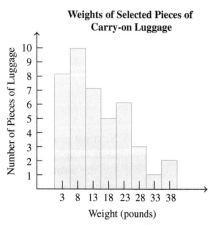

**Figure 13.10**

**Table 13.3**

| Weight (pounds) | Number of Pieces of Luggage |
|---|---|
| 1–5 | 8 |
| 6–10 | 10 |
| 11–15 | 7 |
| 16–20 | 5 |
| 21–25 | 6 |
| 26–30 | 3 |
| 31–35 | 1 |
| 36–40 | 2 |

*Solution*  There are five units between class midpoints, so each class width must also be five units. Since three is the midpoint of the first class, there must be two units below and two units above it. The first class must be 1–5. The second class must therefore be 6–10. The frequency distribution is given in Table 13.3.

## Stem-and-Leaf Displays

Frequency distributions and histograms provide very useful tools to organize and summarize data. However, if the data are grouped, we cannot identify specific data values in a frequency distribution and in a histogram. For example, in Example 7, we know that there are eight pieces of luggage in the class of 1 to 5 pounds, but we don't know the specific weights of those eight pieces of luggage.

A *stem-and-leaf display* is a tool that organizes and groups the data while allowing us to see the actual values that make up the data. To construct a stem-and-leaf display each value is represented with two different groups of digits. The left group of digits is called the *stem*. The remaining group of digits on the right is called the *leaf*. There is no rule for the number of digits to be included in the stem. Usually the units digit is the leaf and the remaining digits are the stem. For example, the number 53 would be broken up into 5 and 3. The 5 would be the stem and the 3 would be the leaf. The number 417 would be broken up into 41 and 7. The 41 would be the stem and the 7 would be the leaf. The number 6, which can be represented as 06, would be broken up into 0 and 6. The stem would be the 0 and the leaf would be the 6. With a stem-and-leaf display, the stems are listed, in ascending order, to the left of a vertical line. Then we place each leaf to the right of its corresponding stem, to the right of the vertical line.* Example 8 illustrates this procedure.

▲ *Captain Fairfield Inn Bed and Breakfast*

### Example 8  *Stem-and-Leaf Display*

The table below indicates the ages of a sample of 20 guests who stayed at Captain Fairfield Inn Bed and Breakfast. Construct a stem-and-leaf display.

| | | | | |
|---|---|---|---|---|
| 29 | 31 | 39 | 43 | 56 |
| 60 | 62 | 59 | 58 | 32 |
| 47 | 27 | 50 | 28 | 71 |
| 72 | 44 | 45 | 44 | 68 |

**Solution**  By quickly glancing at the data, we can see the ages consist of two-digit numbers. Let's use the first digit, the tens digit, as our stem and the second digit, the units digit, as the leaf. For example, for an age of 62, the stem is 6 and the leaf is 2. Our values are numbers in the 20s, 30s, 40s, 50s, 60s, and 70s. Therefore, the stems will be 2, 3, 4, 5, 6, 7 as shown below.

```
2|
3|
4|
5|
6|
7|
```

Next we place each leaf on its stem. We will do so by placing the second digit of each value next to its stem, to the right of the vertical line. Our first value is 29. The 2 is the stem and the 9 is the leaf. Therefore, we place a 9 next to the stem of 2 and to the right of the vertical line.

$$2|9$$

The next value is 31. We will place a leaf of 1 next to the stem of 3.

```
2|9
3|1
```

---

*In stem-and-leaf displays, the leaves are sometimes listed from lowest digit to greatest digit, but that is not necessary.

The next value is 39. Therefore, we will place a leaf of 9 after the leaf of 1 that is next to the stem of 3.

$$
\begin{array}{c|cc}
2 & 9 \\
3 & 1 & 9
\end{array}
$$

We continue this process until we have listed all the leaves on the display. The diagram below shows the stem-and-leaf display for the ages of the guests. In our display, we will also include a legend to indicate the values represented by the stems and leaves. For example, 5|6 represents 56.

$$
5|6 \text{ represents } 56
$$

$$
\begin{array}{c|ccccc}
\text{Stem} & \multicolumn{5}{l}{\text{Leaves}} \\
\hline
2 & 9 & 7 & 8 \\
3 & 1 & 9 & 2 \\
4 & 3 & 7 & 4 & 5 & 4 \\
5 & 6 & 9 & 8 & 0 \\
6 & 0 & 2 & 8 \\
7 & 1 & 2
\end{array}
$$

Every piece of the original data can be seen in a stem-and-leaf display. From the above diagram, we can see that five of the guests' ages were in the 40s. Only two guests were older than 70. Note that the stem-and-leaf display gives the same visual impression as a sideways histogram.

## Circle Graphs

*Circle graphs* (also known as pie charts) are often used to compare parts of one or more components of the whole to the whole. The circle graph in Fig. 13.11 shows what moviegoers say is the most annoying distraction during a movie. Since the total circle represents 100%, the sum of the percents of the sectors should be 100%, and it is.

In the next example, we will discuss a circle graph.

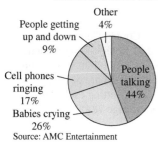

**Distractions at the Movies**

Other 4%
People getting up and down 9%
Cell phones ringing 17%
Babies crying 26%
People talking 44%
Source: AMC Entertainment

**Figure 13.11**

### Example 9  *Circus Performances*

Eight hundred people who attended a Ringling Bros. and Barnum & Bailey Circus were asked to indicate their favorite performance. The circle graph in Fig. 13.12 shows the percentage of respondents that answered tigers, elephants, acrobats, jugglers, and other. Determine the number of respondents for each category.

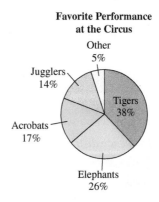

**Favorite Performance at the Circus**

Other 5%
Jugglers 14%
Acrobats 17%
Tigers 38%
Elephants 26%

**Figure 13.12**

*Solution*  To determine the number of respondents in a category, we multiply the percentage for each category, written as a decimal number, by the total number of people, 800. The table on page 792 indicates the results.

| Performance | Percent of Respondents | Percent Written as a Decimal Number | Number of People |
|---|---|---|---|
| Tigers | 38% | 0.38 | $0.38 \times 800 = 304$ |
| Elephants | 26% | 0.26 | $0.26 \times 800 = 208$ |
| Acrobats | 17% | 0.17 | $0.17 \times 800 = 136$ |
| Jugglers | 14% | 0.14 | $0.14 \times 800 = 112$ |
| Other | 5% | 0.05 | $0.05 \times 800 = \phantom{0}40$ |
| Total | | | 800 |

As we can see from the table, 304 people indicated that the tigers were their favorite performance, 208 indicated elephants, 136 people indicated the acrobats, 112 people indicated the jugglers, and 40 people indicated some other performance.   ■

## SECTION 13.3   *Exercises*

### Warm Up Exercises

*In Exercises 1–8, fill in the blank with an appropriate word, phrase, or symbol(s).*

**1.** A listing of observed values and the corresponding frequency of occurrence of each value is called a(n) _____ distribution.

**2.** In a frequency distribution, the class with the greatest frequency is called the _____ class.

**3.** In a frequency distribution, another name for the midpoint of a class is the class _____.

**4.** The class width of a frequency distribution with a first class of 9–16 and a second class of 17–24 is _____.

**5.** A bar graph with observed values on its horizontal scale and frequencies on its vertical scale is called a(n) _____.

**6.** A line graph with observed values on its horizontal scale and frequencies on its vertical scale is called a frequency _____.

**7.** In a stem-and-leaf display, the group of digits in the left-hand column is called the _____.

**8.** In a stem-and-leaf display, the group of digits in the right-hand column is called the _____.

### Practice the Skills/Problem Solving

*In Exercises 9 and 10, use the frequency distribution to determine*

  **a)** *the total number of observations.*

  **b)** *the width of each class.*

  **c)** *the midpoint of the second class.*

  **d)** *the modal class (or classes).*

  **e)** *the class limits of the next class if an additional class were to be added.*

**9.**

| Class | Frequency |
|---|---|
| 9–15 | 4 |
| 16–22 | 7 |
| 23–29 | 1 |
| 30–36 | 0 |
| 37–43 | 3 |
| 44–50 | 5 |

**10.**

| Class | Frequency |
|---|---|
| 40–49 | 7 |
| 50–59 | 5 |
| 60–69 | 3 |
| 70–79 | 2 |
| 80–89 | 7 |
| 90–99 | 1 |

**11.** *Visits to the Library* Johnson County Community College is planning to expand its library. Forty students were asked how many times they visited the library during the previous semester. Their responses are given below. Construct a frequency distribution, letting each class have a width of 1 (as in Example 1 on page 784).

| | | | | | | | |
|---|---|---|---|---|---|---|---|
| 0 | 1 | 1 | 3 | 4 | 5 | 7 | 8 |
| 0 | 1 | 2 | 3 | 5 | 5 | 7 | 8 |
| 0 | 1 | 2 | 3 | 5 | 5 | 7 | 9 |
| 1 | 1 | 2 | 3 | 5 | 6 | 8 | 10 |
| 1 | 1 | 3 | 4 | 5 | 6 | 8 | 10 |

**12.** *Hot Dog Sales* A hot dog vendor is interested in the number of hot dogs he sells each day at his hot dog cart. The number of hot dogs sold is indicated below for 32 consecutive days. Construct a frequency distribution, letting each class have a width of 1.

| | | | | | | | |
|---|---|---|---|---|---|---|---|
| 15 | 16 | 19 | 20 | 21 | 22 | 24 | 27 |
| 15 | 18 | 19 | 20 | 21 | 22 | 25 | 27 |
| 15 | 18 | 19 | 20 | 21 | 23 | 25 | 28 |
| 16 | 18 | 19 | 21 | 21 | 23 | 26 | 29 |

Note that there were no days in which the vendor sold 17 hot dogs. However, it is customary to include a missing value as an observed value and assign to it a frequency of 0.

▲ *See Exercise 12*

**Percent of U.S. Residents Living in Poverty in 2008, by State**

| State | Percent | State | Percent |
|-------|---------|-------|---------|
| AK | 7.9 | MT | 12.9 |
| AL | 14.4 | NC | 14.7 |
| AR | 14.5 | ND | 10.5 |
| AZ | 16.1 | NE | 10.3 |
| CA | 13.6 | NH | 6.4 |
| CO | 10.4 | NJ | 9.0 |
| CT | 8.5 | NM | 16.6 |
| DE | 9.4 | NV | 10.3 |
| FL | 12.8 | NY | 14.3 |
| GA | 14.6 | OH | 13.2 |
| HI | 8.7 | OK | 13.5 |
| IA | 9.2 | OR | 11.7 |
| ID | 11.1 | PA | 10.7 |
| IL | 11.1 | RI | 11.1 |
| IN | 13.1 | SC | 14.0 |
| KS | 12.2 | SD | 11.2 |
| KY | 16.3 | TN | 14.9 |
| LA | 17.1 | TX | 16.2 |
| MA | 11.2 | UT | 8.6 |
| MD | 8.8 | VA | 9.5 |
| ME | 11.4 | VT | 9.4 |
| MI | 11.9 | WA | 10.3 |
| MN | 9.6 | WI | 10.4 |
| MO | 13.1 | WV | 14.6 |
| MS | 20.4 | WY | 10.5 |

Source: *Bureau of the Census*

***Magazine Circulation*** *In Exercises 13–16, use the data given in Table 13.1 on page 786 to construct a frequency distribution with a first class (in ten thousands) of*

**13.** 173–322.    **14.** 170–316.

**15.** 173–272.    **16.** 173–250.

***City Population*** *In Exercises 17–20, use the following data, which represent the population of the 20 most populous cities in the world in 2010, in millions of people (rounded to the nearest 100,000).*

| | | | | |
|---|---|---|---|---|
| 13.8 | 12.5 | 10.1 | 8.8 | 7.6 |
| 13.8 | 11.2 | 9.6 | 8.4 | 7.3 |
| 13.0 | 10.6 | 8.9 | 7.9 | 7.2 |
| 12.6 | 10.5 | 8.9 | 7.8 | 7.1 |

*Construct a frequency distribution with a first class of*

**21.** 6.4–8.3.    **22.** 6.4–9.0.

**23.** 6.4–7.8.    **24.** 6.4–8.8.

**25. *Jogging Distances*** Twenty members of a health club who jog were asked how many miles they jog per week. The responses are as follows. Construct a stem-and-leaf display. For single digit data, use a stem of 0.

| | | | | | | |
|---|---|---|---|---|---|---|
| 12 | 15 | 4 | 7 | 12 | 25 | 21 |
| 33 | 18 | 6 | 8 | 27 | 40 | 22 |
| 19 | 13 | 23 | 34 | 17 | 16 | |

▲ *Shanghai, China, is the world's most populated city.*

*Use these data to construct a frequency distribution with a first class of*

**17.** 7.0–7.9.    **18.** 6.5–7.4.

**19.** 6.5–7.5.    **20.** 7.0–7.4.

***Residents in Poverty*** *In Exercises 21–24, use the data in the table above to the right.*

**26.** *College Credits* Eighteen students in a geology class were asked how many college credits they had earned. The responses are as follows. Construct a stem-and-leaf display.

$$10 \quad 15 \quad 24 \quad 36 \quad 48 \quad 45$$
$$42 \quad 53 \quad 60 \quad 17 \quad 24 \quad 30$$
$$33 \quad 45 \quad 48 \quad 62 \quad 54 \quad 60$$

**27.** *Starting Salaries* Starting salaries (in thousands of dollars) for social workers with a bachelor of science degree and no experience are shown for a random sample of 25 different social workers.

$$27 \quad 28 \quad 29 \quad 31 \quad 33$$
$$28 \quad 28 \quad 29 \quad 31 \quad 33$$
$$28 \quad 28 \quad 30 \quad 32 \quad 33$$
$$28 \quad 29 \quad 30 \quad 32 \quad 34$$
$$28 \quad 29 \quad 30 \quad 32 \quad 34$$

**a)** Construct a frequency distribution. Let each class have a width of one.

**b)** Construct a histogram.

**c)** Construct a frequency polygon.

**d)** Construct a stem-and-leaf display.

**28.** *Visiting a Symphony* The ages of a random sample of 40 people attending a symphony are

$$20 \quad 26 \quad 31 \quad 34 \quad 39 \quad 45 \quad 50 \quad 62$$
$$20 \quad 29 \quad 31 \quad 35 \quad 40 \quad 47 \quad 51 \quad 63$$
$$23 \quad 30 \quad 32 \quad 35 \quad 40 \quad 49 \quad 51 \quad 66$$
$$23 \quad 30 \quad 33 \quad 37 \quad 40 \quad 49 \quad 54 \quad 69$$
$$26 \quad 30 \quad 34 \quad 38 \quad 42 \quad 49 \quad 57 \quad 72$$

**a)** Construct a frequency distribution with a first class of 20–30.

**b)** Construct a histogram.

**c)** Construct a frequency polygon.

**d)** Construct a stem-and-leaf display.

**29.** *Concert Tours* The following table shows the 25 top-grossing North American concert tours, in millions of dollars, for the years 1985–2008.

| Artist | Total Gross ($ millions) |
|---|---|
| 1. The Rolling Stones (2005) | 162 |
| 2. U2 (2005) | 139 |
| 3. The Rolling Stones (2006) | 139 |
| 4. The Police (2007) | 133 |
| 5. The Rolling Stones (1994) | 121 |
| 6. Bruce Springsteen & the E Street Band (2003) | 116 |
| 7. U2 (2001) | 110 |
| 8. Madonna (2008) | 105 |
| 9. Pink Floyd (1994) | 104 |
| 10. Paul McCartney (2002) | 103 |
| 11. The Rolling Stones (1989) | 98 |
| 12. Celine Dion (2008) | 94 |
| 13. Barbra Streisand (2006) | 93 |
| 14. The Rolling Stones (1997) | 89 |
| 15. Tim McGraw/Faith Hill (2006) | 89 |
| 16. The Rolling Stones (2002) | 88 |
| 17. Prince (2004) | 87 |
| 18. 'N Sync (2001) | 87 |
| 19. Madonna (2006) | 86 |
| 20. Backstreet Boys (2001) | 82 |
| 21. Cirque de Soleil: Delirium (2006) | 82 |
| 22. Celine Dion (2005) | 81 |
| 23. Celine Dion (2003) | 81 |
| 24. Celine Dion (2004) | 80 |
| 25. Tina Turner (2000) | 80 |

Source: Pollstar

**a)** Construct a frequency distribution with a first class of 80–91.

**b)** Construct a histogram.

**c)** Construct a frequency polygon.

**30.** *U.S. Presidents* The ages of the 44 U.S. presidents at their first inauguration (as of 2011) are

$$57 \quad 57 \quad 49 \quad 52 \quad 50 \quad 42 \quad 54 \quad 55 \quad 64$$
$$61 \quad 61 \quad 64 \quad 56 \quad 47 \quad 51 \quad 51 \quad 56 \quad 46$$
$$57 \quad 54 \quad 50 \quad 46 \quad 55 \quad 56 \quad 60 \quad 61 \quad 54$$
$$57 \quad 68 \quad 48 \quad 54 \quad 55 \quad 55 \quad 62 \quad 52 \quad 47$$
$$58 \quad 51 \quad 65 \quad 49 \quad 54 \quad 51 \quad 43 \quad 69$$

**a)** Construct a frequency distribution with a first class of 42–47.

**b)** Construct a histogram.

**c)** Construct a frequency polygon.

**31.** *Number of Televisions per Home* Use the histogram below to answer the following questions.

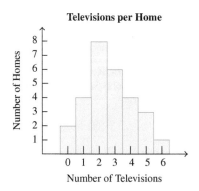

**Televisions per Home**

**a)** How many homes were included in the survey?

**b)** In how many homes were four televisions observed?

**c)** What is the modal class?

**d)** How many televisions were observed?

**e)** Construct a frequency distribution from this histogram.

**32.** *Car Insurance* Use the histogram below to answer the following questions.

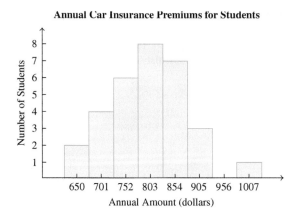

**Annual Car Insurance Premiums for Students**

**a)** How many students were surveyed?

**b)** What are the lower and upper class limits of the first and second classes?

**c)** How many students have an annual car insurance premium in the class with a class mark of $752?

**d)** What is the class mark of the modal class?

**e)** Construct a frequency distribution from this histogram. Use a first class of 625–675.

**33.** *E-mail Messages* Use the frequency polygon below to answer the following questions.

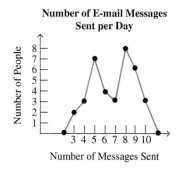

**Number of E-mail Messages Sent per Day**

**a)** How many people sent five e-mail messages?

**b)** How many people sent six or fewer e-mail messages?

**c)** How many people were included in the survey?

**d)** Construct a frequency distribution from the frequency polygon.

**e)** Construct a histogram from the frequency distribution in part (d).

**34.** *San Diego Zoo* Use the frequency polygon below to answer the following questions.

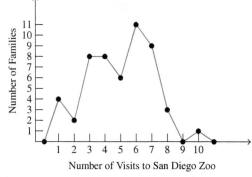

**Number of Visits Selected Families Have Made to the San Diego Zoo**

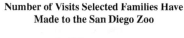

**a)** How many families visited the San Diego Zoo four times?

**b)** How many families visited the San Diego Zoo at least six times?

**c)** How many families were surveyed?

**d)** Construct a frequency distribution from the frequency polygon.

**e)** Construct a histogram from the frequency distribution in part (d).

**35.** *College Costs* The cost for Florida residents to attend the University of Florida for the 2010–2011 school year was $14,570. The circle graph on page 796 shows the percentage of that cost for tuition/fees, room, board, and computer costs. Determine the cost, in dollars, for each category.

**Cost to Attend the University of Florida for 2010–2011**

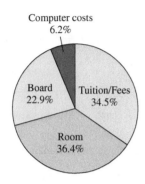

36. *Automobile Accessories*  A sample of 600 people were asked which one automobile accessory they would most prefer to have on a family road trip. The following circle graph shows the percentage of respondents that answered GPS, DVD player, extra cup holders, roof rack, and other. Determine the number of respondents for each category.

**Automobile Accessories for a Family Road Trip**

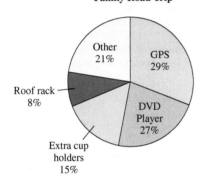

## Challenge Problems/Group Activities

37. **a)** *Birthdays*  What do you believe a histogram of the months in which the students in your class were born (January is month 1 and December is month 12) would look like? Explain.

**b)** By asking, determine the month in which the students in your class were born (include yourself).

**c)** Construct a frequency distribution containing 12 classes.

**d)** Construct a histogram from the frequency distribution in part (c).

**e)** Construct a frequency polygon of the frequency distribution in part (c).

38. *Social Security Numbers*  Repeat Exercise 37 for the last digit of the students' Social Security numbers. Include classes for the digits 0–9.

## Recreational Mathematics

39. **a)** Count the number of F's in the sentence at the bottom of the Recreational Mathematics box on page 785.

**b)** Can you explain why so many people count the number of F's incorrectly?

40. In what month do people take the least number of daily vitamins?

## Internet/Research Activity

41. Over the years many changes have been made in the U.S. Social Security System.

**a)** Do research and determine the number of people receiving Social Security benefits for the years 1945, 1950, 1955, 1960, ..., 2010. Then construct a frequency distribution and histogram of the data.

**b)** Determine the maximum amount that self-employed individuals had to pay into Social Security (the FICA tax) for the years 1945, 1950, 1955, 1960, ..., 2010. Then construct a frequency distribution and a histogram of the data.

# SECTION 13.4    Measures of Central Tendency

▲ *An average is used to describe the fuel efficiency of a car.*

Most people have an intuitive idea of what is meant by an "average." The term is used daily in many familiar ways. "This car averages 19 miles per gallon," "The average test grade was 82," and "The average height of adult males is 5 feet 9 inches" are three examples. In this section, we will introduce four different averages and discuss the circumstances in which each average is used.

**Why** *This is Important*  An average is one of the most common ways to represent a set of data.

## Measures of Central Tendency

An *average* is a number that is representative of a group of data. There are at least four different averages: the mean, the median, the mode, and the midrange. Each is calculated differently and may yield different results for the same set of data. Each will result in a number near the center of the data; for this reason, averages are commonly referred to as *measures of central tendency*.

The *arithmetic mean*, or simply the *mean*, is symbolized either by $\bar{x}$ (read "x bar") or by the Greek letter mu, $\mu$. The symbol $\bar{x}$ is used when the mean of a *sample* of the population is calculated. The symbol $\mu$ is used when the mean of the *entire population* is calculated. Unless otherwise indicated, we will assume that the data featured in this book represent samples; therefore, we will use $\bar{x}$ for the mean.

The Greek letter sigma, $\Sigma$, is used to indicate "summation." The notation $\Sigma x$, read "the sum of x," is used to indicate the sum of all the data. For example, if there are five pieces of data—4, 6, 1, 0, 5—then $\Sigma x = 4 + 6 + 1 + 0 + 5 = 16$.

Now we can discuss the procedure for determining the mean of a set of data.

### Definition: **Mean**

The **mean,** $\bar{x}$, is the sum of the data divided by the number of pieces of data. The formula for calculating the mean is

$$\bar{x} = \frac{\Sigma x}{n}$$

where $\Sigma x$ represents the sum of all the data and $n$ represents the number of pieces of data.

The most common use of the word *average* is the mean.

### Example 1 *Determine the Mean*

Determine the mean age of a group of patients at a doctor's office if the ages of the individuals are 28, 19, 49, 35, and 49.

*Solution*

$$\bar{x} = \frac{\Sigma x}{n} = \frac{28 + 19 + 49 + 35 + 49}{5} = \frac{180}{5} = 36$$

Therefore, the mean, $\bar{x}$, is 36 years.

The mean represents "the balancing point" of a set of data. For example, if a seesaw were pivoted at the mean and uniform weights were placed at points corresponding to the ages in Example 1, the seesaw would balance. Figure. 13.13 shows the five ages given in Example 1 and the calculated mean.

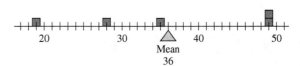

Figure 13.13

A second average is the *median*. To find the median of a set of data, *rank the data from smallest to largest, or largest to smallest, and determine the value in the middle of the set of ranked data.* This value will be the median.

### Definition: **Median**

The **median** is the value in the middle of a set of *ranked data.*

**TIMELY TIP**

Data must be ranked before determining the median. A common error made when determining the median is neglecting to arrange the data in ascending (increasing) or in descending (decreasing) order.

**MATHEMATICS TODAY**

**Buying the American Dream**

San Jose, California

One of the biggest dreams for most people is to own their own home. Yet depending on where you live, the American dream may be hard to achieve. In 2010, San Jose, California, had the highest median home price for major metropolitan housing markets, $630,000. Saginaw, Michigan, had the lowest median home price for major metropolitan housing markets, $59,700.

Saginaw, Michigan

*Source:* National Association of Realtors

---

Example 2  *Determine the Median*

Determine the median of the patients' ages in Example 1 on page 797.

*Solution*   Ranking the data from smallest to largest gives 19, 28, 35, 49, and 49. Since 35 is the value in the middle of this set of ranked data (two pieces of data above it and two pieces below it), 35 years is the median.   ∎

When there are an even number of pieces of data, the median is halfway between the two middle pieces. In this case, to find the median, add the two middle pieces and divide this sum by 2.

Example 3  *Determine the Median of an Even Number of Pieces of Data*

Determine the median of the following sets of data.

a)  9, 14, 16, 17, 11, 16, 11, 12          b)  7, 8, 8, 8, 9, 10

*Solution*

a)  Ranking the data gives 9, 11, 11, 12, 14, 16, 16, 17. There are eight pieces of data. Therefore, the median will lie halfway between the two middle pieces, the 12 and the 14. The median is $\frac{12 + 14}{2}$, or $\frac{26}{2}$, or 13.

b)  There are six pieces of data, and they are already ranked. Therefore, the median lies halfway between the two middle pieces. Both middle pieces are 8's. The median is $\frac{8 + 8}{2}$, or $\frac{16}{2}$, or 8.   ∎

A third average is the *mode*.

**Definition: Mode**

The **mode** is the piece of data that occurs most frequently.

Example 4  *Determine the Mode*

Determine the mode of the patients' ages in Example 1 on page 797.

*Solution*   The ages are 28, 19, 49, 35, and 49. The age 49 is the mode because it occurs twice and the other values occur only once.   ∎

If each piece of data occurs only once, the set of data has no mode. For example, the set of data 1, 2, 3, 4, 5 has no mode. If two values in a set of data occur more often than all the other data, we consider both these values as modes and say that the data are **bimodal**\* (which means two modes). For example, the set of data 1, 1, 2, 3, 3, 5 has two modes, 1 and 3.

The last average we will discuss is the midrange. The *midrange* is the value halfway between the lowest (L) and highest (H) values in a set of data. It is found by adding the lowest and highest values and dividing the sum by 2. A formula for finding the midrange follows.

**Midrange**

The **midrange** of a set of data can be calculated using the following formula.

$$\text{Midrange} = \frac{\text{lowest value} + \text{highest value}}{2}$$

---

\*Some textbooks say that sets of data such as 1, 1, 2, 3, 3, 5 have no mode.

## Example 5  *Determine the Midrange*

Determine the midrange of the patients' ages given in Example 1 on page 797.

**Solution**  The ages of the patients are 28, 19, 49, 35, and 49. The lowest age is 19, and the highest age is 49.

$$\text{Midrange} = \frac{\text{lowest} + \text{highest}}{2} = \frac{19 + 49}{2} = \frac{68}{2} = 34 \text{ years}$$

The "average" of the ages 28, 19, 49, 35, 49 can be considered any one of the follow-ing values: 36 (mean), 35 (median), 49 (mode), or 34 (midrange). Which average do you feel is most representative of the ages? We will discuss this question later in this section.

## Example 6  *Measures of Central Tendency*

The salaries of eight selected social workers rounded to the nearest thousand dollars are 40, 25, 28, 35, 42, 60, 60, and 73. For this set of data, determine the (a) mean, (b) median, (c) mode, and (d) midrange. Then (e) list the measures of central ten-dency from lowest to highest.

**Solution**

a) $\bar{x} = \frac{\Sigma x}{n} = \frac{40 + 25 + 28 + 35 + 42 + 60 + 60 + 73}{8} = \frac{363}{8} = 45.375$

b) Ranking the data from the smallest to largest gives

$$25, 28, 35, 40, 42, 60, 60, 73$$

Since there are an even number of pieces of data, the median is halfway between 40 and 42. The median $= \frac{40 + 42}{2} = \frac{82}{2} = 41$.

c) The mode is the piece of data that occurs most frequently. The mode is 60.

d) The midrange $= \frac{L + H}{2} = \frac{25 + 73}{2} = \frac{98}{2} = 49$.

e) The averages from lowest to highest are the median, mean, midrange, and mode. Their values are 41, 45.375, 49, and 60, respectively.

At this point, you should be able to calculate the four measures of central ten-dency: mean, median, mode, and midrange. Now let's examine the circumstances in which each is used.

The mean is used when each piece of data is to be considered and "weighed" equally. It is the most commonly used average. It is the only average that can be af-fected by *any* change in the set of data; for this reason, it is the most sensitive of all the measures of central tendency (see Exercise 23).

Occasionally, one or more pieces of data may be much greater or much smaller than the rest of the data. When this situation occurs, these "extreme" values have the effect of increasing or decreasing the mean significantly so that the mean will not be representative of the set of data. Under these circumstances, the median should be used instead of the mean. The median is often used in describing average family in-comes because a relatively small number of families have extremely large incomes. These few incomes would inflate the mean income, making it nonrepresentative of the millions of families in the population.

Consider a set of exam scores from a mathematics class: 0, 16, 19, 65, 65, 65, 68, 69, 70, 72, 73, 73, 75, 78, 80, 85, 88, 92. Which average would best represent these grades? The mean is 64.06. The median is 71. Since only 3 of the 18 scores fall below the mean, the mean would not be considered a good representative score. The median of 71 probably would be the better average to use.

The mode is the piece of data, if any, that occurs most frequently. Builders planning houses are interested in the most common family size. Retailers ordering shirts are interested in the most common shirt size. An individual purchasing a thermometer might choose one, from those on display, whose temperature reading is the most common reading among those on display. These examples illustrate how the mode may be used.

The midrange is sometimes used as the average when the item being studied is constantly fluctuating. Average daily temperature, used to compare temperatures in different areas, is calculated by adding the lowest and highest temperatures for the day and dividing the sum by 2. The midrange is actually the mean of the high value and the low value of a set of data. Occasionally, the midrange is used to estimate the mean since it is much easier to calculate.

Sometimes an average itself is of little value, and care must be taken in interpreting its meaning. For example, Jim is told that the average depth of Willow Pond is only 3 feet. He is not a good swimmer but decides that it is safe to go out a short distance in this shallow pond. After he is rescued, he exclaims, "I thought this pond was only 3 feet deep." Jim didn't realize that an average does not indicate extreme values or the spread of the values. The spread of data is discussed in Section 13.5.

## Measures of Position

Measures of position are used to describe the position of a piece of data in relation to the rest of the data. If you took the Scholastic Aptitude Test (SAT) before applying to college, your score was described as a measure of position rather than a measure of central tendency. *Measures of position* are often used to make comparisons, such as comparing the scores of individuals from different populations, and are generally used when the amount of data is large.

Two measures of position are *percentiles* and *quartiles*. There are 99 percentiles dividing a set of data into 100 equal parts; see Fig. 13.14. For example, suppose that you scored 520 on the math portion of the SAT, and the score of 520 was reported to be in the 78th percentile of high school students. This wording *does not* mean that 78% of your answers were correct; it *does* mean that you outperformed about 78% of all those taking the exam. In general, a score in the $n$th percentile means that you outperformed about $n\%$ of the population who took the test and that $(100 - n)\%$ of the people taking the test performed better than you did.

**Percentiles**

1  2  3  4                      100 — 100 equal parts
$P_1$ $P_2$ $P_3$ $P_4$          $P_{99}$ — Percentile indicators

**Figure 13.14**

### Example 7    *English Achievement Test*

Kara Hopkins took an English achievement test to obtain college credit by exam for freshman English. Her score was at the 81st percentile. Explain what that means.

*Solution*    If a score is at the 81st percentile, it means that about 81% of the scores are below that score. Therefore, Kara scored better than about 81% of the students taking the exam. Also, about 19% of all students taking the exam scored higher than she did.

*Quartiles* are another measure of position. Quartiles divide data into four equal parts: The first quartile is the value that is higher than about $\frac{1}{4}$, or 25%, of the population. It is the same as the 25th percentile. The second quartile is the value that is higher than about $\frac{1}{2}$ the population and is the same as the 50th percentile, or the median. The third quartile is the value that is higher than about $\frac{3}{4}$ of the population and is the same as the 75th percentile; see Fig. 13.15.

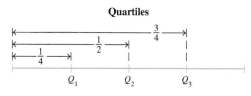

**Quartiles**

Figure 13.15

---

PROCEDURE   **TO DETERMINE THE QUARTILES OF A SET OF DATA**

1. List the data from smallest to largest.

2. Determine the median, or the 2nd quartile, of the set of data. If there is an odd number of pieces of data, the median is the middle value. If there is an even number of pieces of data, the median will be halfway between the two middle pieces of data.

3. The first quartile, $Q_1$, is the median of the lower half of the data; that is, $Q_1$ is the median of the data less than $Q_2$.

4. The third quartile, $Q_3$, is the median of the upper half of the data; that is, $Q_3$ is the median of the data greater than $Q_2$.

---

Example 8   *Finding Quartiles*

Electronics World is concerned about the high turnover of its sales staff. A survey was done to determine how long (in months) the sales staff had been in their current positions. The responses of 27 sales staff follow. Determine $Q_1$, $Q_2$, and $Q_3$.

$$
\begin{array}{ccccccccc}
25 & 3 & 7 & 15 & 31 & 36 & 17 & 21 & 2 \\
11 & 42 & 16 & 23 & 19 & 21 & 9 & 20 & 5 \\
8 & 12 & 27 & 14 & 39 & 24 & 18 & 6 & 10
\end{array}
$$

Solution   First we list the data from smallest to largest.

$$
\begin{array}{ccccccccc}
2 & 3 & 5 & 6 & 7 & 8 & 9 & 10 & 11 \\
12 & 14 & 15 & 16 & 17 & 18 & 19 & 20 & 21 \\
21 & 23 & 24 & 25 & 27 & 31 & 36 & 39 & 42
\end{array}
$$

Next we determine the median. Since there are 27 pieces of data, an odd number, the median will be the middle value. The middle value is 17, with 13 pieces of data less than 17 and 13 pieces of data greater than 17. Therefore, the median, $Q_2$, is 17, shown in red.

To find $Q_1$, the median of the lower half of the data, we need to find the median of the 13 pieces of data that are less than $Q_2$. The middle value of the lower half of the data is 9. There are 6 pieces of data less than 9 and 6 pieces of data greater than 9. Therefore, $Q_1$ is 9, shown in blue.

To find $Q_3$, the median of the upper half of the data, we need to find the median of the 13 pieces of data that are greater than 17, or $Q_2$. The middle value of the upper half of the data is 24. There are 6 pieces of data greater than 17 but less than 24 and 6 pieces of data greater than 24. Therefore, $Q_3$ is 24, shown in blue.  ∎

TECHNOLOGY TIP

Several computer software programs and calculators can be used to determine the mean of a set of data. These programs and calculators can also provide other types of statistical information that we will discuss in this chapter. In this *Technology Tip* we will provide the instructions for using a software program called Microsoft Excel as well as information on how to use Texas Instruments TI-83 Plus and TI-84 Plus graphing calculators. In the example, we will use the data from Example 1 on page 797, which represent the ages of patients in a doctor's office.

**EXCEL**
In our discussion, we will use the symbol > to indicate the next item to be selected from the list or menu of items.
       Begin by entering the five pieces of data in column A. Press the Enter key after each piece of data is entered. Next select

$$\text{Insert} > \text{Function} \ldots > \text{Statistical} > \text{AVERAGE}$$

Then click the OK box at the bottom. The program will then generate a gray box, where you need to enter the data. In the area to the right of **Number1,** you need to enter the data for which you want to find the mean. Since you have already entered the data in column A, rows 1 to 5, if A1:A5 is not already listed, you can enter A1:A5 in the area to the right of **Number1.** Then, at the bottom of the gray box, *Formula Results* = 36 is displayed. The 36 is the mean of the set of data. If you then press the OK box, the mean will be displayed in the cell where the cursor was located. If you do not want the mean displayed in a cell, press CANCEL. To find the median or mode you follow a similar procedure, except that instead of selecting AVERAGE you would select MEDIAN or MODE, respectively.

**TI-83 PLUS AND TI-84 PLUS GRAPHING CALCULATORS**
To enter the data, press STAT. Then highlight **1: Edit** and press the ENTER key. If any data are currently listed in column **L1**, move the cursor to the **L1** and press CLEAR and then the ENTER key. This step will eliminate all data from column **L1**. Now enter the data in column **L1**. After you enter each piece of data, press the ENTER key. After all the data have been entered, press STAT. Then highlight **CALC.** At this point, **1: 1–Var Stats** should be highlighted. Press the ENTER key twice. You will now see $\bar{x}$ = 36. Thus, the mean is 36. Several other descriptive statistics that we will discuss shortly are also shown. If you scroll down, you will eventually see the values of $Q_1$, the median, and $Q_3$.

## SECTION 13.4    *Exercises*

### Warm Up Exercises

*In Exercises 1–10, fill in the blank with an appropriate word, phrase, or symbol(s).*

**1.** A number that is representative of a set of data is called a(n) _____.

**2.** Averages are referred to as measures of central _____.

**3.** The average that is found by summing the data and then dividing the sum by the number of pieces of data is called the _____.

**4.** The value in the middle of a set of ranked data is called the _____.

**5.** The piece of data that occurs most frequently is called the _____.

**6.** The value halfway between the lowest and highest values in a set of data is called the _____.

**7.** The measures of position that divide a set of data into four equal parts are called _____.

**8.** Data that are listed from the lowest value to the highest value or from the highest value to the lowest value are called _____ data.

**9. a)** The symbol for the sample mean is _____.

   **b)** The symbol for the population mean is _____.

**10. a)** Another name for the 25th percentile is the _____ quartile.

   **b)** Another name for the 50th percentile is the _____ quartile.

   **c)** Another name for the 75th percentile is the _____ quartile.

## Practice the Skills

*In Exercises 11–20, determine the mean, median, mode, and midrange of the set of data. Where appropriate, round your answer to the nearest tenth.*

**11.** 8, 9, 9, 11, 13, 13, 13, 24, 26

**12.** 7, 9, 10, 10, 10, 12, 12

**13.** 76, 82, 94, 55, 100, 52, 96

**14.** 4, 6, 10, 12, 10, 9, 365, 40, 37, 8

**15.** 1, 3, 5, 7, 9, 11, 13, 15

**16.** 40, 50, 30, 60, 90, 100, 140

**17.** 1, 7, 11, 27, 36, 14, 12, 9, 1

**18.** 1, 1, 1, 1, 4, 4, 4, 4, 6, 8, 10, 12, 15, 21

**19.** 6, 8, 12, 13, 11, 13, 15, 17

**20.** 5, 15, 5, 15, 5, 15

**21.** *Cholesterol Level* The total cholesterol level of 10 patients of Dr. Novak are 176, 202, 285, 153, 200, 182, 248, 132, 214, and 195. Determine the

**a)** mean.                **b)** median.

**c)** mode.                **d)** midrange.

**22.** *Daily Commission* The amount of money Steve Kline collected in sales commission in each of seven days is $48, $67, $51, $25, $102, $61, $80. Determine the mean, median, mode, and midrange.

## Problem Solving

**23.** *Change in the Data* The mean is the "most sensitive" average because it is affected by any change in the data.

   **a)** Determine the mean, median, mode, and midrange for 1, 2, 3, 5, 5, 7, 11.

   **b)** Change the 7 to a 10 in part (a). Determine the mean, median, mode, and midrange.

   **c)** Which averages were affected by changing the 7 to a 10?

   **d)** Which averages will be affected by changing the 11 to a 10 in part (a)?

**24.** *Life Expectancy* In 2010, the National Center for Health Statistics indicated a record "average life expectancy" of 78.2 years for the total U.S. population. The average life expectancy for men was 75.6 years, and for women it was 80.8 years. Which "average" do you think the National Center for Health is using?

**25.** *A Grade of B* To get a grade of B, a student must have a mean average of 80 or greater. Jim Condor has a mean average of 79 for 10 quizzes. He approaches his teacher and asks for a B, reasoning that he missed a B by only one point. What is wrong with Jim's reasoning?

**26.** *Employee Salaries* The salaries of 10 employees of a small company follow.

| | |
|---|---|
| $29,000 | $65,000 |
| 26,000 | 25,000 |
| 32,000 | 28,000 |
| 27,000 | 82,000 |
| 27,000 | 30,000 |

Determine the

   **a)** mean.                **b)** median.

   **c)** mode.                **d)** midrange.

   **e)** If the employees wanted to demonstrate the need for a raise, which average would they use to show they are being underpaid: the mean or the median? Explain.

   **f)** If the management did not want to give the employees a raise, which average would they use: the mean or the median? Explain.

**27.** *Ice Cream Consumption* The 10 countries with the highest per person consumption of ice cream in 2008 are listed below.

| Country | Consumption (pints per person) |
|---|---|
| Australia | 31.7 |
| USA | 26.0 |
| Nauru | 25.3 |
| New Zealand | 23.4 |
| Canada | 22.7 |
| Norway | 22.3 |
| Finland | 20.9 |
| Sweden | 20.4 |
| Iceland | 18.5 |
| Italy | 18.5 |

Source: *Euromonitor International*

Determine, to the nearest tenth, the

a) mean.                    b) median.

c) mode.                    d) midrange.

28. *Living Expenses* Bob Bennet's monthly living expenses for 1 year are as follows:

| $1200 | $1050 | $1570 | $1600 |
|-------|-------|-------|-------|
| 2000 | 1050 | 1550 | 1450 |
| 1800 | 1100 | 1310 | 1430 |

Where appropriate, round your answer to the nearest cent. Determine the

a) mean.                    b) median.

c) mode.                    d) midrange.

29. *Internet Retailers* The ten U.S. retailers with the highest Internet sales in 2008 are listed below.

| Company | Sales ($ billion) |
|---------|-------------------|
| Amazon.com, Inc. | 14.8 |
| Staples, Inc. | 5.6 |
| Office Depot, Inc. | 4.9 |
| Dell, Inc. | 4.2 |
| HP Home & Home Office Store | 3.4 |
| OfficeMax, Inc. | 3.2 |
| Apple, Inc. | 2.7 |
| Sears Holding Corp. | 2.6 |
| CDW Corp. | 2.4 |
| Newegg.com | 1.9 |

Source: *Internet Retailer*

Determine to the nearest tenth the

a) mean.                    b) median.

c) mode.                    d) midrange.

30. *Exam Average* Malcolm Sander's mean average on five exams is 86. Determine the sum of his scores.

31. *Exam Average* Jeremy Urban's mean average on six exams is 92. Determine the sum of his scores.

32. *Creating a Data Set* Construct a set of five pieces of data in which the mode has a lower value than the median and the median has a lower value than the mean.

33. *Creating a Data Set* Construct a set of six pieces of data with a mean, median, and midrange of 75 and where no two pieces of data are the same.

34. *Creating a Data Set* Construct a set of six pieces of data with a mean of 84 and where no two pieces of data are the same.

35. *Water Park* For the 2011 season, 27,000 people visited the Blue Lagoon Water Park. The park was open 120 days for water activities. The highest number of visitors on a single day was 500. The lowest number of visitors on a single day was 50. Determine whether it is possible to find the following with the given information.

a) the mean number of visitors per day

b) the median number of visitors per day

c) the mode number of visitors per day

d) the midrange number of visitors per day

36. *Determine a Necessary Grade* A mean average of 80 or greater for five exams is needed for a final grade of B in a course. Jorge Rivera's first four exam grades are 73, 69, 85, and 80. What grade does Jorge need on the fifth exam to get a B in the course?

37. *Grading Methods* A mean average of 60 on seven exams is needed to pass a course. On her first six exams, Sheryl Ward received grades of 51, 72, 80, 62, 57, and 69.

a) What grade must she receive on her last exam to pass the course?

b) An average of 70 is needed to get a C in the course. Is it possible for Sheryl to get a C? If so, what grade must she receive on the seventh exam?

c) If her lowest grade of the exams already taken is to be dropped, what grade must she receive on her last exam to pass the course?

d) If her lowest grade of the exams already taken is to be dropped, what grade must she receive on her last exam to get a C in the course?

**38. Central Tendencies** Which of the measures of central tendency *must* be an actual piece of data in the distribution?

**39. Creating a Data Set** Construct a set of six pieces of data such that if only one piece of data is changed, the mean, median, and mode will all change.

**40. Changing One Piece of Data** Consider the set of data 1, 1, 1, 2, 2, 2. If one 2 is changed to a 3, which of the following will change: mean, median, mode, midrange?

**41. Changing One Piece of Data** Is it possible to construct a set of six different pieces of data such that by changing only one piece of data you cause the mean, median, mode, and midrange to change? Explain.

**42. Grocery Expenses** The Taylors have recorded their weekly grocery expenses for the past 12 weeks and determined that the mean weekly expense was $85.20. Later Mrs. Taylor discovered that 1 week's expense of $74 was incorrectly recorded as $47. What is the correct mean?

**43. Percentiles** For any set of data, what must be done to the data before percentiles can be determined?

**44. Percentiles** Josie Waverly scored in the 73rd percentile on the verbal part of her College Board test. What does that mean?

**45. Percentiles** When a national sample of heights of kindergarten children was taken, Kevin Geis was told that he was in the 35th percentile. Explain what that means.

**46. Percentiles** A union leader is told that, when all workers' salaries are considered, the first quartile is $22,750. Explain what that means.

**47. Quartiles** The prices of a gallon of the 21 top-rated interior paints, as rated in the March 2010 issue of *Consumer Reports*, are as follows:

$18  $19  $19  $19  $20  $20  $21
$21  $22  $22  $23  $23  $25  $27
$30  $33  $35  $35  $35  $58  $61

Determine

a) $Q_2$.          b) $Q_1$.          c) $Q_3$.

**48. Quartiles** The prices of the 20 top-rated 16-inch laptops, as rated in the June 2010 issue of *Consumer Reports*, are as follows:

$450   $460   $500   $530   $550
$550   $650   $650   $680   $700
$720   $730   $800   $850   $900
$1000  $1200  $1350  $1700  $1900

Determine

a) $Q_2$.          b) $Q_1$.          c) $Q_3$.

**49. The 50th Percentile** Give the names of two other statistics that have the same value as the 50th percentile.

**50. College Admissions** Jonathan Burd took an admission test for the University of California and scored in the 85th percentile. The following year, Jonathan's sister Kendra took a similar admission test for the University of California and scored in the 90th percentile.

a) Is it possible to determine which of the two answered the higher percent of questions correctly on their respective exams?

b) Is it possible to determine which of the two was in a better relative position with regard to their respective populations? Explain.

**51. Employee Salaries** The following statistics represent weekly salaries at the Midtown Construction Company:

| Mean | $600 | First quartile | $560 |
|------|------|----------------|------|
| Median | $590 | Third quartile | $625 |
| Mode | $580 | 83rd percentile | $665 |

a) What is the most common salary?

b) What salary did half the employees' salaries surpass?

c) About what percent of employees' salaries surpassed $625?

d) About what percent of employees' salaries were less than $560?

e) About what percent of employees' salaries surpassed $665?

f) If the company has 100 employees, what is the total weekly salary of all employees?

## Challenge Problems/Group Activities

**52. The Mean of the Means** Consider the following five sets of values.

i) 5  6  7  7  8  9  14

ii) 3  6  8  9

iii) 1  1  1  2  5

iv) 6  8  9  12  15

v) 50  51  55  60  80  100

a) Compute the mean of each of the five sets of data.

b) Compute the mean of the five means in part (a).

c) Find the mean of the 27 pieces of data.

d) Compare your answer in part (b) to your answer in part (c). Are the values the same? Does your answer make sense?

**53. *Ruth Versus Mantle*** The tables below compare the batting performances for selected years for two well-known former baseball players, Babe Ruth and Mickey Mantle.

Babe Ruth
Boston Red Sox 1914–1919
New York Yankees 1920–1934

| Year | At Bats | Hits | Pct. |
|------|---------|------|------|
| 1925 | 359 | 104 | |
| 1930 | 518 | 186 | |
| 1933 | 459 | 138 | |
| 1916 | 136 | 37 | |
| 1922 | 406 | 128 | |
| Total | 1878 | 593 | |

Mickey Mantle
New York Yankees 1951–1968

| Year | At Bats | Hits | Pct. |
|------|---------|------|------|
| 1954 | 543 | 163 | |
| 1957 | 474 | 173 | |
| 1958 | 519 | 158 | |
| 1960 | 527 | 145 | |
| 1962 | 377 | 121 | |
| Total | 2440 | 760 | |

**a)** For each player, compute the batting average percent (pct.) for each year by dividing the number of hits by the number of at bats. Round to the nearest thousandth. Place the answers in the pct. column.

**b)** Going across each of the five horizontal lines (for example Ruth, 1925, vs. Mantle, 1954), compare the percents (pct.) and determine which is greater in each case.

**c)** For each player, compute the mean batting average percent for the 5 given years by dividing the total hits by the total at bats. Which is greater, Ruth's or Mantle's?

**d)** Based on your answer in part (b), does your answer in part (c) make sense? Explain.

**e)** Find the mean percent for each player by adding the five pcts. and dividing by 5. Which is greater, Ruth's or Mantle's?

**f)** Why do the answers obtained in parts (c) and (e) differ? Explain.

**g)** Who would you say has the better batting average percent for the 5 years selected? Explain.

**54. *Employee Salaries*** The following table gives the annual salary distribution for employees at Kulzer's Home Improvement.

| Annual Salary | Number Receiving Salary |
|---------------|-------------------------|
| $100,000 | 1 |
| 85,000 | 2 |
| 24,000 | 6 |
| 21,000 | 4 |
| 18,000 | 5 |
| 17,000 | 7 |

Using the information provided in the table, determine the

**a)** mean annual salary.

**b)** median annual salary.

**c)** mode annual salary.

**d)** midrange annual salary.

**e)** Which is the best measure of central tendency for this set of data? Explain your answer.

*Weighted Average* Sometimes when we wish to find an average, we may wish to assign more importance, or weight, to some of the pieces of data. To calculate a *weighted average*, we use the formula: *weighted average* $= \dfrac{\Sigma xw}{\Sigma w}$, where *w is the weight of the piece of data, x;* $\Sigma xw$ *is the sum of the products of each piece of data multiplied by its weight; and* $\Sigma w$ *is the sum of the weights. For example, suppose that students in a class need to submit a report* *that counts for 20% of their grade, they need to take a midterm exam that counts for 30% of their grade, and they need to take a final exam that counts for 50% of their grade. Suppose that a student got a 72 on the report, an 85 on the midterm exam, and a 93 on the final exam. To determine this student's weighted average, first find $\Sigma xw$:*

$$\Sigma xw = 72(0.20) + 85(0.30) + 93(0.50) = 86.4.$$

*Next find $\Sigma w$, the sum of the weights: $\Sigma w = 0.20 + 0.30 + 0.50 = 1.00$. Now determine the weighted average as follows.*

$$Weighted\ average = \frac{\Sigma xw}{\Sigma w} = \frac{86.4}{1.00} = 86.4$$

*Thus, the weighted average is 86.4. Note that $\Sigma w$ does not always have to be 1.00. In Exercises 55 and 56, use the weighted average formula.*

55. *Course Average* Suppose that your final grade for a course is determined by a midterm exam and a final exam. The midterm exam is worth 40% of your grade, and the final exam is worth 60%. If your midterm exam grade is 84 and your final exam grade is 94, calculate your final average.

56. *Grade Point Average* In a four-point grade system, an A corresponds to 4.0 points, a B corresponds to 3.0 points, a C corresponds to 2.0 points, and a D corresponds to 1.0 points. No points are awarded for an F. Last semester, Tanya Reeves received a B in a four-credit hour course, an A in a three-credit hour course, a C in a three-credit hour course, and an A in another three-credit hour course. Grade point average (GPA) is calculated as a weighted average using the credit hours as weights and the number

of points corresponding to the grade as pieces of data. Calculate Tanya's GPA for the previous semester. (Round your answer to the nearest hundredth.)

## Recreational Mathematics

57. *Your Exam Average* **a)** Calculate the mean, median, mode, and midrange of your exam grades in your mathematics course.

   **b)** Which measure of central tendency best represents your average grade?

   **c)** Which measure of central tendency would you rather use as your average grade?

58. *Purchases* Matthew Riveria purchased some items at Staples each day for five days. The mode of the number of items Matthew purchased is higher than the median of the number of items he purchased. The median of the number of items Matthew purchased is higher than the mean of the number of items he purchased. He purchased at least two items but no more than seven items each day.

   **a)** How many items did Matthew purchase each day? (*Note:* There is more than one correct answer.)

   **b)** Determine the mean, median, and mode for your answer to part (a).

## Internet/Research Activity

59. Two other measures of location that we did not mention in this section are *stanines* and *deciles*. Use statistics books, books on educational testing and measurements, and Internet Web sites to write a report on what stanines and deciles are and when percentiles, quartiles, stanines, and deciles are used.

---

## SECTION 13.5  Measures of Dispersion

▲ *The average life span of a tablet PC battery may not be enough information to make a sound purchasing decision.*

Measures of central tendency by themselves do not always give sufficient information to analyze a situation and make decisions. For example, suppose Apple Computer is considering two companies to produce batteries for its iPads. Testing shows that Company A batteries have a mean life of 10 hours. Company B batteries have a mean life of 9.5 hours. If both manufacturers' batteries cost the same, which one should be purchased? The average battery life may not be the most important factor. If half of Company A batteries last only 5 hours, while half last 15 hours, there is a large variability in the life of the batteries. If all of Company B batteries last between 9.0 and 10.0 hours, the batteries are more consistent and reliable. This example illustrates the importance of knowing something about the *spread*, or *variability*, of the data. In this section we will discuss two measures of variability or dispersion.

*Why* *This is Important* Knowing the spread, or variability of a set of data helps us make accurate conclusions about the set of data.

*Measures of dispersion* are used to measure the variability of the data, including the *spread of the data*, and how the data varies about the mean. The range and standard deviation* are the measures of dispersion that will be discussed in this section.

## Range and Standard Deviation

The *range* is the difference between the highest and lowest values; it indicates the total spread of the data.

### Range
The range of a set of data can be calculated using the following formula.

$$\textbf{Range} = \text{highest value} - \text{lowest value}$$

### Example 1  *Determine the Range*

The amount of caffeine, in milligrams, of 10 different soft drinks is given below. Determine the range of these data.

$$38, 43, 26, 80, 55, 34, 40, 30, 35, 43$$

Solution   Range = highest value − lowest value = 80 − 26 = 54. The range of the amounts of caffeine is 54 milligrams.                                                    ■

The second measure of dispersion we discuss in this section, the *standard deviation*, measures how much the data *differ from the mean*. It is symbolized either by the letter *s* or by the Greek letter sigma, $\sigma$.[†] The *s* is used when the standard deviation of a *sample* is calculated. The $\sigma$ is used when the standard deviation of the entire *population* is calculated. *Since we are assuming that all data presented in this section are for samples, we use s to represent the standard deviation* (note, however, that on the height and weight charts on page 814, $\sigma$ is used).

The larger the variability of the data about the mean, the larger the standard deviation is. Consider the following two sets of data.

$$5, 8, 9, 10, 12, 13 \qquad 8, 9, 9, 10, 10, 11$$

Both have a mean of 9.5. Which set of values on the whole do you believe differs less from the mean of 9.5? Figure 13.16 may make the answer more apparent. The scores in the second set of data are closer to the mean and therefore have a smaller standard deviation. You will soon be able to verify such relationships yourself.

Sometimes only a very small standard deviation is desirable or acceptable. Consider a cereal box that is to contain 8 oz of cereal. If the amount of cereal put into the boxes varies too much—sometimes underfilling, sometimes overfilling—the manufacturer will soon be in trouble with consumer groups and government agencies.

At other times, a larger spread of data is desirable or expected. For example, intelligence quotients (IQs) are expected to exhibit a considerable spread about the

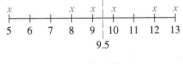

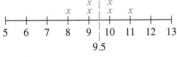

Figure 13.16

---

*Variance*, another measure of dispersion, is the square of the standard deviation.

[†]Our alphabet uses both uppercase and lowercase letters, for example, *A* and *a*. The Greek alphabet also uses both uppercase and lowercase letters. The symbol $\Sigma$ is the capital Greek letter sigma, and $\sigma$ is the lowercase Greek letter sigma.

mean because everyone is different. The following procedure explains how we determine the standard deviation of a set of data.

---

**PROCEDURE**   **TO DETERMINE THE STANDARD DEVIATION OF A SET OF DATA**

1. Determine the mean of the set of data.
2. Make a chart having three columns:

$$\text{Data} \quad \text{Data} - \text{Mean} \quad (\text{Data} - \text{Mean})^2$$

3. List the data vertically under the column marked Data.
4. Subtract the mean from each piece of data and place the difference in the Data − Mean column.
5. Square the values obtained in the Data − Mean column and record these values in the (Data − Mean)$^2$ column.
6. Determine the sum of the values in the (Data − Mean)$^2$ column.
7. Divide the sum obtained in Step 6 by $n - 1$, where $n$ is the number of pieces of data.*
8. Determine the square root of the number obtained in Step 7. This number is the standard deviation of the set of data.

---

Example 2 illustrates the procedure to follow to determine the standard deviation of a set of data.

## Example 2  *Determine the Standard Deviation*

A veterinarian in an animal hospital recorded the following life spans of selected Labrador retrievers (to the nearest year):

$$7, 9, 11, 15, 18, 12$$

Determine the standard deviation of the life spans.

*Solution*   First determine the mean:

$$\bar{x} = \frac{\Sigma x}{n} = \frac{7 + 9 + 11 + 15 + 18 + 12}{6} = \frac{72}{6} = 12$$

Next construct a table with three columns, as illustrated in Table 13.4 on page 810, and list the data in the first column (it is often helpful to list the data in ascending or descending order). Complete the second column by subtracting the mean, 12 in this case, from each piece of data in the first column.

The sum of the values in the Data − Mean column should always be zero; if not, you have made an error. (If a rounded value of $\bar{x}$ is used, the sum of the values in the Data − Mean column will not always be exactly zero; however, the sum will be very close to zero.)

---

*To determine the standard deviation of a sample, divide the sum of (Data − Mean)$^2$ column by $n - 1$. To find the standard deviation of a population, divide the sum by $n$. In this book, we assume that the set of data represents a sample and divide by $n - 1$. The quotient obtained in Step 7 represents a measure of dispersion called the *variance*.

Table 13.4

| Data | Data − Mean | (Data − Mean)$^2$ |
|---|---|---|
| 7 | $7 - 12 = -5$ | |
| 9 | $9 - 12 = -3$ | |
| 11 | $11 - 12 = -1$ | |
| 12 | $12 - 12 = 0$ | |
| 15 | $15 - 12 = 3$ | |
| 18 | $18 - 12 = 6$ | |
| | 0 | |

Next square the values in the second column and place the squares in the third column (Table 13.5).

Table 13.5

| Data | Data − Mean | (Data − Mean)$^2$ |
|---|---|---|
| 7 | −5 | $(-5)^2 = (-5)(-5) = 25$ |
| 9 | −3 | $(-3)^2 = (-3)(-3) = 9$ |
| 11 | −1 | $(-1)^2 = (-1)(-1) = 1$ |
| 12 | 0 | $(0)^2 = (0)(0) = 0$ |
| 15 | 3 | $(3)^2 = (3)(3) = 9$ |
| 18 | 6 | $(6)^2 = (6)(6) = 36$ |
| | 0 | 80 |

Add the squares in the third column. In this case, the sum is 80. Divide this sum by one less than the number of pieces of data ($n - 1$). In this case, the number of pieces of data is 6. Therefore, we divide by 5 and get

$$\frac{80}{5} = 16*$$

Finally, take the square root of this number. Since $\sqrt{16} = 4$, the standard deviation, symbolized $s$, is 4. ∎

Now we will develop a formula for determining the standard deviation of a set of data. If we call the individual data $x$ and the mean $\bar{x}$, we could write the three column heads Data, Data − Mean, and (Data − Mean)$^2$ in Table 13.4 as

$$x \qquad x - \bar{x} \qquad (x - \bar{x})^2$$

Let's follow the procedure we used to obtain the standard deviation in Example 2. We found the sum of the (Data − Mean)$^2$ column, which is the same as the sum of the $(x - \bar{x})^2$ column. We can represent the sum of the $(x - \bar{x})^2$ column by using the summation notation, $\Sigma(x - \bar{x})^2$. Thus, in Table 13.5, $\Sigma(x - \bar{x})^2 = 80$. We then divided this number by 1 less than the number of pieces of data, $n - 1$. Thus, we have

$$\frac{\Sigma(x - \bar{x})^2}{n - 1}$$

---

*16 is the variance, symbolized $s^2$, of this set of data.

Finally, we took the square root of this value to obtain the standard deviation.

## Standard Deviation

The standard deviation, $s$, of a set of data can be calculated using the following formula.

$$s = \sqrt{\frac{\Sigma(x - \bar{x})^2}{n - 1}}$$

## Example 3  *Determine the Standard Deviation of Stock Prices*

The following are the prices of nine stocks on the New York Stock Exchange. Determine the standard deviation of the prices.

$$\$17, \$28, \$32, \$36, \$50, \$52, \$66, \$74, \$104$$

**Solution** The mean, $\bar{x}$, is

$$\bar{x} = \frac{\Sigma x}{n} = \frac{17 + 28 + 32 + 36 + 50 + 52 + 66 + 74 + 104}{9} = \frac{459}{9} = 51$$

The mean is $51.

Table 13.6

| $x$ | $x - \bar{x}$ | $(x - \bar{x})^2$ |
|---|---|---|
| 17 | −34 | 1156 |
| 28 | −23 | 529 |
| 32 | −19 | 361 |
| 36 | −15 | 225 |
| 50 | −1 | 1 |
| 52 | 1 | 1 |
| 66 | 15 | 225 |
| 74 | 23 | 529 |
| 104 | 53 | 2809 |
| | 0 | 5836 |

Table 13.6 shows us that $\Sigma(x - \bar{x})^2 = 5836$. Since there are nine pieces of data, $n - 1 = 9 - 1$, or 8.

$$s = \sqrt{\frac{\Sigma(x - \bar{x})^2}{n - 1}} = \sqrt{\frac{5836}{8}} = \sqrt{729.5} \approx 27.01$$

The standard deviation, to the nearest tenth, is $27.01.

Standard deviation will be used in Section 13.6 to find the percent of data between any two values in a normal curve. Standard deviations are also often used in determining norms for a population (see Exercise 29).

---

**TECHNOLOGY TIP**

In this *Technology Tip*, we will explain how to find the standard deviation using Excel as well as with the TI-83 Plus and TI-84 Plus graphing calculators. In our illustration, we will use the data from Example 3 on page 811, which represent the prices of nine stocks on the New York Stock Exchange.

**EXCEL**
The instructions used to determine the standard deviation are very similar to those used to determine the mean in the *Technology Tip* on page 802 in Section 13.4. Please read that material now. Then enter the nine piece of data in columns A1–A9 and press the Enter key. Now select the following:

Insert  >  Function …  >  Statistical  >  STDEV

Then click the OK box. The program will then generate a gray box where you need to enter the data. In the area to the right of **Number1** you need to enter the data for which you want to find the standard deviation. Since you have already entered the data in column A, rows 1 to 9, if A1:A9 is not already listed, you can enter A1:A9 in the area to the right of **Number1.** At the bottom of the gray box, *Formula Results* = 27.00925767, which is the standard deviation, is displayed. If you click OK, Excel will place the standard deviation in cell A10.

**TI-83 PLUS AND TI-84 PLUS GRAPHING CALCULATORS**
To find the standard deviation on Texas Instruments graphing calculators, follow the instructions for finding the mean in the *Technology Tip* on page 802 in Section 13.4. As explained there, press STAT > EDIT > ENTER. Remove existing data by highlighting **L1** and then pressing CLEAR > ENTER. Then enter the nine pieces of data, pressing the Enter key after each entry. Then press STAT > CALC > ENTER > ENTER. The fourth statistic down is $S_x$ = 27.00925767. This value is the standard deviation.

---

## SECTION 13.5
### Exercises

### Warm Up Exercises

*In Exercises 1–6, fill in the blank with an appropriate word, phrase, or symbol(s).*

**1.** Measures of dispersion are used to indicate the spread or _____ of the data.

**2.** The difference between the highest and lowest values in a set of data is called the _____.

**3.** The measure of dispersion that measures how much the data differ from the mean is called the _____.

**4.** The symbol, $\sigma$, is used to indicate the standard deviation of a(n) _____.

**5.** The symbol, $s$, is used to indicate the standard deviation of a(n) _____.

**6.** The standard deviation of a set of data in which all the data values are the same is _____.

### Practice the Skills

*In Exercises 7–14, determine the range and standard deviation of the set of data. When appropriate, round standard deviations to the nearest hundredth.*

**7.** 11, 9, 6, 12, 17

**8.** 15, 15, 19, 21, 13, 13

**9.** 130, 131, 132, 133, 134, 135, 136

**10.** 3, 7, 8, 12, 0, 9, 11, 12, 6, 2

**11.** 4, 8, 9, 11, 13, 15

**12.** 9, 9, 9, 9, 9, 9, 9

**13.** 7, 9, 7, 9, 9, 10, 12

**14.** 60, 58, 62, 67, 48, 51, 72, 70

## Problem Solving

15. **Digital Cameras** Determine the range and standard deviation of the following prices of selected digital cameras: $158, $95, $175, $180, $95, $129, $228, $300.

16. **Years Until Retirement** Seven employees at a large company were asked the number of additional years they planned to work before retirement. Their responses were 10, 23, 28, 4, 1, 6, 12. Determine the range and standard deviation of the number of years.

17. **Camping Tents** Determine the range and standard deviation of the following prices of selected camping tents: $109, $60, $80, $60, $210, $250, $60, $100, $115.

18. **Prescription Prices** The amount of money seven people spent on prescription medication in a year are as follows: $600, $100, $850, $350, $250, $140, $300. Determine the range and standard deviation of the amounts.

19. Can you think of any situations in which a large standard deviation may be desirable?

20. Can you think of any situations in which a small standard deviation may be desirable?

21. Without actually doing the calculations, decide which, if either, of the following two sets of data will have the greater standard deviation. Explain why.

    10, 13, 14, 15, 17, 21     16, 17, 17, 18, 18, 19

22. Without actually doing the calculations, decide which, if either, of the following two sets of data will have the greater standard deviation. Explain why.

    2, 4, 6, 8, 10     102, 104, 106, 108, 110

23. By studying the standard deviation formula, explain why the standard deviation of a set of data will always be greater than or equal to 0.

24. Patricia Wolff teaches two statistics classes, one in the morning and the other in the evening. On the midterm exam, the morning class had a mean of 75.2 and a standard deviation of 5.7. The evening class had a mean of 75.2 and a standard deviation of 12.5.

    a) How do the means compare?

    b) If we compare the set of scores from the first class with those in the second class, how will the distributions of the two sets of scores compare?

25. **Count Your Money** Six people were asked to determine the amount of money they were carrying, to the nearest dollar. The results were

    $32, $60, $14, $25, $5, $68

    a) Determine the range and standard deviation of the amounts.

    b) Add $10 to each of the six amounts. How do you expect the range and standard deviation of the new set of data to change?

    c) Determine the range and standard deviation of the new set of data. Do the results agree with your answer to part (b)? If not, explain why.

26. a) **Adding to or Subtracting from Each Number** Pick any five numbers. Compute the mean and the standard deviation of this distribution.

    b) Add 20 to each of the numbers in your original distribution and compute the mean and the standard deviation of this new distribution.

    c) Subtract 5 from each number in your original distribution and compute the mean and standard deviation of this new distribution.

    d) What conclusions can you draw about changes in the mean and the standard deviation when the same number is added to or subtracted from each piece of data in a distribution?

    e) How will the mean and standard deviation of the numbers 8, 9, 10, 11, 12, 13, 14 differ from the mean and standard deviation of the numbers 648, 649, 650, 651, 652, 653, 654? Determine the mean and standard deviation of both sets of numbers.

27. a) **Multiplying Each Number** Pick any five numbers. Compute the mean and standard deviation of this distribution.

    b) Multiply each number in your distribution by 3 and compute the mean and the standard deviation of this new distribution.

    c) Multiply each number in your original distribution by 9 and compute the mean and the standard deviation of this new distribution.

**d)** What conclusions can you draw about changes in the mean and the standard deviation when each value in a distribution is multiplied by the same number?

**e)** The mean and standard deviation of the distribution 1, 3, 4, 4, 5, 7 are 4 and 2, respectively. Use the conclusion drawn in part (d) to determine the mean and standard deviation of the distribution

5, 15, 20, 20, 25, 35

**28.** *Waiting in Line* Consider the following illustrations of two bank-customer waiting systems.

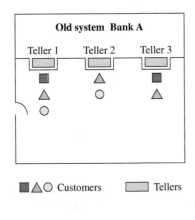

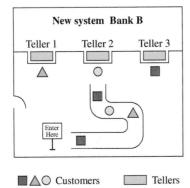

**a)** How would you expect the mean waiting time in Bank A to compare with the mean waiting time in Bank B?

**b)** How would you expect the standard deviation of waiting times in Bank A to compare with the standard deviation of waiting times in Bank B?

**29.** *Height and Weight Distribution* The chart shown on the right uses the symbol $\sigma$ to represent the standard deviation. Note that $2\sigma$ represents the value that is two standard deviations above the mean; $-2\sigma$ represents the value that is two standard deviations below the mean. The unshaded areas, from two standard deviations below the mean to two standard deviations above the mean, are considered the normal range. For example, the average (mean) 8-year-old boy has a height of about 50 inches, but any heights between approximately 45 inches and 55 inches are considered normal for 8-year-old boys. Refer to the chart below to answer the following questions.

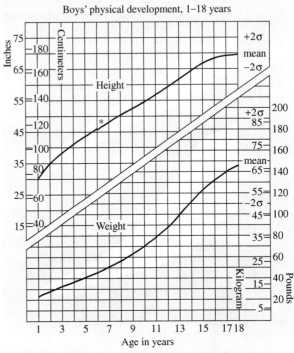

*Supine length to 6 years, standing height from 6 to 18 years

**a)** What happens to the standard deviation for weights of boys as the age of boys increases? What is the significance of this fact?

**b)** At age 16, what is the mean weight, in pounds, of boys?

**c)** What is the approximate standard deviation of boys' weights at age 16?

**d)** Determine the mean weight and normal range for boys at age 13.

**e)** Determine the mean height and normal range for boys at age 13.

**f)** Assuming that this chart was constructed so that approximately 95% of all boys are always in the normal range, determine what percentage of boys are not in the normal range.

## Challenge Problems/Group Activities

**30.** *Athletes' Salaries* The tables on page 815 list the 10 highest-paid athletes in Major League Baseball and in the National Football League.

Major League Baseball (2010 Season)

| Player | Salary (millions of dollars) |
|---|---|
| 1. Alex Rodriguez | 33.0 |
| 2. C. C. Sabathia | 24.3 |
| 3. Derek Jeter | 22.6 |
| 4. Mark Teixeira | 20.6 |
| 5. Johan Santana | 20.1 |
| 6. Miguel Cabrera | 20.0 |
| 7. Carlos Beltran | 19.4 |
| 8. Ryan Howard | 19.0 |
| 9. Carlos Lee | 19.0 |
| 10. Alfonso Soriano | 19.0 |

Source: Major League Baseball Players Association

National Football League (2009–2010 season)

| Player | Salary (millions of dollars) |
|---|---|
| 1. Philip Rivers | 25.6 |
| 2. Jay Cutler | 22.0 |
| 3. Eli Manning | 20.5 |
| 4. Kurt Warner | 19.0 |
| 5. Kelvin Hayden | 17.5 |
| 6. Matt Schaub | 17.0 |
| 7. Julius Peppers | 16.7 |
| 8. Chris Long | 16.6 |
| 9. Greg Jennings | 16.3 |
| 10. Antonio Smith | 15.5 |

Source: National Football League Players Association

a) Without doing any calculations, which do you believe is greater, the mean salary of the 10 baseball players or the mean salary of the 10 football players?

b) Without doing any calculations, which do you believe is greater, the standard deviation of the salary of the 10 baseball players or the standard deviation of the salary of the 10 football players?

c) Compute the mean salary of the 10 baseball players and the mean salary of the 10 football players and determine whether your answer in part (a) was correct.

d) Compute the standard deviation of the salary of the 10 baseball players and the standard deviation of the salary of the 10 football players and determine whether your answer in part (b) is correct. Round each mean to the nearest tenth to determine the standard deviation.

31. *Oil Change* Jiffy Lube has franchises in two different parts of a city. The number of oil changes made daily, for 25 days, is given below.

| East Store | | | | | West Store | | | | |
|---|---|---|---|---|---|---|---|---|---|
| 33 | 59 | 27 | 30 | 42 | 38 | 46 | 38 | 38 | 30 |
| 19 | 42 | 25 | 22 | 32 | 38 | 38 | 37 | 39 | 31 |
| 43 | 27 | 57 | 37 | 52 | 39 | 36 | 40 | 37 | 47 |
| 40 | 67 | 38 | 44 | 43 | 30 | 34 | 42 | 45 | 29 |
| 15 | 31 | 49 | 41 | 35 | 31 | 46 | 28 | 45 | 48 |

a) Construct a frequency distribution for each store with a first class of 15–20.

b) Draw a histogram for each store.

c) Using the histogram, determine which store appears to have a greater mean, or do the means appear about the same? Explain.

d) Using the histogram, determine which store appears to have the greater standard deviation. Explain.

e) Calculate the mean for each store and determine whether your answer in part (c) was correct.

f) Calculate the standard deviation for each store and determine whether your answer in part (d) was correct.

## Recreational Mathematics

32. Calculate the range and standard deviation of your exam grades in this mathematics course. Round the mean to the nearest tenth to calculate the standard deviation.

33. Construct a set of five pieces of data with a mean, median, mode, and midrange of 6 and a standard deviation of 0.

## Internet/Research Activity

34. Use a calculator with statistical function keys to find the mean and standard deviation of the salaries of the 10 Major League Baseball players and the 10 National Football League players in Exercise 30.

# SECTION 13.6    The Normal Curve

▲ Some sets of data, such as exam grades, may form a bell-shaped distribution.

Suppose your mathematics teacher states that exam scores for the previous exam followed a bell-shaped distribution and that your score was 1.5 standard deviations above the mean. How does your exam grade compare with the exam grades of your classmates? What percentage of students in your class had exam grades below your exam grade? In this section, we will discuss sets of data that form bell-shaped distributions and learn how to determine the percentage of data that fall below a particular piece of data in the set of data.

*Why* *This is Important* There are many real-life applications, such as IQ scores, heights and weights of males, heights and weights of females, and wearout mileage of automobile tires, that have a bell-shaped distribution.

When examining data using a histogram, we can refer to the overall appearance of the histogram as the *shape* of the distribution of the data. Certain shapes of distributions of data are more common than others. In this section, we will illustrate and discuss a few of the more common ones. In each case, the vertical scale is the frequency and the horizontal scale is the observed values.

In a *rectangular distribution* (Fig. 13.17), all the observed values occur with the same frequency. If a die is rolled many times, we would expect the numbers 1–6 to occur with about the same frequency. The distribution representing the outcomes of the die is rectangular.

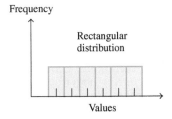

Figure 13.17

In *J-shaped distributions*, the frequency is either constantly increasing (Fig. 13.18(a)) or constantly decreasing (Fig. 13.18(b)). The number of hours studied per week by students may have a distribution like that in Fig. 13.18(b). The bars might represent (from left to right) 0–5 hours, 6–10 hours, 11–15 hours, and so on.

**J-shaped Distributions**

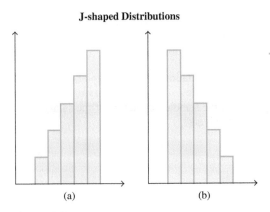

Figure 13.18

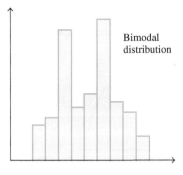

Figure 13.19

A *bimodal distribution* (Fig. 13.19) is one in which two nonadjacent values occur more frequently than any other values in a set of data. For example, if an equal number of men and women were weighed, the distribution of their weights would probably be bimodal, with one mode for the women's weights and the second for the men's weights. For a distribution to be considered bimodal, both modes need not have the same frequency but they must both have a frequency greater than the frequency of each of the other values in the distribution.

The life expectancy of lightbulbs has a bimodal distribution: a small peak very near 0 hours of life, resulting from the bulbs that burned out very quickly because of a manufacturing defect, and a much higher peak representing the nondefective bulbs. A bimodal frequency distribution generally means that you are dealing with two distinct populations, in this case, defective and nondefective lightbulbs.

Another distribution, called a *skewed distribution*, has more of a "tail" on one side than the other. A skewed distribution with a tail on the right (Fig. 13.20(a)) is said to be skewed to the right. If the tail is on the left (Fig. 13.20(b)), the distribution is referred to as skewed to the left.

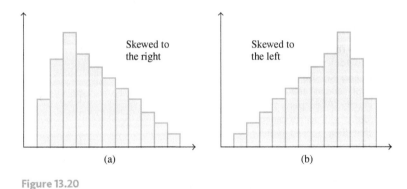

Figure 13.20

The number of children per family might be a distribution skewed to the right. Some families have no children, more families may have one child, the greatest percentage may have two children, fewer may have three children, still fewer may have four children, and so on.

Since few families have high incomes, distributions of family incomes might be skewed to the right.

Smoothing the histograms of the skewed distributions shown in Fig. 13.20 to form curves gives the curves illustrated in Fig. 13.21.

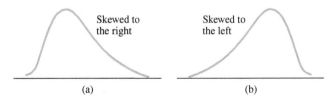

Figure 13.21

In Fig. 13.21(a), the greatest frequency appears on the left side of the curve and the frequency decreases from left to right. Since the mode is the value with the greatest frequency, the mode would appear on the left side of the curve.

Every value in the set of data is considered in determining the mean. The values on the far right side of the curve in Fig. 13.21(a) would tend to increase the value of the mean. Thus, the value of the mean would be farther to the right than the mode.

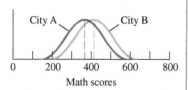
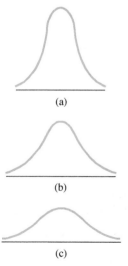

Figure 13.24

The median would be between the mode and the mean. The relationship between the mean, median, and mode for curves that are skewed to the right and left is given in Fig. 13.22.

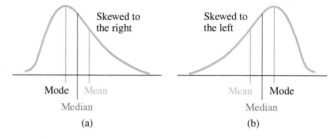

Figure 13.22

## Normal Distributions

Each of these distributions is useful in describing sets of data. However, the most important distribution is the *normal* or *Gaussian distribution*, named for German mathematician Carl Friedrich Gauss. The histogram of a normal distribution is illustrated in Fig. 13.23.

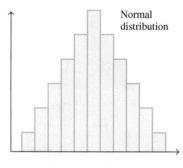

Figure 13.23

The normal distribution is important because many sets of data are normally distributed or closely resemble a normal distribution. Such distributions include intelligence quotients, heights and weights of males, heights and weights of females, lengths of full-grown boa constrictors, weights of watermelons, wearout mileage of automobile brakes, and life spans of refrigerators, to name just a few.

The normal distribution is symmetric about the mean. If you were to fold the histogram of a normal distribution down the middle, the left side would fit the right side exactly. **In a normal distribution, the mean, median, and mode all have the same value.**

When the histogram of a normal distribution is smoothed to form a curve, the curve is bell-shaped. The bell may be high and narrow or short and wide. Each of the three curves in Fig. 13.24 represents a normal curve. Curve 13.24(a) has the smallest standard deviation (spread from the mean); curve 13.24(c) has the largest.

### Properties of a Normal Distribution
- The graph of a normal distribution is called a normal curve.
- The normal curve is bell-shaped and symmetric about the mean.
- The mean, median, and mode of a normal distribution all have the same value and all occur at the center of the distribution.

Since the curve representing the normal distribution is symmetric, 50% of the data always falls above (to the right of) the mean and 50% of the data falls below (to the left of) the mean. In addition, every normal distribution has approximately 68% of the data between the value that is one standard deviation below the mean, and the value that is one standard deviation above the mean, see Fig. 13.25. Approximately 95% of the data falls between the value that is two standard deviations below the mean and the value that is two standard deviations above the mean. Approximately 99.7% of the data falls between the value that is three standard deviations below the mean, and the value that is three standard deviations above the mean. These three percentages, 68%, 95%, and 99.7%, are used in what is referred to as the *empirical rule*.

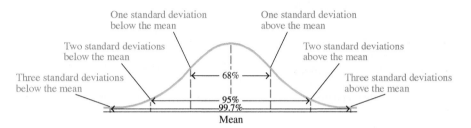

**Figure 13.25**

Thus, if a normal distribution has a mean of 100 and a standard deviation of 10, then approximately 68% of all the data falls between $100 - 10$ and $100 + 10$, or between 90 and 110. Approximately 95% of the data falls between $100 - 20$ and $100 + 20$, or between 80 and 120, and approximately 99.7% of the data falls between $100 - 30$, and $100 + 30$, or between 70 and 130.

The empirical rule is summarized as follows.

### Empirical Rule
In any normal distribution.
- Approximately 68% of all the data lies within one standard deviation of the mean (in both directions).
- Approximately 95% of all the data lies within two standard deviations of the mean (in both directions).
- Approximately 99.7% of all the data lies within three standard deviations of the mean (in both directions).

### Example 1  *Applying the Empirical Rule*

The cholesterol levels for females are normally distributed. In a random sample of 500 females, determine the approximate number of females in the sample who are expected to have a cholesterol level

a) within one standard deviation of the mean.

b) within two standard deviations of the mean.

*Solution*

a) By the empirical rule, about 68% of females have a cholesterol level within one standard deviation of the mean. Since there are 500 females in the sample, the number of females expected to have a cholesterol level within one standard deviation of the mean is

$$68\% \times 500 = 0.68 \times 500 = 340$$

Therefore, about 340 females are expected to have a cholesterol level within one standard deviation of the mean.

b) By the empirical rule, about 95% of females have a cholesterol level within two standard deviations the mean. Since there are 500 females in the sample, the number of females expected to have a cholesterol level within two standard deviations of the mean is

$$95\% \times 500 = 0.95 \times 500 = 475$$

Therefore, about 475 females are expected to have a cholesterol level within two standard deviations of the mean. ∎

## z-Scores

Now we turn our attention to z-scores. We use *z-scores* (or *standard scores*) to determine how far, in terms of standard deviations, a given data value is from the mean of the distribution. For example, a data value that has a z-score of 1.5 indicates the data value is 1.5 standard deviations above the mean. The standard score or z-score is calculated as follows.

### z-Scores or Standard Scores
The formula for finding *z*-scores or standard scores is

$$z = \frac{\text{value of the piece of data} - \text{mean}}{\text{standard deviation}}$$

In this book, the notation $z_x$ represents the z-score, or standard score, of the value $x$. For example, if a normal distribution has a mean of 86 with a standard deviation of 12, a score of 110 has a standard score or z-score of

$$z_{110} = \frac{110 - 86}{12} = \frac{24}{12} = 2$$

Therefore, a value of 110 in this distribution has a z-score of 2 and is two standard deviations above the mean.

Data below the mean will always have negative z-scores; data above the mean will always have positive z-scores. The mean will always have a z-score of 0.

### Example 2 *Finding z-Scores*

A normal distribution has a mean of 80 and a standard deviation of 10. Determine z-scores for the following values.

a) 90      b) 95      c) 80      d) 64

**Solution**

a)

$$z = \frac{\text{value} - \text{mean}}{\text{standard deviation}}$$

$$z_{90} = \frac{90 - 80}{10} = \frac{10}{10} = 1$$

A value of 90 has a $z$-score of 1. Therefore, a value of 90 is one standard deviation above the mean.

b)
$$z_{95} = \frac{95 - 80}{10} = \frac{15}{10} = 1.5$$

A value of 95 has a $z$-score of 1.5, and is 1.5 standard deviations above the mean.

c)
$$z_{80} = \frac{80 - 80}{10} = \frac{0}{10} = 0$$

The mean always has a $z$-score of 0.

d)
$$z_{64} = \frac{64 - 80}{10} = \frac{-16}{10} = -1.6$$

A value of 64 has a $z$-score of $-1.6$, and is 1.6 standard deviations below the mean. ∎

If we are given any normal distribution with a known mean and standard deviation, it is possible through the use of Table 13.7 on pages 822 and 823 (the $z$-table) to determine the percent of data between any two given values. The total area under any normal curve is 1.00. Table 13.7 will be used to determine the cumulative area under the normal curve that lies to the *left of a specified z-score*. We will use Table 13.7(a) when we wish to determine area to the left of a *negative z-score*, and we will use Table 13.7(b) when we wish to determine area to the left of a *positive z-score*.

Example 3 illustrates the procedure to follow when using Table 13.7 to determine the area under the normal curve. When you are determining the area under the normal curve, it is often helpful to draw a picture and shade the area to be determined.

┌ Example **3** *Determining the Area Under the Normal Curve*

Determine the area under the normal curve
a) to the left of $z = -1.00$.
b) to the left of $z = 1.19$.
c) to the right of $z = 1.19$.
d) between $z = -1.62$ and $z = 2.57$.

*Solution*

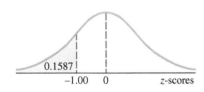

Figure 13.26

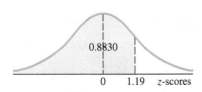

Figure 13.27

a) To determine the area under the normal curve to the left of $z = -1.00$, as illustrated in Fig. 13.26, we use Table 13.7(a) since we are looking for an area to the left of a negative $z$-score. In the upper-left corner of the table, we see the letter $z$. The column under $z$ gives the units and the tenths value for $z$. To locate the hundredths value of $z$, we use the column headings to the right of $z$. In this case, the hundredths value of $z = -1.00$ is 0, so we use the first column labeled .00. To determine the area to the left of $z = -1.00$, we use the row labeled $-1.0$ and move to the column labeled .00. The table entry, .1587, is circled in blue. Therefore, the total area to the left of $z = -1.00$ is 0.1587

b) To determine the area under the normal curve to the left of $z = 1.19$ (Fig. 13.27), we use Table 13.7(b) since we are looking for an area to the left of a positive $z$-score. We first look for 1.1 in the column under $z$. Since the hundredths value

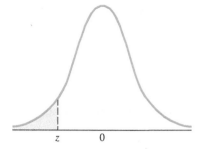

Table entry for $z$ is the area to the left of $z$.

**Table 13.7** Areas of a Standard Normal Distribution

**(a) Table of Areas to the Left of $z$ When $z$ is Negative**

| $z$ | .00 | .01 | .02 | .03 | .04 | .05 | .06 | .07 | .08 | .09 |
|------|------|------|------|------|------|------|------|------|------|------|
| −3.4 | .0003 | .0003 | .0003 | .0003 | .0003 | .0003 | .0003 | .0003 | .0003 | .0002 |
| −3.3 | .0005 | .0005 | .0005 | .0004 | .0004 | .0004 | .0004 | .0004 | .0004 | .0003 |
| −3.2 | .0007 | .0007 | .0006 | .0006 | .0006 | .0006 | .0006 | .0005 | .0005 | .0005 |
| −3.1 | .0010 | .0009 | .0009 | .0009 | .0008 | .0008 | .0008 | .0008 | .0007 | .0007 |
| −3.0 | .0013 | .0013 | .0013 | .0012 | .0012 | .0011 | .0011 | .0011 | .0010 | .0010 |
| −2.9 | .0019 | .0018 | .0018 | .0017 | .0016 | .0016 | .0015 | .0015 | .0014 | .0014 |
| −2.8 | .0026 | .0025 | .0024 | .0023 | .0023 | .0022 | .0021 | .0021 | .0020 | .0019 |
| −2.7 | .0035 | .0034 | .0033 | .0032 | .0031 | .0030 | .0029 | .0028 | .0027 | .0026 |
| −2.6 | .0047 | .0045 | .0044 | .0043 | .0041 | .0040 | .0039 | .0038 | .0037 | .0036 |
| −2.5 | .0062 | .0060 | .0059 | .0057 | .0055 | .0054 | .0052 | .0051 | .0049 | .0048 |
| −2.4 | .0082 | .0080 | .0078 | .0075 | .0073 | .0071 | .0069 | .0068 | .0066 | .0064 |
| −2.3 | .0107 | .0104 | .0102 | .0099 | .0096 | .0094 | .0091 | .0089 | .0087 | .0084 |
| −2.2 | .0139 | .0136 | .0132 | .0129 | .0125 | .0122 | .0119 | .0116 | .0113 | .0110 |
| −2.1 | .0179 | .0174 | .0170 | .0166 | .0162 | .0158 | .0154 | .0150 | .0146 | .0143 |
| −2.0 | .0228 | .0222 | .0217 | .0212 | .0207 | .0202 | .0197 | .0192 | .0188 | .0183 |
| −1.9 | .0287 | .0281 | .0274 | .0268 | .0262 | .0256 | .0250 | .0244 | .0239 | .0233 |
| −1.8 | .0359 | .0351 | .0344 | .0336 | .0329 | .0322 | .0314 | .0307 | .0301 | .0294 |
| −1.7 | .0446 | .0436 | .0427 | .0418 | .0409 | .0401 | .0392 | .0384 | .0375 | .0367 |
| −1.6 | .0548 | .0537 | .0526 | .0516 | .0505 | .0495 | .0485 | .0475 | .0465 | .0455 |
| −1.5 | .0668 | .0655 | .0643 | .0630 | .0618 | .0606 | .0594 | .0582 | .0571 | .0559 |
| −1.4 | .0808 | .0793 | .0778 | .0764 | .0749 | .0735 | .0721 | .0708 | .0694 | .0681 |
| −1.3 | .0968 | .0951 | .0934 | .0918 | .0901 | .0885 | .0869 | .0853 | .0838 | .0823 |
| −1.2 | .1151 | .1131 | .1112 | .1093 | .1075 | .1056 | .1038 | .1020 | .1003 | .0985 |
| −1.1 | .1357 | .1335 | .1314 | .1292 | .1271 | .1251 | .1230 | .1210 | .1190 | (.1170) |
| −1.0 | (.1587) | .1562 | .1539 | .1515 | .1492 | .1469 | .1446 | .1423 | .1401 | .1379 |
| −0.9 | .1841 | .1814 | .1788 | .1762 | .1736 | .1711 | .1685 | .1660 | .1635 | .1611 |
| −0.8 | .2119 | .2090 | .2061 | .2033 | .2005 | .1977 | .1949 | .1922 | .1894 | .1867 |
| −0.7 | .2420 | .2389 | .2358 | .2327 | .2296 | .2266 | .2236 | .2206 | .2177 | .2148 |
| −0.6 | .2743 | .2709 | .2676 | .2643 | .2611 | .2578 | .2546 | .2514 | .2483 | .2451 |
| −0.5 | .3085 | .3050 | .3015 | .2981 | .2947 | .2912 | .2877 | .2843 | .2810 | .2776 |
| −0.4 | .3446 | .3409 | .3372 | .3336 | .3300 | .3264 | .3228 | .3192 | .3156 | .3121 |
| −0.3 | .3821 | .3783 | .3745 | .3707 | .3669 | .3632 | .3594 | .3557 | .3520 | .3483 |
| −0.2 | .4207 | .4168 | .4129 | .4090 | .4052 | .4013 | .3974 | .3936 | .3897 | .3859 |
| −0.1 | .4602 | .4562 | .4522 | .4483 | .4443 | .4404 | .4364 | .4325 | .4286 | .4247 |
| −0.0 | .5000 | .4960 | .4920 | .4880 | .4840 | .4801 | .4761 | .4721 | .4681 | .4641 |

For $z$-scores less than −3.49, use 0.000 to approximate the area.

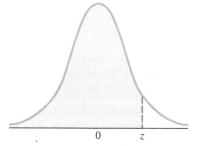

Table entry for *z* is the area to the left of *z*.

**Table 13.7**  Areas of a Standard Normal Distribution *(continued)*

**(b) Table of Areas to the Left of *z* When *z* is Positive**

| z | .00 | .01 | .02 | .03 | .04 | .05 | .06 | .07 | .08 | .09 |
|---|---|---|---|---|---|---|---|---|---|---|
| 0.0 | .5000 | .5040 | .5080 | .5120 | .5160 | .5199 | .5239 | .5279 | .5319 | .5359 |
| 0.1 | .5398 | .5438 | .5478 | .5517 | .5557 | .5596 | .5636 | .5675 | .5714 | .5753 |
| 0.2 | .5793 | .5832 | .5871 | .5910 | .5948 | .5987 | .6026 | .6064 | .6103 | .6141 |
| 0.3 | .6179 | .6217 | .6255 | .6293 | .6331 | .6368 | .6406 | .6443 | .6480 | .6517 |
| 0.4 | .6554 | .6591 | .6628 | .6664 | .6700 | .6736 | .6772 | .6808 | .6844 | .6879 |
| 0.5 | .6915 | .6950 | .6985 | .7019 | .7054 | .7088 | .7123 | .7157 | .7190 | .7224 |
| 0.6 | .7257 | .7291 | .7324 | .7357 | .7389 | .7422 | .7454 | .7486 | .7517 | .7549 |
| 0.7 | .7580 | .7611 | .7642 | .7673 | .7704 | .7734 | .7764 | .7794 | .7823 | .7852 |
| 0.8 | .7881 | .7910 | .7939 | .7967 | .7995 | .8023 | .8051 | .8078 | .8106 | .8133 |
| 0.9 | .8159 | .8186 | .8212 | .8238 | .8264 | .8289 | .8315 | .8340 | .8365 | .8389 |
| 1.0 | .8413 | .8438 | .8461 | .8485 | .8508 | .8531 | .8554 | .8577 | .8599 | .8621 |
| 1.1 | .8643 | .8665 | .8686 | .8708 | .8729 | .8749 | .8770 | .8790 | .8810 | (.8830) |
| 1.2 | .8849 | .8869 | .8888 | .8907 | .8925 | .8944 | .8962 | .8980 | .8997 | .9015 |
| 1.3 | .9032 | .9049 | .9066 | .9082 | .9099 | .9115 | .9131 | .9147 | .9162 | .9177 |
| 1.4 | .9192 | .9207 | .9222 | .9236 | .9251 | .9265 | .9279 | .9292 | .9306 | .9319 |
| 1.5 | .9332 | .9345 | .9357 | .9370 | .9382 | .9394 | .9406 | .9418 | .9429 | .9441 |
| 1.6 | .9452 | .9463 | .9474 | .9484 | .9495 | .9505 | .9515 | .9525 | .9535 | .9545 |
| 1.7 | .9554 | .9564 | .9573 | .9582 | .9591 | .9599 | .9608 | .9616 | .9625 | .9633 |
| 1.8 | .9641 | .9649 | .9656 | .9664 | .9671 | .9678 | .9686 | .9693 | .9699 | .9706 |
| 1.9 | .9713 | .9719 | .9726 | .9732 | .9738 | .9744 | .9750 | .9756 | .9761 | .9767 |
| 2.0 | .9772 | .9778 | .9783 | .9788 | .9793 | .9798 | .9803 | .9808 | .9812 | .9817 |
| 2.1 | .9821 | .9826 | .9830 | .9834 | .9838 | .9842 | .9846 | .9850 | .9854 | .9857 |
| 2.2 | .9861 | .9864 | .9868 | .9871 | .9875 | .9878 | .9881 | .9884 | .9887 | .9890 |
| 2.3 | .9893 | .9896 | .9898 | .9901 | .9904 | .9906 | .9909 | .9911 | .9913 | .9916 |
| 2.4 | .9918 | .9920 | .9922 | .9925 | .9927 | .9929 | .9931 | .9932 | .9934 | .9936 |
| 2.5 | .9938 | .9940 | .9941 | .9943 | .9945 | .9946 | .9948 | .9949 | .9951 | .9952 |
| 2.6 | .9953 | .9955 | .9956 | .9957 | .9959 | .9960 | .9961 | .9962 | .9963 | .9964 |
| 2.7 | .9965 | .9966 | .9967 | .9968 | .9969 | .9970 | .9971 | .9972 | .9973 | .9974 |
| 2.8 | .9974 | .9975 | .9976 | .9977 | .9977 | .9978 | .9979 | .9979 | .9980 | .9981 |
| 2.9 | .9981 | .9982 | .9982 | .9983 | .9984 | .9984 | .9985 | .9985 | .9986 | .9986 |
| 3.0 | .9987 | .9987 | .9987 | .9988 | .9988 | .9989 | .9989 | .9989 | .9990 | .9990 |
| 3.1 | .9990 | .9991 | .9991 | .9991 | .9992 | .9992 | .9992 | .9992 | .9993 | .9993 |
| 3.2 | .9993 | .9993 | .9994 | .9994 | .9994 | .9994 | .9994 | .9995 | .9995 | .9995 |
| 3.3 | .9995 | .9995 | .9995 | .9996 | .9996 | .9996 | .9996 | .9996 | .9996 | .9997 |
| 3.4 | .9997 | .9997 | .9997 | .9997 | .9997 | .9997 | .9997 | .9997 | .9997 | .9998 |

For *z*-scores greater than 3.49, use 1.000 to approximate the area.

of $z = 1.19$ is 9, we move to the column labeled .09. Using the row labeled 1.1 and the column labeled 0.09, the table entry is .8830, circled in green. Therefore, the total area to the left of $z = 1.19$ is 0.8830.

c) To determine the area to the right of $z = 1.19$, we use the fact that the total area under the normal curve is 1. In part (b), we determined that the area to the left of $z = 1.19$ was 0.8830. To determine the area to the right of $z = 1.19$, we can subtract the area to the left of $z = 1.19$ from 1 (Fig. 13.28(a)). Therefore, the area to the right of $z = 1.19$ is $1 - 0.8830$, or 0.1170.

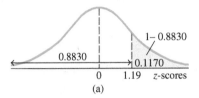
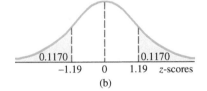

Figure 13.28

Another way to determine the area to the right of $z = 1.19$ is to use the fact that the normal curve is symmetric about the mean. Thus, the area to the left of a negative $z$-score is equal to the area to the right of a positive $z$-score. Therefore, the area to the left of $z = -1.19$ is equal to the area to the right of $z = 1.19$ (Fig. 13.28(b)). Using Table 13.7(a), we see that the area to the left of $z = -1.19$ is .1170. This value is circled in red in the table. Therefore, the area to the right of $z = 1.19$ is also .1170. This answer agrees with our answer obtained by subtracting the area to the left of $z = 1.19$ from 1.

d) To determine the area between two $z$-scores, we subtract the smaller area from the larger area (Fig. 13.29). Using Table 13.7(b), we see that the area to the left of $z = 2.57$ is .9949 (Fig. 13.29(a)). Using Table 13.7(a), we see that the area to the left of $z = -1.62$ is .0526 (Fig. 13.29(b)). Thus, the area between $z = -1.62$ and $z = 2.57$ is $0.9949 - 0.0526$, or 0.9423 (Fig. 13.29(c)).

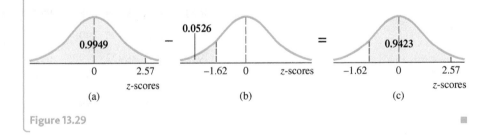

Figure 13.29

To change the area under the normal curve to a percent, multiply the area by 100%. In Example 3(a), we determined the area to the left of $z = -1.00$ to be 0.1587. To change this area to a percent, multiply 0.1587 by 100%.

$$0.1587 = 0.1587 \times 100\% = 15.87\%$$

Therefore 15.87% of the normal curve is less than a score that is one standard deviation below the mean.

Below, we summarize the procedure to determine the percent of data for any interval under the normal curve.

> **PROCEDURE**  **TO DETERMINE THE PERCENT OF DATA BETWEEN ANY TWO VALUES IN A NORMAL DISTRIBUTION**
>
> 1. Draw a diagram of the normal curve, indicating the area or percent to be determined.
>
> 2. Use the formula $z = \dfrac{\text{value of the piece of data} - \text{mean}}{\text{standard deviation}}$ to convert the given values to $z$-scores. Indicate these $z$-scores on the diagram.
>
> 3. Look up the areas that correspond to the specified $z$-scores in Table 13.7.
>    a) When determining the area to the left of a negative $z$-score, use Table 13.7(a).
>
>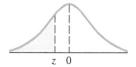
>
>    b) When determining the area to the left of a positive $z$-score, use Table 13.7(b).
>
>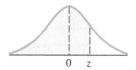
>
>    c) When determining the area to the right of a $z$-score, subtract the percent of data to the left of the specified $z$-score from 100%.
>
>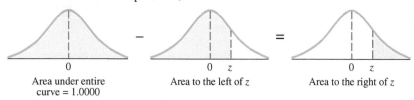
>
>    | Area under entire curve = 1.0000 | Area to the left of $z$ | Area to the right of $z$ |
>
>    Or, use the symmetry of a normal distribution.
>
>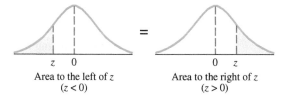
>
>    | Area to the left of $z$ ($z < 0$) | Area to the right of $z$ ($z > 0$) |
>
>    d) When determining the area between two $z$-scores, subtract the smaller area from the larger area.
>
>    In the figure below, we let $z_1$ represent the smaller $z$-score and $z_2$ represent the larger $z$-score.
>
>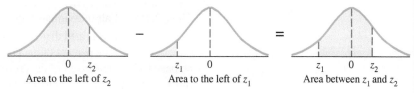
>
>    | Area to the left of $z_2$ | Area to the left of $z_1$ | Area between $z_1$ and $z_2$ |
>
> 4. Change the areas you determined in Step 3 to percents as explained on page 824.

Example **4** *IQ Scores*

Intelligence quotients (IQ scores) are normally distributed with a mean of 100 and a standard deviation of 15. Determine the percent of individuals with IQ scores

a) below 115.

b) below 130.

c) below 70.

d) between 70 and 115.

e) between 115 and 130.

f) above 122.5.

*Solution*

a) We want to determine the area under the normal curve below the value of 115, as illustrated in Fig. 13.30(a). Converting 115 to a $z$-score yields a $z$-score of 1.00.

$$z_{115} = \frac{115 - 100}{15} = \frac{15}{15} = 1.00$$

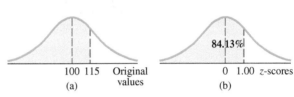

Figure 13.30

The percent of individuals with IQ scores below 115 is the same as the percent of data below a $z$-score of 1.00 (Fig. 13.30(b)). Since our $z$-score is positive, we use Table 13.7(b). From Table 13.7(b), we determine that the area to the left of a $z$-score of 1.00 is .8413. Therefore, 84.13% of all the IQ scores are below a $z$-score of 1.00. Thus, 84.13% of individuals have IQ scores below 115.

b) Begin by finding the $z$-score for 130.

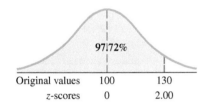

Figure 13.31

$$z_{130} = \frac{130 - 100}{15} = \frac{30}{15} = 2.00$$

The percent of data below a $z$-score of 130 is the same as the percent of data below a $z$-score of 2.00 (Fig. 13.31). Using Table 13.7(b), we determine that the area to the left of a $z$-score of 2.00 is .9772. Therefore, 97.72% of the IQ scores are below a $z$-score of 2.00. Thus, 97.72% of all individuals have IQ scores below 130.

c) Begin by finding the $z$-score for 70.

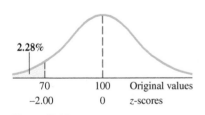

Figure 13.32

$$z_{70} = \frac{70 - 100}{15} = \frac{-30}{15} = -2.00$$

The percent of data below a score of 70 is the same as the percent of data below a $z$-score of $-2.00$ (Fig. 13.32). Since our $z$-score is negative, we use Table 13.7(a). Using the table, we determine that the area to the left of $z = -2.00$ is .0228. Therefore, 2.28% of the data is below a $z$-score of $-2.00$. Thus, 2.28% of all individuals have IQ scores below 70.

d) In part (a), we determined that $z_{115} = 1.00$, and in part (c), we determined that $z_{70} = -2.00$. The percent of data below a $z$-score of 1.00 is 84.13% (Fig. 13.33(a) on page 827). The percent of data below a $z$-score of $-2.00$ is 2.28% (Fig. 13.33(b)). Since we want to find the percent of data between two $z$-scores, we subtract the smaller percent from the larger percent: $84.13\% - 2.28\% = 81.85\%$ (Fig. 13.33(c)). Thus, 81.85% of all individuals have IQ scores between 70 and 115.

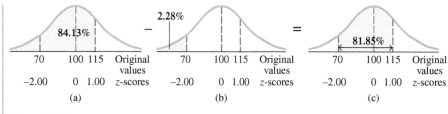

Figure 13.33

e) In part (a), we determined that $z_{115} = 1.00$, and in part (b), we determined $z_{130} = 2.00$. The percent of data below a $z$-score of 1.00 is 84.13%. The percent of data below a $z$-score of 2.00 is 97.72%. Since we want to find the percent of data between two $z$-scores, we subtract the smaller percent from the larger percent: 97.72% – 84.13% = 13.59% (Fig. 13.34). Thus, 13.59% of all individuals have IQ scores between 115 and 130.

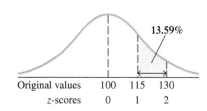

Figure 13.34

f) Begin by determining a $z$-score for 122.5.

$$z_{122.5} = \frac{122.5 - 100}{15} = \frac{22.5}{15} = 1.50$$

The percent of IQ scores above 122.5 is the same as the percent of data above $z = 1.50$ (Fig. 13.35). To determine the percent of data above $z = 1.50$, we can determine the percent of data below $z = 1.50$ and subtract this percent from 100%. In Table 13.7(b), we see that the area to the left of $z = 1.50$ is .9332. Therefore, 93.32% of the IQ scores are below $z = 1.50$. The percent of IQ scores above $z = 1.50$ are 100% – 93.32%, or 6.68%. Thus, 6.68% of all IQ scores are greater than 122.5.

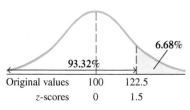

Figure 13.35

## Example 5  Horseback Rides

Assume that the length of time for a horseback ride on the trail at Triple R Ranch is normally distributed with a mean of 3.2 hours and a standard deviation of 0.4 hour.

a) What percent of horseback rides last at least 3.2 hours?
b) What percent of horseback rides last less than 2.8 hours?
c) What percent of horseback rides are at least 3.7 hours?
d) What percent of horseback rides are between 2.8 hours and 4.0 hours?
e) In a random sample of 500 horseback rides at Triple R Ranch, how many are at least 3.7 hours?

*Solution*

a) In a normal distribution, half the data are always above the mean. Since 3.2 hours is the mean, half, or 50%, of the horseback rides last at least 3.2 hours.

b) Convert 2.8 hours to a $z$-score.

$$z_{2.8} = \frac{2.8 - 3.2}{0.4} = -1.00$$

Use Table 13.7(a) to find the area of the normal curve that lies below a $z$-score of –1.00. The area to the left of $z = -1.00$ is 0.1587. Therefore, the percent of horseback rides that last less than 2.8 hours is 15.87% (Fig. 13.36).

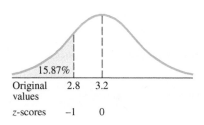

Figure 13.36

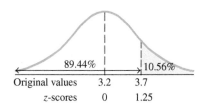

89.44% | 10.56%

| Original values | 3.2 | 3.7 |
| z-scores | 0 | 1.25 |

Figure 13.37

> **TIMELY TIP**
> Following is a summary of some important items presented in this section.
> - The normal curve is symmetric about the mean.
> - The area under the normal curve cannot be negative.
> - A negative z-score indicates that the corresponding value in the original distribution is less than the mean.
> - A positive z-score indicates that the corresponding value in the original distribution is greater than the mean.
> - A z-score of 0 indicates that the corresponding value in the original distribution is the mean.
> - Table 13.7 provides the area to the left of a specified z-score.
> - When using Table 13.7 to determine the area to the left of a specified z-score, locate the units value and tenths value of your specified z-score under the column labeled z. Then move to the column containing the hundredths value of your specified z-score to obtain the area.

c) At least 3.7 hours means greater than or equal to 3.7 hours. Therefore, we are seeking to find the percent of data to the right of 3.7 hours. Convert 3.7 hours to a z-score.

$$z_{3.7} = \frac{3.7 - 3.2}{0.4} = 1.25$$

From Table 13.7(b), we determine that the area to the left of $z = 1.25$ is .8944. Therefore, 89.44% of the data are below $z = 1.25$. The percent of data above $z = 1.25$ (or to the right of $z = 1.25$) is $100\% - 89.44\%$, or 10.56% (Fig. 13.37). Thus, 10.56% of horseback rides last at least 3.7 hours.

d) Convert 4.0 to a z-score.

$$z_{4.0} = \frac{4.0 - 3.2}{0.4} = 2.00$$

From Table 13.7(b), we determine that the area to the left of $z = 2.00$ is .9772 (Fig.13.38(a)). Therefore the percent of data below a z-score of 2.00 is 97.72%. From part (b), we determined that $z_{28} = -1.00$ and that the percent of data below a z-score of $-1.00$ is 15.87% (Fig. 13.38(b)). To find the percent of data between a z-score of $-1.00$ and a z-score of 2.00, we subtract the smaller percent from the larger percent. Thus, the percent of horseback rides that last between 2.8 hours and 4.0 hours is $97.72\% - 15.87\%$, or 81.85% (Fig. 13.38(c)).

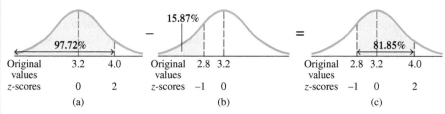

| Original values | 3.2 | 4.0 |
| z-scores | 0 | 2 |

(a)

15.87%

| Original values | 2.8 | 3.2 |
| z-scores | -1 | 0 |

(b)

81.85%

| Original values | 2.8 | 3.2 | 4.0 |
| z-scores | -1 | 0 | 2 |

(c)

Figure 13.38

e) In part (c), we determined that 10.56% of all horseback rides last at least 3.7 hours. We now multiply 0.1056 times the number in the random sample, 500, to determine the number of horseback rides that last at least 3.7 hours. There are $0.1056 \times 500 = 52.8$, or approximately 53, horseback rides that last at least 3.7 hours.

## SECTION 13.6    *Exercises*

### Warm Up Exercises

*In Exercises 1–12, fill in the blank with an appropriate word, phrase, or symbol(s).*

1. A distribution in which all the values have the same frequency is called a(n) _____ distribution.

2. A distribution in which the frequency is either constantly increasing or constantly decreasing is called a(n) _____ distribution.

3. A distribution that has a "tail" on its right is skewed to the _____.

4. A distribution that has a "tail" on its left is skewed to the _____.

5. A distribution in which two nonadjacent values occur more frequently than any other values in a set of data is called a(n) _____ distribution.

6. A normal distribution is a(n) _____ shaped distribution.

7. A measure of how far, in terms of standard deviations, a given data value is from the mean is called a z-score or a(n) _____ score.

8. The mean of a set of data will always have a z-score of _____.

9. A piece of data that has a negative z-score is _____ the mean.

**10.** A piece of data that has a positive *z*-score is _____ the mean.

**11.** According to the empirical rule, in a normal distribution,

   **a)** approximately _____ % of the data lie within plus or minus 1 standard deviation of the mean,

   **b)** approximately _____ % of the data lie within plus or minus 2 standard deviations of the mean, and

   **c)** approximately _____ % of the data lie within plus or minus 3 standard deviations of the mean.

**12.** In a normal distribution, the mean, median, and mode all have the same _____.

*In Exercises 13–16, give an example of the type of distribution.*

**13.** Rectangular

**14.** Skewed

**15.** J-shaped

**16.** Bimodal

*For the distributions in Exercises 17–20, state whether you think the distribution would be normal, J-shaped, bimodal, rectangular, skewed left, or skewed right.*

**17.** The wearout mileage of automobile tires

**18.** The numbers resulting from tossing a die many times

**19.** The number of people per household in the United States

**20.** The heights of a sample of high school seniors, where there are an equal number of males and females

## Practice the Skills

*In Exercises 21–32, use Table 13.7 on pages 822 and 823 to find the specified area.*

**21.** Above the mean

**22.** Below the mean

**23.** Between two standard deviations below the mean and one standard deviation above the mean

**24.** Between 1.10 and 1.60 standard deviations above the mean

**25.** To the right of $z = 1.53$   **26.** To the left of $z = 1.62$

**27.** To the left of $z = -1.78$   **28.** To the right of $z = -1.78$

**29.** Between $z = -1.32$ and $z = -1.64$

**30.** To the left of $z = 1.84$

**31.** To the left of $z = -2.13$

**32.** To the left of $z = -0.92$

*In Exercises 33–42, use Table 13.7 on pages 822 and 823 to determine the percent of data specified.*

**33.** Less than $z = 0.71$   **34.** Less than $z = -0.82$

**35.** Between $z = -1.34$ and $z = 2.24$

**36.** Between $z = -2.18$ and $z = -1.90$

**37.** Greater than $z = -1.90$

**38.** Greater than $z = 2.66$

**39.** Less than $z = 1.96$

**40.** Between $z = -1.53$ and $z = -1.82$

**41.** Between $z = 0.72$ and $z = 2.14$

**42.** Between $z = -2.15$ and $z = 3.31$

## Problem Solving

***Heights of Girls*** In Exercises 43 and 44, assume that the heights of 7-year-old girls are normally distributed. The heights of 8 girls are given in z-scores below.

| Emily | 0.9 | Jenny | 0.0 | Heather | $-1.3$ | Shenice | 0.0 |
|-------|-----|-------|-----|---------|--------|---------|-----|
| Sarah | 1.7 | Sadaf | $-0.2$ | Carol | 0.8 | Kim | $-1.2$ |

**43. a)** Which of these girls are taller than the mean?

   **b)** Which of these girls are at the mean?

   **c)** Which of these girls are shorter than the mean?

**44. a)** Which girl is the tallest?

   **b)** Which girl is the shortest?

*Police Officer's Salaries* In Exercises 45–48, assume the annual salaries of police officers are normally distributed with a mean of $50,000 and a standard deviation of $7000.

45. Determine the percent of police officers with an annual salary of at least $50,000.

46. Determine the percent of police officers with an annual salary between $43,000 and $64,000.

47. Determine the percent of police officers with an annual salary of at least $58,750.

48. In a random sample of 500 police officers, how many have an annual salary of at least $58,750.

*SAT Scores* In Exercises 49–54, assume that the mathematics scores on the SAT are normally distributed with a mean of 500 and a standard deviation of 100.

49. What percent of students who took the test have a mathematics score below 550?

50. What percent of students who took the test have a mathematics score above 650?

51. What percent of students who took the test have a mathematics score between 550 and 650?

52. What percent of students who took the test have a mathematics score below 300?

53. What percent of students who took the test have a mathematics score between 400 and 525?

54. What percent of students who took the test have a mathematics score above 380?

*Vending Machine* In Exercises 55–58, a vending machine is designed to dispense a mean of 7.6 oz of coffee into an 8-oz cup. If the standard deviation of the amount of coffee dispensed is 0.4 oz and the amount is normally distributed, find the percent of times the machine will

55. dispense from 7.4 oz to 7.7 oz.

56. dispense less than 7.0 oz.

57. dispense less than 7.7 oz.

58. result in the cup overflowing (therefore dispense more than 8 oz).

▲ *See Exercises 55–58*

*Automobile Speed* In Exercises 59–64, assume that the speed of automobiles on an expressway during rush hour is normally distributed with a mean of 62 mph and a standard deviation of 5 mph.

59. What percent of cars are traveling faster than 62 mph?

60. What percent of cars are traveling between 58 mph and 66 mph?

61. What percent of cars are traveling slower than 56 mph?

62. What percent of cars are traveling faster than 70 mph?

63. If 200 cars are selected at random, how many will be traveling slower than 56 mph?

64. If 200 cars are selected at random, how many will be traveling faster than 70 mph?

*Corn Flakes* In Exercises 65–68, assume that the amount of corn flakes in a box is normally distributed with a mean of 16 oz and a standard deviation of 0.1 oz.

65. Determine the percent of boxes that will contain between 15.83 oz and 16.32 oz of corn flakes.

66. Determine the percent of boxes that will contain more than 16.16 oz of corn flakes.

67. If the manufacturer produces 300,000 boxes, how many of them will contain less than 15.83 oz of corn flakes?

68. If the manufacturer produces 300,000 boxes, how many of them will contain more than 16.16 oz of corn flakes?

*Cost of Day Care* In Exercises 69–74, assume the annual day care cost per child is normally distributed with a mean of $8000 and a standard deviation of $1500.

**69.** What percent of day care costs are more than $7250 annually?

**70.** What percent of day care costs are between $6500 and $8750 annually?

**71.** What percent of day care costs are more than $11,750 annually?

**72.** What percent of day care costs are less than $11,750 annually?

**73.** In a random sample of 120 families, how many pay more than $7250 annually for day care per child?

**74.** In a random sample of 120 families, how many pay between $6500 and $8750 annually for day care per child?

**75.** *Weight Loss* A weight-loss clinic guarantees that its new customers will lose at least 5 lb by the end of their first month of participation or their money will be refunded. If the weight loss of customers at the end of their first month is normally distributed, with a mean of 6.7 lb and a standard deviation of 0.81 lb, determine the percent of customers who will be able to claim a refund.

**76.** *Battery Warranty* The warranty on a car battery is 36 months. If the breakdown times of this battery are normally distributed with a mean of 46 months and a standard deviation of 8 months, determine the percent of batteries that can be expected to require repair or replacement under warranty.

**77.** *Coffee Machine* A vending machine that dispenses coffee does not appear to be working correctly. The machine rarely gives the proper amount of coffee. Some of the time the cup is underfilled, and some of the time the cup overflows. Does this variation indicate that the mean number of ounces dispensed has to be adjusted, or does it indicate that the standard deviation of the amount of coffee dispensed by the machine is too large?

**78.** *Grading on a Normal Curve* Mr. Sanderson marks his class on a normal curve. Those with $z$-scores above 1.8 will receive an A, those between 1.8 and 1.1 will receive a B, those between 1.1 and $-1.2$ will receive a C, those between $-1.2$ and $-1.9$ will receive a D, and those under $-1.9$ will receive an F. Determine the percent of grades that will be A, B, C, D, and F.

**79.** Consider the following normal curve, representing a normal distribution, with points *A*, *B*, and *C*. One of these points corresponds to the mean, one point corresponds to the mean plus one standard deviation and one point corresponds to the mean minus two standard deviations.

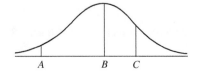

**a)** Which point corresponds to the mean?

**b)** Which point corresponds to the mean plus one standard deviation?

**c)** Which point corresponds to the mean minus two standard deviations?

**80.** Consider the following two normal curves.

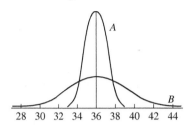

**a)** Do these distributions have the same mean? If so, what is the mean?

**b)** One of these curves corresponds to a normal distribution with a standard deviation of 1. The other curve corresponds to a normal distribution with a standard deviation of 3. Which curve, *A* or *B*, has a standard deviation of 3?

## Concept/Writing Exercises

**81.** In a distribution that is skewed to the right, which has the greatest value: the mean, median, or mode? Which has the smallest value? Explain.

**82.** In a distribution skewed to the left, which has the greatest value: the mean, median, or mode? Which has the smallest value? Explain.

**83.** List three populations other than those given in the text that may be normally distributed.

**84.** List three populations other than those given in the text that may not be normally distributed.

## Challenge Problems/Group Activities

**85.** *Salesperson Promotion* The owner at Kim's Home Interiors is reviewing the sales records of two managers who are up for promotion, Katie and Stella, who work in different stores. At Katie's store, the mean sales have been $23,200 per month, with a standard deviation of $2170. At Stella's store, the mean sales have been $25,600 per month, with a standard deviation of $2300. Last month, Katie's store

sales were $28,408 and Stella's store sales were $29,510. At both stores, the distribution of monthly sales is normal.

a) Convert last month's sales for Katie's store and for Stella's store to $z$-scores.

b) If one of the two were to be promoted based solely on the increase in sales last month, who should be promoted? Explain.

86. *Chebyshev's Theorem* How can you determine whether a distribution is approximately normal? A statistical theorem called *Chebyshev's theorem* states that the *minimum percent* of data between plus and minus $K$ standard deviations from the mean $(K > 1)$ in *any distribution* can be found by the formula

$$\text{Minimum percent} = 1 - \frac{1}{K^2}$$

Thus, for example, between $\pm 2$ standard deviations from the mean there will always be a minimum of 75% of data. This minimum percent applies to any distribution. For $K = 2$,

$$\text{Minimum percent} = 1 - \frac{1}{2^2}$$

$$= 1 - \frac{1}{4} = \frac{3}{4}, \quad \text{or} \quad 75\%$$

Likewise, between $\pm 3$ standard deviations from the mean there will always be a minimum of 89% of the data. For $K = 3$,

$$\text{Minimum percent} = 1 - \frac{1}{3^2}$$

$$= 1 - \frac{1}{9} = \frac{8}{9}, \quad \text{or} \quad 89\%$$

The following table lists the minimum percent of data in *any distribution* and the actual percent of data in *the normal distribution* between $\pm 1.1$, $\pm 1.5$, $\pm 2.0$, and $\pm 2.5$ standard deviations from the mean. The minimum percents of data in any distribution were calculated by using Chebyshev's theorem. The actual percents of data for the normal distribution were calculated by using the area given in the standard normal, or $z$, table.

| | $K = 1.1$ | $K = 1.5$ | $K = 2$ | $K = 2.5$ |
|---|---|---|---|---|
| Minimum (for any distribution) | 17.4% | 55.6% | 75% | 84% |
| Normal distribution | 72.9% | 86.6% | 95.4% | 98.8% |
| Given distribution | | | | |

The third row of the chart has been left blank for you to fill in the percents when you reach part (e).

Consider the following 30 pieces of data obtained from a quiz.

1, 1, 1, 1, 2, 2, 2, 2, 3, 3, 4, 4, 4, 5, 6,

6, 6, 7, 7, 7, 7, 8, 8, 8, 8, 9, 9, 9, 10, 10

a) Determine the mean of the set of scores.

b) Determine the standard deviation of the set of scores.

c) Determine the values that correspond to 1.1, 1.5, 2, and 2.5 standard deviations above the mean.
    Then determine the values that correspond to 1.1, 1.5, 2, and 2.5 standard deviations below the mean.

d) By observing the 30 pieces of data, determine the actual percent of quiz scores between

   $\pm 1.1$ standard deviations from the mean.

   $\pm 1.5$ standard deviations from the mean.

   $\pm 2$ standard deviations from the mean.

   $\pm 2.5$ standard deviations from the mean.

e) Place the percents found in part (d) in the third row of the chart.

f) Compare the percents in the third row of the chart with the minimum percents in the first row and the normal percents in the second row, and then make a judgment as to whether this set of 30 scores is approximately normally distributed.

87. *Test Scores* Obtain a set of test scores from your instructor.

a) Determine the mean, median, mode, and midrange of the test scores.

b) Determine the range and standard deviation of the set of scores. (You may round the mean to the nearest tenth when finding the standard deviation.)

c) Construct a frequency distribution of the set of scores. Select your first class so that there will be between 5 and 12 classes.

d) Construct a histogram and frequency polygon of the frequency distribution in part (c).

e) Does the histogram in part (d) appear to represent a normal distribution? Explain.

f) Use the procedure explained in Exercise 86 to determine whether the set of scores approximates a normal distribution. Explain.

88. Determine a value of $z$ such that $z \geq 0$ and 47.5% of the standard normal curve lies between 0 and the $z$-value.

89. Determine a value of $z$ such that $z \leq 0$ and 38.1% of the standard normal curve lies between 0 and the $z$-value.

## Recreational Mathematics

**90.** Ask your instructor for the class mean and class standard deviation for one of the exams taken by your class. For that exam, calculate the $z$-score for your exam grade. How many standard deviations is your exam grade away from the mean?

**91.** If the mean score on a math quiz is 12.0 and 77% of the students in your class scored between 9.6 and 14.4, determine the standard deviation of the quiz scores.

## Internet/Research Activity

**92.** In this project, you actually become the statistician.

**a)** Select a project of interest to you in which data must be collected.

**b)** Write a proposal and submit it to your instructor for approval. In the proposal, discuss the aims of your project and how you plan to gather the data to make your sample unbiased.

**c)** After your proposal has been approved, gather 50 pieces of data by the method you proposed.

**d)** Rank the data from smallest to largest.

**e)** Compute the mean, median, mode, and midrange.

**f)** Determine the range and standard deviation of the data. You may round the mean to the nearest tenth when computing the standard deviation.

**g)** Construct a frequency distribution, histogram, frequency polygon, and stem-and-leaf display of your data. Select your first class so that there will be between 5 and 12 classes. Be sure to label your histogram and frequency polygon.

**h)** Does your distribution appear to be normal? Explain your answer. Does it appear to be another type of distribution discussed? Explain.

**i)** Determine whether your distribution is approximately normal by using the technique discussed in Exercise 86.

---

## SECTION 13.7     Linear Correlation and Regression

▲ *You can predict the value of a car based on the age of the car.*

Do you believe that there is a relationship between the time a person studies for an exam and the exam grade the person receives? Is there a relationship between the age of a car and the value of the car? Can we predict the value of a car based on the age of the car? In this section, we will learn how to determine whether there is a relationship between two quantities and, if so, how strong that relationship is. We will also learn how to determine the equation of the line that best describes the relationship between two quantities.

*Why* **This is Important** There are many real-life applications in which a relationship exists between two variables, such as the amount of time spent studying for an exam and the exam score.

---

In this section, we discuss two important statistical topics: correlation and regression. *Correlation* is used to determine whether there is a relationship between two quantities and, if so, how strong the relationship is. *Regression* is used to determine the equation that relates the two quantities. Although there are other types of correlation and regression, in this section we discuss only linear correlation and linear regression. We begin by discussing linear correlation.

## Linear Correlation

The *linear correlation coefficient*, $r$, is a unitless measure that describes the strength of the linear relationship between two variables. A positive value of $r$, or a positive correlation, means that as one variable increases, the other variable also increases. A negative value of $r$, or a negative correlation, means that as one variable increases, the other variable decreases. The correlation coefficient, $r$, will always be a value between $-1$ and $1$ inclusive. A value of $1$ indicates the strongest possible positive correlation, a value of $-1$ indicates the strongest possible negative correlation, and a value of $0$ indicates no correlation (Fig. 13.39).

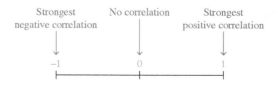

Figure 13.39

A visual aid used with correlation is the *scatter diagram*, a plot of data points. To help understand how to construct a scatter diagram, consider the following data from Egan Electronics. During a 6-day period, Egan Electronics kept daily records of the number of assembly line workers absent and the number of defective parts produced. The information is provided in the following chart.

| Day | 1 | 2 | 3 | 4 | 5 | 6 |
|---|---|---|---|---|---|---|
| Number of workers absent | 3 | 5 | 0 | 1 | 2 | 6 |
| Number of defective parts | 15 | 22 | 7 | 12 | 20 | 30 |

For each of the 6 days, two pieces of data are provided: number of workers absent and number of defective parts. We call the set of data *bivariate data*. Often when we have a set of bivariate data, we can control one of the quantities. We generally denote the quantity that can be controlled, the *independent variable*, $x$. The other variable, the *dependent variable*, is denoted as $y$. In this problem, we will assume that the number of defective parts produced is affected by the number of workers absent. Therefore, we will call the number of workers absent $x$ and the number of defective parts produced $y$. When we plot bivariate data, the independent variable is marked on the horizontal axis and the dependent variable is marked on the vertical axis. Therefore, for this problem, number of workers absent is marked on the horizontal axis and number of defective parts is marked on the vertical axis. If we plot the six pieces of bivariate data in the Cartesian coordinate system, we get a scatter diagram, as shown in Fig. 13.40.

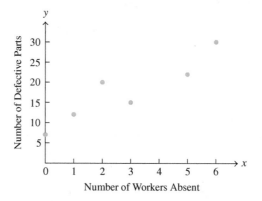

Figure 13.40

The figure shows that, generally, the more workers that are absent, the more defective parts are produced.

In Fig. 13.41, we show some scatter diagrams and indicate the corresponding strength of correlation between the quantities on the horizontal and vertical axes.

Earlier, we mentioned that $r$ will always be a value between $-1$ and $1$ inclusive. A value of $r = 1$ is obtained only when every point of the bivariate data on a scatter diagram lies in a straight line and the line is increasing from left to right (Fig. 13.41(a)). In other words, the line has a positive slope, as discussed in Section 6.7.

A value of $r = -1$ will be obtained only when every point of the bivariate data on a scatter diagram lies in a straight line and the line is decreasing from left to right. (Fig. 13.41(e)). In other words, the line has a negative slope.

The value of $r$ is a measure of how far a set of points varies from a straight line. The greater the spread, the weaker the correlation and the closer the value of $r$ is to 0. Figure 13.41 shows that the more the points diverge from a straight line, the weaker the correlation becomes.

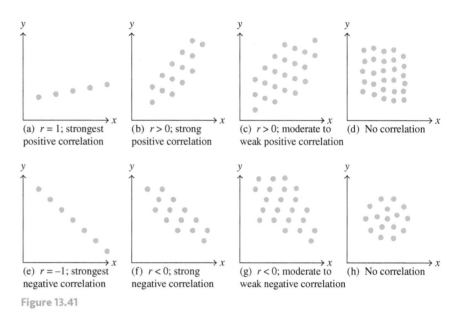

(a) $r = 1$; strongest positive correlation

(b) $r > 0$; strong positive correlation

(c) $r > 0$; moderate to weak positive correlation

(d) No correlation

(e) $r = -1$; strongest negative correlation

(f) $r < 0$; strong negative correlation

(g) $r < 0$; moderate to weak negative correlation

(h) No correlation

**Figure 13.41**

The following formula is used to calculate $r$.

### Linear Correlation Coefficient

The formula to calculate the **correlation coefficient, $r$,** is as follows.

$$r = \frac{n(\Sigma xy) - (\Sigma x)(\Sigma y)}{\sqrt{n(\Sigma x^2) - (\Sigma x)^2} \sqrt{n(\Sigma y^2) - (\Sigma y)^2}}$$

To determine the correlation coefficient, $r$, and the equation of the line of best fit (to be discussed shortly), a statistical calculator may be used. On the statistical calculator, you enter the ordered pairs, $(x, y)$ and press the appropriate keys. At the end of this section, we indicate the procedure to follow to use the computer software spreadsheet program, Microsoft Excel, and the TI-83 Plus or the TI-84 Plus calculators to determine the correlation coefficient.

In Example 1, we show how to determine $r$ for a set of bivariate data without the use of a statistical calculator. We will use the same set of bivariate data given on page 834 that was used to make the scatter diagram in Fig. 13.40.

Example **1** *Number of Absences Versus Number of Defective Parts*

Egan Electronics provided the following daily records about the number of assembly line workers absent and the number of defective parts produced for 6 days. Determine the correlation coefficient between the number of workers absent and the number of defective parts produced.

| Day | 1 | 2 | 3 | 4 | 5 | 6 |
|---|---|---|---|---|---|---|
| Number of workers absent | 3 | 5 | 0 | 1 | 2 | 6 |
| Number of defective parts | 15 | 22 | 7 | 12 | 20 | 30 |

**Solution** We plotted this set of data on the scatter diagram in Fig. 13.40 on page 834. We will call the number of workers absent $x$. We will call the number of defective parts produced $y$. We list the values of $x$ and $y$ and calculate the necessary sums: $\Sigma x, \Sigma y, \Sigma xy, \Sigma x^2, \Sigma y^2$. We determine the values in the column labeled $x^2$ by squaring the $x$'s (multiplying the $x$'s by themselves). We determine the values in the column labeled $y^2$ by squaring the $y$'s. We determine the values in the column labeled $xy$ by multiplying each $x$-value by its corresponding $y$-value.

| Number of Workers Absent | Number of Defective Parts | | | |
|---|---|---|---|---|
| $x$ | $y$ | $x^2$ | $y^2$ | $xy$ |
| 3 | 15 | 9 | 225 | 45 |
| 5 | 22 | 25 | 484 | 110 |
| 0 | 7 | 0 | 49 | 0 |
| 1 | 12 | 1 | 144 | 12 |
| 2 | 20 | 4 | 400 | 40 |
| 6 | 30 | 36 | 900 | 180 |
| 17 | 106 | 75 | 2202 | 387 |

Thus, $\Sigma x = 17$, $\Sigma y = 106$, $\Sigma x^2 = 75$, $\Sigma y^2 = 2202$, and $\Sigma xy = 387$. In the formula for $r$, we use both $(\Sigma x)^2$ and $\Sigma x^2$. Note that $(\Sigma x)^2 = (17)^2 = 289$ and that $\Sigma x^2 = 75$. Similarly, $(\Sigma y)^2 = (106)^2 = 11{,}236$ and $\Sigma y^2 = 2202$.

The $n$ in the formula represents the number of pieces of bivariate data. Here $n = 6$. Now let's determine $r$.

$$r = \frac{n(\Sigma xy) - (\Sigma x)(\Sigma y)}{\sqrt{n(\Sigma x^2) - (\Sigma x)^2}\sqrt{n(\Sigma y^2) - (\Sigma y)^2}}$$

$$= \frac{6(387) - (17)(106)}{\sqrt{6(75) - (17)^2}\sqrt{6(2202) - (106)^2}}$$

$$= \frac{2322 - 1802}{\sqrt{6(75) - 289}\sqrt{6(2202) - 11{,}236}}$$

$$= \frac{520}{\sqrt{450 - 289}\sqrt{13{,}212 - 11{,}236}}$$

$$= \frac{520}{\sqrt{161}\sqrt{1976}} \approx 0.922$$

Since the maximum possible value for $r$ is 1.00, a correlation coefficient of 0.922 is a strong, positive correlation. This result implies that, generally, the more assembly line workers absent, the more defective parts produced. ∎

In Example 1, had we found $r$ to be a value greater than 1 or less than $-1$, it would have indicated that we had made an error. Also, from the scatter diagram, we should realize that $r$ should be a positive value and not negative.

Table 13.8 Correlation Coefficient, *r*

| n | α = 0.05 | α = 0.01 |
|---|---|---|
| 4 | 0.950 | 0.990 |
| 5 | 0.878 | 0.959 |
| 6 | 0.811 | 0.917 |
| 7 | 0.754 | 0.875 |
| 8 | 0.707 | 0.834 |
| 9 | 0.666 | 0.798 |
| 10 | 0.632 | 0.765 |
| 11 | 0.602 | 0.735 |
| 12 | 0.576 | 0.708 |
| 13 | 0.553 | 0.684 |
| 14 | 0.532 | 0.661 |
| 15 | 0.514 | 0.641 |
| 16 | 0.497 | 0.623 |
| 17 | 0.482 | 0.606 |
| 18 | 0.468 | 0.590 |
| 19 | 0.456 | 0.575 |
| 20 | 0.444 | 0.561 |
| 22 | 0.423 | 0.537 |
| 27 | 0.381 | 0.487 |
| 32 | 0.349 | 0.449 |
| 37 | 0.325 | 0.418 |
| 42 | 0.304 | 0.393 |
| 47 | 0.288 | 0.372 |
| 52 | 0.273 | 0.354 |
| 62 | 0.250 | 0.325 |
| 72 | 0.232 | 0.302 |
| 82 | 0.217 | 0.283 |
| 92 | 0.205 | 0.267 |
| 102 | 0.195 | 0.254 |

*The derivation of this table is beyond the scope of this text. It shows the critical values of the Pearson correlation coefficient.*

In Example 1, there appears to be a cause–effect relationship. That is, the more assembly line workers who are absent, the more defective parts are produced. *However, a correlation does not necessarily indicate a cause–effect relationship.* For example, there is a positive correlation between police officers' salaries and the cost of medical insurance over the past 10 years (both have increased), but that does not mean that the increase in police officers' salaries caused the increase in the cost of medical insurance.

Suppose in Example 1 that *r* had been 0.53. Would this value have indicated a correlation? What is the minimum value of *r* needed to assume that a correlation exists between the variables? To answer this question, we introduce the term *level of significance*. The *level of significance*, denoted α (alpha), is used to identify the cutoff between results attributed to chance and results attributed to an actual relationship between the two variables. Table 13.8 gives *critical values** (or cutoff values) that are sometimes used for determining whether two variables are related. The table indicates two different levels of significance: α = 0.05 and α = 0.01. A level of significance of 5%, written α = 0.05, means that there is a 5% chance that, when you say the variables are related, they actually are *not* related. Similarly, a level of significance of 1%, or α = 0.01, means that there is a 1% chance that, when you say the variables are related, they actually are *not* related. More complete critical value tables are available in statistics books.

To explain the use of the table, we use *absolute value*, symbolized $| \ |$. The absolute value of a nonzero number is the positive value of the number, and the absolute value of 0 is 0. Therefore,

$$|3| = 3, \quad |-3| = 3, \quad |5| = 5, \quad |-5| = 5, \quad \text{and} \quad |0| = 0$$

If the absolute value of *r*, written $|r|$, is *greater than* the value given in the table under the specified α and appropriate sample size *n*, we assume that a correlation does exist between the variables. If $|r|$ is less than the table value, we assume that no correlation exists.

Returning to Example 1, if we want to determine whether there is a correlation at a 5% level of significance, we find the critical value (or cutoff value) that corresponds to *n* = 6 (there are 6 pieces of bivariate data) and α = 0.05. The value to the right of *n* = 6 and under the α = 0.05 column is the critical value 0.811. From the formula, we had obtained *r* = 0.922. Since $|0.922| > 0.811$, or 0.922 > 0.811, we assume that a correlation between the variables exists.

Note in Table 13.8 that the larger the sample size, the smaller is the value of *r* needed for a significant correlation.

## Example 2  *Amount of Drug Remaining in the Bloodstream*

To test the length of time that an infection-fighting drug stays in a person's bloodstream, a doctor gives 300 milligrams of the drug to 10 patients, labeled 1–10 in the table below. Once each hour, for 10 hours, one of the 10 patients is selected at random and that person's blood is tested to determine the amount of the drug remaining in the bloodstream. The results are as follows.

| Patient | 1 | 2 | 3 | 4 | 5 | 6 | 7 | 8 | 9 | 10 |
|---|---|---|---|---|---|---|---|---|---|---|
| Time (hr) | 1 | 2 | 3 | 4 | 5 | 6 | 7 | 8 | 9 | 10 |
| Drug remaining (mg) | 250 | 230 | 200 | 210 | 140 | 120 | 210 | 100 | 90 | 85 |

*This table of values may be used only under certain conditions. If you take a statistics course, you will learn more about which critical values to use to determine whether a linear correlation exists.

Determine at a level of significance of 5% whether a correlation exists between the time elapsed and the amount of drug remaining.

*Solution*  Let time be represented by $x$ and the amount of drug remaining by $y$. We first draw a scatter diagram (Fig. 13.42).

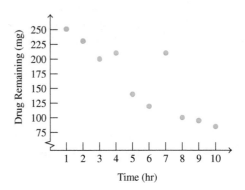

Figure 13.42

The scatter diagram suggests that, if a correlation exists, it will be negative. We now construct a table of values and calculate $r$.

| $x$ | $y$ | $x^2$ | $y^2$ | $xy$ |
|-----|-----|-------|-------|------|
| 1 | 250 | 1 | 62,500 | 250 |
| 2 | 230 | 4 | 52,900 | 460 |
| 3 | 200 | 9 | 40,000 | 600 |
| 4 | 210 | 16 | 44,100 | 840 |
| 5 | 140 | 25 | 19,600 | 700 |
| 6 | 120 | 36 | 14,400 | 720 |
| 7 | 210 | 49 | 44,100 | 1470 |
| 8 | 100 | 64 | 10,000 | 800 |
| 9 | 90 | 81 | 8100 | 810 |
| 10 | 85 | 100 | 7225 | 850 |
| 55 | 1635 | 385 | 302,925 | 7500 |

$$r = \frac{n(\Sigma xy) - (\Sigma x)(\Sigma y)}{\sqrt{n(\Sigma x^2) - (\Sigma x)^2}\,\sqrt{n(\Sigma y^2) - (\Sigma y)^2}}$$

$$= \frac{10(7500) - (55)(1635)}{\sqrt{10(385) - (55)^2}\,\sqrt{10(302,925) - (1635)^2}}$$

$$= \frac{-14,925}{\sqrt{825}\sqrt{356,025}} \approx \frac{-14,925}{17,138.28} \approx -0.871$$

From Table 13.8, for $n = 10$ and $\alpha = 0.05$, we get 0.632. Since $|-0.871| = 0.871$ and $0.871 > 0.632$, a correlation exists. The correlation is negative, which indicates that the longer the time period, the smaller is the amount of drug remaining. ∎

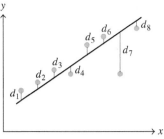

**Figure 13.43**

## Linear Regression

Let's now turn to regression. *Linear regression* is the process of determining the linear relationship between two variables. Recall from Section 6.7 that the slope–intercept form of a straight line is $y = mx + b$, where $m$ is the slope and $b$ is the $y$-intercept.

Using the set of bivariate data, we will determine the equation of *the line of best fit*. The line of best fit is also called *the regression line*, or *the least squares line*. The *line of best fit* is the line such that the sum of the squares of the vertical distances from the line to the data points (on the scatter diagram) is a minimum, as shown in Fig. 13.43. In Fig. 13.43, the line of best fit minimizes the sum of $d_1$ through $d_8$. To determine the equation of the line of best fit, $y = mx + b$,* we must find $m$ and then $b$. The formulas for finding $m$ and $b$ are as follows.*

### The Line of Best Fit
The equation of the line of best fit is

$$y = mx + b,$$

$$\text{where } m = \frac{n(\Sigma xy) - (\Sigma x)(\Sigma y)}{n(\Sigma x^2) - (\Sigma x)^2} \quad \text{and} \quad b = \frac{\Sigma y - m(\Sigma x)}{n}$$

Note that the numerator of the fraction used to find $m$ is identical to the numerator used to find $r$. Therefore, if you have previously found $r$, you do not need to repeat this calculation. Also, the denominator of the fraction used to find $m$ is identical to the radicand of the first square root in the denominator of the fraction used to find $r$.

### Example 3  *The Line of Best Fit*

a) Use the data in Example 1 on pages 835–836 to find the equation of the line of best fit that relates the number of workers absent on an assembly line and the number of defective parts produced.
b) Graph the equation of the line of best fit on a scatter diagram that illustrates the set of bivariate points.

*Solution*

a) In Example 1, we found $n(\Sigma xy) - (\Sigma x)(\Sigma y) = 520$ and $n(\Sigma x^2) - (\Sigma x)^2 = 161$. Thus,

$$m = \frac{n(\Sigma xy) - (\Sigma x)(\Sigma y)}{n(\Sigma x^2) - (\Sigma x)^2} = \frac{520}{161} \approx 3.23$$

Now we find the $y$-intercept, $b$. In Example 1, we found $n = 6$, $\Sigma x = 17$, and $\Sigma y = 106$.

$$b = \frac{\Sigma y - m(\Sigma x)}{n}$$

$$\approx \frac{106 - 3.23(17)}{6} \approx \frac{51.09}{6} \approx 8.52$$

*Some statistics books use $y = ax + b$, $y = b_0 + b_1 x$, or something similar, for the equation of the line of best fit. In any case, the letter next to the variable $x$ represents the slope of the line of best fit, and the other letter represents the $y$-intercept of the graph.

Therefore, the equation of the line of best fit is

$$y = mx + b$$
$$y = 3.23x + 8.52$$

where $x$ represents the number of workers absent and $y$ represents the predicted number of defective parts produced.

b) To graph $y = 3.23x + 8.52$, we need to plot at least two points. We will plot three points and then draw the graph.

| | $y = 3.23x + 8.52$ | | $x$ | $y$ |
|---|---|---|---|---|
| $x = 2$ | $y = 3.23(2) + 8.52 = 14.98$ | | 2 | 14.98 |
| $x = 4$ | $y = 3.23(4) + 8.52 = 21.44$ | | 4 | 21.44 |
| $x = 6$ | $y = 3.23(6) + 8.52 = 27.90$ | | 6 | 27.90 |

These three calculations indicate that if 2 assembly line workers are absent on the assembly line, the predicted number of defective parts produced is about 15. If 4 assembly line workers are absent, the predicted number of defective parts produced is about 21, and if 6 assembly line workers are absent, the predicted number of defective parts produced is about 28. Plot the three points (the three black points in Fig. 13.44) and then draw a straight line through the three points. The scatter diagram and graph of the equation of the line of best fit are plotted in Fig. 13.44.

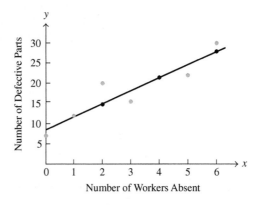

Figure 13.44

In Example 3, the line of best fit intersects the $y$-axis at 8.52, the value we determined for the $y$-intercept, $b$, in part (a).

## Example 4  Line of Best Fit for Example 2

a) Determine the equation of the line of best fit between the time elapsed and the amount of drug remaining in a person's bloodstream in Example 2 on pages 837–838.

b) If the average person is given 300 mg of the drug, how much will remain in the person's bloodstream after 5 hr?

### Solution

a) From the scatter diagram on page 838, we see that the slope of the line of best fit, $m$, will be negative. In Example 2, we found that $n(\Sigma xy) - (\Sigma x)(\Sigma y) = -14{,}925$ and that $n(\Sigma x^2) - (\Sigma x)^2 = 825$. Thus,

$$m = \frac{n(\Sigma xy) - (\Sigma x)(\Sigma y)}{n(\Sigma x^2) - (\Sigma x)^2}$$

$$= \frac{-14{,}925}{825}$$

$$\approx -18.09$$

From Example 2, $n = 10$, $\Sigma x = 55$, and $\Sigma y = 1635$.

$$b = \frac{\Sigma y - m\Sigma x}{n}$$

$$= \frac{1635 - (-18.09)(55)}{10}$$

$$\approx 263.00$$

Thus, the equation of the line of best fit is

$$y = mx + b$$
$$y = -18.09x + 263.00$$

where $x$ is the elapsed time and $y$ is the amount of drug remaining.

b)  We evaluate $y = -18.09x + 263.00$ at $x = 5$.

$$y = -18.09x + 263.00$$
$$y = -18.09(5) + 263.00 = 172.55$$

Thus, after 5 hr, about 173 mg of the drug remains in the average person's bloodstream.

**TECHNOLOGY TIP**

We can use EXCEL and both the TI-83 Plus and the TI-84 Plus graphing calculators to determine the correlation coefficient, $r$, and the equation of the line of best fit. Below we use the data from Example 1 on page 835–836, where $x$ represents the number of workers absent and $y$ represents the number of defective parts for 6 selected days.

**Excel**

Begin by reading the *Technology Tip* on page 802. The instructions for determining the correlation coefficient and equation of the line of best fit are similar to the instructions given on page 802. In column A, rows 1 through 6, enter the 6 values representing the number of workers absent. In column B, rows 1 through 6, enter the 6 values that represent the number of defective parts. In general, the items listed on the horizontal axis in the scatter diagram (the independent variable if there is one) are placed in column A and the items listed on the vertical axis are placed in column B. Then select the following:

Insert > Function ... > Statistical

Then to determine the value of the correlation coefficient, select **CORREL** and click OK. Excel will then generate a gray box and ask you for information about your data. In the box to the right of **Array1**, type in A1:A6, and in the box to the right of **Array2**, type in B1:B6. Then at the bottom of the box you will see *Formula results* = .921927852, which is the correlation coefficient. If you then wish to find the equation of the line of best fit, press CANCEL on the bottom of the gray box. Then select

Insert > Function ... > Statistical > SLOPE > OK

Excel will then generate a gray box. In the box to the right of **Known_y's**, type in B1:B6. In the box to the right of **Known_x's**, type in A1:A6. At that point, at the bottom of the box you will see *Formula results* = 3.229813665, which is the slope of the equation of the line of best fit. To find the y-intercept, press cancel to remove the gray box. Then select

Insert > Function ... > Statistical ... > INTERCEPT > OK

Excel will then generate a gray box. In the box to the right of **Known_y's**, type in B1:B6. In the box to the right of **Known_x's**, type in A1:A6. At that point, at the bottom of the box you will see *Formula results* = 8.51552795, which is the *y*-intercept of the equation of the line of best fit.

**TI-83 Plus And TI-84 Plus Graphing Calculators**

To determine the correlation coefficient and the equation of the line of best fit on a graphing calculator, press $\boxed{STAT}$. Then select Edit. If you have any data in **L1** or **L2**, delete the data by going to **L1** and pressing $\boxed{CLEAR}$ and then $\boxed{ENTER}$. Follow a similar procedure to clear column **L2**. Now enter the 6 pieces of data representing the number of workers absent in column **L1** and enter the 6 pieces of data representing the number of defective parts in **L2**. Then press $\boxed{STAT}$ and highlight **CALC**. At this point, **1: 1 − Var Stats** should be highlighted. Scroll down to highlight **4: LinReg (ax+b)**. Then press the Enter key twice. You will get *r* = .921927852, which represents the correlation coefficient. On the screen, you will also see values for *a* and *b*. Note that *a* represents the slope and *b* represents the *y*-intercept of the equation of the line of best fit. Thus, the slope is 3.229813665 and the *y*-intercept is 8.51552795.

## SECTION 13.7    *Exercises*

### Warm Up Exercises

*In Exercises 1–10, fill in the blank with an appropriate word, phrase, or symbol(s).*

1. A unitless measure that describes the strength of the linear relationship between two variables is called the linear correlation _____.

2. The process of determining the linear relationship between two variables is called linear _____.

3. The value of *r*, the linear correlation coefficient, that represents the strongest positive correlation is _____.

4. The value of *r*, the linear correlation coefficient, that represents the strongest negative correlation is _____.

5. The value of *r*, the linear correlation coefficient, that represents no correlation between two variables is _____.

6. If one quantity increases as the other quantity decreases, the two variables are said to have a(n) _____ correlation.

7. If one quantity increases as the other quantity increases, the two variables are said to have a(n) _____ correlation.

8. A plot of data points is called a(n) _____ diagram.

9. The line such that the sum of the squares of the vertical distances between the data points in the scatter diagram and the line is a minimum is called the line of best _____.

10. The cutoff between results attributed to chance and results attributed to an actual relationship between two variables is called the level of _____.

*In Exercises 11–14, indicate if you believe that a correlation exists between the quantities on the horizontal and vertical axis. If so, indicate if you believe that the correlation is a strong positive correlation, a strong negative correla-*

*tion, a weak positive correlation, a weak negative correlation, or no correlation. Explain your answer.*

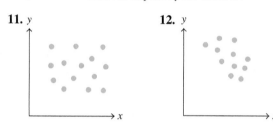

11. | 12.

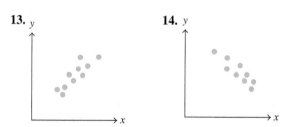

13. | 14.

### Practice the Skills

*In Exercises 15–22, assume that a sample of bivariate data yields the correlation coefficient, r, indicated. Use Table 13.8 on page 837 for the specified sample size and level of significance to determine whether a linear correlation exists.*

15. $r = 0.87$ when $n = 10$ at $\alpha = 0.01$

16. $r = 0.43$ when $n = 27$ at $\alpha = 0.01$

17. $r = -0.92$ when $n = 6$ at $\alpha = 0.05$

18. $r = -0.49$ when $n = 11$ at $\alpha = 0.05$

19. $r = -0.23$ when $n = 102$ at $\alpha = 0.01$

20. $r = -0.49$ when $n = 18$ at $\alpha = 0.01$

21. $r = 0.75$ when $n = 6$ at $\alpha = 0.01$

22. $r = 0.96$ when $n = 5$ at $\alpha = 0.01$

*In Exercises 23–30, (a) draw a scatter diagram; (b) determine the value of r, rounded to the nearest thousandth;(c) determine whether a correlation exists at α = 0.05; and (d) determine whether a correlation exists at α = 0.01.*

**23.**

| x | y |
|---|---|
| 5 | 8 |
| 6 | 10 |
| 7 | 12 |
| 8 | 12 |
| 11 | 16 |

**24.**

| x | y |
|---|---|
| 7 | 14 |
| 9 | 12 |
| 12 | 10 |
| 15 | 11 |
| 18 | 8 |

**25.**

| x | y |
|---|---|
| 23 | 29 |
| 35 | 37 |
| 31 | 26 |
| 43 | 20 |
| 49 | 39 |

**26.**

| x | y |
|---|---|
| 90 | 3 |
| 80 | 4 |
| 60 | 6 |
| 60 | 5 |
| 40 | 5 |
| 20 | 7 |

**27.**

| x | y |
|---|---|
| 5.3 | 10.3 |
| 4.7 | 9.6 |
| 8.4 | 12.5 |
| 12.7 | 16.2 |
| 4.9 | 9.8 |

**28.**

| x | y |
|---|---|
| 12 | 15 |
| 16 | 19 |
| 13 | 45 |
| 24 | 30 |
| 100 | 60 |
| 50 | 28 |

**29.**

| x | y |
|---|---|
| 100 | 2 |
| 80 | 3 |
| 60 | 5 |
| 60 | 6 |
| 40 | 6 |
| 20 | 8 |

**30.**

| x | y |
|---|---|
| 90 | 90 |
| 70 | 70 |
| 65 | 65 |
| 60 | 60 |
| 50 | 50 |
| 40 | 40 |
| 15 | 15 |

*In Exercises 31–38, determine the equation of the line of best fit from the data in the exercise indicated. Round both the slope and the y-intercept to the nearest hundredth.*

**31.** Exercise 23

**32.** Exercise 24

**33.** Exercise 25

**34.** Exercise 26

**35.** Exercise 27

**36.** Exercise 28

**37.** Exercise 29

**38.** Exercise 30

## Problem Solving

*In Exercises 39–49, round both the slope and y-intercept to the nearest hundredth.*

**39.** *Fitness* Six students provided the following data about the number of sit-ups completed and the number of push-ups completed during a fitness test in their physical education class.

| Sit-ups | 50 | 53 | 60 | 35 | 43 | 62 |
|---|---|---|---|---|---|---|
| Push-ups | 40 | 42 | 45 | 25 | 34 | 45 |

a) Determine the correlation coefficient between the number of sit-ups completed and the number of push-ups completed.

b) Determine whether a correlation exists at α = 0.05.

c) Determine the equation of the line of best fit for the number of sit-ups completed and the number of push-ups completed.

**40.** *Amount of Fat in Chicken Nuggets* The June 2010 issue of *Consumer Reports* provided the following information regarding the number of calories and the number of grams of fat per 3-ounce serving of chicken nuggets for the 6 top-rated chicken nuggets.

| Calories | 210 | 310 | 240 | 210 | 160 | 130 |
|---|---|---|---|---|---|---|
| Fat (grams) | 10 | 21 | 16 | 13 | 8 | 4 |

a) Determine the correlation coefficient between the number of calories and the number of grams of fat.

b) Determine whether a correlation exists at α = 0.05.

c) Determine the equation of the line of best fit for the number of calories and the number of grams of fat.

**41.** *Time Spent Studying* Six students provided the following data on page 844 about the lengths of time they studied for a psychology exam and the grades they received on the exam.

| Time studied (minutes) | 20 | 40 | 50 | 60 | 80 | 100 |
|---|---|---|---|---|---|---|
| Grade received (percent) | 40 | 45 | 70 | 76 | 92 | 95 |

a) Determine the correlation coefficient between the length of time studied and the grade received.

b) Determine whether a correlation exists at $\alpha = 0.01$.

c) Find the equation of the line of best fit for the length of time studied and the grade received

42. *Price of a Home*   The following table shows the listing price and the selling price, in thousands of dollars, for eight houses listed and sold.

| List price (thousands $) | 139 | 165 | 210 | 287 | 189 | 115 | 125 | 95 |
|---|---|---|---|---|---|---|---|---|
| Sale price (thousands $) | 120 | 165 | 208 | 275 | 160 | 100 | 118 | 90 |

a) Determine the correlation coefficient between the listing price and the selling price of a house.

b) Determine whether a correlation exists at $\alpha = 0.01$.

c) Determine the equation of the line of best fit for the listing price and selling price of a house.

d) Use the equation in part (c) to estimate the selling price of a house listed for $130,000.

43. *Blood Pressure*   The following table shows the systolic blood pressure and diastolic blood pressure readings for six adults.

| Systolic | 110 | 153 | 120 | 143 | 100 | 112 |
|---|---|---|---|---|---|---|
| Diastolic | 70 | 110 | 80 | 98 | 70 | 75 |

a) Determine the correlation coefficient between the systolic blood pressure and the diastolic blood pressure readings.

b) Determine whether a correlation exists at $\alpha = 0.05$.

c) Determine the equation of the line of best fit for the systolic blood pressure and the diastolic blood pressure readings.

d) Use the equation in part (c) to estimate the diastolic blood pressure for an adult with a systolic blood pressure reading of 115.

44. *Selling Popcorn at the Movies*   The number of movie tickets sold and the number of units of popcorn sold at AMC Cinema for 8 days is shown below.

| Ticket sales | 89 | 110 | 125 | 92 | 100 | 95 | 108 | 97 |
|---|---|---|---|---|---|---|---|---|
| Units of popcorn | 22 | 28 | 30 | 26 | 22 | 21 | 28 | 25 |

a) Determine the correlation coefficient between ticket sales and units of popcorn sold.

b) Determine whether a correlation exists at $\alpha = 0.05$.

c) Determine the equation of the line of best fit for tickets sold and units of popcorn sold.

d) Use the equation in part (c) to estimate the units of popcorn sold if 115 tickets are sold.

45. *Fuel Efficiency of Cars*   The following table shows the weights, in hundreds of pounds, for six selected cars. Also shown is the corresponding fuel efficiency, in miles per gallon (mpg), for the car in city driving.

| Weight (hundreds of pounds) | 27 | 31 | 35 | 32 | 30 | 30 |
|---|---|---|---|---|---|---|
| Fuel efficiency (mpg) | 23 | 22 | 20 | 21 | 24 | 22 |

a) Determine the correlation coefficient between the weight of a car and the fuel efficiency.

b) Determine whether a correlation exists at $\alpha = 0.01$.

c) Determine the equation of the line of best fit for the weight of a car and the fuel efficiency of a car.

d) Use the equation in part (c) to estimate the fuel efficiency of a car that weighs 33 hundred pounds.

46. *City Muggings*   In a certain section of a city, muggings have been a problem. The number of police officers patrolling that section of the city has varied. The following chart shows the number of police officers and the number of muggings for 8 successive days.

| Police officers | 20 | 12 | 18 | 15 | 22 | 10 | 20 | 12 |
|---|---|---|---|---|---|---|---|---|
| Muggings | 8 | 10 | 12 | 9 | 6 | 15 | 7 | 18 |

**a)** Determine the correlation coefficient for number of police officers and number of muggings.

**b)** Determine whether a correlation exists at $\alpha = 0.05$.

**c)** Find the equation of the line of best fit for number of police officers and number of muggings.

**d)** Use the equation in part (c) to estimate the average number of muggings when 14 police officers are patrolling that section of the city.

**47.** *Chlorine in a Swimming Pool* A gallon of chlorine is put into a swimming pool. Each hour later for the following 6 hours the percent of chlorine that remains in the pool is measured. The following information is obtained.

| Time | 1 | 2 | 3 | 4 | 5 | 6 |
|---|---|---|---|---|---|---|
| Chlorine remaining (percent) | 80.0 | 76.2 | 68.7 | 50.1 | 30.2 | 20.8 |

**a)** Determine the correlation coefficient for time and percent of chlorine remaining.

**b)** Determine whether a correlation exists at $\alpha = 0.01$.

**c)** Determine the equation of the line of best fit for time and amount of chlorine remaining.

**d)** Use the equation in part (c) to estimate the average amount of chlorine remaining after 4.5 hr.

**48.** *Social Security Numbers* **a)** Match the first 9 digits of your phone number (including area code) with the 9 digits in your Social Security number. To do so, match the first digit in your phone number with the first digit in your Social Security number to get one ordered pair. Match the second digits to get a second ordered pair. Continue this process until you get a total of nine ordered pairs.

**b)** Do you believe that this set of bivariate data has a positive correlation, a negative correlation, or no correlation? Explain your answer.

**c)** Construct a scatter diagram for the nine ordered pairs.

**d)** Calculate the correlation coefficient, *r*.

**e)** Is there a correlation at $\alpha = 0.05$? Explain.

**f)** Calculate the equation of the line of best fit.

**g)** Use the equation in part (f) to estimate the digit in a social Security number that corresponds with a 7 in a telephone number.

**49.** *Hitting the Brakes* **a)** Examine the art below. Do you believe that there is a positive correlation, a negative correlation, or no correlation between speed of a car and stopping distance when the brakes are applied?

**b)** Do you believe that there is a stronger correlation between speed of a car and stopping distance on wet or dry roads?

**c)** Use the figure to construct two scatter diagrams, one for dry pavement and the other for wet pavement. Place the speed of the car on the horizontal axis.

**d)** Compute the correlation coefficient for speed of the car and stopping distance for dry pavement.

**e)** Repeat part (d) for wet pavement.

**f)** Were your answers to parts (a) and (b) correct? Explain.

**g)** Determine the equation of the line of best fit for dry pavement.

**h)** Repeat part (g) for wet pavement.

**i)** Use the equations in parts (g) and (h) to estimate the stopping distance of a car going 77 mph on both dry and wet pavements.

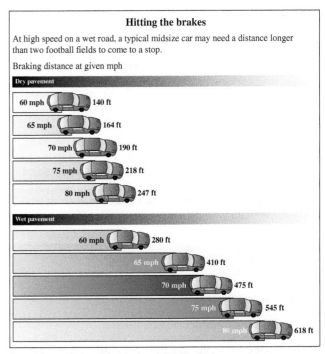

**Hitting the brakes**

At high speed on a wet road, a typical midsize car may need a distance longer than two football fields to come to a stop.

Braking distance at given mph

Dry pavement

60 mph 140 ft
65 mph 164 ft
70 mph 190 ft
75 mph 218 ft
80 mph 247 ft

Wet pavement

60 mph 280 ft
65 mph 410 ft
70 mph 475 ft
75 mph 545 ft
80 mph 618 ft

Source: *Car and Driver*, American Automobile Association

## Challenge Problems/Group Activities

**50.** *Interchanging Variables* **a)** Assume that a set of bi-variate data yields a specific correlation coefficient. If the *x*- and *y*-values are interchanged and the correlation coefficient is recalculated, will the correlation coefficient change?

**b)** Make up a table of five pieces of bivariate data and determine *r* using the data. Then switch the values of the *x*'s and *y*'s and recompute the correlation coefficient. Has the value of *r* changed?

**51.** *Height vs. Length* **a)** Do you believe that a correlation exists between a person's height and the length of a person's arm?

**b)** Select 10 people from your class and measure (in inches) their heights and the lengths of their arms.

**c)** Plot the 10 ordered pairs on a scatter diagram.

**d)** Calculate the correlation coefficient, *r*.

**e)** Determine the equation of the line of best fit.

**f)** Estimate the length of the arm of a person who is 58 in. tall.

**52.** *Calculating a Correlation Coefficient* **a)** Have your group select a category of bivariate data that it thinks has a strong positive correlation. Designate the independent variable and the dependent variable. Explain why your group believes that the bivariate data have a strong positive correlation.

**b)** Collect at least 10 pieces of bivariate data that can be used to determine the correlation coefficient. Explain how your group chose these data.

**c)** Plot a scatter diagram.

**d)** Calculate the correlation coefficient.

**e)** Does there appear to be a strong positive correlation? Explain your answer.

**f)** Calculate the equation of the line of best fit.

**g)** Explain how the equation in part (f) may be used.

**53.** *CPI* Use the following table. CPI represents consumer price index.

| Year | 2005 | 2006 | 2007 | 2008 | 2009 | 2010 |
|------|------|------|------|------|------|------|
| CPI | 195.3 | 201.6 | 207.3 | 215.3 | 214.5 | 218.1 |

**a)** Calculate *r*.

**b)** If 2005 is subtracted from each year, the table obtained becomes:

| Year | 0 | 1 | 2 | 3 | 4 | 5 |
|------|---|---|---|---|---|---|
| CPI | 195.3 | 201.6 | 207.3 | 215.3 | 214.5 | 218.1 |

If *r* is calculated from these values, how will it compare with the *r* determined in part (a)? Explain.

**c)** Calculate *r* from the values in part (b) and compare the results with the value of *r* found in part (a). Are they the same? If not, explain why.

**54. a)** There are equivalent formulas that can be used to find the correlation coefficient and the equation of the line of best fit. A formula used in some statistics books to find the correlation coefficient is

$$r = \frac{SS(xy)}{\sqrt{SS(x)SS(y)}}$$

where

$$SS(x) = \Sigma x^2 - \frac{(\Sigma x)^2}{n}$$

$$SS(y) = \Sigma y^2 - \frac{(\Sigma y)^2}{n}$$

$$SS(xy) = \Sigma xy - \frac{(\Sigma x)(\Sigma y)}{n}$$

Use this formula to find the correlation coefficient of the set of bivariate data given in Example 1 on page 835–836.

**b)** Compare your answer with the answer obtained in Example 1.

## Internet/Research Activity

**55. a)** Obtain a set of bivariate data from a newspaper or magazine.

**b)** Plot the information on a scatter diagram.

**c)** Indicate whether you believe that the data show a positive correlation, a negative correlation, or no correlation. Explain your answer.

**d)** Calculate *r* and determine whether your answer to part (c) was correct.

**e)** Determine the equation of the line of best fit for the bivariate data.

**56.** Find a scatter diagram in a newspaper or magazine and write a paper on what the diagram indicates. Indicate whether you believe that the bivariate data show a positive correlation, a negative correlation, or no correlation and explain why.

## CHAPTER 13 ) *Summary*

| Important Facts and Concepts | Examples and Discussion |
|---|---|
| **Section 13.1** | |
| *Sampling Techniques* | |
| Random sampling | Example 1, page 777 |
| Systematic sampling | |
| Cluster sampling | |
| Stratified sampling | |
| Convenience sampling | |
| **Section 13.2** | |
| Misuses of statistics | Discussion pages 779–781 |
| **Section 13.3** | |
| Frequency Distribution | Examples 1–2, pages 784–786 |
| *Rules for Data Grouped by Classes* | |
| 1. The classes should be the same width. | Discussion, page 784; Examples 1–3, |
| 2. The classes should not overlap. | pages 784–787 |
| 3. Each piece of data should belong to only one class. | |
| *Statistical Graphs* | |
| Histogram | Examples 4, 6, 7, pages 787–789 |
| Frequency polygon | Examples 5–6, pages 788–789 |
| Stem-and-leaf display | Examples 8, pages 790–791 |
| Circle graph | Examples 9, pages 791–792 |
| **Section 13.4** | |
| *Measures of Central Tendency* | |
| The **mean** is the sum of the data divided by the number of pieces of data: $\bar{x} = \dfrac{\Sigma x}{n}$. | Example 1, page 797 |
| The **median** is the value in the middle of a set of ranked data. | Examples 2–3, 6, pages 798–799 |
| The **mode** is the piece of data that occurs most frequently (if there is one). | Examples 4, 6, pages 798–799 |
| The **midrange** is the value halfway between the lowest and highest values: midrange $= \dfrac{L + H}{2}$. | Examples 5, 6, page 799 |
| **Percentiles** and **Quartiles** are measures of position. | Examples 7–8, pages 800–801 |

**Section 13.5**
**Measures of Dispersion**

The **range** is the difference between the highest value and lowest value in a set of data.

The **standard deviation,** $s$, is a measure of the spread of a set of data about the mean: $s = \sqrt{\dfrac{\Sigma(x - \bar{x})^2}{n - 1}}$.

Discussion pages 808–812;
Example 1, page 808
Examples 2–3, pages 809–811

**Section 13.6**
**z–SCORES**

$$z = \frac{\text{value of the piece of data} - \text{mean}}{\text{standard deviation}}$$

Discussion pages 820–828;
Examples 2–5, pages 820–828

**Section 13.7**
**Linear Correlation And Regression**

**Linear correlation coefficient,** $r$, is

$$r = \frac{n(\Sigma xy) - (\Sigma x)(\Sigma y)}{\sqrt{n(\Sigma x^2) - (\Sigma x)^2} \sqrt{n(\Sigma y^2) - (\Sigma y)^2}}$$

Discussion pages 833–835;
Examples 1–2, pages 835–838

**Equation of the Line of the Best Fit**

$y = mx + b$, where

$$m = \frac{n(\Sigma xy) - (\Sigma x)(\Sigma y)}{n(\Sigma x^2) - (\Sigma x)^2}$$

$$b = \frac{\Sigma y - m(\Sigma x)}{n}$$

Discussion pages 839–840;
Examples 3–4, pages 839–841

## CHAPTER 13 ) *Review Exercises*

### 13.1

**1. a)** What is a population?

  **b)** What is a sample?

**2.** What is a random sample?

### 13.2

*In Exercises 3 and 4, tell what possible misuses or misinterpretations may exist in the statements.*

**3.** The Stay Healthy Candy Bar indicates on its label that it has no cholesterol. Therefore, it is safe to eat as many of these candy bars as you want.

**4.** More copies of *Time* magazine are sold than are copies of *Money* magazine. Therefore, *Time* is a more profitable magazine than *Money*.

**5.** *U.S. Households with Cable Television* In 2008, 99.7 million households in the United States subscribed to cable

television. In 2009, 103.0 million households in the United States subscribed to cable television. Draw a graph that appears to show a

**a)** small increase in the number of households subscribing to cable television from 2008 to 2009.

**b)** large increase in the number of households subscribing to cable television from 2008 to 2009.

### 13.3

**6.** Consider the following set of data.

| | | | | |
|---|---|---|---|---|
| 35 | 37 | 38 | 41 | 43 |
| 36 | 37 | 38 | 41 | 43 |
| 36 | 37 | 39 | 41 | 43 |
| 36 | 37 | 39 | 41 | 44 |
| 37 | 37 | 39 | 42 | 45 |

**a)** Construct a frequency distribution letting each class have a width of 1.

**b)** Construct a histogram.

**c)** Construct a frequency polygon.

**7.** *Average Monthly High Temperature*  Consider the following average monthly high temperature in July for 40 selected U.S. cities.

71  79  58  73  80  75  84  77
82  72  80  70  75  66  73  72
80  66  74  68  81  84  75  67
91  76  82  79  63  69  68  79
71  76  80  83  73  87  82  71

**a)** Construct a frequency distribution. Let the first class be 58–62.

**b)** Construct a histogram of the frequency distribution.

**c)** Construct a frequency polygon of the frequency distribution.

**d)** Construct a stem-and-leaf display.

## 13.4, 13.5

*In Exercises 8–13, for the following test scores 67, 74, 79, 83, 84, 93, determine the*

**8.** mean.                    **9.** median.

**10.** mode.                   **11.** midrange.

**12.** range.                  **13.** standard deviation.

*In Exercises 14–19, for the set of data 4, 5, 12, 14, 19, 7, 12, 23, 7, 17, 15, 21, determine the*

**14.** mean.                   **15.** median.

**16.** mode.                   **17.** midrange.

**18.** range.                  **19.** standard deviation.

## 13.6

*Police Response Time  In Exercises 20–24, assume that police response time to emergency calls is normally distributed with a mean of 9 minutes and a standard deviation of 2 minutes. Determine the percent of emergency calls with a police response time*

**20.** between 7 and 11 minutes.  **21.** between 5 and 13 minutes.

**22.** less than 12.2 minutes.    **23.** more than 12.2 minutes.

**24.** more than 7.8 minutes.

*Pizza Delivery  In Exercises 25–28, assume that the amount of time to prepare and deliver a pizza from Pepe's Pizza*

*is normally distributed with a mean of 20 minutes and standard deviation of 5 minutes. Determine the percent of pizzas that were prepared and delivered*

**25.** between 20 and 25 minutes.  **26.** in less than 18 minutes.

**27.** between 22 and 28 minutes.

**28.** If Pepe's Pizza advertises that the pizza is free if it takes more than 30 min to deliver, what percent of the pizza will be free?

## 13.7

**29.** *Hiking*  The following table shows the number of hiking permits issued for a specific trail at Yellowstone National Park for selected years and the corresponding number of bears sighted by the hikers on that trail.

| Hiking permits | 765 | 926 | 1145 | 842 | 1485 | 1702 |
|---|---|---|---|---|---|---|
| Bears | 119 | 127 | 150 | 119 | 153 | 156 |

**a)** Construct a scatter diagram with hiking permits on the horizontal axis.

**b)** Use the scatter diagram in part (a) to determine whether you believe that a correlation exists between the number of hiking permits issued and the number of bears sighted by hikers. If so, is it a positive or negative correlation?

**c)** Calculate the correlation coefficient between the number of hiking permits issued and the number of bears sighted by hikers.

**d)** Determine whether a correlation exists at $\alpha = 0.05$.

**e)** Determine the equation of the line of best fit between the number of hiking permits issued and the number of bears sighted by hikers. Round both the slope and $y$-intercept to the nearest hundredth.

**f)** Assuming that this trend continues, use the equation of the line of best fit to estimate the number of bears sighted if 1500 hiking permits were issued.

**30. *Daily Sales*** Ace Hardware recorded the number of a particular item sold per week for 6 weeks and the corresponding weekly price, in dollars, of the item as shown in the table below.

| Price ($) | 0.75 | 1.00 | 1.25 | 1.50 | 1.75 | 2.00 |
|-----------|------|------|------|------|------|------|
| Number sold | 200 | 160 | 140 | 120 | 110 | 95 |

**a)** Construct a scatter diagram with price on the horizontal axis.

**b)** Use the scatter diagram in part (a) to determine whether you believe that a correlation exists between the price of the item and number sold. If so, it is a positive or a negative correlation?

**c)** Determine the correlation coefficient between the price and the number sold.

**d)** Determine whether a correlation exists at $\alpha = 0.05$.

**e)** Determine the equation of the line of best fit for the price and the number sold.

**f)** Use the equation in part (e) to estimate the number sold if the price is $1.60.

## 13.4–13.6

***Men's Weight*** *In Exercises 31–38, use the following data obtained from a study of the weights of adult men.*

| Mean | 192 lb | First quartile | 178 lb |
|------|--------|----------------|--------|
| Median | 185 lb | Third quartile | 232 lb |
| Mode | 180 lb | 86th percentile | 239 lb |
| Standard deviation | 23 lb | | |

**31.** What is the most common weight?

**32.** What weight did half of those surveyed exceed?

**33.** About what percent of those surveyed weighed more than 232 lb?

**34.** About what percent of those surveyed weighed less than 178 lb?

**35.** About what percent of those surveyed weighed more than 239 lb?

**36.** If 100 men were surveyed, what is the total weight of all men?

**37.** What weight represents two standard deviations above the mean?

**38.** What weight represents 1.8 standard deviations below the mean?

## 13.2–13.6

***Presidential Children*** *The following list shows the names of the 43 U.S. presidents and the number of children in their families.*

| | | | |
|---|---|---|---|
| Washington | 0 | B. Harrison | 3 |
| J. Adams | 5 | McKinley | 2 |
| Jefferson | 6 | T. Roosevelt | 6 |
| Madison | 0 | Taft | 3 |
| Monroe | 2 | Wilson | 3 |
| J. Q. Adams | 4 | Harding | 0 |
| Jackson | 0 | Coolidge | 2 |
| Van Buren | 4 | Hoover | 2 |
| W. H. Harrison | 10 | F. D. Roosevelt | 6 |
| Tyler | 14 | Truman | 1 |
| Polk | 0 | Eisenhower | 2 |
| Taylor | 6 | Kennedy | 3 |
| Fillmore | 2 | L. B. Johnson | 2 |
| Pierce | 3 | Nixon | 2 |
| Buchanan | 0 | Ford | 4 |
| Lincoln | 4 | Carter | 4 |
| A. Johnson | 5 | Reagan | 4 |
| Grant | 4 | G. Bush | 6 |
| Hayes | 8 | Clinton | 1 |
| Garfield | 7 | G. W. Bush | 2 |
| Arthur | 3 | Obama | 2 |
| Cleveland | 5 | | |

*In Exercises 39–50, use the data to determine the following.*

**39.** Mean

**40.** Mode

**41.** Median

**42.** Midrange

**43.** Range

**44.** Standard deviation (round the mean to the nearest tenth)

**45.** Construct a frequency distribution; let the first class be 0–1.

**46.** Construct a histogram of the frequency distribution.

**47.** Construct a frequency polygon of the frequency distribution.

**48.** Does this distribution appear to be normal? Explain.

**49.** Do you think the number of children per family in the United States is a normal distribution? Explain.

**50.** Is this set of data representative of the U.S. population? Explain.

## CHAPTER 13  Test

*In Exercises 1–6, for the set of data 27, 43, 43, 45, 52, determine the*

**1.** mean.

**2.** median.

**3.** mode.

**4.** midrange.

**5.** range.

**6.** standard deviation.

*In Exercises 7–9, use the set of data*

| | | | | | |
|---|---|---|---|---|---|
| 26 | 28 | 35 | 46 | 49 | 56 |
| 26 | 30 | 36 | 46 | 49 | 58 |
| 26 | 32 | 40 | 47 | 50 | 58 |
| 26 | 32 | 44 | 47 | 52 | 62 |
| 27 | 35 | 46 | 47 | 54 | 66 |

*to construct the following.*

**7.** a frequency distribution; let the first class be 25–30

**8.** a histogram of the frequency distribution

**9.** a frequency polygon of the frequency distribution

**Statistics on Salaries**  *In Exercises 10–16, use the following data on weekly salaries at Donovan's Construction Company.*

| | | | |
|---|---|---|---|
| Mean | $740 | First quartile | $690 |
| Median | $710 | Third quartile | $745 |
| Mode | $735 | 79th percentile | $752 |
| Standard deviation | $40 | | |

**10.** What is the most common salary?

**11.** What salary did half the employees exceed?

**12.** About what percent of employees' salaries exceeded $690?

**13.** About what percent of employees' salaries was less than $752?

**14.** If the company has 100 employees, what is the total weekly salary of all employees?

**15.** What salary represents one standard deviation above the mean?

*Anthropology  In Exercises 16–19, assume that anthropologists have determined that the akidolestes, a small primitive mammal believed to have lived with the dinosaurs, had a head circumference that was normally distributed with a mean of 42 cm and a standard deviation of 5 cm.*

**16.** What percent of head circumferences were between 36 and 53 cm?

**17.** What percent of head circumferences were greater than 35.75 cm?

**18.** What percent of head circumferences were greater than 48.25 cm?

**19.** What percent of head circumferences were less than 50 cm?

**20.** *Minimum Wage*  The following table shows the hourly minimum wage in the U.S. for the years 2006–2010, where the column labeled Year refers to the number of years since 2006.

| Year | Minimum Wage |
|---|---|
| 0 | $5.15 |
| 1 | $5.85 |
| 2 | $6.55 |
| 3 | $7.25 |
| 4 | $7.25 |

Source: *Bureau of Labor Statistics*

a) Construct a scatter diagram placing the year on the horizontal axis.

b) Use the scatter diagram in part (a) to determine whether you believe a correlation exists between the year and the minimum wage.

c) Determine the correlation coefficient between the year and the minimum wage.

d) Determine whether a correlation exists at $\alpha = 0.05$.

e) Determine the equation of the line of best fit between the year and the minimum wage. Round both the slope and $y$-intercept to the nearest hundredth.

f) Use the equation in part (e) to predict the minimum wage in 2014.

## GROUP PROJECTS

### Watching TV

1. Do you think that men or women, aged 17–20, watch more hours of TV weekly, or do you think that they watch the same number of hours?

   a) Write a procedure to use to determine the answer to that question. In your procedure, use a sample of 30 men and 30 women. State how you will obtain an unbiased sample.

   b) Collect 30 pieces of data from men aged 17–20 and 30 pieces of data from women aged 17–20. Round answers to the nearest 0.5 hr. Follow the procedure developed in part (a) to obtain your unbiased sample.

   c) Compute the mean for your two groups of data to the nearest tenth.

   d) Using the means obtained in part (c), answer the question asked at the beginning of the problem.

   e) Is it possible that your conclusion in part (d) is wrong? Explain.

   f) Compute the standard deviation for each group to the nearest tenth. How do the standard deviations compare?

   g) Do you believe that the distribution of data from either or both groups resembles a normal distribution? Explain.

   h) Add the two groups of data to get one group of 60 pieces of data. If these 60 pieces of data are added and divided by 60, will you obtain the same mean as when you add the two means from part (c) and divide the sum by 2? Explain.

   i) Compute the mean of the 60 pieces of data by using both methods mentioned in part (h). Are they the same? If so, why? If not, why not?

   j) Do you believe that this group of 60 pieces of data represents a normal distribution? Explain.

### Bivariate Data Experiment

2. a) Have your group select a category of bivariate data that it thinks has a strong negative correlation. Indicate the variable that you will designate as the independent variable and the variable that you will designate as the dependent variable. Explain why your group believes that the bivariate data have a strong negative correlation.

   b) Collect at least 10 pieces of bivariate data that can be used to determine the correlation coefficient. Explain how your group chose these data.

   c) Plot a scatter diagram.

   d) Calculate the correlation coefficient.

   e) Is there a negative correlation at $\alpha = 0.05$? Explain your answer.

   f) Calculate the equation of the line of best fit.

   g) Explain how the equation in part (f) may be used.

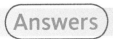

**Chapter 2**

SECTION 2.1, PAGE 47

1. Set  3. Description, roster form, set-builder notation.

5. Infinite  7. Equivalent  9. Empty or null

11. Universal  13. Not well defined  15. Well defined

17. Well defined  19. Infinite  21. Infinite  23. Infinite

25. $\{$ Maine, Maryland, Massachusetts, Michigan, Minnesota, Mississippi, Missouri, Montana $\}$

27. $\{11, 12, 13, 14, \ldots, 177\}$  29. $B = \{2, 4, 6, 8, \ldots\}$

31. $\{\ \}$ or $\varnothing$  33. $E = \{14, 15, 16, 17, \ldots, 84\}$

35. $\{$Louvre Museum, British Museum, National Gallery of Art, Tate Modern, Metropolitan Museum of Art$\}$

37. $\{$Musee d'Orsay, Musee d'Art Moderne Prado, Museum of Modern Art$\}$

39. $\{2007, 2008\}$

41. $\{2004, 2005, 2006, 2007\}$

43. $B = \{x \mid x \in N \text{ and } 6 < x < 15\}$ or $B = \{x \mid x \in N \text{ and } 7 \le x \le 14\}$

45. $C = \{x \mid x \in N \text{ and } x \text{ is a multiple of } 3\}$

47. $E = \{x \mid x \in N \text{ and } x \text{ is odd}\}$

49. $C = \{x \mid x \text{ is February}\}$

51. Set $A$ is the set of natural numbers less than or equal to 7.

53. Set $V$ is the set of vowels in the English alphabet.

55. Set $T$ is the set of species of trees.

57. Set $S$ is the set of seasons.

59. $\{$China, India, United States$\}$

61. $\{$Russia, Brazil, Indonesia, Japan, Germany$\}$

63. $\{2008, 2009, 2010, 2011\}$

65. $\{2000, 2001, 2002, 2003, 2004, 2005, 2007\}$

67. False; $\{e\}$ is a set, and not an element of the set.

69. False; $h$ is not an element of the set.

71. False; 3 is an element of the set.

73. True  75. 4  77. 0  79. Both

81. Neither  83. Equivalent

85. a) Set $A$ is the set of natural numbers greater than 2. Set $B$ is the set of all numbers greater than 2.

   b) Set $A$ contains only natural numbers. Set $B$ contains other types of numbers, including fractions and decimal numbers.

   c) $A = \{3, 4, 5, 6, \ldots\}$

   d) No; because there are an infinite number of elements between any two elements in set $B$, we cannot write set $B$ in roster form.

87. Cardinal  89. Ordinal  91. Answers will vary.

93. Answers will vary.

SECTION 2.2, PAGE 55

1. Subset  3. $2^n$  5. True

7. False; McIntosh is not in the second set.

9. True  11. False; no set is a proper subset of itself.

13. True  15. False; $\{$swimming$\}$ is a set not an element

17. True  19. True

21. False; the set $\{\varnothing\}$ contains the element $\varnothing$.

23. False; the set $\{0\}$ contains the element 0.

25. False; 0 is a numbner and $\{\ \}$ is a set.

27. $B \subseteq A, B \subset A$  29. $A \subseteq B, A \subset B$,  31. $B \subseteq A, B \subset A$

33. $A = B, A \subseteq B, B \subseteq A$  35. $\{\ \}$

37. $\{\}, \{\text{cow}\}, \{\text{horse}\}, \{\text{cow, horse}\}$

39. a) $\{\ \}, \{a\}, \{b\}, \{c\}, \{d\}, \{a,b\}, \{a,c\}, \{a,d\}, \{b,c\}, \{b,d\}, \{c,d\}, \{a,b,c\}, \{a,b,d\}, \{a,c,d\}, \{b,c,d\}, \{a,b,c,d\}$

   b) $\{a, b, c, d\}$

41. False  43. True  45. True  47. True  49. True

51. True  53. $2^8$ or 256  55. $2^7$ or 128  57. $E = F$

59. a) Yes  b) No  c) Yes  61. 1  62. Yes  63. Yes

64. No

SECTION 2.3, PAGE 63

1. Complement  3. Intersection  5. Cartesian  7. Disjoint

9.

11.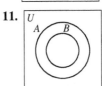

13.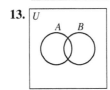

15. *And* is generally interpreted to mean *intersection*.

17.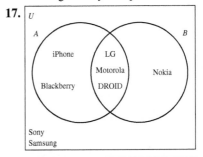

19.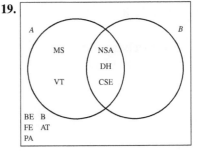

**21.** The set of animals in U.S. zoos that are not in the San Diego Zoo

**23.** The set of farms in the United States that do not produce corn

**25.** The set of farms in the United States that produce corn or produce tomatoes

**27.** The set of farms in the United States that produce corn and do not produce tomatoes

**29.** The set of furniture stores that sell mattresses or leather furniture

**31.** The set of furniture stores that do not sell outdoor furniture and sell leather furniture

**33.** The set of furniture stores that sell mattresses or outdoor furniture or leather furniture

**35.** $\{b, c, t, w, a, h\}$    **37.** $\{a, h\}$

**39.** $\{c, w, b, t, a, h, f, r, d, g\}$    **41.** $\{p, m, z\}$

**43.** $\{L, \Delta, @, \$, *\}$    **45.** $\{L, \Delta, @, *, \$, R, \square, \alpha, \infty, \Sigma, Z\}$

**47.** $\{R, \square, \alpha, *, \$, \infty, Z, \Sigma\}$    **49.** $\{R, \square, \alpha\}$

**51.** $\{1, 2, 3, 4, 5, 6, 7\}$    **53.** $\{1, 4, 7, 8\}$    **55.** $\{8\}$

**57.** $\{\ \}$    **59.** $\{8\}$    **61.** $\{a, e, h, i, j, k\}$    **63.** $\{a, f, i\}$

**65.** $\{b, c, d, e, g, h, j, k\}$    **67.** $\{a, c, d, e, f, g, h, i, j, k\}$

**69.** $\{a, b, c, d, e, f, g, h, i, j, k\}$, or $U$    **71.** $\{2, 6, 9\}$

**73.** $\{1, 4\}$    **75.** $\{1, 3, 4, 5, 7, 8, 10\}$    **77.** $\{4, 9\}$

**79.** $\{(a, 1), (a, 2), (b, 1), (b, 2), (c, 1), (c, 2)\}$

**81.** No. The ordered pairs are not the same. For example, $(a, 1) \neq (1, a)$.

**83.** 6    **85.** $\{\ \}$    **87.** $\{2, 4, 6, 8\}$, or $B$    **89.** $\{7, 9\}$

**91.** $\{1, 3, 5, 6, 7, 8, 9\}$    **93.** $\{6, 8\}$

**95.** $\{1, 2, 3, 4, 5, 6, 7, 8, 9\}$, or $U$

**97.** $\{1, 2, 3, 4, 5\}$, or $C$

**99.** A set and its complement will always be disjoint. For example, if $U = \{1, 2, 3\}$ and $A = \{1, 2\}$, then $A' = \{3\}$, and $A \cap A' = \{\ \}$.

**101.** 49

**103.** a) $8 = 4 + 6 - 2$
  b) Answers will vary.
  c) Answers will vary.

**105.** $\{1, 2, 3, 4, \dots\}$, or $A$

**107.** $\{2, 4, 6, 8, \dots\}$, or $C$

**109.** $\{2, 4, 6, 8, \dots\}$, or $C$

**111.** $\{2, 6, 10, 14, 18, \dots\}$

**113.** $\{2, 6, 10, 14, 18, \dots\}$

**115.** $\{\ \}$    **117.** $A$    **119.** $U$    **121.** $U$    **123.** $B \subseteq A$

**125.** $A$ and $B$ are disjoint sets.    **127.** $A \subseteq B$

**SECTION 2.4, PAGE 72**

**1.** 8    **3.** a) $A' \cap B'$    b) $A' \cup B'$    **5.** 8

**7.** a) Yes
  b) No, one specific case cannot be used as proof.
  c) No, not equal

**9.**

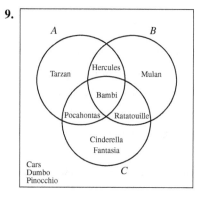

**11.**

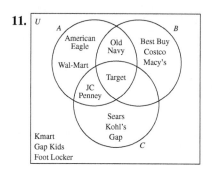

**13.**

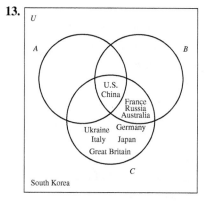

**15.** II    **17.** VIII    **19.** III    **21.** VI    **23.** III    **25.** III    **27.** V

**29.** II    **31.** VII    **33.** I    **35.** VIII    **37.** VI

**39.** $\{1, 2, 3, 4, 5, 7\}$    **41.** $\{3, 4, 5, 6, 8, 9, 12, 14\}$

**43.** $\{3, 4, 5\}$    **45.** $\{1, 2, 3, 7, 9, 10, 11, 12, 13, 14\}$

**47.** $\{1, 2, 3, 4, 5, 6, 7, 8, 9, 12, 14\}$    **49.** $\{9, 10, 12, 13, 14\}$

**51.** $\{6, 8, 9, 10, 11, 12, 13, 14\}$    **53.** Yes    **55.** No

**57.** No    **59.** Yes    **61.** No    **63.** Yes    **65.** Yes    **67.** Yes

**69.** No    **71.** $(A \cup B)'$    **73.** $(A \cup B) \cap C'$

**75.** a) Both equal $\{6, 7\}$.    b) Answers will vary.
  c) Both are represented by the regions IV, V, VI.

**77.**

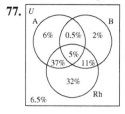

**79. a)**

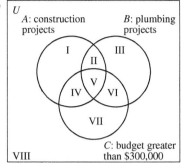

U
A: construction projects
B: plumbing projects
I   II   III
V
IV   VI
VII
C: budget greater than $300,000
VIII

**b)** V; $A \cap B \cap C$   **c)** VI; $A' \cap B \cap C$
**d)** I; $A \cap B' \cap C'$

**81. a)**

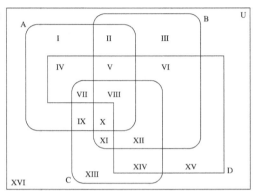

U
A
B
I   II   III
IV   V   VI
VII   VIII
IX   X
XI   XII
XIII   XIV   XV   D
XVI   C

**b)**

| Region | Set | Region | Set |
|---|---|---|---|
| I | $A \cap B' \cap C' \cap D'$ | IX | $A \cap B' \cap C \cap D'$ |
| II | $A \cap B \cap C' \cap D'$ | X | $A \cap B \cap C \cap D'$ |
| III | $A' \cap B \cap C' \cap D'$ | XI | $A' \cap B \cap C \cap D'$ |
| IV | $A \cap B' \cap C' \cap D$ | XII | $A' \cap B \cap C \cap D$ |
| V | $A \cap B \cap C' \cap D$ | XIII | $A' \cap B' \cap C \cap D'$ |
| VI | $A' \cap B \cap C' \cap D$ | XIV | $A' \cap B' \cap C \cap D$ |
| VII | $A \cap B' \cap C \cap D$ | XV | $A' \cap B' \cap C' \cap D$ |
| VIII | $A \cap B \cap C \cap D$ | XVI | $A' \cap B' \cap C' \cap D'$ |

**SECTION 2.5, PAGE 80**

**1.**

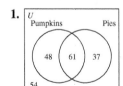

U
Pumpkins   Pies
48   61   37
54

**a)** 48   **b)** 37   **c)** 54

**3.**

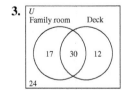

U
Family room   Deck
17   30   12
24

**a)** 17   **b)** 12   **c)** 59

**5.**

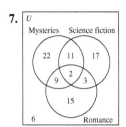

U   Professional sports team   Symphony
3   6   2
5
2   4
4
7   Children's museum

**a)** 3   **b)** 6   **c)** 22   **d)** 11   **e)** 12

**7.**

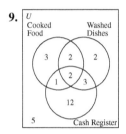

U
Mysteries   Science fiction
22   11   17
2
9   3
15
6   Romance

**a)** 22   **b)** 11   **c)** 64   **d)** 50   **e)** 23

**9.**

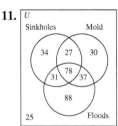

U
Cooked Food   Washed Dishes
3   2   2
2
1   3
12
5   Cash Register

**a)** 3   **b)** 12   **c)** 3   **d)** 17   **e)** 8

**11.**

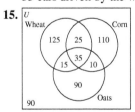

U
Sinkholes   Mold
34   27   30
78
31   37
88
25   Floods

**a)** 67   **b)** 237   **c)** 37   **d)** 25

**13.** In a Venn diagram, regions II, IV, and V contain a total of 37 cars driven by women. This total is greater than the 35 cars driven by the women, as given in the exercise.

**15.**

U
Wheat   Corn
125   25   110
35
15   10
90
90   Oats

**a)** 410   **b)** 35   **c)** 90   **d)** 50

**17. a)** 10   **b)** 10   **c)** 6

**SECTION 2.6, PAGE 86**

**1.** Infinite

**3.** $\{3, 4, 5, 6, \ 7, \ \ldots, \ n + 2, \ \ldots\}$
$\downarrow \downarrow \downarrow \downarrow \downarrow \quad\quad\quad \downarrow$
$\{4, 5, 6, 7, 8, \ \ldots, \ n + 3, \ \ldots\}$

**5.** $\{3, 5, 7, \ 9, 11, \ \ldots, 2n + 1, \ \ldots\}$
$\downarrow \downarrow \downarrow \downarrow \ \downarrow \quad\quad\quad \downarrow$
$\{5, 7, 9, 11, 13, \ \ldots, \ 2n + 3, \ \ldots\}$

**7.** $\{5, \ 9, 13, 17, \ 21, \ \ldots, \ 4n + 1, \ \ldots\}$
$\downarrow \ \downarrow \ \downarrow \ \downarrow \ \downarrow \quad\quad\quad\quad \downarrow$
$\{9, 13, 17, 21, \ 25, \ \ldots, \ 4n + 5, \ \ldots\}$

**9.** $\left\{\dfrac{1}{2}, \dfrac{1}{4}, \dfrac{1}{6}, \dfrac{1}{8}, \dfrac{1}{10}, \ \ldots, \quad \dfrac{1}{2n}, \ \ldots\right\}$
$\downarrow \downarrow \downarrow \ \downarrow \ \downarrow \quad\quad\quad \downarrow$
$\left\{\dfrac{1}{4}, \dfrac{1}{6}, \dfrac{1}{8}, \dfrac{1}{10}, \dfrac{1}{12}, \ \ldots, \quad \dfrac{1}{2n + 2}, \ \ldots\right\}$

**11.** $\left\{\dfrac{4}{11}, \dfrac{5}{11}, \dfrac{6}{11}, \dfrac{7}{11}, \dfrac{8}{11}, \ \ldots, \dfrac{n + 3}{11}, \ \ldots\right\}$
$\downarrow \ \downarrow \ \downarrow \ \downarrow \ \downarrow \quad\quad\quad \downarrow$
$\left\{\dfrac{5}{11}, \dfrac{6}{11}, \dfrac{7}{11}, \dfrac{8}{11}, \dfrac{9}{11}, \ \ldots, \dfrac{n + 4}{11}, \ \ldots\right\}$

**13.** $\{1, 2, 3, \ 4, \ 5, \ \ldots, \ n, \ \ldots\}$
$\downarrow \ \downarrow \ \downarrow \ \downarrow \ \downarrow \quad\quad \downarrow$
$\{3, 6, 9, 12, 15, \ \ldots, 3n, \ \ldots\}$

**15.** $\{1, 2, 3, \ 4, \ 5, \ \ldots, \quad n, \ \ldots\}$
$\downarrow \downarrow \downarrow \ \downarrow \ \downarrow \quad\quad\quad \downarrow$
$\{4, 6, 8, 10, 12, \ \ldots, 2n + 2, \ \ldots\}$

**17.** $\{1, 2, 3, \ 4, \ 5, \ \ldots, \quad n, \ \ldots\}$
$\downarrow \ \downarrow \ \downarrow \ \downarrow \ \downarrow \quad\quad\quad \downarrow$
$\{2, 5, 8, 11, 14, \ \ldots, 3n - 1, \ \ldots\}$

**19.** $\{1, 2, 3, \ \ 4, \ \ 5, \ \ldots, \ \ n, \ \ldots\}$
$\downarrow \ \downarrow \ \downarrow \ \ \downarrow \ \ \downarrow \quad\quad\quad \downarrow$
$\left\{\dfrac{1}{3}, \dfrac{1}{6}, \dfrac{1}{9}, \dfrac{1}{12}, \dfrac{1}{15}, \ \ldots, \dfrac{1}{3n}, \ \ldots\right\}$

**21.** $\{\ 1, \ 2, \ 3, \ 4, \ 5, \ \ldots, \quad n, \ \ldots\}$
$\downarrow \ \downarrow \ \downarrow \ \downarrow \ \downarrow \quad\quad\quad \downarrow$
$\left\{\dfrac{1}{3}, \dfrac{1}{4}, \dfrac{1}{5}, \dfrac{1}{6}, \dfrac{1}{7}, \ \ldots, \dfrac{1}{n + 2}, \ \ldots\right\}$

**23.** $\{1, 2, 3, 4, \ \ 5, \ \ldots, \ \ n, \ \ldots\}$
$\downarrow \downarrow \downarrow \ \downarrow \ \downarrow \quad\quad \downarrow$
$\{1, 4, 9, 16, 25, \ \ldots, n^2, \ \ldots\}$

**25.** $\{1, 2, \ 3, \ \ 4, \ \ 5, \ \ldots, \ \ n, \ \ldots\}$
$\downarrow \downarrow \ \downarrow \ \ \downarrow \ \ \downarrow \quad\quad \downarrow$
$\{3, 9, 27, 81, 243, \ \ldots, 3^n, \ \ldots\}$

**27.** =    **29.** =    **31.** =

**REVIEW EXERCISES, PAGE 88**

**1.** True

**2.** False; the word best makes the statement not well defined.

**3.** True   **4.** False; no set is a proper subset of itself.

**5.** False; the elements 6, 12, 18, 24, … are members of both sets.

**6.** True

**7.** False; both sets do not contain exactly the same elements.

**8.** True   **9.** True   **10.** True   **11.** True   **12.** True

**13.** True   **14.** True   **15.** $A = \{7, 9, 11, 13, 15\}$

**16.** {Colorado, Nebraska, Missouri, Oklahoma}

**17.** $C = \{1, 2, 3, 4, \ldots, 161\}$

**18.** $D = \{9, 10, 11, 12, \ldots, 80\}$

**19.** $A = \{x \mid x \in N \text{ and } 50 < x < 150\}$

**20.** $B = \{x \mid x \in N \text{ and } x > 42\}$

**21.** $C = \{x \mid x \in N \text{ and } x < 7\}$

**22.** $D = \{x \mid x \in N \text{ and } 27 \le x \le 51\}$

**23.** $A$ is the set of capital letters in the English alphabet from E through M, inclusive.

**24.** $B$ is the set of U.S. coins with a value of less than a dollar.

**25.** $C$ is the set of the first three lowercase letters in the English alphabet.

**26.** $D$ is the set of numbers greater than or equal to 3 and less than 9

**27.** $\{3, 7\}$   **28.** $\{1, 2, 3, 4, 5, 6, 7, 8\}$   **29.** $\{9, 10\}$

**30.** $\{1, 2, 4, 6, 7, 8, 10\}$   **31.** $\{1, 5\}$   **32.** $\{1, 7\}$

**33.** $\{(1, 1), (1, 7), (1, 10), (3, 1), (3, 7), (3, 10), (5, 1), (5, 7), (5, 10), (7, 1), (7, 7), (7, 10)\}$

**34.** $\{(3, 1), (3, 3), (3, 5), (3, 7), (7, 1), (7, 3), (7, 5), (7, 7), (9, 1), (9, 3), (9, 5), (9, 7), (10, 1), (10, 3), (10, 5), (10, 7)\}$

**35.** 16   **36.** 15

**37.**

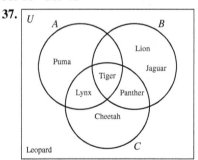

**38.** $\{a, c, d, f, g, i, k, l\}$   **39.** $\{i, k\}$

**40.** $\{a, b, c, d, f, g, h, i, k, l\}$   **41.** $\{f\}$

**42.** $\{a, f, i\}$   **43.** $\{a, b, d, f, h, i, l\}$   **44.** True

**45.** True   **46.** II   **47.** III   **48.** I   **49.** IV   **50.** IV

**51.** II   **52.** II   **53.** $450

**54.**

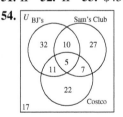

**a)** 131   **b)** 32   **c)** 10   **d)** 65

**55.**

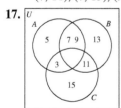

U
CSI: NY    CSI: Miami
38   41   99
37   59   28
161
CSI: Crime
Scene
47            Investigation

**a)** 38   **b)** 298   **c)** 28   **d)** 236   **e)** 106

**56.** $\{2, 4, 6, 8, 10, \ldots, \qquad 2n, \ldots\}$
↓ ↓ ↓ ↓ ↓          ↓
$\{4, 6, 8, 10, 12, \ldots, 2n + 2, \ldots\}$

**57.** $\{3, 5, 7, 9, 11, \ldots, 2n + 1, \ldots\}$
↓ ↓ ↓ ↓ ↓          ↓
$\{5, 7, 9, 11, 13, \ldots, 2n + 3, \ldots\}$

**58.** $\{1, 2, 3, 4, 5, \ldots, \quad n, \quad \ldots\}$
↓ ↓ ↓ ↓ ↓          ↓
$\{5, 8, 11, 14, 17, \ldots, 3n + 2, \ldots\}$

**59.** $\{1, 2, 3, 4, 5, \ldots, \quad n, \quad \ldots\}$
↓ ↓ ↓ ↓ ↓          ↓
$\{4, 9, 14, 19, 24, \ldots, 5n - 1, \ldots\}$

**CHAPTER TEST, PAGE 91**

**1.** True

**2.** False; the sets do not contain exactly the same elements.

**3.** True

**4.** False; the second set has no subset that contains the element 7.

**5.** False; the set has $2^4$, or 16 subsets.   **6.** True

**7.** False; for any set $A$, $A \cup A' = U$, not $\{\ \}$.

**8.** True   **9.** $A = \{1, 2, 3, 4, 5, 6, 7, 8, 9\}$

**10.** Set A is the set of natural numbers less than 10.

**11.** $\{7, 9\}$   **12.** $\{3, 5, 7, 9, 13\}$

**13.** $\{7, 9\}$   **14.** 2   **15.** $\{3, 5\}$

**16.** $\{ (3, 3), (3, 11), (3, 15), (5, 3), (5, 11), (5, 15), (7, 3),$
$(7, 11), (7, 15), (9, 3), (9, 11), (9, 15) \}$

**17.**

U
A       B
5   7 9   13
3   11
15
C

**18.** Equal

**19.**

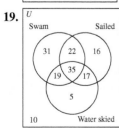

U
Swam        Sailed
31   22   16
19   35   17
5
10          Water skied

**a)** 52   **b)** 10   **c)** 93   **d)** 22   **e)** 69   **f)** 5

**20.** $\{7, 8, 9, 10, 11, \ldots, n + 6, \ldots\}$
↓ ↓ ↓ ↓ ↓          ↓
$\{8, 9, 10, 11, 12, \ldots, n + 7, \ldots\}$

**Chapter 3**

Answer to Recreational Math on page 97

| 7 | 1 | 9 | 4 | 8 | 2 | 5 | 6 | 3 |
|---|---|---|---|---|---|---|---|---|
| 5 | 4 | 6 | 7 | 3 | 9 | 8 | 1 | 2 |
| 2 | 3 | 8 | 6 | 5 | 1 | 4 | 9 | 7 |
| 8 | 2 | 4 | 3 | 9 | 5 | 1 | 7 | 6 |
| 6 | 7 | 5 | 1 | 2 | 4 | 3 | 8 | 9 |
| 1 | 9 | 3 | 8 | 6 | 7 | 2 | 4 | 5 |
| 9 | 6 | 1 | 5 | 4 | 3 | 7 | 2 | 8 |
| 3 | 8 | 7 | 2 | 1 | 6 | 9 | 5 | 4 |
| 4 | 5 | 2 | 9 | 7 | 8 | 6 | 3 | 1 |

**SECTION 3.1, PAGE 101**

**1.** Statement   **3.** Compound

**5. a)** Not   **b)** And   **c)** Or   **d)** If-then   **e)** If and only if

**7.** Some   **9.** Simple statement

**11.** Compound; biconditional, $\leftrightarrow$

**13.** Compound; conjunction, $\wedge$

**15.** Compound; conditional, $\rightarrow$

**17.** Compound; negation, $\sim$

**19.** Some butterflies are not insects.

**21.** All turtles have claws.

**23.** Some bicycles have three wheels.

**25.** No pedestrians are in the crosswalk.

**27.** Some Holsteins are Guernseys.

**29.** $\sim p$   **31.** $\sim q \vee \sim p$

**33.** $\sim p \rightarrow \sim q$

**35.** $\sim p \wedge q$   **37.** $\sim q \leftrightarrow p$

**39.** $\sim (p \vee q)$

**41.** Brie does not have a MacBook.

**43.** Joe has an iPad and Brie has a MacBook.

**45.** If Joe does not have an iPad then Brie has a MacBook.

**47.** Joe does not have an iPad or Brie does not have a MacBook.

**49.** It is false that Joe has an iPad and Brie has a MacBook.

**51.** $(p \wedge \sim q) \wedge r$   **53.** $(p \wedge q) \vee r$

**55.** $p \rightarrow (q \vee \sim r)$   **57.** $(r \leftrightarrow q) \wedge p$

**59.** $q \rightarrow (p \leftrightarrow r)$

**61.** The water is 70° or the sun is shining, and we do not go swimming.

**63.** The water is not 70°, and the sun is shining or we go swimming.

**65.** If we do not go swimming, then the sun is shining and the water is 70°.

**67.** If the sun is shining then we go swimming, and the water is 70°.

**69.** The sun is shining if and only if the water is 70°, and we go swimming.

**71.** Not permissible, you cannot have both soup and salad. The *or* used on menus is the *exclusive or*.

**73.** Not permissible, you cannot have both potatoes and pasta. The *or* used on menus is the *exclusive or*.

**75. a)** $w \land \sim p$   **b)** Conjunction

**77. a)** $\sim (b \rightarrow \sim p)$   **b)** Negation

**79. a)** $(f \lor v) \rightarrow h$   **b)** Conditional

**81. a)** $c \leftrightarrow (\sim f \lor p)$   **b)** Biconditional

**83. a)** $(c \leftrightarrow w) \lor s$   **b)** Disjunction

**85. a)** Answers will vary.   **b)** Answers will vary.

**86.**

| 6 | 4 | 8 | 7 | 5 | 3 | 2 | 1 | 9 |
|---|---|---|---|---|---|---|---|---|
| 3 | 9 | 2 | 8 | 6 | 1 | 7 | 5 | 4 |
| 7 | 5 | 1 | 9 | 4 | 2 | 8 | 6 | 3 |
| 9 | 1 | 6 | 3 | 2 | 5 | 4 | 8 | 7 |
| 5 | 7 | 3 | 4 | 8 | 6 | 9 | 2 | 1 |
| 8 | 2 | 4 | 1 | 9 | 7 | 5 | 3 | 6 |
| 4 | 3 | 5 | 6 | 7 | 8 | 1 | 9 | 2 |
| 2 | 6 | 9 | 5 | 1 | 4 | 3 | 7 | 8 |
| 1 | 8 | 7 | 2 | 3 | 9 | 6 | 4 | 5 |

**SECTION 3.2, PAGE 114**

**1.** Opposite   **3.** False

**5.** F
F

**7.** T
F
T
T

**9.** F
T
T
T

**11.** T
F
T
T

**13.** T
F
F
T
F
F
T
T

**15.** T
F
T
T
T
F
T
F

**17.** F
F
T
F
F
F
T
T

**19.** $p \land q$
T
F
F
F

**21.** $p \land \sim q$
F
T
F
F

**23.** $\sim(p \land q)$
F
T
T
T

**25.** $p \lor (q \lor r)$
T
T
T
T
T
T
T
F

**27. a)** False   **b)** False   **29. a)** False   **b)** False

**31. a)** True   **b)** False   **33. a)** False   **b)** True

**35. a)** True   **b)** True   **37.** True   **39.** True

**41.** False   **43.** False   **45.** False   **47.** True

**49.** True   **51.** False

**53.** $p \land \sim q$
F
T
F
F
True in case 2

**55.** $p \lor \sim q$
T
T
F
T
True in cases 1, 2, and 4.

**57.** $(r \lor q) \land p$
T
T
T
F
F
F
F
F
True in cases 1, 2, and 3

**59.** $q \lor (p \land \sim r)$
T
T
F
T
T
T
F
F
True in cases 1, 2, 4, 5, and 6.

**61. a)** Mr. Duncan and Mrs. Tuttle qualify.

**b)** Mrs. Rusinek does not qualify, since their combined income is less than $46,000.

**63. b)** Gina Vela is returning on April 3. Kara Sharo is returning on a Monday. Christos Supernaw is not staying over on a Saturday. Alex Chang is returning on a Monday.

**65.** T
T
T
T
F
T
F
T

**67.** Yes

**SECTION 3.3, PAGE 124**

**1.** False   **3.** True   **5.** Self-contradiction

**7.** T
T
T
F

**9.** T
F
F
F

**11.** F
T
T
F

**13.** T
T
F
T

**15.** F
T
T
T

**17.** T
T
T
T
T
F
F
F

**19.** F
F
T
F
T
T
F
T

**21.** T
T
T
T
T
F
F
F

**23.** T
T
T
F
T
T
T
F

**25.** $p \rightarrow (q \land r)$
T
F
F
F
T
T
T
T

**27.** $(p \leftrightarrow q) \vee r$

T
T
T
F
T
F
T
T

**29.** $(\sim p \rightarrow q) \vee r$

T
T
T
T
T
T
T
F

**31.** Neither   **33.** Self-contradiction   **35.** Tautology
**37.** Not an implication   **39.** Implication   **41.** Implication
**43.** True   **45.** False   **47.** False   **49.** True   **51.** True
**53.** True   **55.** False   **57.** True   **59.** True   **61.** True
**63.** False   **65.** False   **67.** True   **69.** False   **71.** True
**73.** No, the statement only states what will occur if your sister gets straight A's. If your sister does not get straight A's, your parents may still get her a computer.

**75.** F
F
T
T
T
F
F
F

**77.** It is a tautology. The statement may be expressed as $(p \rightarrow q) \vee (\sim p \rightarrow q)$, where $p$: It is a head and $q$: I win. This statement is a tautology.

**79.** Allen was born in January. Booker was born in February. Chris was born in March. Dennis was born in April.

**80.**
| Tiger | Boots | Sam | Sue |
|---|---|---|---|
| Blue | Yellow | Red | Green |
| Nine Lives | Whiskas | Friskies | Meow Mix |

**81.** Katie was born last. Katie and Mary are saying the same thing.

**SECTION 3.4, PAGE 136**

Answer to Recreational Math on page 134

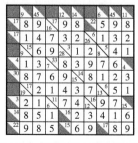

**1.** Equivalent   **3.** $\sim p \vee q$   **5.** $q \rightarrow p$   **7.** $\sim q \rightarrow \sim p$

**9.** Not equivalent   **11.** Equivalent   **13.** Not equivalent

**15.** Equivalent   **17.** Equivalent   **19.** Equivalent

**21.** Equivalent   **23.** Equivalent

**25.** Not equivalent   **27.** Equivalent

**29.** Oregon does not border the Atlantic Ocean or Delaware does not border the Pacific Ocean.

**31.** It is false that the dog was a bulldog or the dog was a boxer.

**33.** If Ashley Tabai takes the new job, then it is false that she will move and she will not buy a new house in town.

**35.** Janette Campbell does not buy a new car or she sells her old car.

**37.** If Bob the Tomato did not visit the nursing home then he did not visit the Cub Scout meeting.

**39.** If Chase is hiding, then the pitcher is broken.

**41.** We go to Chicago and we do not go to Navy Pier.

**43.** It is false that if I am cold then the heater is working.

**45.** Amazon has a sale and we will not buy $100 worth of books.

**47.** It is false that if John Deere will hire new workers then the city of Dubuque will not retrain the workers.

**49.** *Converse:* If she needs extra yarn, then Nanette Berry teaches macramé.

*Inverse:* If Nanette Berry does not teach macramé, then she does not need extra yarn.

*Contrapositive:* If she does not need extra yarn, then Nanette Berry does not teach macramé.

**51.** *Converse:* If I buy silver jewelry, then I go to Mexico.

*Inverse:* If I do not go to Mexico, then I do not buy silver jewelry.

*Contrapositive:* If I do not buy silver jewelry, then I do not go to Mexico.

**53.** *Converse*: If I scream, then that annoying paper clip shows up on my computer screen.

*Inverse*: If that annoying paper clip does not show up on my computer screen, then I will not scream.

*Contrapositive*: If I do not scream, then that annoying paper clip does not show up on my screen.

**55.** If a natural number is not divisible by 7, then the natural number is not divisible by 14. True.

**57.** If a natural number is not divisible by 6, then the natural number is not divisible by 3. False.

**59.** If two lines are not parallel, then the two lines intersect in at least one point. True.

**61.** b) and c) are equivalent.   **63.** a) and c) are equivalent.

**65.** b) and c) are equivalent.   **67.** b) and c) are equivalent.

**69.** None are equivalent.   **71.** None are equivalent.

**73.** a) and c) are equivalent.

**75.** True. If $p \rightarrow q$ is false, it must be of the form T → F. Therefore, the converse must be of the form F → T, which is true.

**77.** False. A conditional statement and its contrapositive always have the same truth values.

**79.** Answers will vary.

**81.** Answers will vary.

**83.**

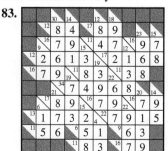

**SECTION 3.5, PAGE 147**

**1.** Valid   **3.** Fallacy   **5.** Valid   **7.** Inverse   **9.** Syllogism
**11.** Syllogism   **13.** Invalid   **15.** Valid   **17.** Valid
**19.** Invalid   **21.** Invalid   **23.** Valid   **25.** Valid
**27.** Invalid   **29.** Invalid   **31.** Valid

**33. a)** $p \rightarrow q$   **b)** Valid   **35. a)** $p \rightarrow q$   **b)** Valid

$$\frac{\sim q}{\therefore \sim p} \qquad\qquad \frac{p}{\therefore q}$$

**37. a)** $p \rightarrow q$   **b)** Valid   **39. a)** $p \rightarrow q$   **b)** Invalid

$$\frac{\sim q}{\therefore \sim p} \qquad\qquad \frac{q}{\therefore p}$$

**41. a)** $p \vee q$   **b)** Valid   **43. a)** $p \rightarrow q$   **b)** Valid

$$\frac{\sim p}{\therefore q} \qquad\qquad \frac{q \rightarrow r}{\therefore p \rightarrow r}$$

**45. a)** $p \wedge q$   **b)** Valid   **47. a)** $s \wedge g$   **b)** Valid

$$\frac{q \rightarrow r}{\therefore r \rightarrow p} \qquad\qquad \frac{g \rightarrow c}{\therefore s \rightarrow c}$$

**49. a)** $p \rightarrow q$   **b)** Valid   **51. a)** $p \vee q$   **b)** Valid

$$\frac{\sim q}{\therefore \sim p} \qquad\qquad \frac{\sim p}{\therefore q}$$

**53. a)** $t \wedge g$   **b)** Valid   **55. a)** $c \wedge \sim h$   **b)** Invalid

$$\frac{\sim t \vee \sim g}{\therefore \sim t} \qquad\qquad \frac{h \rightarrow c}{\therefore h}$$

**57. a)** $p \rightarrow q$   **b)** Invalid

$$\frac{q \rightarrow \sim r}{\therefore p \rightarrow r}$$

**59.** Therefore, you must rest for three days.
**61.** Therefore, I am stressed out.
**63.** Therefore, you did not close the deal.
**65.** Yes, if the conclusion does not necessarily follow from the premises, the argument is invalid, even if the conclusion is true.
**67.** Yes, if the conclusion does not necessarily follow from the premises, the argument is invalid, even if the premises are true.
**69.** Valid   **71. a)** $p \rightarrow q$   **b)** No   **c)** This argument is the fallacy of the inverse.

$$\frac{\sim p}{\therefore \sim q}$$

**SECTION 3.6, PAGE 154**

**1.** Euler   **3.** Invalid   **5.** No   **7.** Valid   **9.** Valid
**11.** Invalid   **13.** Valid   **15.** Invalid   **17.** Invalid
**19.** Invalid   **21.** Valid   **23.** Invalid
**25.** Invalid   **27.** Valid
**29.** Yes, if the conclusion necessarily follows from the premises, the argument is valid.

**SECTION 3.7, PAGE 161**

**1.** Series   **3.** Closed
**5. a)** $p \vee q$
   **b)** The lightbulb will be on when either $p$ or $q$ are closed.
**7. a)** $(p \vee q) \wedge \sim q$
   **b)** The lightbulb will be on when $p$ is closed and $q$ is open.
**9. a)** $(p \wedge q) \wedge [(p \wedge \sim q) \vee r]$
   **b)** The lightbulb will be on when $p$, $q$, and $r$ are all closed.
**11. a)** $p \vee q \vee (r \wedge \sim p)$
   **b)** The lightbulb will be on in all cases except when $p$, $q$, and $r$ are all open.

**13.**

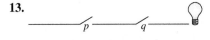

**15.**

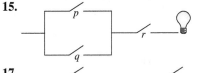

**17.**

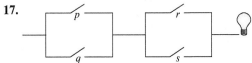

**19.**

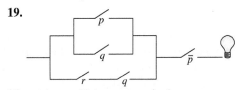

**21.** $p \vee \sim q; \overline{p} \wedge q$ not equivalent
**23.** $[(p \wedge q) \vee r] \wedge p; (q \vee r) \wedge p$; equivalent
**25.** $(p \vee \sim p) \wedge q \wedge r; p \wedge q \wedge r$; not equivalent
**27.** It is a series circuit; therefore, both switches must be closed for current to flow and the lightbulb to go on. When the $p$ switch is closed, the $\overline{p}$ switch is open and no current will flow through the circuit. When the $\overline{p}$ switch is closed, the $p$ switch is open and no current will flow through the circuit.

**29. a)**                      **b)**

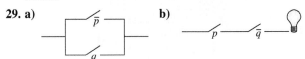

**REVIEW EXERCISE, PAGE 164**

**1.** Some Scions are not Toyotas.
**2.** Some pets are allowed in this park.
**3.** No women are presidents.   **4.** All pine trees are green.
**5.** The coffee is Maxwell House or the coffee is hot.
**6.** The coffee is not hot and the coffee is strong.
**7.** If the coffee is hot, then the coffee is strong and the coffee is not Maxwell House.
**8.** The coffee is Maxwell House if and only if the coffee is not strong.
**9.** The coffee is not Maxwell House, if and only if the coffee is strong and the coffee is not hot.
**10.** The coffee is Maxwell House or the coffee is not hot, and the coffee is not strong.

**11.** $p \vee r$   **12.** $r \rightarrow {\sim} p$   **13.** $(r \rightarrow q) \vee {\sim} p$

**14.** $(q \leftrightarrow p) \wedge {\sim} r$   **15.** $(r \wedge q) \vee {\sim} p$   **16.** ${\sim}(r \wedge q)$

| **17.** | **18.** | **19.** | **20.** | **21.** | **22.** |
|---|---|---|---|---|---|
| F | T | T | T | F | F |
| F | F | T | F | T | T |
| T | F | T | T | F | T |
| F | F | T | T | F | T |
|   |   | T | F | T | T |
|   |   | F | F | T | T |
|   |   | F | F | T | T |
|   |   | T | F | T | T |

**23.** False   **24.** True   **25.** False   **26.** True   **27.** True

**28.** True   **29.** False   **30.** False   **31.** Not equivalent

**32.** Equivalent   **33.** Equivalent   **34.** Not equivalent

**35.** It is false that if Lady Gaga sang "Poker Face", then Jay-Z sang "Beamer, Benz, or Bentley".

**36.** If Lynn Swann did not play for the Steelers, then Jack Tatum played for the Raiders.

**37.** Altec Lansing does not produce only speakers and Harman Kardon does not produce only stereo receivers.

**38.** It is false that Travis Tritt won an Academy Award or Randy Jackson does commercials for Milk Bone Dog Biscuits.

**39.** The temperature is above 32° or we will go ice fishing at O'Leary's Lake.

**40. a)** If you know Jay Stu, then you listen to Jim Rome.

   **b)** If you do not listen to Jim Rome, then you do not know Jay Stu.

   **c)** If you do not know Jay Stu, then you do not listen to Jim Rome.

**41. a)** If we will learn the table's value, then we take the table to *Antiques Roadshow*.

   **b)** If we do not take the table to *Antiques Roadshow*, then we will not learn the table's value.

   **c)** If we will not learn the table's value, then we do not take the table to *Antiques Roadshow*.

**42. a)** If you do not sell more doughnuts, then you do not advertise.

   **b)** If you advertise, then you sell more doughnuts.

   **c)** If you sell more doughnuts, then you advertise.

**43. a)** If we will not buy a desk at Miller's Furniture, then the desk is made by Winner's Only and the desk is in the Rose catalog.

   **b)** If the desk is not made by Winner's Only or the desk is not in the Rose catalog, then we will buy a desk at Miller's Furniture.

   **c)** If we will buy a desk at Miller's Furniture, then the desk is not made by Winner's Only or the desk is not in the Rose catalog.

**44. a)** If I let you attend the prom, then you will get straight A's on your report card.

   **b)** If you do not get straight A's on your report card, then I will not let you attend the prom.

   **c)** If I will not let you attend the prom, then you did not get straight A's on your report card.

**45. a)**, **b)** and **c)** are equivalent.   **46.** None are equivalent.

**47. a)** and **c)** are equivalent.   **48.** None are equivalent.

**49.** Invalid   **50.** Valid   **51.** Valid   **52.** Invalid

**53.** Invalid   **54.** Valid   **55.** Invalid   **56.** Invalid

**57. a)** $p \wedge [(q \wedge r) \vee {\sim} p]$

   **b)** The lightbulb will be on when $p$, $q$, and $r$ are all closed.

**58.**

**59.** Equivalent

**CHAPTER TEST, PAGE 167**

**1.** $(p \wedge r) \vee {\sim} q$   **2.** $(r \rightarrow q) \vee {\sim} p$   **3.** ${\sim}(r \leftrightarrow {\sim} q)$

**4.** Phobos is not a moon of Mars and Rosalind is a moon of Uranus, if and only if Callisto is not a moon of Jupiter.

**5.** If Phobos is a moon of Mars or Callisto is not a moon of Jupiter, then Rosalind is a moon of Uranus.

| **6.** | **7.** |
|---|---|
| F | T |
| T | T |
| F | T |
| F | T |
| F | F |
| F | T |
| F | T |
| F | F |

**8.** True   **9.** True   **10.** True   **11.** True   **12.** Equivalent.

**13. a)** and **b)** are equivalent.   **14. a)** and **b)** are equivalent.

**15.** $s \rightarrow f$
$f \rightarrow p$
$\therefore s \rightarrow p$
Valid

**16.** Invalid   **17.** Some highways are not roads.

**18.** Nick did not play football or Max did not play baseball.

**19.** *Converse:* If today is Saturday, then the garbage truck comes.

   *Inverse:* If the garbage truck does not come, then today is not Saturday.

   *Contrapositive:* If today is not Saturday, then the garbage truck does not come.

**20.**

**Chapter 9**

**SECTION 9.1, PAGE 486**

**1.** Parallel   **3.** Angle   **5.** Supplementary   **7.** Straight

**9.** Obtuse   **11.** Vertical   **13.** Ray, $\overrightarrow{AB}$

**15.** Half line, $\overset{\circ}{\overrightarrow{BA}}$   **17.** Ray, $\overrightarrow{BA}$

**19.** Half open line segment, $\overset{\circ}{\overline{AB}}$

**21.** $\overline{AD}$   **23.** $\overline{BD}^{\circ}$   **25.** $\{B, F\}$   **27.** $\{C\}$

**29.** $\measuredangle CBF$ or $\measuredangle FBC$   **31.** $\overleftrightarrow{BC}$   **33.** $\overleftrightarrow{DE}$   **35.** $\overrightarrow{BC}$

**37.** $\measuredangle ABE$   **39.** $\overline{BF}$   **41.** $\overset{\circ}{\overline{AC}}{}^{\circ}$   **43.** $\overline{BE}$   **45.** Right

**47.** Straight   **49.** Obtuse   **51.** None of these angles

**53.** 80°   **55.** $57\frac{1}{4}°$   **57.** 25.3°   **59.** 100°   **61.** 159.5°

**63.** $136\frac{2}{7}°$   **65.** (f)   **67.** (b)   **69.** (a)

**71.** $m\angle 1 = 75°, m\angle 2 = 15°$   **73.** 134° and 46°

**75.** Angles 3, 4, and 7 each measure 125°; angles 1, 2, 5, and 6 each measure 55°.

**77.** Angles 1, 4, and 7 each measure 30°; angles 2, 3, 5, and 6 each measure 150°.

**79.** $m\angle 1 = 64°, m\angle 2 = 26°$

**81.** $m\angle 1 = 33°, m\angle 2 = 57°$

**83.** $m\angle 1 = 134°, m\angle 2 = 46°$

**85.** $m\angle 1 = 29°, m\angle 2 = 151°$

**87.** Plane $ABG$ and plane $JCD$

**89.** $\overleftrightarrow{BG}$ and $\overleftrightarrow{DG}$

**91.** Plane $AGB \cap$ plane $ABC \cap$ plane $BCD = \{B\}$

**93.** $\overleftrightarrow{BC} \cap$ plane $ABG = \{B\}$

**95. a)** Undefined terms, definitions, postulates (axioms), and theorems
   **b)** First, Euclid introduced undefined terms. Second, he introduced certain definitions. Third, he stated primitive propositions called postulates about the undefined terms and definitions. Fourth, he proved, using deductive reasoning, other propositions called theorems.

**97. a)** An infinite number   **b)** An infinite number

**99.** An infinite number

**101.** Always true. If any two lines are parallel to a third line, then they must be parallel to each other.

**103.** Sometimes true. Vertical angles are only complementary when each is equal to 45°.

**105.** Sometimes true. Alternate interior angles are only complementary when each is equal to 45°.

**107.** Answers will vary.

**109.** No. Line $l$ and line $n$ may be parallel or skew.   **111.** 360°

## SECTION 9.2, PAGE 496

**1.** Polygon   **3.** Proportion   **5.** Congruent

**7. a)** Octagon   **b)** Regular   **9. a)** Triangle   **b)** Regular

**11. a)** Parallelogram   **b)** Not regular

**13. a)** Heptagon   **b)** Not regular

**15. a)** Isosceles   **b)** Right   **17. a)** Isosceles   **b)** Acute

**19. a)** Scalene   **b)** Acute   **21. a)** Scalene   **b)** Right

**23.** Trapezoid   **25.** Square   **27.** Rhombus

**29.** 96°   **31.** 150°

**33.** $m\angle 1 = 90°, m\angle 2 = 50°, m\angle 3 = 130°, m\angle 4 = 50°,$
$m\angle 5 = 50°, m\angle 6 = 40°, m\angle 7 = 90°, m\angle 8 = 130°,$
$m\angle 9 = 140°, m\angle 10 = 40°, m\angle 11 = 140°, m\angle 12 = 40°$

**35.** 540°   **37.** 1260°   **39.** 3240°   **41. a)** 60°   **b)** 120°

**43. a)** 135°   **b)** 45°   **45. a)** 144°   **b)** 36°

**47.** $x = 2, y = 1.6$   **49.** $x = 2\frac{2}{5}, y = 7\frac{1}{2}$

**51.** $x = 20, y = 21\frac{1}{4}$   **53.** 3   **55.** $3\frac{1}{3}$   **57.** 14   **59.** 15

**61.** 28°   **63.** 9   **65.** 10   **67.** 70°   **69.** 55°   **71.** 35°

**73.** 70 ft   **75. a)** $\approx 113.14$ mi   **b)** $\approx 75.43$ mi

**77.** The different types of triangles are acute, obtuse, right, isosceles, equilateral, and scalene. Descriptions will vary.

**79.** $D'E' = 4, E'F' = 5, D'F' = 3$

**81. a)** $m\angle HMF = m\angle TMB, m\angle HFM = m\angle TBM,$
   $m\angle MHF = m\angle MTB$
   **b)** 44 ft

**82. a)** $m\angle CED = m\angle ABC, m\angle ACB = m\angle DCE,$
   $m\angle BAC = m\angle CDE$
   **b)** $\approx 2141.49$ ft

## SECTION 9.3, PAGE 507

**1. a)** Perimeter   **b)** Area   **3.** Circle   **5.** $12\ \text{cm}^2$

**7.** $17.5\ \text{cm}^2$   **9. a)** $50\ \text{ft}^2$   **b)** 30 ft

**11. a)** $6000\ \text{cm}^2$   **b)** 654 cm

**13. a)** $288\ \text{in}^2$   **b)** 74 in.   **15. a)** $78.54\ \text{m}^2$   **b)** 31.42 m

**17. a)** $132.73\ \text{ft}^2$   **b)** 40.84 ft

**19. a)** 17 yd   **b)** 40 yd   **c)** $60\ \text{yd}^2$

**21. a)** 12 km   **b)** 30 km   **c)** $30\ \text{km}^2$

**23.** $7.73\ \text{ft}^2$   **25.** $8\ \text{in}^2$   **27.** $90\ \text{yd}^2$   **29.** $65.73\ \text{in}^2$

**31.** $56.55\ \text{mm}^2$   **33.** $8\ \text{yd}^2$   **35.** $132.3\ \text{ft}^2$   **37.** $50{,}000\ \text{cm}^2$

**39.** $0.8625\ \text{m}^2$   **41. a)** \$5494.50   **b)** \$6594.50

**43.** \$3056.60   **45.** \$3835.20   **47.** \$234.21

**49. a)** 288 ft   **b)** 4700 tiles   **51.** 21 ft   **53.** 312 ft

**55. a)** $A = s^2$   **b)** $A = 4s^2$   **c)** Four times larger

**57.** $24\ \text{cm}^2$   **59.** Answers will vary.

**60.** Answers will vary.

## SECTION 9.4, PAGE 520

**1.** Volume   **3.** Platonic   **5.** Right   **7. a)** $64\ \text{ft}^3$   **b)** $112\ \text{ft}^2$

**9. a)** $8\ \text{yd}^3$   **b)** $24\ \text{yd}^2$   **11. a)** $150.80\ \text{in}^3$   **b)** $175.93\ \text{in}^2$

**13. a)** $131.95\ \text{cm}^3$   **b)** $163.22\ \text{cm}^2$

**15. a)** $381.70\ \text{cm}^3$   **b)** $254.47\ \text{cm}^2$   **17.** $750\ \text{m}^3$

**19.** $720\ \text{cm}^3$   **21.** $768\ \text{ft}^3$   **23.** $392\ \text{ft}^3$   **25.** $284.46\ \text{cm}^3$

**27.** $24\ \text{ft}^3$   **29.** $81\ \text{ft}^3$   **31.** $\approx 5.67\ \text{yd}^3$   **33.** $560{,}000\ \text{cm}^3$

**35.** $7.5\ \text{m}^3$   **37. a)** $225\ \text{ft}^3$   **b)** \$2475   **39.** $40{,}840\ \text{mm}^2$

**41.** $\approx 2.50$ qt   **43. a)** $120{,}000\ \text{cm}^3$
   **b)** $120{,}000\ \text{m}\ell$   **c)** $120\ \ell$

**45.** $\approx 283.04\ \text{in}^3$   **47. a)** $\approx 323.98\ \text{in}^3$   **b)** $\approx 0.19\ \text{ft}^3$

**49.** $\approx 14.14\ \text{in}^3$   **51.** Ten edges   **53.** Six vertices

**55.** Seven faces

**57. a)** $\approx 5.11 \times 10^8\ \text{km}^2$   **b)** $\approx 3.79 \times 10^7\ \text{km}^2$
   **c)** $\approx 13$ times larger   **d)** $\approx 1.09 \times 10^{12}\ \text{km}^3$
   **e)** $\approx 2.20 \times 10^{10}\ \text{km}^3$   **f)** $\approx 50$ times larger

**59. a)** Answers will vary.   **b)** Answers will vary.
   **c)** Answers will vary.   **d)** Answers will vary.
   **e)** Answers will vary.
   **f)** If we double the length of each edge of a cube, the new volume will be eight times the original volume.

**61. a)** Answers will vary.

**b)** $V_1 = a^3$; $V_2 = a^2b$; $V_3 = a^2b$; $V_4 = ab^2$;
$V_5 = a^2b$; $V_6 = ab^2$; $V_7 = b^3$

**c)** $ab^2$

**62. a)** $330 \text{ in}^3$   **b)** $\approx 330.84 \text{ in}^3$

**SECTION 9.5, PAGE 537**

**1.** Rigid   **3.** Axis   **5.** Vector   **7.** Center   **9.** Glide
**11.** Reflective   **13.** Tessellation

*This figure contains the answers for Exercises 15 and 16.*

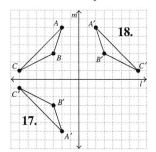

*This figure contains the answers for Exercises 17 and 18.*

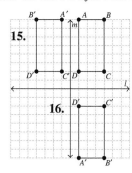

*This figure contains the answers for Exercises 19 and 20.*

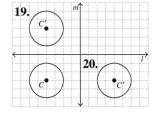

*This figure contains the answers for Exercises 21 and 22.*

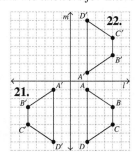

*This figure contains the answers for Exercises 23 and 24.*

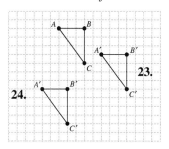

*This figure contains the answers for Exercises 25 and 26.*

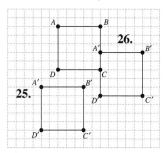

*This figure contains the answers for Exercises 27 and 28.*

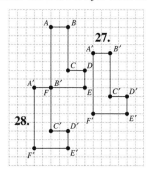

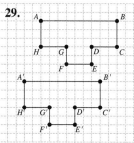

*This figure contains the answers for Exercises 31 and 32.*

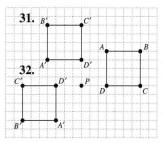

*This figure contains the answers for Exercises 33 and 34.*

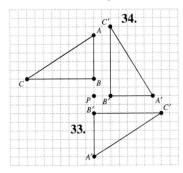

*This figure contains the answers for Exercises 35 and 36.*

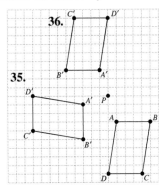

*This figure contains the answers for Exercises 37 and 38.*

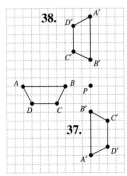

*This figure contains the answers for Exercises 39 and 40.*

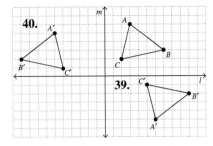

*This figure contains the answers for Exercises 41 and 42.*

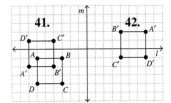

*This figure contains the answers for Exercises 43 and 44.*

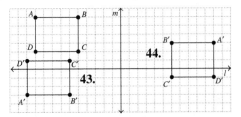

*This figure contains the answers for Exercises 45 and 46.*

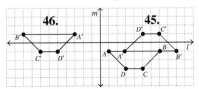

**47. a)**    **b)** Yes   **c)** Yes

**49. a)**    **b)** No   **c)** No

**51. a)**    **b)** No   **c)** No

**d)**    **e)** Yes   **f)** Yes

**53. a)–c)**

**b)** No. Any 90° rotation will result in the figure being in a different position than the starting position.

**55. a)–b)**

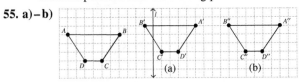

**c)** No

**d)** The order in which the translation and the reflection are performed is important. The figure obtained in part (a) is the glide reflection.

**57.** Answers will vary.    **59.** A regular pentagon cannot be used as a tessellating shape.

**60.** Although answers will vary depending on the font, the following capital letters have reflective symmetry about a horizontal line drawn through the center of the letter: B, C, D, E, H, I, K, O, X.

**61.** Although answers will vary depending on the font, the following capital letters have reflective symmetry about a vertical line drawn through the center of the letter: A, H, I, M, O, T, U, V, W, X, Y.

**62.** Although answers will vary depending on the font, the following capital letters have 180° rotational symmetry about a point in the center of the letter: H, I, N, O, S, X, Z.

### SECTION 9.6, PAGE 547

**1.** Rubber    **3.** Klein    **5.** Jordan    **7.** One

**9.** Answers will vary.    **11.** Answers will vary.

**13.** Answers will vary.    **15.** Answers will vary.

**17.** Outside    **19.** Outside    **21.** Inside    **23.** 1    **25.** 5

**27.** Larger than 5    **29.** 5    **31.** 0    **33.** Larger than 5

**35. a)** Answers will vary.    **b)** Answers will vary.
   **c)** Answers will vary.    **d)** Answers will vary.

**37.** One    **39.** Two

**41. a)** No, it has an inside and an outside.    **b)** Two
   **c)** Two    **d)** Two strips, one inside the other

**43.** Answers will vary.    **45.** Answers will vary.

### SECTION 9.7, PAGE 556

**1.** Parallel    **3.** Two    **5.** Sphere    **7.** Geodesic

**9.**

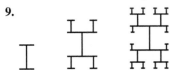

**11.**

**13. a)**

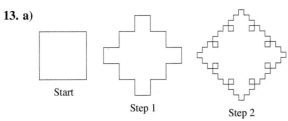

Start            Step 1            Step 2

   **b)** Infinite    **c)** Finite

**15.** Each type of geometry can be used in its own frame of reference.

**17.** Coastlines, trees, mountains, galaxies, polymers, rivers, weather patterns, brains, lungs, blood supply

**19.** Answers will vary.    **21.** Answers will vary.

**23.** Answers will vary.

**1.** $\overrightarrow{BF}$    **2.** $\overline{AD}$    **3.** $\triangle BFC$    **4.** $\overleftrightarrow{BH}$    **5.** $\{F\}$

**6.** $\{\ \}$    **7.** 54.6°    **8.** 79.5°    **9.** 10.2 in.

**10.** 2 in.    **11.** 58°    **12.** 92°

**13.** $m\angle 1 = 45°$, $m\angle 2 = 110°$, $m\angle 3 = 110°$, $m\angle 4 = 65°$, $m\angle 5 = 115°$, $m\angle 6 = 65°$

**14.** 1080°    **15. a)** 99 mi²    **b)** 40 mi

**16. a)** 13 in²    **b)** 19.4 in.    **17. a)** 84 in²    **b)** 42 in.

**18. a)** 6 km²    **b)** 12 km    **19. a)** 153.94 ft²    **b)** 43.98 ft

**20.** 64.38m²    **21.** 79.73 yd²    **22.** $1176

**23. a)** 120 cm³    **b)** 164 cm²

**24. a)** 254.47 ft³    **b)** 226.19 ft²

**25. a)** 603.19 mm³    **b)** 435.20 mm²

**26. a)** 1436.76 yd³    **b)** 615.75 yd²

**27.** 432 m³    **28.** 28 ft³    **29.** 75.40 cm³    **30.** 458.15 in³

**31. a)** $\approx 67.88$ ft³    **b)** 4610.7 lb; yes    **c)** $\approx 510.3$ gal

*This figure contains the answers for Exercises 32 and 33.*

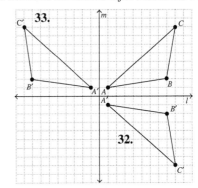

*This figure contains the answers for Exercises 34 and 35.*

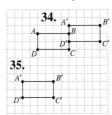

*This figure contains the answers for Exercises 36–38.*

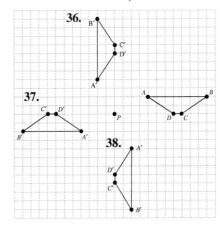

*This figure contains the answers for Exercises 39 and 40.*

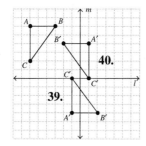

**41.** Yes   **42.** No   **43.** No   **44.** Yes

**45. a)** Answers will vary.   **b)** Answers will vary.

  **c)** Answers will vary.   **d)** Answers will vary.

**46.** Answers will vary.   **47.** Outside

**48.** Euclidean: Given a line and a point not on the line, one and only one line can be drawn parallel to the given line through the given point. Elliptical: Given a line and a point not on the line, no line can be drawn through the given point parallel to the given line. Hyperbolic: Given a line and a point not on the line, two or more lines can be drawn through the given point parallel to the given line.

**49.**

**50.**

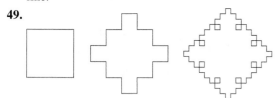

**CHAPTER TEST, PAGE 563**

**1.** $\overleftrightarrow{EF}$   **2.** $\triangle BCD$   **3.** {D}   **4.** $\overleftrightarrow{AC}$   **5.** 15.1°

**6.** 169.6°   **7.** 65°   **8.** 540°   **9.** ≈2.69 cm

**10. a)** 5 in.   **b)** 30 in.   **c)** 30 in.²

**11. a)** 1436.76 cm³   **b)** 615.75 cm²

**12.** 59.43 m³   **13.** 112 ft³

**14.**

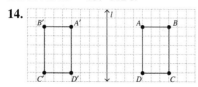

**15.**

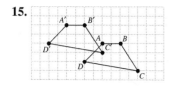

**16.**

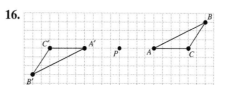

**17.**

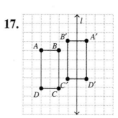

**18. a)** No   **b)** Yes

**19.** A surface with one side and one edge

**20. a)** Answers will vary.   **b)** Answers will vary.

**Chapter 12**

**SECTION 12.1, PAGE 679**

**1.** Experiment   **3.** Event   **5.** Empirical

**7. a)** Answers will vary.   **b)** Answers will vary.
  **c)** Answers will vary.

**9. a)** Answers will vary.   **b)** Answers will vary.
  **c)** Answers will vary.

**11. a)** $\frac{7}{15}$   **b)** $\frac{1}{3}$   **c)** $\frac{1}{5}$   **13. a)** $\frac{3}{7}$   **b)** $\frac{8}{21}$   **c)** $\frac{1}{21}$

**15. a)** $\frac{13,674}{153,468}$, or ≈ 0.0891   **b)** $\frac{27,362}{153,468}$ ≈ 0.1783

  **c)** $\frac{11,140}{153,468}$, or ≈ 0.0726

**17. a)** $\frac{16,600,000}{66,950,000}$ ≈ 0.2479   **b)** $\frac{8,870,000}{66,950,000}$ ≈ 0.1325

  **c)** $\frac{18,880,000}{66,950,000}$, or ≈ 0.2820

**19. a)** $\frac{11}{40}$   **b)** $\frac{9}{40}$   **c)** $\frac{1}{4}$   **d)** $\frac{7}{40}$   **e)** $\frac{3}{40}$

**21. a)** $\frac{6}{20} = \frac{3}{10}$   **b)** $\frac{14}{20} = \frac{7}{10}$   **c)** $\frac{14}{20} = \frac{7}{10}$   **d)** $\frac{2}{20} = \frac{1}{10}$

**23. a)** 0   **b)** $\frac{50}{250} = 0.2$   **c)** 1

**25. a)** $\frac{224}{929}$ ≈ 0.2411   **b)** $\frac{705}{929}$ ≈ 0.7589

**27.** No, it means that if a coin was flipped many times, about $\frac{1}{2}$ of the tosses would land heads up.

**29. a)** Roll a die many times and then find the relative frequency of 5's to the total number of rolls.
  **b)** Answers will vary.   **c)** Answers will vary.

**31. a)** Answers will vary.   **b)** Answers will vary.
  **c)** Answers will vary.   **d)** Answers will vary.

**32. a)** Answers will vary.   **b)** Answers will vary.
  **c)** Answers will vary.

**SECTION 12.2, PAGE 687**

**1.** Equally  **3.** 1  **5.** 1  **7.** $\frac{4}{7}$  **9.** 0.1  **11. a)** $\frac{1}{5}$  **b)** $\frac{1}{4}$

**13.** $\frac{1}{40}$  **15.** $\frac{1}{13}$  **17.** $\frac{12}{13}$  **19.** $\frac{1}{2}$  **21.** 1  **23.** $\frac{4}{13}$

**25. a)** $\frac{1}{4}$  **b)** $\frac{1}{2}$  **c)** $\frac{1}{4}$  **d)** 0

**27. a)** $\frac{1}{2}$  **b)** $\frac{1}{8}$  **c)** $\frac{1}{8}$  **d)** $\frac{1}{4}$

**29.** $\frac{1}{5}$  **31.** $\frac{9}{10}$  **33.** $\frac{1}{12}$  **35.** $\frac{1}{6}$  **37.** $\frac{1}{2}$  **39.** $\frac{2}{3}$  **41.** $\frac{11}{17}$

**43.** $\frac{12}{17}$  **45.** $\frac{2}{11}$  **47.** $\frac{6}{11}$  **49.** 0  **51.** $\frac{1}{10}$  **53.** $\frac{1}{5}$

**55.** $\frac{1}{26}$  **57.** $\frac{5}{26}$  **59.** $\frac{17}{26}$  **61.** $\frac{83}{130}$  **63.** $\frac{11}{26}$  **65.** $\frac{5}{21}$

**67.** $\frac{11}{42}$  **69.** $\frac{4}{21}$  **71.** $\frac{13}{36}$  **73.** $\frac{1}{3}$  **75.** $\frac{23}{36}$

**77. a)** 0  **b)** 1  **79. a)** $\frac{1}{4}$  **b)** $\frac{1}{4}$  **c)** $\frac{1}{4}$  **81.** 29 dots

**SECTION 12.3, PAGE 694**

**1.** Against  **3.** 3:1  **5.** 2:1  **7.** $\frac{1}{4}$

**9. a)** $\frac{5}{12}$  **b)** $\frac{7}{12}$  **c)** 7:5  **d)** 5:7

**11.** 6:1, 1:6  **13.** 5:1  **15.** 4:2 or 2:1  **17.** 12:1, 1:12
**19.** 10:3, 3:10  **21.** 1:1  **23.** 5:3  **25. a)** 8:7  **b)** 7:8
**27.** 8:7  **29.** 7:8  **31.** 8:7  **33. a)** $\frac{4}{5}$  **b)** 1:4  **35.** 1:16
**37. a)** $\frac{7}{11}$  **b)** $\frac{4}{11}$  **39.** $\frac{11}{15}$  **41.** $\frac{1}{5}$  **43.** 1:4  **45.** 74:1
**47.** 0.34  **49.** 33:17  **51.** 43:57  **53.** 1:9  **55.** 7:1

**57. a)** $\frac{1}{33}$  **b)** 32:1

**59.** Horse 2, $\frac{2}{9}$; Horse 3, $\frac{1}{3}$; Horse 4, $\frac{1}{16}$; Horse 5, $\frac{5}{12}$;

Horse 6, $\frac{1}{2}$  **61.** $\approx 97:3$

**SECTION 12.4, PAGE 703**

**1.** Expected  **3.** Positive  **5.** 32,700 people  **7.** 70 points
**9.** 1.44 million viewers  **11.** $5500  **13.** $1.60 off
**15. a)** $\approx -\$0.17$  **b)** $\approx \$0.17$

**17. a)** Yes, because you have a positive expectation of $\frac{1}{5}$

**b)** Yes, because you have a positive expectation of $\frac{1}{2}$

**19.** $3.00  **21. a)** $-\$2.00$  **b)** $1.00
**23. a)** $-\$2.00$  **b)** $1.00  **25.** $3.00  **27.** $-\$1.25$

**29.** $750  **31.** $416.67  **33. a)** $3.50  **b)** $5.50
**35. a)** $2.25  **b)** $4.25  **37.** $2.50  **39.** $-\$8.25$
**41.** 0.75 base  **43.** 2.9 points  **45.** 56 employees
**47.** $14,550  **49.** 3.5  **51.** $\approx 141.51$ service calls
**53. a)** $\frac{9}{16}, \frac{1}{4}, \frac{1}{8}, \frac{1}{16}$  **b)** $11.81
**55.** An amount greater than $1200
**57.** $-\$0.053$ or $-5.3¢$  **59. a)** $458.33  **b)** $308.33

**SECTION 12.5, PAGE 712**

**1.** Sample  **3.** 14  **5. a)** 2500 **b)** 2450
**7. a)** 216  **b)** 120  **9. a)** 4

**9. b)**  Sample Space  **c)** $\frac{1}{4}$  **d)** $\frac{1}{2}$  **e)** $\frac{1}{4}$

```
        H ──── H    HH
   H
        └──── T    HT
        H ──── H    TH
   T
        └──── T    TT
```

**11. a)** 9  **b)** Sample Space  **c)** $\frac{1}{9}$  **d)** $\frac{1}{9}$  **e)** $\frac{5}{9}$

```
        S    SS
   S    Q    SQ
        A    SA
        S    QS
   Q    Q    QQ
        A    QA
        S    AS
   A    Q    AQ
        A    AA
```

**13. a)** 12  **b)**  Sample Space

```
        R    YR
   Y    B    YB
        G    YG
        Y    RY
   R    B    RB
        G    RG
        Y    BY
   B    R    BR
        G    BG
        Y    GY
   G    R    GR
        B    GB
```

**c)** $\frac{1}{2}$  **d)** 1  **e)** $\frac{1}{2}$

**15. a)** 9  **b)**  Sample Space  **c)** $\frac{1}{3}$  **d)** $\frac{1}{9}$  **e)** $\frac{2}{3}$

```
        A    SA
   S    W    SW
        O    SO
        A    JA
   J    W    JW
        O    JO
        A    CA
   C    W    CW
        O    CO
```

**17. a)** 36    **b)**

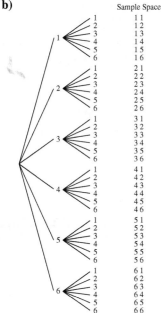

Sample Space

**c)** $\dfrac{1}{6}$    **d)** $\dfrac{5}{36}$    **e)** $\dfrac{1}{36}$    **f)** No

**19. a)** 12    **b)**

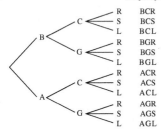

Sample Space

**c)** $\dfrac{1}{2}$    **d)** $\dfrac{1}{6}$    **e)** $\dfrac{2}{3}$

**21. a)** 18    **b)**

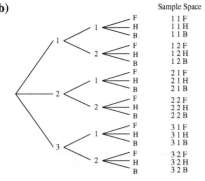

Sample Space

**c)** $\dfrac{1}{3}$    **d)** $\dfrac{1}{9}$    **e)** $\dfrac{2}{3}$

**23. a)** 27    **b)**

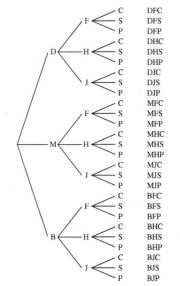

Sample Space

**c)** $\dfrac{1}{3}$    **d)** $\dfrac{1}{9}$    **e)** $\dfrac{2}{3}$

**25. a)** 24    **b)**

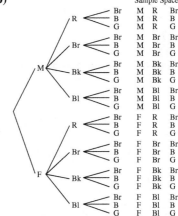

Sample Space

**c)** $\dfrac{1}{24}$    **d)** $\dfrac{1}{8}$

**27. a)** $\dfrac{1}{3}$    **b)** $\dfrac{2}{3}$

**c)** No, the probability of selecting a red chip is not the same as the probability of selecting a white chip.
**d)** Answers will vary.

**29.** 3; 1 red, 1 blue, and 1 brown    **30.** 5 faces

**31. a)** 120    **b)** CHAIR    **32. a)** 720    **b)** BASKET

SECTION 12.6, PAGE 723

**1.** Compound    **3.** And    **5.** Independent    **7.** Independent
**9.** $P(A) + P(B) - P(A \text{ and } B)$    **11.** 0.7    **13.** 0.4
**15.** 0.75    **17.** $\dfrac{1}{3}$    **19.** $\dfrac{1}{2}$    **21.** $\dfrac{2}{13}$    **23.** $\dfrac{8}{13}$    **25.** $\dfrac{7}{13}$
**27. a)** $\dfrac{1}{16}$    **b)** $\dfrac{1}{19}$    **29. a)** $\dfrac{1}{16}$    **b)** $\dfrac{5}{76}$
**31. a)** $\dfrac{1}{40}$    **b)** $\dfrac{1}{38}$    **33. a)** $\dfrac{9}{25}$    **b)** $\dfrac{33}{95}$    **35.** $\dfrac{11}{20}$

**37.** $\dfrac{2}{5}$   **39.** $\dfrac{1}{4}$   **41.** $\dfrac{1}{8}$   **43.** $\dfrac{9}{64}$   **45.** $\dfrac{1}{8}$   **47.** $\dfrac{3}{8}$

**49.** $\dfrac{3}{7}$   **51.** $\dfrac{9}{49}$   **53.** $\dfrac{1}{35}$   **55.** $\dfrac{1}{35}$   **57.** $\dfrac{1}{8}$   **59.** $\dfrac{1}{8}$

**61. a)** $\dfrac{1}{32}$   **b)** $\dfrac{1}{2}$   **63. a)** $\dfrac{4}{49}$   **b)** $\dfrac{2}{21}$   **65. a)** $\dfrac{24}{49}$   **b)** $\dfrac{11}{21}$

**67.** $\dfrac{376}{925}$   **69.** $\dfrac{549}{925}$   **71.** $\dfrac{1771}{9880}$   **73.** $\dfrac{7}{988}$   **75.** $\dfrac{7}{10}$

**77.** $\dfrac{343}{1000}$   **79.** $\dfrac{1}{4}$   **81.** $\dfrac{27}{1024}$   **83.** $\dfrac{243}{1024}$   **85.** $\dfrac{5}{22}$

**87.** $\dfrac{1050}{1331}$   **89.** $\dfrac{1}{24}$   **91.** $\dfrac{5}{12}$   **93.** 0.36   **95.** 0.36

**97. a)** No   **b)** 0.001   **c)** 0.00004   **d)** 0.00096
   **e)** 0.000999   **f)** 0.998001

**99.** $\dfrac{9}{250}$   **101.** $\dfrac{2169}{62,500}$   **103.** $\dfrac{14}{45}$

**105.** Favors dealer. The probability of at least one diamond is $\approx 0.44$, which is less than 0.5.

**107.** $\dfrac{1}{9}$   **108.** $\dfrac{1}{4}$   **109.** $\dfrac{1}{2}$   **110.** 1

### SECTION 12.7, PAGE 731

**1.** Conditional   **3.** $\dfrac{1}{3}$   **5.** $\dfrac{1}{3}$   **7.** $\dfrac{2}{3}$   **9.** $\dfrac{2}{3}$   **11.** $\dfrac{2}{3}$

**13.** $\dfrac{2}{3}$   **15.** $\dfrac{2}{3}$   **17.** $\dfrac{1}{5}$   **19.** $\dfrac{1}{3}$   **21.** $\dfrac{3}{5}$   **23.** $\dfrac{1}{7}$

**25.** $\dfrac{1}{16}$   **27.** $\dfrac{1}{7}$   **29.** $\dfrac{1}{6}$   **31.** $\dfrac{1}{6}$   **33.** $\dfrac{2}{3}$   **35.** $\dfrac{2}{9}$   **37.** $\dfrac{1}{2}$

**39.** $\dfrac{1}{2}$   **41.** 0.5941   **43.** 0.3605   **45.** 0.6251   **47.** $\dfrac{7}{13}$

**49.** $\dfrac{4}{15}$   **51.** $\dfrac{11}{15}$   **53.** 0.6337   **55.** 0.2459

**57.** 0.2897   **59.** $\dfrac{10}{11}$   **61.** $\dfrac{3}{19}$   **63.** $\dfrac{44}{47}$   **65.** $\dfrac{11}{27}$

**67.** $\dfrac{10}{29}$   **69.** $\dfrac{11}{29}$   **71.** $\dfrac{93}{200}$   **73.** $\dfrac{15}{52}$

**75. a)** 140   **b)** 120   **c)** $\dfrac{7}{10}$   **d)** $\dfrac{3}{5}$   **e)** $\dfrac{2}{3}$   **f)** $\dfrac{4}{7}$
   **g)** Because A and B are not independent events

**77. a)** 0.3   **b)** 0.5   **c)** Yes; $P(A|B) = P(A) \cdot P(B)$

**78.** $\dfrac{1}{3}$   **79.** $\dfrac{1}{2}$   **80.** $\dfrac{1}{3}$   **81.** $\dfrac{1}{3}$   **82.** 1   **83.** $\dfrac{1}{3}$

### SECTION 12.8, PAGE 742

**1.** Counting   **3.** $n!$   **5.** $\dfrac{n!}{(n-r)!}$   **7.** $_5P_3$   **9.** 120

**11.** 12   **13.** 1   **15.** 1   **17.** 15,120   **19.** 336   **21.** 10,000

**23.** 24   **25. a)** $5^5 = 3125$   **b)** $\dfrac{1}{3125} = 0.00032$

**27. a)** 456,976,000   **b)** 258,336,000   **29.** 336

**31. a)** 720   **b)** 120   **c)** 24   **d)** 600   **33.** 720

**35. a)** 479,001,600   **b)** 3,628,800   **c)** 14,400

**37.** 78,624,000   **39.** 131,040   **41.** 676,000   **43.** 104,000

**45. a)** 8,000,000   **b)** 6,400,000,000   **c)** 64,000,000,000

**47.** 524,160   **49.** 5040   **51.** 280   **53.** 362,880   **55.** 3780

**57.** 630   **59.** 15,120   **61. a)** 40,320   **b)** 362,880

**63. a)** 3125   **b)** 128   **c)** 0.00032

**65.** 12,600 sec, or 3.5 hr   **67.** No   **68.** 56   **69.** 600

**70. a)** 360   **b)** CHOICE

**71. a)** 2520   **b)** SCROOGE

### SECTION 12.9, PAGE 749

**1.** Combination   **3.** Permutations   **5.** $_7C_3$   **7.** 15

**9. a)** 70   **b)** 1680   **11. a)** 1   **b)** 1   **13.** **a)** 120   **b)** 720

**15.** $\dfrac{1}{6}$   **17.** $\dfrac{3}{4}$   **19.** 12   **21.** 495   **23.** 5   **25.** 56   **27.** 35

**29.** 495   **31.** 210   **33.** 1260   **35.** 6160   **37.** 5880

**39.** 8820   **41.** 700   **43.** 600   **45. a)** 45   **b)** 56

**47. a)**

```
                1
            1       1
        1       2       1
    1       3       3       1
1       4       6       4       1
```

   **b)**   1     5     10     10     5     1

**49. a)** 24   **b)** 24   **51.** 60,060

**52. a)** The order is important. Since the numbers may be repeated, it is not a true permutation lock.
   **b)** 64,000   **c)** 59,280

### SECTION 12.10, PAGE 755

**1.** $\dfrac{_{10}C_4}{_{14}C_4}$   **3.** $\dfrac{_5C_3}{_{26}C_3}$   **5.** $\dfrac{_8C_5}{_{15}C_5}$   **7.** $\dfrac{_{23}C_5}{_{120}C_5}$   **9.** $\dfrac{1}{15}$

**11.** $\dfrac{4}{143}$   **13.** $\dfrac{1}{30}$   **15.** $\dfrac{2}{11}$   **17.** $\dfrac{1}{9,366,819}$   **19.** $\dfrac{3}{10}$

**21.** $\dfrac{7}{10}$   **23.** $\dfrac{1}{115}$   **25.** $\dfrac{27}{230}$   **27.** 0.0012   **29.** 0.3083

**31.** $\dfrac{2}{55}$   **33.** $\dfrac{4}{33}$   **35.** $\dfrac{1}{77}$   **37.** $\dfrac{5}{77}$   **39.** $\dfrac{15}{253}$

**41. a)** $\dfrac{1}{123,760}$   **b)** $\dfrac{1}{30,940}$

**43. a)** $\dfrac{33}{54,145}$   **b)** $\dfrac{1}{2,598,960}$   **45. a)** $\dfrac{1}{2,162,160}$   **b)** $\dfrac{1}{6435}$

**47.** 1; Since there are more hairs than people, two or more people must have the same number of hairs on their head.

### SECTION 12.11, PAGE 764

**1.** Probability   **3.** Success   **5.** 0.0036   **7.** 0.3456

**9.** 0.015625

**11. a)** $P(x) = (_nC_x)(0.14)^x(0.86)^{n-x}$
   **b)** $P(2) = (_{12}C_2)(0.14)^2(0.86)^{10}$

**13.** 0.27869   **15.** 0.12248   **17.** 0.06877   **19.** 0.4096

**21. a)** 0.00098   **b)** 0.08789   **c)** 0.10352

**23. a)** $\approx 0.1119$   **b)** $\approx 0.2966$   **25.** 0; it will be midnight.

**REVIEW EXERCISES, PAGE 767**

**1.** Answers will vary.   **2.** Answers will vary.

**3.** $\dfrac{1}{5}$   **4.** Answers will vary.   **5.** $\dfrac{8}{25}$   **6.** $\dfrac{1}{2}$   **7.** $\dfrac{4}{5}$

**8.** 1   **9.** $\dfrac{1}{5}$   **10.** $\dfrac{9}{25}$   **11.** $\dfrac{11}{50}$   **12.** $\dfrac{16}{25}$   **13.** $\dfrac{43}{50}$

**14. a)** 4:1   **b)** 1:4   **15.** 5:3   **16.** $\dfrac{3}{85}$   **17.** 17:3

**18. a)** $-\$1.20$   **b)** $-\$3.60$   **19. a)** $-\$0.23$   **b)** \$0.23

  **c)** Lose \$23.08   **20.** 660 people   **21.** \$4.00   **22.** \$3.50

**23. a)**

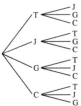

  **b)** Sample Space    **c)** $\dfrac{1}{12}$

    TJ
    TG
    TC
    JT
    JG
    JC
    GT
    GJ
    GC
    CT
    CJ
    CG

**24. a)**    **b)** Sample Space    **c)** $\dfrac{1}{4}$   **d)** $\dfrac{3}{4}$

    H1
    H2
    H3
    H4
    T1
    T2
    T3
    T4

**25.** $\dfrac{1}{4}$   **26.** $\dfrac{9}{64}$   **27.** $\dfrac{5}{16}$   **28.** $\dfrac{7}{8}$   **29.** 1   **30.** $\dfrac{3}{16}$

**31.** $\dfrac{1}{22}$   **32.** $\dfrac{14}{55}$   **33.** $\dfrac{41}{55}$   **34.** $\dfrac{1}{22}$

**35.** $\dfrac{1}{4}$   **36.** Against, 3:1; in favor, 1:3   **37.** \$13.75

**38.** $\dfrac{1}{8}$   **39.** $\dfrac{5}{8}$   **40.** In favor, 3:5; against, 5:3   **41.** \$3.75

**42.** $\dfrac{7}{8}$   **43.** $\dfrac{15}{17}$   **44.** $\dfrac{17}{19}$   **45.** $\dfrac{2}{15}$   **46.** $\dfrac{1}{2}$   **47.** $\dfrac{23}{40}$

**48.** $\dfrac{3}{17}$   **49.** $\dfrac{3}{4}$   **50.** $\dfrac{12}{17}$   **51. a)** 24   **b)** \$4500   **52.** 30

**53.** 720   **54.** 504   **55.** 20   **56.** 3,628,800

**57. a)** $\dfrac{1}{3,819,816}$   **b)** $\dfrac{1}{175,711,536}$   **58.** 35,640

**59.** 560   **60.** $\dfrac{1}{221}$   **61.** $\dfrac{1}{12}$   **62.** $\dfrac{1}{18}$   **63.** $\dfrac{1}{24}$   **64.** $\dfrac{11}{12}$

**65.** $\dfrac{5}{182}$   **66.** $\dfrac{45}{364}$   **67.** $\dfrac{2}{13}$   **68.** $\dfrac{11}{13}$

**69. a)** $P(x) = (_nC_x)(0.6)^x(0.4)^{n-x}$

  **b)** $P(75) = (_{100}C_{75})(0.6)^{75}(0.4)^{25}$

**70.** 0.0512   **71. a)** 0.01024   **b)** 0.98976

**CHAPTER TEST, PAGE 771**

**1.** $\dfrac{7}{25}$   **2.** $\dfrac{5}{9}$   **3.** $\dfrac{4}{9}$   **4.** $\dfrac{2}{3}$   **5.** $\dfrac{1}{6}$   **6.** $\dfrac{5}{18}$   **7.** $\dfrac{5}{12}$

**8.** $\dfrac{8}{13}$   **9.** 18   **10.**    Sample Space    **11.** $\dfrac{1}{18}$

    R1
    R2
    R3
    R4
    R5
    R6
    B1
    B2
    B3
    B4
    B5
    B6
    G1
    G2
    G3
    G4
    G5
    G6

**12.** $\dfrac{4}{9}$   **13.** $\dfrac{5}{6}$   **14.** 1,581,840   **15. a)** 5:4   **b)** 5:4

**16.** \$0   **17.**   **a)** $\dfrac{107}{228}$   **b)** $\dfrac{113}{228}$   **c)** $\dfrac{53}{113}$   **d)** $\dfrac{47}{107}$

**18.** 120   **19. a)** $\dfrac{3}{38}$   **b)** $\dfrac{35}{38}$   **20.** 0.2304

**Chapter 13**

**SECTION 13.1, PAGE 778**

**1.** Statistics   **3.** Descriptive   **5.** Sample   **7.** Random

**9.** Cluster   **11.** Unbiased   **13.** Stratified sample

**15.** Cluster sample   **17.** Systematic sample

**19.** Convenience sample   **21.** Random sample

**23. a)** Answers will vary.   **b)** Answers will vary.

  **c)** Answers will vary.

**25.** President; four out of 44 U.S. presidents have been assassinated (Lincoln, Garfield, McKinley, Kennedy).

**SECTION 13.2, PAGE 781**

**1.** The patients may have improved on their own without taking honey.

**3.** Mama Mia's may have more empty spaces and more cars in the parking lot than Shanghi's due to a larger parking lot or because more people may walk to Mama Mia's than to Shanghi's.

**5.** More people drive on Saturday evening. Thus, one might expect more accidents.

**7.** Most driving is done close to home. Thus, one might expect more accidents close to home.

**9.** We don't know how many of each professor's students were surveyed. Perhaps more of Professor Malone's students than Professor Wagner's students were surveyed. Also, because more students prefer a teacher does not mean that he or she is a better teacher. For example, a particular teacher may be an easier grader and that may be why that teacher is preferred.

**11.** Just because they are more expensive does not mean that they will last longer.

**13.** There may be deep sections in the pond, so it may not be safe to go wading.

**15. a)**  **b)**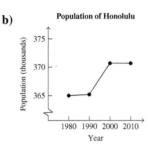

**17. a)**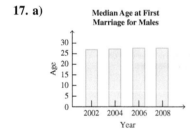

**b)**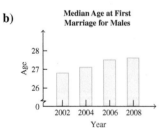

**19. a)**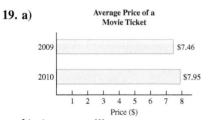

**b)** Answers will vary.

**21.** Yes, the sum of its parts is 121%. The sum of the parts of a circle graph should be 100%. When the total percent of responses is more than 100%, a circle graph is not an appropriate graph to display the data. A bar graph is more appropriate in this situation.

**23.** A decimal point

SECTION 13.3, PAGE 792

**1.** Frequency **3.** Mark **5.** Histogram **7.** Stem

**9. a)** 20 **b)** 7 **c)** 19 **d)** 16–22 **e)** 51–57

**11.**

| Number of Visits | Number of Students |
|:---:|:---:|
| 0 | 3 |
| 1 | 8 |
| 2 | 3 |
| 3 | 5 |
| 4 | 2 |
| 5 | 7 |
| 6 | 2 |
| 7 | 3 |
| 8 | 4 |
| 9 | 1 |
| 10 | 2 |

**13.**

| Circulation (ten thousands) | Number of Magazines |
|:---:|:---:|
| 173–322 | 33 |
| 323–472 | 10 |
| 473–622 | 1 |
| 623–772 | 1 |
| 773–922 | 1 |

**15.**

| Circulation (ten thousands) | Number of Magazines |
|:---:|:---:|
| 173–272 | 28 |
| 273–372 | 10 |
| 373–472 | 5 |
| 473–572 | 1 |
| 573–672 | 0 |
| 673–772 | 1 |
| 773–872 | 1 |

**17.**

| Population (millions) | Number of Cities |
|:---:|:---:|
| 7.0–7.9 | 6 |
| 8.0–8.9 | 4 |
| 9.0–9.9 | 1 |
| 10.0–10.9 | 3 |
| 11.0–11.9 | 1 |
| 12.0–12.9 | 2 |
| 13.0–13.9 | 3 |

**19.**

| Population (millions) | Number of Cities |
|---|---|
| 6.5–7.5 | 3 |
| 7.6–8.6 | 4 |
| 8.7–9.7 | 4 |
| 9.8–10.8 | 3 |
| 10.9–11.9 | 1 |
| 12.0–13.0 | 3 |
| 13.1–14.1 | 2 |

**21.**

| Percent | Number of States |
|---|---|
| 6.4–8.3 | 2 |
| 8.4–10.3 | 13 |
| 10.4–12.3 | 14 |
| 12.4–14.3 | 9 |
| 14.4–16.3 | 9 |
| 16.4–18.3 | 2 |
| 18.4–20.3 | 0 |
| 20.4–22.3 | 1 |

**23.**

| Percent | Number of States |
|---|---|
| 6.4–7.8 | 1 |
| 7.9–9.3 | 7 |
| 9.4–10.8 | 12 |
| 10.9–12.3 | 9 |
| 12.4–13.8 | 7 |
| 13.9–15.3 | 8 |
| 15.4–16.8 | 4 |
| 16.9–18.3 | 1 |
| 18.4–19.8 | 0 |
| 19.9–21.3 | 1 |

**25.** 1|2 represents 12

```
0 4  6  7  8
1 2  2  3  5  6  7  8  9
2 1  2  3  5  7
3 3  4
4 0
```

**27. a)**

| Salaries (1000s of dollars) | Number of Social Workers |
|---|---|
| 27 | 1 |
| 28 | 7 |
| 29 | 4 |
| 30 | 3 |
| 31 | 2 |
| 32 | 3 |
| 33 | 3 |
| 34 | 2 |

**b) and c)**

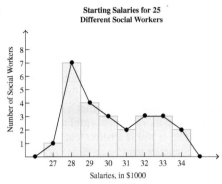

Starting Salaries for 25 Different Social Workers

**d)** 2|8 represents 28

```
2 7  8  8  8  8  8  8  8  9  9  9  9
3 0  0  0  1  1  2  2  2  3  3  3  4  4
```

**29. a)**

| Total Gross (millions of dollars) | Number of Tours |
|---|---|
| 80–91 | 12 |
| 92–103 | 4 |
| 104–115 | 3 |
| 116–127 | 2 |
| 128–139 | 3 |
| 140–151 | 0 |
| 152–163 | 1 |

**b) and c)**

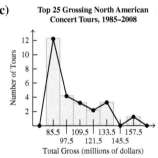

Top 25 Grossing North American Concert Tours, 1985–2008

**31. a)** 28  **b)** 4  **c)** 2  **d)** 75

**e)**

| Number of Televisions | Number of Homes |
|---|---|
| 0 | 2 |
| 1 | 4 |
| 2 | 8 |
| 3 | 6 |
| 4 | 4 |
| 5 | 3 |
| 6 | 1 |

**33. a)** 7   **b)** 16   **c)** 36

**d)**

| Number of Messages | Number of People | Number of Messages | Number of People |
|---|---|---|---|
| 3 | 2 | 7 | 3 |
| 4 | 3 | 8 | 8 |
| 5 | 7 | 9 | 6 |
| 6 | 4 | 10 | 3 |

**e)**

Number of E-Mail Messages Sent

**35.**

| Tution/Fees: | $5026.65 |
|---|---|
| Room: | $5303.48 |
| Board: | $3336.53 |
| Computer costs: | $903.34 |

**37. a)** Answers will vary.   **b)** Answers will vary.
   **c)** Answers will vary.   **d)** Answers will vary.
   **e)** Answers will vary.

**39. a)** There are 6 F's.   **b)** Answers will vary.

**40.** February, since it has the fewest number of days

SECTION 13.4, PAGE 802

**1.** Average   **3.** Mean   **5.** Mode   **7.** Quartiles
**9. a)** $\bar{x}$   **b)** $\mu$
**11.** 14, 13, 13, 17   **13.** 79.3, 82, none, 76
**15.** 8,8, none, 8   **17.** 13.1, 11, 1, 18.5
**19.** 11.9, 12.5, 13, 11.5
**21. a)** 198.7   **b)** 197.5   **c)** None   **d)** 208.5
**23. a)** 4.9, 5, 5, 6   **b)** 5.3, 5, 5, 6   **c)** Only the mean
   **d)** The mean and the midrange
**25.** A 79 mean average on 10 quizzes gives a total of
   790 points. An 80 mean average on 10 quizzes requires
   a total of 800 points. Thus, Jim missed a B by 10 points,
   not 1 point.
**27. a)** 23.0 pints   **b)** 22.5 pints   **c)** 18.5 pints   **d)** 25.1 pints
**29. a)** $4.6 billion   **b)** $3.3 billion
   **c)** None   **d)** $8.4 billion
**31.** 552
**33.** One example is 72, 73, 74, 76, 77, 78.
**35. a)** Yes   **b)** No   **c)** No   **d)** Yes
**37. a)** 29 or greater   **b)** Yes, 99 or greater
   **c)** 20 or greater   **d)** 80 or greater
**39.** One example: 1, 2, 3, 3, 4, 5 changed to 1, 2, 3, 4, 4, 5.

**41.** No. By changing only one piece of the 6 pieces of data,
   you cannot alter both the median and the midrange.
**43.** The data must be ranked.
**45.** He is taller than approximately 35 percent of all kindergarten
   children.
**47. a)** $23   **b)** $20   **c)** $34   **49.** Second quartile, median
**51. a)** $580   **b)** $590   **c)** 25%
   **d)** 25%   **e)** 17%   **f)** $60,000
**53. a)**

| Ruth | Mantle |
|---|---|
| 0.290 | 0.300 |
| 0.359 | 0.365 |
| 0.301 | 0.304 |
| 0.272 | 0.275 |
| 0.315 | 0.321 |

   **b)** Mantle's is greater in every case.
   **c)** Ruth: 0.316; Mantle: 0.311; Ruth's is greater.
   **d)** Answers will vary.
   **e)** Ruth: 0.307; Mantle: 0.313; Mantle's is greater.
   **f)** Answers will vary.
   **g)** Answers will vary.
**55.** 90   **57. a)** Answers will vary.   **b)** Answers will vary.
   **c)** Answers will vary.
**58. a)** Answers will vary. One example is 2, 3, 5, 7, 7.
   **b)** Answers will vary.

SECTION 13.5, PAGE 812

**1.** Variability   **3.** Standard deviation   **5.** Sample
**7.** 11, $\sqrt{16.5} \approx 4.06$   **9.** 6, $\sqrt{4.67} \approx 2.16$
**11.** 11, $\sqrt{15.2} \approx 3.90$   **13.** 5, $\sqrt{3} \approx 1.73$
**15.** $205, $\sqrt{4780.57} \approx \$69.14$
**17.** $190, $\sqrt{4725.25} \approx \$68.74$   **19.** Answers will vary.
**21.** The first set will have the greater standard deviation because the scores have a greater spread about the mean.
**23.** The sum of the values in the (Data $-$ Mean)$^2$ column will
   always be greater than or equal to 0.
**25. a)** $63, $\sqrt{631.6} \approx \$25.13$   **b)** Answers will vary.
   **c)** Answers remain the same, range: $63, standard devia-
   tion $\approx \$25.13$.
**27. a)** Answers will vary.   **b)** Answers will vary.
   **c)** Answers will vary.
   **d)** If each number in a distribution is multiplied by $n$, the
   mean and standard deviation of the new distribution
   will be $n$ times that of the original distribution.
   **e)** 20, 10
**29. a)** The standard deviation increases. There is a greater
   spread from the mean as they get older.
   **b)** $\approx 133$ lb   **c)** $\approx 21$ lb
   **d)** Mean: $\approx 100$ lb; normal range: $\approx 60$ to 140 lb
   **e)** Mean: $\approx 62$ in.; normal range: $\approx 53$ to 68 in.   **f)** 5%

**31. a)**

| East | | West | |
|---|---|---|---|
| Number of Oil Changes Made | Number of Days | Number of Oil Changes Made | Number of Days |
| 15–20 | 2 | 15–20 | 0 |
| 21–26 | 2 | 21–26 | 0 |
| 27–32 | 5 | 27–32 | 6 |
| 33–38 | 4 | 33–38 | 9 |
| 39–44 | 7 | 39–44 | 4 |
| 45–50 | 1 | 45–50 | 6 |
| 51–56 | 1 | 51–56 | 0 |
| 57–62 | 2 | 57–62 | 0 |
| 63–68 | 1 | 63–68 | 0 |

**b)**

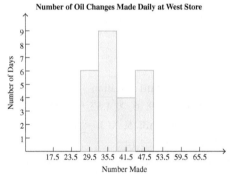

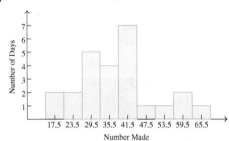

**c)** They appear to have about the same mean since they are both centered around 38.

**d)** The distribution for East is more spread out. Therefore, East has a greater standard deviation.

**e)** East: 38, West: 38  **f)** East: $\approx 12.64$, West: $\approx 5.98$

**32.** Answers will vary.

**33.** 6, 6, 6, 6, 6

**SECTION 13.6, PAGE 828**

**1.** Rectangular  **3.** Right  **5.** Bimodal  **7.** Standard
**9.** Below  **11. a)** 68%  **b)** 95%  **c)** 99.7%
**13.** Answers will vary.  **15.** Answers will vary.
**17.** Normal  **19.** Skewed right  **21.** 0.5000  **23.** 0.8185
**25.** 0.0630  **27.** 0.0375  **29.** 0.0429  **31.** 0.0166
**33.** 76.11%  **35.** 89.74%  **37.** 97.13%  **39.** 97.50%
**41.** 21.96%  **43. a)** Emily, Sarah, Carol  **b)** Jenny, Shenice
**c)** Sadaf, Heather, Kim

**45.** 50%  **47.** 10.56%  **49.** 69.15%  **51.** 24.17%
**53.** 44.00%  **55.** 29.02%  **57.** 59.87%  **59.** 50.00%
**61.** 11.51%  **63.** $\approx 23$ cars  **65.** 95.47%  **67.** 13,380 boxes
**69.** 69.15%  **71.** 0.62%  **73.** $\approx 83$ families  **75.** 1.79%
**77.** The standard deviation is too large.
**79. a)** $B$  **b)** $C$  **c)** $A$
**81.** The mean is the greatest value. The median is lower than the mean. The mode is the lowest value.
**83.** Answers will vary.
**85. a)** Katie: $z = 2.4$; Stella: $z = 1.7$
**b)** Katie. Her $z$-score is higher than Stella's $z$-score, which means her sales are further above the mean than Stella's sales.
**87. a)** Answers will vary.  **b)** Answers will vary.
**c)** Answers will vary.  **d)** Answers will vary.
**e)** Answers will vary.  **f)** Answers will vary.
**89.** $-1.18$  **90.** Answers will vary.  **91.** 2

**SECTION 13.7, PAGE 842**

**1.** Coefficient  **3.** 1  **5.** 0  **7.** Positive  **9.** fit
**11.** No correlation  **13.** Strong positive correlation
**15.** Yes  **17.** Yes  **19. No**  **21.** No

**23. a)**

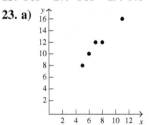

**b)** 0.981  **c)** Yes  **d)** Yes

**25. a)**

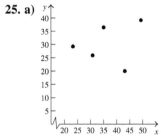

**b)** 0.228  **c)** No  **d)** No

**27. a)**

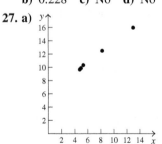

**b)** 0.999  **c)** Yes  **d)** Yes

**29. a)** 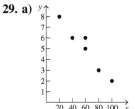    **b)** −0.968   **c)** Yes   **d)** Yes

**31.** $y = 1.26x + 2.25$   **33.** $y = 0.18x + 23.82$

**35.** $y = 0.81x + 5.84$   **37.** $y = -0.08x + 9.50$

**39. a)** 0.974   **b)** Yes   **c)** $y = 0.74x + 1.26$

**41. a)** 0.950   **b)** Yes   **c)** $y = 0.77x + 24.86$

**43. a)** 0.984   **b)** Yes   **c)** $y = 0.79x - 12.98$   **d)** 78

**45. a)** −0.804   **b)** No

**c)** $y = -0.43x + 35.28$   **d)** 21.1 mpg

**47. a)** −0.977   **b)** Yes

**c)** $y = -12.93x + 99.59$   **d)** 41.4%

**49. a)** Answers will vary.   **b)** Answers will vary.

**c)**

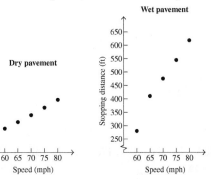

**d)** 0.999   **e)** 0.990   **f)** Answers will vary.

**g)** $y = 5.36x - 183.40$   **h)** $y = 16.22x - 669.80$

**i)** Dry, 229.3 ft; wet, 579.1 ft

**51. a)** Answers will vary.   **b)** Answers will vary.

**c)** Answers will vary.   **d)** Answers will vary.

**e)** Answers will vary.   **f)** Answers will vary.

**53. a)** 0.963   **b)** Should be the same.

**c)** 0.963; the values are the same.

**REVIEW EXERCISES, PAGE 848**

**1. a)** A population consists of all items or people of interest.

**b)** A sample is a subset of the population.

**2.** A random sample is one where every item in the population has the same chance of being selected.

**3.** The candy bars may have lots of calories, or fat, or sodium. Therefore, it may not be healthy to eat them.

**4.** Sales may not necessarily be a good indicator of profit. Expenses must also be considered.

**5. a)** **b)**

**6. a)**

| Class | Frequency |
|---|---|
| 35 | 1 |
| 36 | 3 |
| 37 | 6 |
| 38 | 2 |
| 39 | 3 |
| 40 | 0 |
| 41 | 4 |
| 42 | 1 |
| 43 | 3 |
| 44 | 1 |
| 45 | 1 |

**b) and c)**

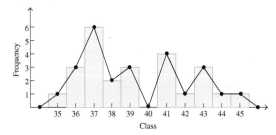

**7. a)**

| High Temperature | Number of Cities |
|---|---|
| 58–62 | 1 |
| 63–67 | 4 |
| 68–72 | 9 |
| 73–77 | 10 |
| 78–82 | 11 |
| 83–87 | 4 |
| 88–92 | 1 |

**b) and c)**

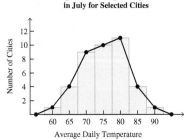

**d)** 5|8 represents 58

```
5|8
6|3 6 6 7 8 8 9
7|0 1 1 1 2 2 3 3 3 4 5 5 5 6 6 7 9 9 9
8|0 0 0 0 1 2 2 2 3 4 4 7
9|1
```

**8.** 80   **9.** 81   **10.** None   **11.** 80   **12.** 26
**13.** $\sqrt{80} \approx 8.94$   **14.** 13   **15.** 13   **16.** 7 and 12
**17.** 13.5   **18.** 19   **19.** $\sqrt{40} \approx 6.32$   **20.** 68.26%

**21.** 95.44%  **22.** 94.52%  **23.** 5.48%  **24.** 72.57%
**25.** 34.1%  **26.** 34.5%  **27.** 29.0%  **28.** 2.3%
**29. a)**

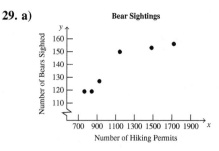

**b)** Yes; positive  **c)** 0.925  **d)** Yes
**e)** $y = 0.04x + 88.17$  **f)** $\approx 148$ bears

**30. a)**

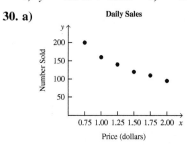

**b)** Yes; negative  **c)** $-0.973$  **d)** Yes
**e)** $y = -79.4x + 246.7$  **f)** $\approx 120$ sold

**31.** 180 lb  **32.** 185 lb  **33.** 25%  **34.** 25%  **35.** 14%
**36.** 19,200 lb  **37.** 238 lb  **38.** 150.6 lb  **39.** 3.53
**40.** 2  **41.** 3  **42.** 7  **43.** 14  **44.** $\sqrt{7.97} \approx 2.82$

**45.**

| Number of Children | Number of Presidents |
|---|---|
| 0–1 | 8 |
| 2–3 | 16 |
| 4–5 | 10 |
| 6–7 | 6 |
| 8–9 | 1 |
| 10–11 | 1 |
| 12–13 | 0 |
| 14–15 | 1 |

**46. and 47.**

Number of Children of U.S. Presidents

**48.** No, it is skewed to the right.  **49.** Answers will vary.
**50.** Answers will vary.

**1.** 42  **2.** 43  **3.** 43  **4.** 39.5  **5.** 25  **6.** $\sqrt{84} \approx 9.17$
**7.**

| Class | Frequency |
|---|---|
| 25–30 | 7 |
| 31–36 | 5 |
| 37–42 | 1 |
| 43–48 | 7 |
| 49–54 | 5 |
| 55–60 | 3 |
| 61–66 | 2 |

**8.**

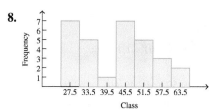

**9.**

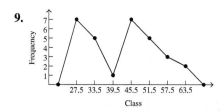

**10.** $735  **11.** $710  **12.** 75%  **13.** 79%  **14.** $74,000
**15.** $780  **16.** 87.10%  **17.** 89.44%  **18.** 10.56%
**19.** 94.52%
**20. a)**  Hourly Minimum Wage in the U.S.  **b)** Yes  **c)** 0.970  **d)** Yes

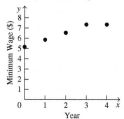

**e)** $y = 0.56x + 5.29$  **f)** $9.77

# Student's Solutions Manual

# Table of Contents

**CHAPTER 13    STATISTICS**

# CHAPTER TWO

## SETS

**Exercise Set 2.1**

1. Set
3. Description, Roster form, Set-builder notation
5. Infinite
7. Equivalent
9. Empty set or null
11. Universal
13. Not well defined, "best" is interpreted differently by different people.
15. Well defined, the contents can be clearly determined.
17. Well defined, the contents can be clearly determined.
19. Infinite, the number of elements in the set is not a natural number.
21. Infinite, the number of elements in the set is not a natural number.
23. Infinite, the number of elements in the set is not a natural number.

25. $\{$ Maine, Maryland, Massachusetts, Michigan, Minnesota, Misssissippi, Missouri, Montana $\}$

27. $\{11, 12, 13, 14, \ldots, 177\}$

29. $B = \{2, 4, 6, 8, \ldots\}$

31. $\{\ \}$ or $\varnothing$

33. $E = \{14, 15, 16, 17, \ldots, 84\}$

35. $\{$Metropolitan Museum of Art, Tate Modern, National Gallery of Art, British Museum, Louvre Museum$\}$

37. $\{$ Museum of Modern Art, Musee d'Art Moderne Prado, Musee d'Orsay $\}$

39. $\{2007, 2008\}$

41. $\{2004, \ 2005, 2006, 2007\}$

43. $B = \{x \mid x \in N \text{ and } 6 < x < 15\}$ or $B = \{x \mid x \in N \text{ and } 7 \le x \le 14\}$

45. $C = \{x \mid x \in N \text{ and } x \text{ is a multiple of } 3\}$

47. $E = \{x \mid x \in N \text{ and } x \text{ is odd}\}$

49. $C = \{x \mid x \text{ is February}\}$

51. Set $A$ is the set of natural numbers less than or equal to 7.
53. Set $V$ is the set of vowels in the English alphabet.
55. Set $T$ is the set of species of trees.
57. Set $S$ is the set of seasons.

59. $\{$ China, India, United States $\}$

61. $\{$ Russia, Brazil, Indonesia, Japan, Germany $\}$

63.  $\{2008,\ 2009,\ 2010,\ 2011\}$   65.  $\{2000,\ 2001,\ 2002,\ 2003,\ 2004, 2005\}$

67.  False; $\{e\}$ is a set, and not an element of the set.   69.  False; $h$ is not an element of the set.

71.  False; 3 is an element of the set.   73.  True; *Titanic* is an element of the set.

75.  $n(A)=4$   77.  $n(C)=0$

79.  Both; $A$ and $B$ contain exactly the same elements.

81.  Neither; the sets have a different number of elements.

83.  Equivalent; both sets contain the same number of elements, 4.

85.  a) Set $A$ is the set of natural numbers greater than 2.  Set $B$ is the set of all numbers greater than 2.

   b) Set $A$ contains only natural numbers.  Set $B$ contains other types of numbers, including fractions and decimal numbers.

   c) $A=\{3,4,5,6,\ldots\}$

   d) No

87.  Cardinal; 7 tells how many.   89.  Ordinal; 16th tells Lincoln's relative position.

91.  Answers will vary   93.  Answers will vary

**Exercise Set 2.2**

1.  Subset

3.  $2^n$, where $n$ is the number of elements in the set.

5.  True; $\{book\}$ is a subset of $\{$ magazine, newspaper, book $\}$.

7.  False; McIntosh is not in the second set.

9.  True; $\{$ motorboat, kayak $\}$ is a subset of $\{$ kayak, fishing boat, sailboat, motorboat $\}$.

11.  False; no subset is a proper subset of itself.

13.  True; Xbox 360 is an element of $\{$ PSIII, Wii, Xbox 360 $\}$.

15.  False; $\{swimming\}$ is a set, not an element.

17.  True; 5 is not an element of $\{2,4,6\}$.

19.  True; $\{red\}$ is a proper subset of $\{red, blue, green\}$.

21.  False; the set $\{\varnothing\}$ contains the element $\varnothing$.

23.  False; the set $\{0\}$ contains the element 0.

25.  False; 0 is a number and $\{\ \}$ is a set.

27.  $B\subseteq A, B\subset A$   29.  $A\subseteq B, A\subset B$

31.  $B\subseteq A, B\subset A$   33.  $A=B, A\subseteq B, B\subseteq A$

35.  $\{\ \}$ is the only subset.

37.  a) $\{\ \},\{a\},\{b\},\{c\},\{d\},\{a,b\},\{a,c\},\{a,d\},$ $\{b,c\},\{b,d\},\{c,d\},\{a,b,c\},\{a,b,d\},$ $\{a,c,d\},\{b,c,d\},\{a,b,c,d\}$

   b) All the sets in part (a) are proper subsets of $A$ except $\{a,b,c,d\}$.

39.   a) $\{\ \},\{a\},\{b\},\{c\},\{d\},\{a,b\},\{a,c\},\{a,d\},$
$\{b,c\},\{b,d\},\{c,d\},\{a,b,c\},\{a,b,d\},$
$\{a,c,d\},\{b,c,d\},\{a,b,c,d\}$
   b) All the sets in part (a) are proper subsets of
   $A$ except $\{a,b,c,d\}$.

41.   False; $A$ could be equal to $B$.

43.   True; every set is a subset of itself.

45.   True; $\varnothing$ is a proper subset of every set except
   itself.

47.   True; every set is a subset of the universal set.

49.      True; $\varnothing$ is a proper subset of every set
   except itself and $U \neq \varnothing$.

51.   True; $\varnothing$ is a subset of every set.

53.   The number of different variations is equal to the number of subsets of
   $\{$cheese, pepperoni, sausage, onions, green peppers, mushrooms, anchovies, ham$\}$,

   which is $2^8 = 2\times2\times2\times2\times2\times2\times2\times2 = 256$.

55.   The number of options is equal to the number of subsets of
   $\{$ cucumber, onion, tomato, carrot, green pepper, olive, mushroom $\}$, which is

   $2^7 = 2\times2\times2\times2\times2\times2\times2 = 128$.

57.   $E = F$ since they are both subsets of each other.

59. a) Yes.
   b) No, $c$ is an element of set $D$.
   c) Yes, each element of $\{a,b\}$ is an element of set $D$.

61. A one element set has one proper subset, namely the empty set.  A one element set has two subsets, namely
   itself and the empty set.  One is one-half of two.  Thus, the set must have one element.

### Section 2.3

1.   Complement

3. Intersection

5.   Cartesian

7.   Disjoint

9.

11.

13.

15.  *And* is generally interpreted to mean *intersection*.

17.

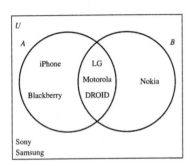

19.

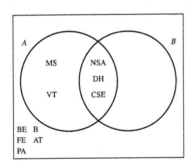

21.  The set of animals in U.S. zoos that are not in the San Diego Zoo
23.  The set of farms in the U.S. that do not produce corn
25.  The set of farms in the U.S. that produce corn or tomatoes
27.  The set of farms in the U.S. that produce corn and do not produce tomatoes
29.  The set of furniture stores in the U.S. that sell mattresses or leather furniture
31.  The set of furniture stores in the U.S. that do not sell outdoor furniture and sell leather furniture
33.  The set of furniture stores in the U.S. that sell mattresses or outdoor furniture or leather furniture
35.  $A = \{ b, c, t, w, a, h \}$
37.  $A \cap B = \{ w, b, c, t, a, h \} \cap \{ a, h, f, r, d, g \} = \{ a, h \}$
39.  $A \cup B = \{ w, b, c, t, a, h \} \cup \{ a, h, f, r, d, g \} = \{ w, b, c, t, a, h, f, r, d, g \}$

41. $A' \cap B' = \{w, c, b, t, a, h\}\{a, h, f, r, d, g\} \cap \{w, c, b, t, p, m, z\} = \{p, m, z\}$

43. $A = \{L, \Delta, @, *, \$\}$

45. $U = \{L, \Delta, @, *, \$, R, \square, \alpha, \infty, Z, \Sigma\}$

47. $A' \cup B = \{R, \square, \alpha, \infty, Z, \Sigma\} \cup \{*, \$, R, \square, \alpha\} = \{R, \square, \alpha, \infty, Z, \Sigma, *, \$\}$

49. $A' \cap B = \{L, \Delta, @, *, \$\}' \cap \{*, \$, R, \square, \alpha\} = \{R, \square, \alpha, \infty, Z, \Sigma\} \cap \{*, \$, R, \square, \alpha\} = \{R, \square, \alpha\}$

51. $A \cup B = \{1, 2, 4, 5, 7\} \cup \{2, 3, 5, 6\} = \{1, 2, 3, 4, 5, 6, 7\}$

53. $B' = \{2, 3, 5, 6\}' = \{1, 4, 7, 8\}$

55. $(A \cup B)'$ From #51, $A \cup B = \{1, 2, 3, 4, 5, 6, 7\}$. $(A \cup B)' = \{1, 2, 3, 4, 5, 6, 7\}' = \{8\}$

57. $(A \cup B)' \cap B$: From #53, $(A \cup B)' = \{7\}$. $(A \cup B)' \cap B = \{7\} \cap \{2, 3, 4, 6\} = \{\ \}$

59. $(B \cup A)' \cap (B' \cup A')$: From #53, $(A \cup B)' = (B \cup A)' = \{8\}$.

$(B \cup A)' \cap (B' \cup A') = \{8\} \cap \Big[\{2, 3, 4, 6\}' \cup \{1, 2, 4, 5, 8\}'\Big] = \{8\} \cap (\{1, 5, 7, 8\} \cup \{3, 6, 7\})$

$= \{8\} \cap \{1, 3, 4, 6, 7, 8\} = \{8\}$

61. $B' = \{b, c, d, f, g\}' = \{a, e, h, i, j, k\}$

63. $A \cap C = \{a, c, d, f, g, i\} \cap \{a, b, f, i, j\} = \{a, f, i\}$

65. $(A \cap C)'$: From #63, $A \cap C = \{a, f, i\}$. $(A \cap C)' = \{a, f, i\}' = \{b, c, d, e, g, h, j, k\}$

67. $A \cup (C \cap B)' = \{a, c, d, f, g, i\} \cup (\{a, b, f, i, j\} \cap \{b, c, d, f, g\})' = \{a, c, d, f, g, i\} \cup \{b, f\}'$

$= \{a, c, d, f, g, i\} \cup \{a, c, d, e, g, h, i, j, k\} = \{a, c, d, e, f, g, h, i, j, k\}$

69. $(A' \cup C) \cup (A \cap B) = \Big[\{a, c, d, f, g, i\}' \cup \{a, b, f, i, j\}\Big] \cup (\{a, c, d, f, g, i\} \cap \{b, c, d, f, g\})$

$= (\{b, e, h, j, k\} \cup \{a, b, f, i, j\}) \cup \{c, d, f, g\} = \{a, b, e, f, h, i, j, k\} \cup \{c, d, f, g\}$

$= \{a, b, c, d, e, f, g, h, i, j, k\}$, or $U$

For exercises 71-77: $U = \{1, 2, 3, 4, 5, 6, 7, 8, 9, 10\}$, $A = \{1, 2, 4, 6, 9\}$, $B = \{1, 3, 4, 5, 8\}$, $C = \{4, 5, 9\}$

71. $A - B = \{1, 2, 4, 6, 9\} - \{1, 3, 4, 5, 8\} = \{2, 6, 9\}$

73. $A - B'$: This leaves only $A \cap B$, which is $\{1, 4\}$

75. $(A - B)' = \{2, 6, 9\}' = \{1, 3, 4, 5, 7, 8, 10\}$

77. $C - A' = \{4, 5, 9\} - \{3, 5, 7, 8, 10\} = \{4, 9\}$

For exercises 79-83: $A = \{a, b, c\}$ and $B = \{1, 2\}$

79. $\{(a, 1), (a, 2), (b, 1), (b, 2), (c, 1), (c, 2)\}$

81. No; the ordered pairs are not the same.

83. 6

85. $A \cap B = \{1, 3, 5, 7, 9\} \cap \{2, 4, 6, 8\} = \{\ \}$

87. $A' \cup B = \{1, 3, 5, 7, 9\}' \cup \{2, 4, 6, 8\} = \{2, 4, 6, 8\} \cup \{2, 4, 6, 8\} = \{2, 4, 6, 8\}$, or $B$

89. $A \cap C' = \{1, 3, 5, 7, 9\} \cap \{1, 2, 3, 4, 5\}' = \{1, 3, 5, 7, 9\} \cap \{6, 7, 8, 9\} = \{7, 9\}$

91. $(B \cap C)' = (\{2, 4, 6, 8\} \cap \{1, 2, 3, 4, 5\})' = \{2, 4\}' = \{1, 3, 5, 6, 7, 8, 9\}$

93. $(C' \cup A) \cap B = \left(\{1, 2, 3, 4, 5\}' \cup \{1, 3, 5, 7, 9\}\right) \cap \{2, 4, 6, 8\} = (\{6, 7, 8, 9\} \cup \{1, 3, 5, 7, 9\}) \cap \{2, 4, 6, 8\}$

$= \{1, 3, 5, 6, 7, 8, 9\} \cap \{2, 4, 6, 8\} = \{6, 8\}$

95. $(A \cap B)' \cup C$:  From #83, $A \cap B = \{\ \}$.

$(A \cap B)' \cup C = \{\ \}' \cup \{1, 2, 3, 4, 5\} = \{1, 2, 3, 4, 5, 6, 7, 8, 9\} \cup \{1, 2, 3, 4, 5\} = \{1, 2, 3, 4, 5, 6, 7, 8, 9\}$, or $U$

97. $(A' \cup B') \cap C = \left(\{1, 3, 5, 7, 9\}' \cup \{2, 4, 6, 8\}'\right) \cap \{1, 2, 3, 4, 5\}$

$= (\{2, 4, 6, 8\} \cup \{1, 3, 5, 7, 9\}) \cap \{1, 2, 3, 4, 5\} = \{1, 2, 3, 4, 5, 6, 7, 8, 9\} \cap \{1, 2, 3, 4, 5\} = \{1, 2, 3, 4, 5\}$, or $C$

99. A set and its complement will always be disjoint since the complement of a set is all of the elements in the universal set that are not in the set.  Therefore, a set and its complement will have no elements in common.

For example, if $U = \{1, 2, 3\}$, $A = \{1, 2\}$, and $A' = \{3\}$, then $A \cap A' = \{\ \}$.

101. Let $A = \{$ customers who owned dogs $\}$ and $B = \{$ customers who owned cats $\}$.

$n(A \cup B) = n(A) + n(B) - n(A \cap B) = 27 + 38 - 16 = 49$

103. a)  $A \cup B = \{a, b, c, d\} \cup \{b, d, e, f, g, h\} = \{a, b, c, d, e, f, g, h\}$, $n(A \cup B) = 8$,

$A \cap B = \{a, b, c, d\} \cap \{b, d, e, f, g, h\} = \{b, d\}$, $n(A \cap B) = 2$.

$n(A) + n(B) - n(A \cap B) = 4 + 6 - 2 = 8$

Therefore, $n(A \cup B) = n(A) + n(B) - n(A \cap B)$.

b)  Answers will vary.

c)  Elements in the intersection of $A$ and $B$ are counted twice in $n(A) + n(B)$.

105. $A \cup B = \{1, 2, 3, 4, \dots\} \cup \{4, 8, 12, 16, \dots\} = \{1, 2, 3, 4, \dots\}$, or $A$

105. $B \cap C = \{4, 8, 12, 16, \dots\} \cap \{2, 4, 6, 8, \dots\} = \{4, 8, 12, 16, \dots\}$, or $B$

107. $B \cup C = \{4, 8, 12, 16, \dots\} \cup \{2, 4, 6, 8, \dots\} = \{2, 4, 6, 8, \dots\}$, or $C$

109. $A \cap C = \{1, 2, 3, 4, \dots\} \cap \{2, 4, 6, 8, \dots\} = \{2, 4, 6, 8, \dots\}$, or $C$

111. $B' \cap C = \{4, 8, 12, 16, \dots\}' \cap \{2, 4, 6, 8, \dots\} = \{0, 1, 2, 3, 5, 6, 7, 9, 10, 11, 13, 14, 15, \dots\} \cap \{2, 4, 6, 8, \dots\}$

$= \{2, 6, 10, 14, 18, \dots\}$

113. $(A \cap C) \cap B'$:  From #109, $A \cap C = C$.  $(A \cap C) \cap B' = C \cap B'$.

From #111, $B' \cap C = C \cap B' = \{2, 6, 10, 14, 18, \dots\}$

115. $A \cap A' = \{\ \}$

117. $A \cup \varnothing = A$

119. $A' \cup U = U$

121. $A \cup U = U$

123. If $A \cap B = B$, then $B \subseteq A$.

125. If $A \cap B = \varnothing$, then $A$ and $B$ are disjoint sets.

127. If $A \cap B = A$, then $A \subseteq B$.

## Exercise Set 2.4

1.  8

3.  a)  $A' \cap B'$

    b)  $A' \cup B'$

5.  $A' \cap B'$ is represented by regions V and VI.  If $B \cap C$ contains 12 elements and region V contains 4 elements, then region VI contains $12 - 4 = 8$ elements

7.  a)  Yes

    $$A \cup B = \{1,4,5\} \cup \{1,4,5\} = \{1,4,5\}$$
    $$A \cap B = \{1,4,5\} \cap \{1,4,5\} = \{1,4,5\}$$

    b)  No, one specific case cannot be used as proof.

    c)  No

| $A \cup B$ | | $A \cap B$ | |
|---|---|---|---|
| Set | Regions | Set | Regions |
| $A$ | I, II | $A$ | I, II |
| $B$ | II, III | $B$ | II, III |
| $A \cup B$ | I, II, III | $A \cap B$ | II |

Since the two statements are not represented by the same regions, $A \cup B \neq A \cap B$ for all sets $A$ and $B$.

9.

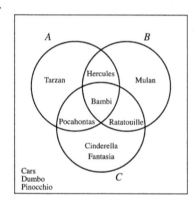

11.

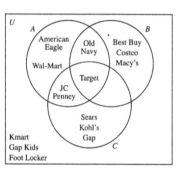

13.

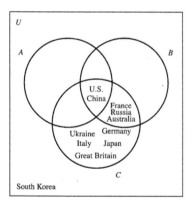

15.  Italy, V

19.  Spain, VI

21.  VI

17.  Canada, I

23.  Department of Energy, II

23.  III

25. III

27. V

29. II

31. VII

33. I

35. VIII

37. VI

39. $A = \{1, 2, 3, 4, 5, 7\}$

41. $B = \{3, 4, 5, 6, 8, 9, 12, 14\}$

43. $A \cap B = \{3, 4, 5\}$

45. $(B \cap C)' = \{1, 2, 3, 7, 9, 10, 11, 12, 13, 14\}$

47. $A \cup B = \{1, 2, 3, 4, 5, 6, 7, 8, 9, 12, 14\}$

49. $(A \cup C)' = \{9, 10, 12, 13, 14\}$

51. $A' = \{6, 8, 9, 10, 11, 12, 13, 14\}$

53. $(A \cap B)'$        $A' \cup B'$

| Set | Regions | Set | Regions |
|---|---|---|---|
| $A$ | I, II | $A$ | I, II |
| $B$ | II, III | $A'$ | III, IV |
| $A \cap B$ | II | $B$ | II, III |
| $(A \cap B)'$ | I, III, IV | $B'$ | I, IV |
| | | $A' \cup B'$ | I, III, IV |

Both statements are represented by the same regions, I, III, IV, of the Venn diagram. Therefore,

$(A \cap B)' = A' \cup B'$ for all sets $A$ and $B$.

55. $A' \cup B'$        $A \cap B$

| Set | Regions | Set | Regions |
|---|---|---|---|
| $A$ | I, II | $A$ | I, II |
| $A'$ | III, IV | $B$ | II, III |
| $B$ | II, III | $A \cap B$ | II |
| $B'$ | I, IV | | |
| $A' \cup B'$ | I, III, IV | | |

Since the two statements are not represented by the same regions, it is not true that $A' \cup B' = A \cap B$ for all sets $A$ and $B$.

57. $A' \cup B'$        $A \cup B'$

| Set | Regions | Set | Regions |
|---|---|---|---|
| $A$ | I, II | $A$ | I, II |
| $A'$ | III, IV | $B$ | II, III |
| $B$ | II, III | $B'$ | I, IV |
| $B'$ | I, IV | $A \cup B'$ | I, II, IV |
| $A' \cup B'$ | I, III, IV | | |

Since the two statements are not represented by the same regions, it is not true that $A' \cup B' = A \cup B'$ for all sets $A$ and $B$.

59. $(A' \cap B)'$        $A \cup B'$

| Set | Regions | Set | Regions |
|---|---|---|---|
| $A$ | I, II | $A$ | I, II |
| $A'$ | III, IV | $B$ | II, III |
| $B$ | II, III | $B'$ | I, IV |
| $A' \cap B$ | III | $A \cup B'$ | I, II, IV |
| $(A' \cap B)'$ | I, II, IV | | |

Both statements are represented by the same regions, I, II, IV, of the Venn diagram. Therefore,

$(A' \cap B)' = A \cup B'$ for all sets $A$ and $B$.

61.     $A \cap (B \cup C)$                                              $(A \cap B) \cup C$

| Set | Regions | Set | Regions |
|-----|---------|-----|---------|
| $B$ | II, III, V, VI | $A$ | I, II, IV, V |
| $C$ | IV , V, VI, VII | $B$ | II, III, V, VI |
| $B \cup C$ | II, III, IV, V, VI, VII | $A \cap B$ | II, V |
| $A$ | I, II, IV, V | $C$ | IV, V, VI, VII |
| $A \cap (B \cup C)$ | II, IV, V | $(A \cap B) \cup C$ | II, IV, V, VI, VII |

Since the two statements are not represented by the same regions, it is not true that
$A \cap (B \cup C) = (A \cap B) \cup C$ for all sets $A, B$, and $C$.

63.     $A \cap (B \cup C)$                                              $(B \cup C) \cap A$

| Set | Regions | Set | Regions |
|-----|---------|-----|---------|
| $B$ | II, III, V, VI | $B$ | II, III, V, VI |
| $C$ | IV , V, VI, VII | $C$ | IV, V, VI, VII |
| $B \cup C$ | II, III, IV, V, VI, VII | $B \cup C$ | II, III, IV, V, VI, VII |
| $A$ | I, II, IV, V | $A$ | I, II, IV, V |
| $A \cap (B \cup C)$ | II, IV, V | $(B \cup C) \cap A$ | II, IV, V |

Both statements are represented by the same regions, II, IV, V, of the Venn diagram.

Therefore, $A \cap (B \cup C) = (B \cup C) \cap A$ for all sets $A, B$, and $C$.

65.     $A \cap (B \cup C)$                                              $(A \cap B) \cup (A \cap C)$

| Set | Regions | Set | Regions |
|-----|---------|-----|---------|
| $B$ | II, III, V, VI | $A$ | I, II, IV, V |
| $C$ | IV, V, VI, VII | $B$ | II, III, V, VI |
| $B \cup C$ | II, III, IV, V, VI, VII | $A \cap B$ | II, V |
| $A$ | I, II, IV, V | $C$ | IV, V, VI, VII |
| $A \cap (B \cup C)$ | II, IV, V | $A \cap C$ | IV, V |
| | | $(A \cap B) \cup (A \cap C)$ | II, IV, V |

Both statements are represented by the same regions, II, IV, V, of the Venn diagram.

Therefore, $A \cap (B \cup C) = (A \cap B) \cup (A \cap C)$ for all sets $A, B$, and $C$.

67.     $A \cup (B \cup C)'$                                              $A \cup (B' \cap C')$

| Set | Regions | Set | Regions |
|-----|---------|-----|---------|
| $B$ | II, III, V, VI | $B$ | II, III, V, VI |
| $C$ | IV, V, VI, VII | $B'$ | I, IV, VII, VIII |
| $B \cup C$ | II, III, IV, V, VI, VII | $C$ | IV, V, VI, VII |
| $(B \cup C)'$ | I, VIII | $C'$ | I, II, III, VIII |
| $A$ | I, II, IV, V | $B' \cap C'$ | I, VIII |
| $A \cup (B \cup C)'$ | I, II, IV, V, VIII | $A$ | I, II, IV, V |
| | | $A \cup (B' \cap C')$ | I, II, IV, V, VIII |

Both statements are represented by the same region, I, II, IV, V, VIII of the Venn diagram.

Therefore, $A \cup (B \cup C)' = A \cup (B' \cap C')$ for all sets $A, B$, and $C$.

69.    $(A \cup B)' \cap C$                                          $(A' \cup C) \cap (B' \cup C)$

| Set | Regions |
|-----|---------|
| $A$ | I, II, IV, V |
| $B$ | II, III, V, VI |
| $A \cup B$ | I, II, III, IV, V, VI |
| $(A \cup B)'$ | VII, VIII |
| $C$ | IV, V, VI, VII |
| $(A \cup B)' \cap C$ | VII |

| Set | Regions |
|-----|---------|
| $A$ | I, II, IV, V |
| $A'$ | III, VI, VII, VIII |
| $C$ | IV, V, VI, VII |
| $A' \cup C$ | III, IV, V, VI, VII, VIII |
| $B$ | II, III, V, VI |
| $B'$ | I, IV, VII, VIII |
| $B' \cup C$ | I, IV, V, VI, VII, VIII |
| $(A' \cup C) \cap (B' \cup C)$ | IV, V, VI, VII, VIII |

Since the two statements are not represented by the same regions,  it is not true

that $(A \cup B)' \cap C = (A' \cup C) \cap (B' \cup C)$

for all sets $A, B,$ and $C$.

71.  $(A \cup B)'$                          73.   $(A \cup B) \cap C'$

75.  a) $(A \cup B) \cap C = (\{1,2,3,4\} \cup \{3,6,7\}) \cap \{6,7,9\} = \{1,2,3,4,6,7\} \cap \{6,7,9\} = \{6,7\}$

$(A \cap C) \cup (B \cap C) = (\{1,2,3,4\} \cap \{6,7,9\}) \cup (\{3,6,7\} \cap \{6,7,9\}) = \varnothing \cup \{6,7\} = \{6,7\}$

Therefore, for the specific sets, $(A \cup B) \cap C = (A \cap C) \cup (B \cap C)$.

b) Answers will vary.

c)     $(A \cup B) \cap C$                          $(A \cap C) \cup (B \cap C)$

| Set | Regions |
|-----|---------|
| $A$ | I, II, IV, V |
| $B$ | II, III, V, VI |
| $A \cup B$ | I, II, III, IV, V, VI |
| $C$ | IV, V, VI, VII |
| $(A \cup B) \cap C$ | IV, V, VI |

| Set | Regions |
|-----|---------|
| $A$ | I, II, IV, V |
| $C$ | IV, V, VI, VII |
| $A \cap C$ | IV, V |
| $B$ | II, III, V, VI |
| $B \cap C$ | V, VI |
| $(A \cap C) \cup (B \cap C)$ | IV, V, VI |

Both statements are represented by the same regions, IV, V, VI, of the Venn diagram.

Therefore, $(A \cup B) \cap C = (A \cap C) \cup (B \cap C)$ for all sets $A, B,$ and $C$.

77.

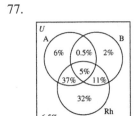

79.  a)  *A* : Office Building Construction Projects,  *B* : Plumbing Projects,  *C* : Budget Greater Than $300,000

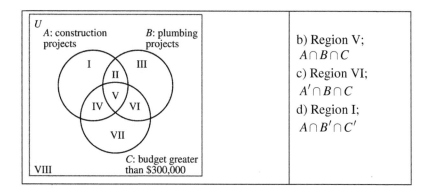

b) Region V;
$A \cap B \cap C$

c) Region VI;
$A' \cap B \cap C$

d) Region I;
$A \cap B' \cap C'$

81.  a)

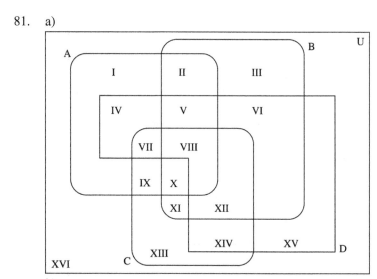

b)

| Region | Set | Region | Set |
|---|---|---|---|
| I | $A \cap B' \cap C' \cap D'$ | IX | $A \cap B' \cap C \cap D'$ |
| II | $A \cap B \cap C' \cap D'$ | X | $A \cap B \cap C \cap D'$ |
| III | $A' \cap B \cap C' \cap D'$ | XI | $A' \cap B \cap C \cap D'$ |
| IV | $A \cap B' \cap C' \cap D$ | XII | $A' \cap B \cap C \cap D$ |
| V | $A \cap B \cap C' \cap D$ | XIII | $A' \cap B' \cap C \cap D'$ |
| VI | $A' \cap B \cap C' \cap D$ | XIV | $A' \cap B' \cap C \cap D$ |
| VII | $A \cap B' \cap C \cap D$ | XV | $A' \cap B' \cap C' \cap D$ |
| VIII | $A \cap B \cap C \cap D$ | XVI | $A' \cap B' \cap C' \cap D'$ |

**Exercise Set 2.5**

1.

a) 48
b) 37
c) $200 - (48 + 61 + 37)$, or 54

3.

a) 17     b) 12
c) 59, the sum of the numbers in Regions I, II, III

5.

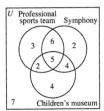

a) 3     b) 6
c) $3 + 2 + 6 + 5 + 2 + 4$, or 22
d) $3 + 6 + 2$, or 11
e) $2 + 6 + 4$, or 12

7.

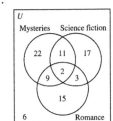

a) 22     b) 11
c) $85 - 15 - 6$, or 64
d) $22 + 11 + 17$, or 50
e) $9 + 11 + 3$, or 23

9.

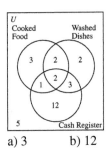

a) 3     b) 12
c) 3
d) $12 + 3 + 2$, or 17
e) 8

11.

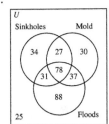

a) $30 + 37$, or 67
b) $350 - 25 - 88$, or 237
c) 37     d) 25

13. The Venn diagram shows the number of cars driven by women is 37, the sum of the numbers in Regions II, IV, V. This exceeds the 35 women the agent claims to have surveyed.

15. First fill in 15, 20 and 35 on the Venn diagram. Referring to the labels in the Venn diagram and the given information, we see that

$a+c=60$

$b+c=50$

$a+b+c=200-125=75$

Adding the first two equations and subtracting the third from this sum gives $c=60+50-75=35$. Then $a=25$ and $b=15$. Then $d=180-110-25-35=10$. We now have labeled all the regions except the region outside the three circles, so the number of farmers growing at least one of the crops is $125+25+110+15+35+10+90$, or 410. Thus the number growing none of the crops is $500-410$, or 90.

a) 410

b) 35

c) 90

d) $15+25+10$, or 50

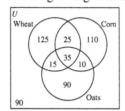

17. From the given information we can generate the Venn diagram. First fill in 4 for Region V. Then since the intersections in pairs all have 6 elements, we can fill in 2 for each of Regions II, IV, and VI. This already accounts for the 10 elements $A\cup B\cup C$, so the remaining 2 elements in $U$ must be in Region VIII.

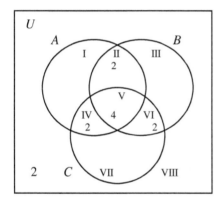

a) 10, the sum of the numbers in Regions I, II, III, IV, V, VI

b) 10, the sum of the numbers in Regions III, IV, V, VI, VIII

c) 6, the sum of the numbers in Regions I, III, IV, VI, VIII

## Exercise Set 2.6

1. An **infinite set** is a set that can be placed in a one-to-one correspondence with a proper subset of itself.

3. $\{3, 4, 5, 6, 7, ..., n+2, ...\}$

   $\downarrow \downarrow \downarrow \downarrow \downarrow \quad \downarrow$

   $\{4, 5, 6, 7, 8, ..., n+3, ...\}$

5. $\{3, 5, 7, 9, 11, ..., 2n+1, ...\}$

   $\downarrow \downarrow \downarrow \downarrow \downarrow \quad \downarrow$

   $\{5, 7, 9, 11, 13, ..., 2n+3, ...\}$

7. $\{5, 9, 13, 17, 21 ..., 4n+1, ...\}$

   $\downarrow \downarrow \downarrow \downarrow \downarrow \quad \downarrow$

   $\{9, 13, 17, 21, 25, ..., 4n+5, ...\}$

9.  $\left\{\dfrac{1}{2},\dfrac{1}{4},\dfrac{1}{6},\dfrac{1}{8},\dfrac{1}{10},...,\dfrac{1}{2n},...\right\}$

$\downarrow\;\downarrow\;\downarrow\;\downarrow\;\downarrow\qquad\downarrow$

$\left\{\dfrac{1}{4},\dfrac{1}{6},\dfrac{1}{8},\dfrac{1}{10},...,\dfrac{1}{2n+2},...\right\}$

11.  $\left\{\dfrac{4}{11},\dfrac{5}{11},\dfrac{6}{11},\dfrac{7}{11},...,\dfrac{n+3}{11},...\right\}$

$\downarrow\;\downarrow\;\downarrow\;\downarrow\qquad\downarrow$

$\left\{\dfrac{5}{11},\dfrac{6}{11},\dfrac{7}{11},\dfrac{8}{11},...,\dfrac{n+4}{11},...\right\}$

13.  $\{1,\ 2,\ 3,\ 4,\ 5,\ ...,\ n,\ ...\}$
$\downarrow\downarrow\downarrow\;\downarrow\;\downarrow\qquad\downarrow$
$\{3,\ 6,\ 9,\ 12,\ 15,\ ...,3n,\ ...\}$

15.  $\{1,2,3,\ 4,\ 5,\ ...,\quad n,\ ...\}$
$\downarrow\downarrow\downarrow\downarrow\;\downarrow\qquad\downarrow$
$\{4,6,8,10,12,...,2n+2,\ ...\}$

17.  $\{1,2,3,\ 4,\ 5,\ ...,\qquad n,\ ...\}$
$\downarrow\downarrow\downarrow\downarrow\;\downarrow\qquad\downarrow$
$\{2,5,8,11,14,...,3n-1,\ ...\}$

19.  $\{1,\ 2,\ 3,\ 4,\ 5,\ ...,\quad n,\ ...\}$
$\downarrow\;\downarrow\;\downarrow\;\downarrow\;\downarrow\qquad\downarrow$
$\left\{\dfrac{1}{3},\dfrac{1}{6},\dfrac{1}{9},\dfrac{1}{12},\dfrac{1}{15},...,\dfrac{1}{3n},...\right\}$

21.  $\{\ 1,2,\ 3,4,7,\ ...,\ n,\ ...\}$
$\downarrow\downarrow\downarrow\downarrow\downarrow\qquad\downarrow$
$\left\{\dfrac{1}{3},\dfrac{1}{4},\dfrac{1}{5},\dfrac{1}{6},\dfrac{1}{7},...,\dfrac{1}{n+2},...\right\}$

23.  $\{1,\ 2,3,\ 4,\ \ 5,\ ...,\ n,\ ...\}$
$\downarrow\;\downarrow\;\downarrow\;\downarrow\;\downarrow\qquad\downarrow$
$\{1,4,\ 9\ ,16,25,...,n^2,\ ...\}$

25.  $\{1,2,\ 3,\ 4,\ \ 5,\ ...,\quad n,\ ...\}$
$\downarrow\downarrow\;\downarrow\;\downarrow\;\downarrow\qquad\downarrow$
$\{3,9,27,81,243,...,3^n,\ ...\}$

27.  =

29.  =

31.  =

### Review Exercises

1. True

2. False; the word *best* makes the statement not well defined.

3. True

4. False; no set is a proper subset of itself.

5. False; the elements 6, 12, 18, 24, ... are members of both sets.

6. True

7. False; the two sets do not contain exactly the same elements.

8. True

9. True

10. True

11. True

12. True

13. True

14. True

15. $A = \{7, 9, 11, 13, 15\}$

16. $B = \{$ Colorado, Nebraska, Missouri, Oklahoma $\}$

17. $C = \{1, 2, 3, 4, ..., 161\}$

18. $D = \{9, 10, 11, 12, ..., 80\}$

19. $A = \{x \mid x \in N \text{ and } 50 < x < 150\}$

20. $B = \{x \mid x \in N \text{ and } x > 42\}$

21. $C = \{x \mid x \in N \text{ and } x < 5\}$

22. $D = \{x \mid x \in N \text{ and } 27 \le x \le 51\}$

23. $A$ is the set of capital letters in the English alphabet from E through M, inclusive.

24. $B$ is the set of U.S. coins with a value of less than one dollar.

25. $C$ is the set of the first three lowercase letters in the English alphabet.

26. $D$ is the set of numbers greater than or equal to 3 and less than 9.

27. $A \cap B = \{1, 3, 5, 7\} \cap \{3, 7, 9, 10\} = \{3, 7\}$

28. $A \cup B' = \{1, 3, 5, 7\} \cup \{3, 7, 9, 10\}' = \{1, 3, 5, 7\} \cup \{1, 2, 4, 5, 6, 8\} = \{1, 2, 3, 4, 5, 6, 7, 8\}$

29. $A' \cap B = \{1, 3, 5, 7\}' \cap \{3, 7, 9, 10\} = \{2, 4, 6, 8, 9, 10\} \cap \{5, 7, 9, 10\} = \{9, 10\}$

30. $(A \cup B)' \cup C = (\{1, 3, 5, 7\} \cup \{3, 7, 9, 10\})' \cup \{1, 7, 10\} = \{1, 3, 5, 7, 9, 10\}' \cup \{1, 7, 10\}$

    $= \{2, 4, 6, 8\} \cup \{1, 7, 10\} = \{1, 2, 4, 6, 7, 8, 10\}$

31. $A - B = \{1, 3, 5, 7\} - \{3, 7, 9, 10\} = \{1, 5\}$

32. $A - C' = \{1, 3, 5, 7\} - \{1, 7, 10\}' = \{1, 3, 5, 7\} - \{2, 3, 4, 5, 6, 8, 9\} = \{1, 7\}$

33. $\{(1, 1), (1, 7), (1, 10), (3, 1), (3, 7), (3, 10), (5, 1), (5, 7), (5, 10), (7, 1), (7, 7), (7, 10)\}$

34. $\{(3, 1), (3, 3), (3, 5), (3, 7), (7, 1), (7, 3), (7, 5), (7, 7), (9, 1), (9, 3), (9, 5), (9, 7), (10, 1), (10, 3), (10, 5), (10, 7)\}$

35. $2^4 = 2 \times 2 \times 2 \times 2 = 16$

36. $2^4 - 1 = (2 \times 2 \times 2 \times 2) - 1 = 16 - 1 = 15$

37.

38. $A \cup B = \{$ a, c, d, f, g, i, k, l $\}$

39.  $A \cap B' = \{ i, k \}$

41.  $A \cap B \cap C = \{ f \}$

43.  $(A \cap B) \cup C = \{ a, b, d, f, h, i, l \}$

40.  $A \cup B \cup C = \{ a, b, c, d, f, g, h, i, k, l \}$

42.  $(A \cup B) \cap C = \{ a, f, i \}$

44.  $(A' \cup B')'$          $A \cap B$

| Set | Regions | Set | Regions |
|---|---|---|---|
| $A$ | I, II | $A$ | I, II |
| $A'$ | III, IV | $B$ | II, III |
| $B$ | II, III | $A \cap B$ | II |
| $B'$ | I, IV | | |
| $A' \cup B'$ | I, III, IV | | |
| $(A' \cup B')'$ | II | | |

Both statements are represented by the same region, II, of the Venn diagram.  Therefore, $(A' \cup B')' = A \cap B$ for all sets $A$ and $B$.

45.  $(A \cup B') \cup (A \cup C')$          $A \cup (B \cap C)'$

| Set | Regions | Set | Regions |
|---|---|---|---|
| $A$ | I, II, IV, V | $B$ | II, III, V, VI |
| $B$ | II, III, V, VI | $C$ | IV, V, VI, VII |
| $B'$ | I, IV, VII, VIII | $B \cap C$ | V, VI |
| $A \cup B'$ | I, II, IV, V, VII, VIII | $(B \cap C)'$ | I, II, III, IV, VII, VIII |
| $C$ | IV, V, VI, VII | $A$ | I, II, IV, V |
| $C'$ | I, II, III, VIII | $A \cup (B \cap C)'$ | I, II, III, IV, V, VII, VIII |
| $A \cup C'$ | I, II, III, IV, V, VIII | | |
| $(A \cup B') \cup (A \cup C')$ | I, II, III, IV, V, VII, VIII | | |

Both statements are represented by the same regions, I, II, III, IV, V, VII, VIII, of the Venn diagram.

Therefore, $(A \cup B') \cup (A \cup C') = A \cup (B \cap C)'$ for all sets $A, B$, and $C$.

46.  II

48.  I

50.  IV

52.  II

47.  III

49.  IV

51.  II

53. The company paid $450 since the sum of the numbers in Regions I through IV is 450.

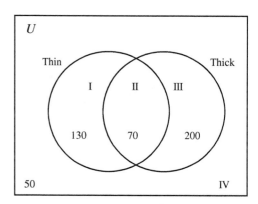

54. a) 131, the sum of the numbers in Regions I through VII
   b) 32, Region I
   c) 10, Region II
   d) 65, the sum of the numbers in Regions I, IV, VII

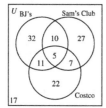

55. a) 38, Region I
   b) 298, the sum of the numbers in Regions I, III, VII
   c) 28, Region VI
   d) 236, the sum of the numbers in Regions I, IV, VII
   e) 106, the sum of the numbers in Regions II, IV, VI

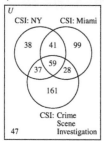

56. $\{2, 4, 6, \ 8, \ 10, \ldots, 2n, \ldots\}$
    $\downarrow \downarrow \downarrow \downarrow \ \downarrow \ \ \ \ \ \ \downarrow$
    $\{4, 6, \ 8, \ 10, \ 12, \ldots, 2n + 2, \ldots\}$

57. $\{3, 5, 7, \ 9, \ 11, \ldots, 2n + 1, \ldots\}$
    $\downarrow \downarrow \downarrow \downarrow \ \downarrow \ \ \ \ \ \ \downarrow$
    $\{5, 7, 9, \ 11, \ 13, \ldots, 2n + 3, \ldots\}$

58. $\{1, 2, \ 3, \ 4, \ 5, \ldots, \ \ \ n, \ldots\}$
    $\downarrow \downarrow \downarrow \downarrow \ \downarrow \ \ \ \ \ \ \downarrow$
    $\{5, 8, \ 11, \ 14, \ 17, \ldots, 3n + 2, \ldots\}$

59. $\{1, 2, \ 3, \ 4, \ \ 5, \ldots, \ \ \ n, \ldots\}$
    $\downarrow \downarrow \downarrow \downarrow \ \downarrow \ \ \ \ \ \ \downarrow$
    $\{4, 9, \ 14, \ 19, \ 24, \ldots, 5n - 1, \ldots\}$

## Chapter Test

1. True

2. False; the sets do not contain exactly the same elements.

3. True

4. False; the second set has no subset that contains the element 7.

5. False; the set has $2^4 = 2 \times 2 \times 2 \times 2 = 16$ subsets.

6. True

7. False; for any set $A$, $A \cup A' = U$, not $\{ \ \}$.

8. True

9. $A = \{1, 2, 3, 4, 5, 6, 7, 8, 9\}$

10. Set $A$ is the set of natural numbers less than 10.

11. $A \cap B = \{3, 5, 7, 9\} \cap \{7, 9, 11, 13\} = \{7, 9\}$

12. $A \cup C' = \{3, 5, 7, 9\} \cup \{3, 11, 15\}'$
    $= \{3, 5, 7, 9\} \cup \{5, 7, 9, 13\} = \{3, 5, 7, 9, 13\}$

13. $A \cap (B \cap C)' = \{3, 5, 7, 9\} \cap (\{7, 9, 11, 13\} \cap \{3, 11, 15\})' = \{3, 5, 7, 9\} \cap \{11\}'$
    $= \{3, 5, 7, 9\} \cap \{3, 5, 7, 9, 13, 15\} = \{3, 5, 7, 9\}$, or $A$.

14. $n(A \cap B') = n(\{3, 5, 7, 9\} \cap \{7, 9, 11, 13\}') = n(\{3, 5, 7, 9\} \cap \{3, 5, 15\}) = n(\{3, 5\}) = 2$

15. $A - B = \{3, 5, 7, 9\} - \{7, 9, 11, 13\} = \{3, 5\}$

16. $A \times C = \{(3, 3), (3, 11), (3, 15), (5, 3), (5, 11), (5, 15), (7, 3), (7, 11), (7, 15), (9, 3), (9, 11), (9, 15)\}$

17.

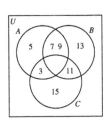

18.     $A \cap (B \cup C')$                                                   $(A \cap B) \cup (A \cap C')$

| Set | Regions |
|-----|---------|
| $B$ | II, III, V, VI |
| $C$ | IV, V, VI, VII |
| $C'$ | I, II, III, VIII |
| $B \cup C'$ | I, II, III, V, VI, VIII |
| $A$ | I, II, IV, V |
| $A \cap (B \cup C')$ | I, II, V |

| Set | Regions |
|-----|---------|
| $A$ | I, II, IV, V |
| $B$ | II, III, V, VI |
| $A \cap B$ | II, V |
| $C$ | IV, V, VI, VII |
| $C'$ | I, II, III, VIII |
| $A \cap C'$ | I, II |
| $(A \cap B) \cup (A \cap C')$ | I, II, V |

Both statements are represented by the same regions, I, II, V, of the Venn diagram.

Therefore, $A \cap (B \cup C') = (A \cap B) \cup (A \cap C')$ for all sets $A, B,$ and $C$.

19.
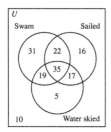

a) 52, the sum of the numbers in Regions I, III, VII
b) 10, Region VIII
c) 93, the sum of the numbers in Regions II, IV, V, VI
d) 17, Region II
e) 38, the sum of the numbers in Regions I, II, III
f) 31, Region VII

20.  $\{7, 8, \ 9, \ 10, 11, ..., n+6, ...\}$
$\quad \downarrow \downarrow \downarrow \ \downarrow \ \downarrow \qquad \downarrow$
$\{8, 9, \ 10, 11, 12, ..., n+7, ...\}$

# CHAPTER THREE

## LOGIC

**Exercise Set 3.1**

1. Statement

3. Compound

5. a) Not       b) And
   c) Or          d) If then
   e) If and only if

7. Some

9. Simple statement

11. Compound; biconditional $\leftrightarrow$

13. Compound; conjunction, $\wedge$

15. Compound; conditional, $\rightarrow$

17. Compound; negation, $\sim$

19. Some butterflies are not insects.

21. All turtles have claws.

23. Some bicycles have three wheels.

25. No pedestrians are in the crosswalk.

27. Some Holsteins are Guernseys.

29. $\sim p$

31. $\sim q \vee \sim p$

33. $\sim p \rightarrow \sim q$

35. $\sim p \wedge q$

37. $\sim q \leftrightarrow p$

39. $\sim (p \vee q)$

41. Brie does not have a MacBook.

43. Joe has an iPad and Brie has a Macbook.

45. If Joe does not have an iPad then Brie has a MacBook.

47. Joe does not have an iPad or Brie does not have a MacBook.

49. It is false that Joe has an iPad and Brie has a MacBook..

51. $(p \wedge \sim q) \wedge r$

53. $(p \wedge q) \vee r$

55. $p \rightarrow (q \vee \sim r)$

57. $(r \leftrightarrow q) \wedge p$

59. $q \rightarrow (p \leftrightarrow r)$

61. The water is 70° or the sun is shining, and we do not go swimming.

63. The water is not 70°, and the sun is shining or we go swimming.

65. If we do not go swimming, then the sun is shining and the water is 70°.

67. If the sun is shining then we go swimming, and the water is 70°.

69. The sun is shining if and only if the water is 70°, and we go swimming.

71. Not permissible. In the list of choices, the connective "or" is the exclusive or, thus one can order either the soup or the salad but not both items.

73. Not permissible. Potatoes and pasta cannot be ordered together.

75. a) $w$: I bought the watch in Tijuana; $p$: I paid $100;
    $w \wedge \sim p$

   b) Conjunction

77. a) $b$: below speed limit; $p$: pulled over;
    $\sim (b \rightarrow \sim p)$

   b) Negation

79. a) *f*: food has fiber;  *v*: food has vitamins; *h*: be healthy;  $(f \lor v) \to h$

   b) Conditional

83. a) *c*: classroom is empty;  *w*: is the weekend;  *s*: is 7:00 a.m.;  $(c \leftrightarrow w) \lor s$

   b) Disjunction

81. a) *c*: may take course;  *f*: fail previous exam; *p*: passed placement test;  $c \leftrightarrow (\sim f \lor p)$

   b) Biconditional

85.  Answers will vary.

## Exercise Set 3.2

1. Opposite
3. False

5.

| p | p | $\land$ | $\sim$p |
|---|---|---|---|
| T | T | F | F |
| F | F | F | T |
|   | 1 | 3 | 2 |

7.

| p | q | q | $\lor$ | $\sim$p |
|---|---|---|---|---|
| T | T | T | T | F |
| T | F | F | F | T |
| F | T | T | T | T |
| F | F | F | T | T |
|   |   | 1 | 3 | 2 |

9.

| p | q | $\sim$p | $\lor$ | $\sim$q |
|---|---|---|---|---|
| T | T | F | F | F |
| T | F | F | T | T |
| F | T | T | T | F |
| F | F | T | T | T |
|   |   | 1 | 3 | 2 |

11.

| p | q | $\sim$(p | $\land$ | $\sim$ | q) |
|---|---|---|---|---|---|
| T | T | T | T | F | F |
| T | F | F | T | T | T |
| F | T | T | F | F | F |
| F | F | T | F | F | T |
|   |   | 4 | 1 | 3 | 2 |

13.

| p | q | r | ~ q ∨ (p ∧ r) |
|---|---|---|---|
| T | T | T | F T T T T |
| T | T | F | F F T F F |
| T | F | T | T T T T T |
| T | F | F | T T T F F |
| F | T | T | F F F F T |
| F | T | F | F F F F F |
| F | F | T | T T F F T |
| F | F | F | T T F F F |
|   |   |   | 1 5 2 4 3 |

15.

| p | q | r | r ∨ (p ∧ ~ q) |
|---|---|---|---|
| T | T | T | T T T F F |
| T | T | F | F F T F F |
| T | F | T | T T T T T |
| T | F | F | F T T T T |
| F | T | T | T T F F F |
| F | T | F | F F F F F |
| F | F | T | T T F F T |
| F | F | F | F F F F T |
|   |   |   | 1 5 2 4 3 |

17.

| p | q | r | ( r ∨ ~ p) ∧ ~ q |
|---|---|---|---|
| T | T | T | T T F F F |
| T | T | F | F F F F F |
| T | F | T | T T F T F |
| T | F | F | T T F T T |
| F | T | T | T F T F F |
| F | T | F | F T T F F |
| F | F | T | T T T T T |
| F | F | F | F T T T T |
|   |   |   | 1 4 2 5 3 |

19. p: Train recorded *Hey, Soul Sister*.

q: The Black Eyed Peas recorded *Where Is the Love?*.

In symbolic form the statement is p ∧ q.

| p | q | p ∧ q |
|---|---|---|
| T | T | T |
| T | F | F |
| F | T | F |
| F | F | F |
|   |   | 1 |

21. p: I have worked all week.

q: I have been paid.

In symbolic form the statement is p ∧ ~ q.

| p | q | p | ∧ | ~ q |
|---|---|---|---|---|
| T | T | T | F | F |
| T | F | T | T | T |
| F | T | F | F | F |
| F | F | F | F | T |
| | | 1 | 3 | 2 |

23. p: Jasper Adams is the tutor.

q: Mark Russo is a secretary.

In symbolic form the statement is ~ (p ∧ q).

| p | q | ~ (p ∧ q) |
|---|---|---|
| T | T | F T T T |
| T | F | T T F F |
| F | T | T F F T |
| F | F | T F F F |
| | | 4 1 3 2 |

25. p: The copier is out of toner.

q: The lens is dirty.

r : The corona wires are broken.

The statement is p ∨ (q ∨ r).

| p | q | r | p ∨ (q ∨ r) |
|---|---|---|---|
| T | T | T | T T T |
| T | T | F | T T T |
| T | F | T | T T T |
| T | F | F | T T F |
| F | T | T | F T T |
| F | T | F | F T T |
| F | F | T | F T T |
| F | F | F | F F F |
| | | | 2 3 1 |

27. (a) (p ∨ q) ∧ ~ r

( T ∨ F) ∧ F

T  ∧ F

F

Therefore the statement is false.

(b) (p ∨ q) ∧ ~ r

( F ∨ T) ∧ F

T  ∧ F

F

Therefore the statement is false.

29. (a) (~ p ∧ ~q) ∨ ~ r

(F ∧ T) ∨ F

F  ∨ F

F

Therefore the statement is false.

(b) (~ p ∧ ~q) ∨ ~ r

(T ∧ F) ∨ F

F  ∨ F

F

Therefore the statement is false.

31. (a) (p ∨ ~q) ∧ ~ (p ∧ ~ r)

(T ∨ T) ∧ ~ (T ∧ F)

T  ∧  ~F

T

Therefore the statement is true.

(b) (p ∨ ~q) ∧ ~ (p ∧ ~ r)

(F ∨ F) ∧ ~ (F ∧ F)

F  ∧  ~F

F

33. (a) (~ r ∧ p) ∨ q

(F ∧ T) ∨ F

F  ∨ F

F

Therefore the statement is false.

(b) (~ r ∧ p) ∨ q

(F ∧ F) ∨ T

F  ∨ T

T

35. (a) (~p ∨ ~q) ∨ (~r ∨ q)

(F ∨ T) ∨ (F ∨ F)

T  ∨  F

T

Therefore the statement is true.

(b) (~p ∨ ~q) ∨ (~r ∨ q)

(T ∨ F) ∨ (F ∨ T)

T  ∨  T

T

37. $8 + 7 = 20 - 5$  and  $63 \div 7 = 3 \cdot 3$

       T     $\wedge$     T

            T

Therefore the statement is true.

39. C: Florida is in Canada.

    M: Texas borders Mexico.

       C  $\vee$  M

       F  $\vee$  T

           T

    Therefore the statement is true.

41. Q: Quentin Tarantio is a movie director.

    Z: Zac Efron is an actor.

    M: Scarlett Johansson is an actress.

     (Q $\wedge$ Z) $\wedge$ ~S

    (T $\wedge$ T) $\wedge$ F

       T     $\wedge$  F

          F

Therefore the statement is false.

43. IQ: Iraq is in Africa.

    IN: Iran is in South America.

    S: Syria is in the Middle East.

    ( IQ $\vee$ IN ) $\wedge$ S

     ( F $\vee$ F ) $\wedge$ T

        F    $\wedge$  T

           F

    Therefore the statement is false.

45. p: India produced more feature films than the United States.

    q: China produced more feature films than Japan.

     p $\wedge$ q

     T $\wedge$ F

      False

47. p: The United States produced more feature films than Japan.

    q: Japan produced more feature films than China.

     p $\wedge$ q

     T $\wedge$ T

     True

49. p: 30% of Americans get 6 hours of sleep.

    q: 9% get 5 hours of sleep.

     ~ (p $\wedge$ q)

     ~ (F $\wedge$ T)

      ~F

     True

51. p: 13% of Americans get $\leq$ 5 hrs. of sleep.

    q: 32% of Americans get $\geq$ 6 hrs. of sleep.

    r: 30% of Americans get $\geq$ 8 hrs. of sleep.

     (p $\vee$ q) $\wedge$ r

     (T $\vee$ F) $\wedge$ F

      T  $\wedge$ F

     False

53. p $\wedge$ ~q; true when p is true and q is false.

55. p $\vee$ ~q; true when p is true or when p and q are both false.

57. (r $\vee$ q) $\wedge$ p; true when p is true and when either r or q is true.

59. q $\vee$ (p $\wedge$ ~r); true except when p, q, r have truth values TFT, FFT, or FFF.

61. (a) Mr. Duncan qualifies for the loan.

       Mrs. Tuttle qualifies for the loan.

    (b) The Rusineks do not qualify because their gross income is too low.

63. (a) Wing Park qualifies for the special fare.

    (b) The other 4 do not qualify:

       Gina V. returns after 04/01;

       Kara S. returns on Monday;

       Christos S. does not stay at least one Saturday; and

   Alex C. returns on Monday.

65.

| p | q | r | [(q ∧ ~ r) ∧ (~ p ∨ ~ q)] ∨ (p ∨ ~ r) | | | | |
|---|---|---|---|---|---|---|---|
| T | T | T | F | F | F | T | T |
| T | T | F | T | F | F | T | T |
| T | F | T | F | F | T | T | T |
| T | F | F | F | F | T | T | T |
| F | T | T | F | F | T | F | F |
| F | T | F | T | T | T | T | T |
| F | F | T | F | F | T | F | F |
| F | F | F | F | F | T | T | T |
| | | | 1 | 3 | 2 | 5 | 4 |

67. Yes

| p | q | r | (p ∧~q) ∨ r | | | (q ∧ ~r) ∨ p | | |
|---|---|---|---|---|---|---|---|---|
| T | T | T | F | T | T | F | T | T |
| T | T | F | F | F | F | T | T | T |
| T | F | T | T | T | T | F | T | T |
| T | F | F | T | T | F | F | T | T |
| F | T | T | F | T | T | F | F | F |
| F | T | F | F | F | F | T | T | F |
| F | F | T | F | T | T | F | F | F |
| F | F | F | F | F | F | F | F | F |

## Exercise Set 3.3

1. False

3. True

5. Self-contradiction

7.

| p | q | ~ p → q | | |
|---|---|---|---|---|
| T | T | F | T | T |
| T | F | F | T | F |
| F | T | T | T | T |
| F | F | T | F | F |
| | | | | |
| | | 1 | 3 | 2 |

9.

| p | q | ~ (p→~ q) | |
|---|---|---|---|
| T | T | T | F |
| T | F | F | T |
| F | T | F | T |
| F | F | F | T |
|   |   | 2 | 1 |

11.

| p | q | ~ q | ↔ | p |
|---|---|---|---|---|
| T | T | F | F | T |
| T | F | T | T | T |
| F | T | F | T | F |
| F | F | T | F | F |
|   |   | 1 | 3 | 2 |

13.

| p | q | p | ↔ | (q ∨ p) |
|---|---|---|---|---|
| T | T | T | T | T |
| T | F | T | T | T |
| F | T | F | F | T |
| F | F | F | T | F |
|   |   | 1 | 3 | 2 |

15.

| p | q | q → (p → ~ q) | | | | |
|---|---|---|---|---|---|---|
| T | T | T | F | T | F | F |
| T | F | F | T | T | T | T |
| F | T | T | T | F | T | F |
| F | F | F | T | F | T | T |
|   |   | 4 | 5 | 1 | 3 | 2 |

17.

| p | q | r | ~p | → | (q | ∧ | r) |
|---|---|---|---|---|---|---|---|
| T | T | T | F | T | T | T | T |
| T | T | F | F | T | T | F | F |
| T | F | T | F | T | F | F | T |
| T | F | F | F | T | F | F | F |
| F | T | T | T | T | T | T | T |
| F | T | F | T | F | T | F | F |
| F | F | T | T | F | F | F | T |
| F | F | F | T | F | F | F | F |
|   |   |   | 4 | 5 | 1 | 3 | 2 |

19.

| p | q | r | (q | ∨ | ~ r | ↔ | ~ p |
|---|---|---|---|---|---|---|---|
| T | T | T | T | T | F | F | F |
| T | T | F | T | T | T | F | F |
| T | F | T | F | F | F | T | F |
| T | F | F | F | T | T | F | F |
| F | T | T | T | T | F | T | T |
| F | T | F | T | T | T | T | T |
| F | F | T | F | F | F | F | T |
| F | F | F | F | T | T | T | T |
|   |   |   | 1 | 3 | 2 | 5 | 4 |

21.

| p | q | r | (~ r | ∨ | ~q) | → | p |
|---|---|---|---|---|---|---|---|
| T | T | T | F | F | F | T | T |
| T | T | F | T | T | F | T | T |
| T | F | T | F | T | T | T | T |
| T | F | F | T | T | T | T | T |
| F | T | T | F | F | F | T | F |
| F | T | F | T | T | F | F | F |
| F | F | T | F | T | T | F | F |
| F | F | F | T | T | T | F | F |
|   |   |   | 1 | 3 | 2 | 5 | 4 |

23.

| p | q | r | (p | → | q) | ↔ | (~q | → | ~r) |
|---|---|---|---|---|---|---|---|---|---|
| T | T | T | | T | | T | F | T | F |
| T | T | F | | T | | T | F | T | T |
| T | F | T | | F | | T | T | F | F |
| T | F | F | | F | | F | T | T | T |
| F | T | T | | T | | T | F | T | F |
| F | T | F | | T | | T | F | T | T |
| F | F | T | | T | | F | T | F | F |
| F | F | F | | T | | T | T | T | T |
|   |   |   | | 1 | | 5 | 2 | 4 | 3 |

25.    p: It is raining;  q: The baseball game is cancelled;
r:  We can eat dinner together.

| p | q | r | p | → | (q | ∧ | r) |
|---|---|---|---|---|---|---|---|
| T | T | T | T | T | | T | |
| T | T | F | T | F | | F | |
| T | F | T | T | F | | F | |
| T | F | F | T | F | | F | |
| F | T | T | F | T | | T | |
| F | T | F | F | T | | F | |
| F | F | T | F | T | | F | |
| F | F | F | F | T | | F | |
|   |   |   | 1 | 3 | | 2 | |

27.    p: The election was fair;  q: The polling station stayed open until 8 P.M.;  r: We will request a recount.

| p | q | r | (p | ↔ | q) | ∨ | r |
|---|---|---|---|---|---|---|---|
| T | T | T | | T | | T | T |
| T | T | F | | T | | T | F |
| T | F | T | | F | | T | T |
| T | F | F | | F | | F | F |
| F | T | T | | F | | T | T |
| F | T | F | | F | | F | F |
| F | F | T | | T | | T | T |
| F | F | F | | T | | T | F |
|   |   |   | | 1 | | 3 | 2 |

29.    p: Mary Andrews sends me an e-mail;
       q: We can call her;  r: We can write to Mom.

| p | q | r | (~ p | → | q) | ∨ | r |
|---|---|---|---|---|---|---|---|
| T | T | T | | T | | T | T |
| T | T | F | | T | | T | F |
| T | F | T | | T | | T | T |
| T | F | F | | T | | T | F |
| F | T | T | | T | | T | T |
| F | T | F | | T | | T | F |
| F | F | T | | F | | T | T |
| F | F | F | | F | | F | F |
| | | | | 1 | | 3 | 2 |

31.

| p | ~p | → | p |
|---|---|---|---|
| T | F | T | T |
| F | T | F | F |
| | 1 | 3 | 2 |
| | | | |
| | | | |

     Neither

33.

| p | q | ~ p | ∧ | (q ↔ ~ q) |
|---|---|---|---|---|
| T | T | F | F | F |
| T | F | F | F | F |
| F | T | T | F | F |
| F | F | T | F | F |
| | | 1 | 3 | 2 |

     Self-contradiction

35.

| p | q | (~ q | → | p ) | ∨ | ~ q |
|---|---|---|---|---|---|---|
| T | T | | T | | T | F |
| T | F | | T | | T | T |
| F | T | | T | | T | F |
| F | F | | F | | T | T |
| | | | 1 | | 3 | 2 |

     Tautology

37.

| p | ~ p | → | p |
|---|---|---|---|
| T | F | T | T |
| F | T | F | F |
| | 1 | 3 | 2 |

     Not an implication

39.

| p | q | ~p | → | ~(p ∧ q) |
|---|---|----|---|----------|
| T | T | F | T | F |
| T | F | F | T | T |
| F | T | T | T | T |
| F | F | T | T | T |
|   |   | 1 | 3 | 2 |

An implication

41.

| p | q | [ (p → q) | ∧ | (q → p) ] | → | (p ↔ q) |
|---|---|-----------|---|----------|---|---------|
| T | T | T | T | T | T | T |
| T | F | F | F | T | T | F |
| T | T | T | F | F | T | F |
| T | F | T | T | T | T | T |
|   |   | 1 | 3 | 2 | 5 | 4 |

Implication

43.  $p \rightarrow (q \rightarrow r)$
  $T \rightarrow (F \rightarrow T)$
  $T \rightarrow \quad T$
  $\quad T$

45.  $(p \land q) \leftrightarrow (q \lor r)$
  $(T \land F) \leftrightarrow (F \lor T)$
  $\quad F \quad \leftrightarrow \quad T$
  $\quad F$

47.  $(\sim p \land \sim q) \lor \sim r$
  $( F \land T) \lor F$
  $\quad F \quad \lor F$
  $\quad F$

49.  $(\sim p \leftrightarrow r) \lor (\sim q \leftrightarrow r)$
  $(F \leftrightarrow T) \lor ( T \leftrightarrow T)$
  $\quad F \quad \lor \quad T$
  $\quad T$

51.  $\sim [(p \lor q) \leftrightarrow ( p \rightarrow \sim r)]$
  $\sim [(T \lor F) \leftrightarrow ( T \rightarrow F)]$
  $\sim [T \quad \leftrightarrow \quad F]$
  $\quad \sim F$
  $\quad T$

53.  If $\sqrt{25} = 5$ , then $\sqrt{49} = 7$.
  $\quad T \rightarrow T$
  $\quad T$

55. A cat has whiskers or a fish can swim, then a dog lays eggs.
  $(T \lor T) \rightarrow F$
  $\quad T \quad \rightarrow \quad F$
  $\quad F$

57. Apple makes computers, if and only if Nike makes sports shoes or Rolex makes watches.
  $T \leftrightarrow (T \lor T)$
  $T \leftrightarrow \quad T$
  $\quad T$

59. Mother's Day is in May and Father's Day is in December, if and only if Thanksgiving is in April.
  $(T \land F) \leftrightarrow F$
  $\quad F \quad \leftrightarrow F$
  $\quad T$

61. Io has a diameter of 1000–3161 miles, or Thebe may have water, and Io may have atmosphere.
  $(T \lor F) \land T$
  $\quad T \land T$
  $\quad T$

63. Phoebe has a larger diameter than Rhea if and only if Callisto may have water ice, and Calypso has a diameter of 6–49 miles.

$(F \leftrightarrow T) \wedge T$

$\quad F \quad \wedge T$

$\qquad F$

65. The number of communications credits needed is more than the number of mathematics credits needed and the number of cultural issues credits needed is equal to the number of humanities credits needed, if and only if the number of social sciences credits needed is more than the numbe of natural sciences credits needed..

$(T \wedge T) \leftrightarrow F$

$\quad T \quad \leftrightarrow F$

$\qquad F$

For 67–71  $p$: Muhundan spoke at the teachers' conference.
$\qquad q$: Muhundan received the outstanding teacher award
$\qquad$ Assume $p$ and $q$ are false.

67. $\quad q \rightarrow p$

$\quad F \rightarrow F$

$\qquad T$

69. $\quad \sim q \rightarrow p$

$\quad T \rightarrow F$

$\qquad F$

71. $\quad q \leftrightarrow p$

$\quad F \leftrightarrow F$

$\qquad T$

73. No, the statement only states what will occur if your sister gets straight A's. If your sister does not get straight A's, your parents may still get her a computer.

75.

| p | q | r | [p | ∨ | ( q | → | ~ r)] | ↔ | (p ∧ ~ q) |
|---|---|---|----|---|-----|---|-------|---|-----------|
| T | T | T | T |   |     | F | F     | F | F         |
| T | T | F | T |   |     | T | T     | F | F         |
| T | F | T | T |   |     | T | F     | T | T         |
| T | F | F | T |   |     | T | T     | T | T         |
| F | T | T | F |   |     | F | F     | T | F         |
| F | T | F | T |   |     | T | T     | F | F         |
| F | F | T | T |   |     | T | F     | F | F         |
| F | F | F | T |   |     | T | T     | F | F         |
|   |   |   | 3 |   |     | 2 | 1     | 5 | 4         |

77. The statement may be expressed as $(p \rightarrow q) \vee (\sim p \rightarrow q)$, where $p$: It is a head and $q$: I win.

| p | q | ( p → q ) | ∨ | (~ p → q ) |
|---|---|-----------|---|------------|
| T | T | T         | T | T          |
| T | F | F         | T | T          |
| F | T | T         | T | T          |
| F | F | T         | T | F          |
|   |   | 1         | 3 | 2          |

The statement is a tautology.

79. Allen was born in January.  Booker was born in February, Chris was born in March. Dennis was born in April.

81. Katie was born last.  Katie and Mary are telling the truth.

## Exercise Set 3.4

1. Equivalent

3. $p \rightarrow q$ is equivalent to $\sim p \vee q$.

5. $q \rightarrow p$

7. $\sim q \rightarrow \sim p$

9. $\sim(p \wedge q) \Leftrightarrow \sim p \vee q$ (by law 1) and this is not equivalent to $\sim p \wedge \sim q$.

11. Equivalent by law 2.

13. $\sim(\sim p \wedge q) \Leftrightarrow \sim(\sim p) \vee \sim q$ by law 1 and $\sim(\sim p) \vee \sim q \Leftrightarrow p \vee \sim q$ by law 2. $p \vee \sim q$ is not equivalent to $p \wedge \sim q$.

15. Yes, equivalent

17. Yes, $\sim(p \rightarrow \sim q) \Leftrightarrow \sim(\sim p \vee \sim q) \Leftrightarrow p \wedge q$

19.

| p | q | $p \rightarrow q$ | $\sim p \vee q$ |
|---|---|---|---|
| T | T | T | F  T  T |
| T | F | F | F  F  F |
| F | T |   | T  T  T |
| F | F | T | T  T  F |
|   |   | 1 | 1  3  2 |

The statements are equivalent.

21.

| p | q | $\sim q \rightarrow \sim p$ | $p \rightarrow q$ |
|---|---|---|---|
|   | T | F  T  F | T |
| T | F | T  F  F | F |
| F | T | F  T  T | T |
| F | F | T  T  T | T |
|   |   | 1  3  2 | 1 |

The statements are equivalent.

23.

| p | q | r | $(p \vee q) \vee r$ | $p \vee (q \vee r)$ |
|---|---|---|---|---|
| T | T | T | T □□ T | T  T □  T |
| T | T | F | T   T F | T  T   T |
| T | F | T | T   T T | T  T   T |
| T | F | F | T   T F | T  T   F |
| F | T | T | T   T T | F  T   T |
| F | T | F | T   T F | F  T   T |
| F | F | T | F   T T | F  T   T |
| F | F | F | F   F F | F  F   F |
|   |   |   | 1   3 2 | 2  3   1 |

The statements are equivalent.

25.

| p | q | r | $p \wedge (q \vee r)$ | $(p \wedge q) \vee r$ |
|---|---|---|---|---|
| T | T | T | T T  T T T | T T T T T |
| T | T | F | T T  T T F | T T T T T |
| T | F | T | T T  F T T | T F F T T |
| T | F | F | T F  F F F | T F F F F |
| F | T | T | F F  T T T | F F T T T |
| F | T | F | F F  T T F | F F T F F |
| F | F | T | F F  F T T | F F F T T |
| F | F | F | F F  F F F | F F F F F |
|   |   |   | 1 5  2 4 3 | 1 3 2 5 4 |

The statements are not equivalent.

27.

| p | q | $(p \rightarrow q) \wedge (q \rightarrow p)$ | $p \leftrightarrow q$ |
|---|---|---|---|
| T | T | T  T□□ T | □□ T |
| T | F | □  F  F  T | F |
| F | T | T  F  F | F |
| F | F | T  T  T | T |
|   |   | 1  3  2 | 1 |

The statements are equivalent.

29. p: Oregon borders the Atlantic Ocean.

q: Delaware borders the Pacific Ocean.

In symbolic form, the statement is $\sim(p \wedge q)$.

Applying DeMorgan's Laws we get: $\sim p \vee \sim q$.

Oregon does not border the Atlantic Ocean or Delaware does not border the Pacific Ocean.

31. p: The dog was a bulldog.

q: The dog was a boxer.

In symbolic form, the statement is $\sim p \wedge \sim q$.

Applying DeMorgan's Laws we get: $\sim(p \vee q)$.

It is false that the dog was a bulldog or the dog was a boxer.

33. p: Ashley takes the new job.

q: Ashley will move.

r: Ashley will buy a new house in town.

In symbolic form, the statement is $p \rightarrow (\sim q \vee r)$. Applying DeMorgan's Laws we get: $p \rightarrow \sim(q \wedge \sim r)$. If Ashley takes the new job, it is false that she will move and will not buy a new house in town.

35. p: Janette buys a new car.

   q: Janette sells her old car.

   In symbolic form, the statement is p → q.

   Since p → q ⟺ ~ p ∨ q, an equivalent statement is: Janette does not buy a new car or she sells her old car.

37. p: Bob the Tomato visited the nursing home.

   q: Bob the Tomato visited the Cub Scout meeting.

   In symbolic form, the statement is p ∨ ~ q.

   Since ~p → ~q ⟺ ~ p ∨q, an equivalent Statement is: If Bob the Tomato did not visit the nursing home, then he did not visit the Cub Scout meeting.

39. p: Chase is hiding.

   q: The pitcher is broken.

   In symbolic form, the statement is ~p ∨ q .

   ~p ∨ q ⟺ p → q. If Chase is hiding, then the pitcher is broken.

41. p: We go to Chicago.

   q: We go to Navy Pier.

   In symbolic form, the statement is ~(p → q) .

   ~(p → q) ⟺ p ∧ ~ q.

   We go to Chicago and we do not go to Navy Pier.

43. p: I am cold.

   q: The heater is working.

   In symbolic form, the statement is p ∧ ~ q .

   p ∧ ~ q ⟺ ~(p → q) .

   It is false that if I am cold then the heater is working.

45. p: Amazon has a sale.

   q: We will buy $100 worth of books.

   In symbolic form, the statement is ~(p → q) .

   ~(p → q) ⟺ p ∧ ~ q.

   Amazon has a sale and we will not buy $100 worth of books.

47. p: John Deere will hire new workers.

   q: Dubuque will retrain the workers.

   In symbolic form, the statement is p ∧ q.

   p ∧ q ⟺ ~(p → ~q).

   It is false that if John Deere will hire new workers then the city of Dubuque will not retain the workers.

49. Converse: If Nanette Berry needs extra yarn, then she teaches macramé.

   Inverse: If Nanette Berry does not teach macramé, then she does not need extra yarn.

   Contrapositive: If Nanette Berry does not need extra yarn, then she does not teach macramé.

51. Converse: If I buy silver jewelry, then I go to Mexico.

   Inverse: If I do not go to Mexico, then I do not buy silver jewelry.

   Contrapositive: If I do not buy silver jewelry then I do not go to Mexico.

53. Converse: If I scream, then that annoying paper clip (Clippie) shows up on my screen.

   Inverse: If Clippie does not show up on my screen, then I will not scream.

   Contrapositive: If I do not scream, then Clippie does not show up on my screen.

55. If a natural number is not divisible by 7, then it is not divisible by 14. True

57. If a natural number is not divisible by 6, then it is not divisible by 3. False

59. If two lines are not parallel, then the two lines intersect in at least one point.  True

61. p:  The ball lands in foul territory.

q:  The runner returns to the base.

In symbolic form, the statements are:

a) $p \rightarrow q$, b) $q \rightarrow p$, c) $\sim q \vee p$.

| | | a) | b) | c) |
|---|---|---|---|---|
| p | q | $p \rightarrow q$ | $q \rightarrow p$ | $\sim q \vee p$ |
| T | T | T T T | T T☐T | F☐ T T |
| T | F | T F F | F T T | T T ☐ |
| F | T | F T☐☐ F | T F F | F F F |
| F | F | F T F | F T F | T T F |
| | | 1 3 2 | 1 3 2 | 1 3 2 |

Since the truth tables for (a) and (b) are different we conclude that only statements (b) and (c) are equivalent.

63. p: The office is cool.

q: The copier is jammed.

In symbolic form, the statements are: a) $\sim p \wedge q$, b) $\sim p \rightarrow \sim q$, c) $\sim (p \vee \sim q)$.  If we use DeMorgan's Laws on statement (a), we get statement (c).

Therefore, statements (a) and (c) are equivalent. If we look at the truth tables for statements (a), (b), and (c), we see that only statements (a) and (c) are equivalent.

| | | a) | b) | c) |
|---|---|---|---|---|
| p | q | $\sim p \wedge q$ | $\sim p \rightarrow \sim q$ | $\sim (p \vee \sim q)$ |
| T | T | F F T | F T F | F T T ☐ |
| T | F | F F F | F T ☐ ☐ | F T T T |
| F | T | ☐T T T | T F F | T F F F |
| F | F | T F F | T T T | F F T T |
| | | 1 3 2 | 1 3 2 | 4 1 3 2 |

65. p: Today is Sunday.

q: The library is open.

In symbolic form, the statements are: a) $\sim p \vee q$, b) $p \rightarrow \sim q$, c) $q \rightarrow \sim p$.  Looking at the truth table for all three statements, we can determine that only statements (b) and (c) are equivalent.

| | | a) | b) | c) |
|---|---|---|---|---|
| p | q | $\sim p \vee$ ☐ ☐ | $p \rightarrow \sim q$ | $q \rightarrow \sim p$ |
| T | T | F T T | T F F | T F F |
| T | F | F F F | T T T | F T F |
| F | T | T T T | F T F | T T T |
| F | F | T T F | F T T | F T T |
| | | 1 3 2 | 1 3 2 | 1 3 2 |

67. p: The grass grows.

    q: The trees are blooming.

    In symbolic form, the statements are: a) $p \wedge q$,

    b) $q \rightarrow \sim p$, c) $\sim q \vee \sim p$. Using the fact that $p \rightarrow q$

    $\Leftrightarrow \sim p \vee q$, on statement (b) we get $\sim q \vee p$.

    Therefore, statements (b) and (c) are equivalent.

    Looking at the truth table for statements (a) and (b)

    we can conclude that only statements (b) and (c) are

    equivalent.

| p | q | $p \wedge q$ | $q \rightarrow \sim p$ | | |
|---|---|---|---|---|---|
| T | T | T | T | F | F |
| T | F | F | F | T | F |
| F | T | F | T | T | T |
| F | F | F | F | T | T |
|   |   | 1 | 1 | 3 | 2 |

71. p: The pay is good.

    q: Today is Monday.

    r : I will take the job.

    Looking at the truth tables for statements (a), (b), and

    (c), we see that none of the statements are equivalent.

| p | q | r | a) $(p \wedge q) \rightarrow r$ | | b) $\sim r \rightarrow \sim (p \vee q)$ | | | | c) $(p \wedge q) \vee r$ | | |
|---|---|---|---|---|---|---|---|---|---|---|---|
| T | T | T | T | T T | F T | F | T | | T | T T |
| T | T | F | T | F F | T F | F | T | | T | T F |
| T | F | T | F | T T | F T | F | T | | F | T T |
| T | F | F | F | T F | T F | F | T | | F | F F |
| F | T | T | F | T T | F T | F | T | | F | T T |
| F | T | F | F | T F | T F | F | T | | F | F F |
| F | F | T | F | T T | F T | T | F | | F | T T |
| F | F | F | F | T F | T T | T | F | | F | F F |
|   |   |   | 1 | 3 2 | 1 4 | 3 | 2 | | 1 | 3 2 |

69. p: The corn bag goes in the hole.

    q: you are awarded three points.

    In symbolic form, the statements are:

    a)   $p \rightarrow q$,  b) $\sim (p \wedge q)$, and  c) $\sim p \wedge \sim q$.

| p | q | $p \rightarrow q$ | | $\sim (p \wedge q)$, | | | | $\sim p \wedge \sim q$ | | |
|---|---|---|---|---|---|---|---|---|---|---|
| T | T | T T T | | F T T T | | | | F F F | | |
| T | F | T F F | | T T F F | | | | F F T | | |
| F | T | F T T | | T F F T | | | | T F F | | |
| F | F | F T F | | T F | | | | T T T | | |
|   |   |   | | F F F | | | | | | |
|   |   | 1 3 2 | | 4 1 3 2 | | | | 1 3 2 | | |

Therefore, none of the statements are equivalent.

73. p: The package was sent by Federal Express.

q: The package was sent by United Parcel Service.

r : The package arrived on time.

Using the fact that $p \to q \Leftrightarrow {\sim} p \vee q$ to rewrite statement (c), we get $p \vee ({\sim} q \wedge r)$. Therefore, statements (a) and (c) are equivalent. Looking at the truth table for statements (a) and (b), we can conclude that only statements (a) and (c) are equivalent.

|   |   |   | a) | b) | c) |
|---|---|---|----|----|----|
| p | q | r | $p \vee ({\sim} q \wedge r)$ | $r \Leftrightarrow (p \vee {\sim} q)$ | ${\sim} r \to ({\sim} q \wedge r)$ |
| T | T | T | T T F F T | T T T T F | F T F F T |
| T | T | F | T T F F F | F F T T F | T T F F F |
| T | F | T | T T T T T | T T T T T | F T T T T |
| T | F | F | T T T F F | F F T T T | T T T F F |
| F | T | T | F F F F T | T F F F F | F F F F T |
| F | T | F | F F F F F | F T F F F | T F F F F |
| F | F | T | F T T T T | T T F T T | F T T T T |
| F | F | F | F F T F F | F F F T T | T F T F F |
|   |   |   | 1 5  2 4 3 | 1 5  2 4 3 | 1 5  2 4 3 |

75. True. If $p \to q$ is false, it must be of the form $T \to F$. Therefore, the converse must be of the form $F \to T$, which is true.

77. False. A conditional statement and its contrapositive always have the same truth values.

79. If we use DeMorgan's Laws to rewrite ${\sim} p \vee q$, we get ${\sim} (p \wedge {\sim} q)$. Since ${\sim} p \vee q \Leftrightarrow {\sim} (p \wedge {\sim} q)$ and $p \to q \Leftrightarrow {\sim} p \vee q$, we can conclude that $p \to q \Leftrightarrow {\sim} (p \wedge {\sim} q)$. Other answers are possible.

81. Research problem -- Answers will vary.

83.

**Exercise Set 3.5**
1. Valid
3. Fallacy
5. Valid
7. Inverse
9. Syllogism
11. Syllogism

13. This argument is the fallacy of the inverse, therefore it is invalid.

15. This is the law of detachment, so it is a valid argument.

17. This argument is a disjunctive syllogism and therefore is valid.

19. This argument is the fallacy of the converse. Therefore it is invalid.

21. This argument is the fallacy of the inverse, Therefore it is invalid.

23. This argument is the law of syllogism and therefore it is valid.

25.

| p | q | r | [(p ↔ q) ∧ (q ∧ r)] → (p ∨ r) | | | | |
|---|---|---|---|---|---|---|---|
| T | T | T | T | T | T | T | T |
| T | T | F | T | F | F | T | T |
| T | F | T | F | F | F | T | T |
| T | F | F | F | F | F | T | T |
| F | T | T | F | F | F | T | T |
| F | T | F | F | F | F | T | F |
| F | F | T | T | F | F | T | T |
| F | F | F | T | F | F | T | F |
| | | | 1 | 3 | 2 | 5 | 4 |

The argument is valid.

27.

| p | q | r | [(r ↔ p) ∧ (~p ∧ q)] → (p ∧ r) | | | | | | |
|---|---|---|---|---|---|---|---|---|---|
| T | T | T | T | F | F | T | T | T | T |
| T | T | F | F | F | F | F | T | T | F |
| T | F | T | T | F | F | F | F | T | T |
| T | F | F | F | F | F | F | F | T | F |
| F | T | T | F | F | T | T | T | T | F |
| F | T | F | T | T | T | T | T | F | F |
| F | F | T | F | F | T | F | F | T | F |
| F | F | F | T | F | T | F | F | T | F |
| | | | 1 | 5 | 2 | 4 | 3 | 7 | 6 |

The argument is invalid.

29.

| p | q | r | [(p→ q) ∧ (q ∨ r) ∧ (r ∨ p)] → p | | | | | | |
|---|---|---|---|---|---|---|---|---|---|
| T | T | T | T | T | T | T | T | T | T |
| T | T | F | T | T | T | T | T | T | T |
| T | F | T | F | F | T | F | T | T | T |
| T | F | F | F | F | F | F | T | T | T |
| F | T | T | T | T | T | T | T | | F |
| F | T | F | T | T | T | F | F | T | F |
| F | F | T | T | T | T | T | T | F | F |
| F | F | F | T | F | F | F | F | T | F |
| | | | 1 | 3 | 2 | 5 | 4 | 7 | 6 |

The argument is invalid.

31.

| p | q | r | [(p → q) ∧ (r → ~ p) ∧ (p ∨ r)] → (q ∨ ~ p) |
|---|---|---|---|
| T | T | T | T   F   TF   F F   T   T   TT F |
| T | T | F | T   T   FT   F T   T   T   TT F |
| T | F | T | F   F   TF   F F   T   T   FF F |
| T | F | F | F   F   FT   F F   T   T   FF F |
| F | T | T | T   T   TT   T T   T   T   TT T |
| F | T | F | T   T   FT   T F   F   T   TT T |
| F | F | T | T   T   TT   T T   T   T   FT T |
| F | F | F | T   T   FT   T F   F   T   FT T |
|   |   |   | 1   5   2 4   3   7   6   11 9 10 8 |

The argument is valid.

33. p: The lighthouse works.
   q: The boat stays out late.

   p → q

   ~q
   ∴ ~p

   The argument is valid (law of contraposition).

35. p: The baby is a boy.
   q: The baby will be named Alexander Martin.

   p → q

   p
   ∴ q

   The argument is valid (law of detachment).

37. p: The guitar is a Les Paul model.
   q: The guitar is made by Gibson.

   p → q

   ~q
   ∴ ~p

   This argument is valid by the law of contraposition.

39. p: We planted the garden by the first Friday in April.
   q: We will have potatoes by the Fourth of July.

   p → q

   q
   ∴ p

   This is the fallacy of the converse; thus the argument is invalid.

41. p: Erica Kane will marry Samuel Woods.
   q: Erica Kane will marry David Hayward.

   p ∨ q

   ~p
   ∴ q

   The argument is a disjunctive syllogism and is therefore valid.

43. p: It is cold.
   q: The graduation will be held indoors.
   r: The fireworks will be postponed.
   [(p → q) ∧ (q → r)] → (p → r)

   This argument is valid because of the law of syllogism.

45. m: Marie works for the post office
    j: Jim works for target.
    t: Tommy gets an internship.

| m | j | t | [(m ∧ j) ∧ (j → t)] → (t → m) |
|---|---|---|---|
| T | T | T | T  T  T  T  T |
| T | T | F | T  F  F  T  T |
| T | F | T | F  F  T  T  T |
| T | F | F | F  F  T  T  T |
| F | T | T | F  F  T  T  F |
| F | T | F | F  F  F  T  T |
| F | F | T | F  F  T  T  F |
| F | F | F | F  F  T  T  T |
|   |   |   | 1  3  2  5  4 |

The argument is valid.

47. s: It is snowing.
    g: I am going skiing.
    c: I will wear a coat.

| s | g | c | [(s ∧ g) ∧ (g → c)] → (s → c) |
|---|---|---|---|
| T | T | T | T  T  T  T  T |
| T | T | F | T  F  F  T  F |
| T | F | T | F  F  T  T  T |
| T | F | F | F  F  T  T  F |
| F | T | T | F  F  T  T  T |
| F | T | F | F  F  F  T  T |
| F | F | T | F  F  T  T  T |
| F | F | F | F  F  T  T  T |
|   |   |   | 1  3  2  5  4 |

The argument is valid.

49. p: You read *The Order of the Phoenix*.
    h: You can understand *The Half-Blood Prince*.

   $$p \to h$$
   $$\underline{\sim h}$$
   $$\therefore \sim p$$

The argument is the law of contraposition and is valid.

51. s: Max is playing Game Boy with the sound off.
    h: Max is wearing headphones.

   $$s \vee h$$
   $$\underline{\sim s}$$
   $$\therefore h$$

This argument is an example of disjunctive syllogism and is therefore valid.

53. t: The test was easy.
    g: I received a good grade.

| t | g | [(t ∧ g) ∧ (~ t ∨ ~ g)] → ~ t |
|---|---|---|
| T | T | T  F  F  F F  T  F |
| T | F | F  F  F  T T  T  F |
| F | T | F  F  T  T F  T  T |
| F | F | F  F  T  T T  T  T |
|   |   | 1  5  2  4 3  7  6 |

The argument is valid.

55. c: The baby is crying.
    h: The baby is hungry.

| c | h | [(c ∧ ~ h) ∧ (h → c)] → h |
|---|---|---|
| T | T | T F  F  F  T  T |
| T | F | T T  T  T  T  F F |
| F | T | F F  F  F  T  T |
| F | F | F F  T  F  T  T F |
|   |   | 1 3  2  5  4  7 6 |

The argument is invalid.

57. s: You liked *This Is Spinal Tap*.    s → b
    b: You liked *Best In Show*.          b → ~ m
    m: You liked *A Mighty Wind*.        ∴ s → m

Using the law of syllogism s → ~m, so this argument is invalid.

59. You must rest for three days. (law of detachment)

61. Therefore, I am stressed out. (disjunctive syllogism)

63. Therefore, you did not close the deal. (law of contraposition)

65. Yes. For example,

$$p \rightarrow q$$

$$\underline{q}$$

$$\therefore \ p$$

is an invalid argument, but if p happens to be true, then its conclusion is true.

67. Yes. If the conclusion does not follow from the set of premises, then the argument is invalid.

69. p: Lynn wins the contest.

q: Lynn strikes oil.

r : Lynn will be rich.

s: Lynn will stop working.

| p | q | r | s | [((p ∨ q) | → | r) ∧ (r | → | s)] → (~ s | → | ~ p) |
|---|---|---|---|---|---|---|---|---|---|---|
| T | T | T | T | T | T T | T | T | T | | T |
| T | T | T | F | T | T T | F | F | T | | F |
| T | T | F | T | T | F F | F | T | T | | T |
| T | T | F | F | T | F F | F | T | T | | F |
| T | F | T | T | T | T T | T | T | T | | T |
| T | F | T | F | T | T T | F | F | T | | F |
| T | F | F | T | T | F F | F | T | T | | T |
| T | F | F | F | T | F F | F | T | T | | F |
| F | T | T | T | T | T T | T | T | T | | T |
| F | T | T | F | T | T T | F | F | T | | T |
| F | T | F | T | T | F F | F | T | T | | T |
| F | T | F | F | T | F F | F | T | T | | T |
| F | F | T | T | F | T T | T | T | T | | T |
| F | F | T | F | F | T T | F | F | T | | T |
| F | F | F | T | F | T F | T | T | T | | T |
| F | F | F | F | F | T F | T | T | T | | T |
| | | | | 1 | 3 2 | 5 | 4 | 7 | | 6 |

The argument is valid.

71. p: I think.

q: I am.

$$p \rightarrow q$$

$$\underline{\sim q}$$

$$\therefore \ \sim p$$

By the Fallacy of the Inverse, the argument is invalid.

**<u>Exercise Set 3.6</u>**
1. Euler
3. Invalid
5. No

7.

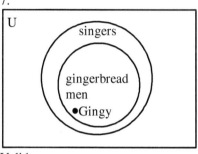

Valid

9. Valid

11. Invalid

13.

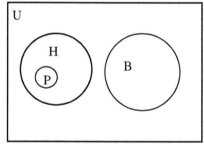

Valid

15.

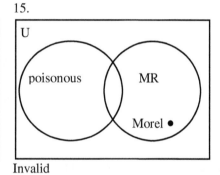

Invalid

17. Invalid

19.

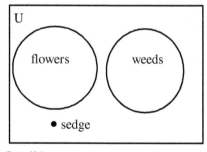

Invalid

21.

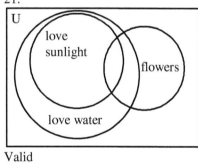

Valid

23.

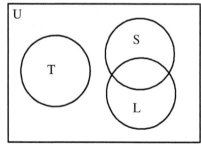

Invalid

25.

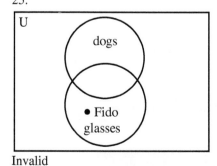

Invalid

27.

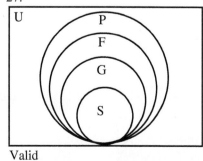

Valid

29. Yes. If the conjunction of the premises is false in all cases, then the argument is valid regardless of the truth value of the conclusion.

31. $[(p \to q) \land (p \lor q)] \to \sim p$ can be expressed as a set statement by $[(P' \cup Q) \cap (P \cup Q)] \subseteq P'$. If this statement is true, then the argument is valid; otherwise, the argument is invalid.

| Set | Regions |
|-----|---------|
| $P' \cup Q$ | II, III, IV |
| $P \cup Q$ | I, II, III |
| $(P' \cup Q) \cap (P \cup Q)$ | II, III |
| $P'$ | III, IV |

Since $(P' \cup Q) \cap (P \cup Q)$ is not a subset of $P'$, the argument is invalid.

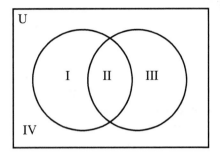

## Exercise Set 3.7

1. Series

3. Closed

5. $p \lor q$

| | | Light |
|---|---|-------|
| $p$ | $q$ | $p \lor q$ |
| T | T | T |
| T | F | T |
| F | T | T |
| F | F | F |

7. $(p \lor q) \land \overline{q}$

| | | | Light | |
|---|---|---------|---|----------|
| $p$ | $q$ | $(p \lor q)$ | $\land$ | $\overline{q}$ |
| T | T | T | F | F |
| T | F | T | T | T |
| F | T | T | F | F |
| F | F | F | F | T |

9. $(p \land q) \land [(p \land \overline{q}) \lor r]$

It is clear from the $(p \land q)$ condition that both $p$ and $q$ must be closed for the bulb to light. In this case the upper branch of the parallel portion of the circuit is open since it includes $\overline{q}$, so for the bulb to light, $r$ must be closed. Thus the bulb lights only if $p$, $q$ and $r$ are all T.

11. $p \lor q \lor (r \land \overline{p})$

Reading from the circuit, we can see that the only case in which the bulb will *not* light is: $p$ is F, $q$ is F, and $r$ is F.

13.

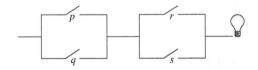

15.

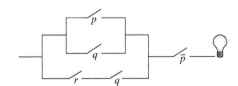

17.

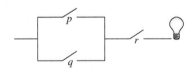

19.

21.  $p \lor \sim q;\ \overline{p} \land q$

Not equivalent; in fact, by De Morgan's laws,
$(p \lor q) \Leftrightarrow \overline{(\overline{p} \land \overline{q})}$, so the first circuit will light
the bulb exactly when the second one does not.

23.  $[(p \land q) \lor r] \land p;\ (q \lor r) \land p$

Clearly both circuits light the bulb only if $p$ is T.
In this case $p \land q$ has the same value as $q$ alone,
so $(p \land q) \lor r$ will have the same value as $q \lor r$.
Thus the two circuits are equivalent.

25.  $(p \lor \overline{p}) \land q \land r;\ p \land q \land r$

Not equivalent, since the first circuit will light the bulb when $p$ is F, $q$ is T and $r$ is T, while
$p$ being F breaks the second circuit.

27.  One of the two switches will always be open.  NEED ART

29.  a)                                              b)

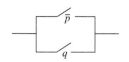                                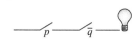

## Review Exercises

1.  Some Scions are not Toyotas.

2.  Some pets are allowed in this park.

3.  No women are presidents.

4.  All pine trees are green.

5.  The coffee is Maxwell House or the coffee is hot.

6.  The coffee is not hot and the coffee is strong.

7.  If the coffee is hot, then the coffee is strong and it is not Maxwell House.

8.  The coffee is Maxwell House if and only if the coffee is not strong.

9.  The coffee is not Maxwell House, if and only if the coffee is strong and the coffee is not hot.

10. The coffee is Maxwell House or the coffee is not hot, and the coffee is not strong.

11. $p \lor r$

12. $r \rightarrow \sim p$

13. $(r \rightarrow q) \lor \sim p$

14. $(q \leftrightarrow p) \land \sim r$

15. $(r \land q) \lor \sim p$

16. $\sim (r \land q)$

17.

| p | q | (p | ∨ | q) | ∧ | ~ p |
|---|---|----|---|----|---|-----|
| T | T |    | T |    | F | F |
| T | F |    | T |    | F | F |
| F | T |    | T |    | T | T |
| F | F |    | F |    | F | T |
|   |   |    | 1 |    | 3 | 2 |

18.

| p | q | q ↔ (p ∨ ~ q) |
|---|---|---|
| T | T | T  T  T T  F |
| T | F | F  F  T T  T |
| F | T | T  F  F F  F |
| F | F | F  F  F T  T |
|   |   | 1  5  2 4  3 |

19.

| p | q | r | (p ∨ q) ↔ (p ∨ r) |
|---|---|---|---|
| T | T | T | T    T    T |
| T | T | F | T    T    T |
| T | F | T | T    T    T |
| T | F | F | T    T    T |
| F | T | T | T    T    T |
| F | T | F | T    F    F |
| F | F | T | F    F    T |
| F | F | F | F    T    F |
|   |   |   | 1    3    2 |

20.

| p | q | r | p ∧ (~ q ∨ r) |
|---|---|---|---|
| T | T | T | T  T  F T  T |
| T | T | F | T  F  F F  F |
| T | F | T | T  T  T T  T |
| T | F | F | T  T  T T  F |
| F | T | T | F  F  F T  T |
| F | T | F | F  F  F F  F |
| F | F | T | F  F  T T  T |
| F | F | F | F  F  T T  F |
|   |   |   | 4  5  1 3  2 |

21.

| p | q | r | P → (q ∧ ~ r) |
|---|---|---|---|
| T | T | T | T  F  T F  F |
| T | T | F | T  T  T T  T |
| T | F | T | T  F  F F  F |
| T | F | F | T  F  F F  T |
| F | T | T | F  T  T F  F |
| F | T | F | F  T  T T  T |
| F | F | T | F  T  F F  F |
| F | F | F | F  T  F F  T |
|   |   |   | 4  5  1 3  2 |

22.

| p | q | r | (p ∧ q) → ~ r |
|---|---|---|---|
| T | T | T | T    F  F |
| T | T | F | T    T  T |
| T | F | T | F    T  F |
| T | F | F | F    T  T |
| F | T | T | F    T  F |
| F | T | F | F    T  T |
| F | F | T | F    T  F |
| F | F | F | F    T  T |
|   |   |   | 1    3  2 |

23.  p: ESPN is a sports network.
   q: CNN is a news network.
   r: Nickelodeon is a cooking network.
   (p → q) ↔ r
   T → T) ↔ F
      T    ↔ F
            F

24.  p: President's Day is in February.
   q: Memorial Day is in May.
   r: Labor Day is in December.
   p ∨ (q ∧ r)
   T ∨ (T ∧ F)
   T ∨    F
      T

25.  p: Oregon borders the Pacific Ocean.
   q: California borders the Atlantic Ocean.
   r: Minnesota is south of Texas.
   (p ∨ q) → r
   (T ∨ F) → F
      T  → F
         F

26.  p: 15 − 7 = 22      (p ∨ q) ∧ r
   q: 4 + 9 = 13      (F ∨ T) ∧ T
   r : 9 − 8 = 1        T   ∧ T
                  T

27.  (~ p → q) ∧ ~ (q ∨ r)
   (F →  F ) ∧ ~ (F ∨ F)
      T      ∧  ~ F
            T

28.  (p ↔ q) → (~ p ∨ r)
   (T ↔ F) → (F ∨ F)
      F    →    F
            T

29.  ~ r ↔ [(p ∨ q) ↔ ~ p]
   T ↔ [(T ∨ F) ↔ F]
   T ↔ [   T   ↔ F]
   T ↔         F
      F

30.  ~ [(q ∧ r) → (~ p ∨ r)]
   ~ [(F ∧ F) → ( F ∨ F)]
   ~ [   F   →     F]
         ~ T
         F

31.

| p | q | ~ (p ∧ ~ q) | ~ p ∧ q |
|---|---|-------------|---------|
| T | T | T T F F | F F T |
| T | F | F T T T | F F F |
| F | T | T F F F | T T T |
| F | F | T F F T | T F F |
|   |   | 4 1 3 □ 2 | 1 3 □ |

The statements are not equivalent.

32.

| p | q | p ∨ q | ~ p → q |
|---|---|-------|---------|
| T | T | T T T | F T T |
| T | F | T T F | F T F |
| F | T | F T T | T T T |
| F | F | F F F | T F F |
|   |   | 1 3 2 | 1 3 □ |

33.

| p | q | r | ~ p ∨ (q ∧ r) | | | (~ p ∨ q) ∧ (~ p ∨ r) | | | | | | |
|---|---|---|---|---|---|---|---|---|---|---|---|---|
| T | T | T | F | T | T | F | T | T | T | F | T | T |
| T | T | F | F | F | F | F | T | T | F | F | F | F |
| T | F | T | F | F | F | F | F | F | F | F | T | T |
| T | F | F | F | F | F | F | F | F | F | F | F | F |
| F | T | T | T | T | T | T | T | T | T | T | T | T |
| F | T | F | T | T | F | T | T | T | T | T | F | F |
| F | F | T | T | T | F | T | T | F | T | T | T | T |
| F | F | F | T | T | F | T | T | F | T | T | T | F |
|   |   |   | 2 | 3 | 1 | 1 | 3 | 2 | 7 | 4 | 6 | 5 |

The statements are equivalent.

34.

| p | q | (~ q → p) ∧ p | | | | | ~ (~ p ↔ q) ∨ p | | | | | |
|---|---|---|---|---|---|---|---|---|---|---|---|---|
| T | T | F | T | T | T | T | T | F | F | T | T | T |
| T | F | T | T | T | T | T | F | F | T | F | T | T |
| F | T | F | T | F | F | F | F | T | T | T | F | F |
| F | F | T | F | F | F | F | T | T | F | F | T | F |
|   |   | 1 | 3 | 2 | 5 | 4 | 4 | 1 | 3 | 2 | 6 | 5 |

The statements are not equivalent.

35. p: Lady Gaga sang *Poker Face*.

q: Jay-Z sang *Beamer, Benz, or Bentley*.
In symbolic form, the statement is p ∧ ~q. We are
given that p ∧ ~q ⇔ ~(p → q). So an equivalent
statement is: It is false that if Lady Gaga sang
*Poker Face*, then Jay-Z sang *Beamer, Benz, or Bentley*.

36. p: Lynn Swann played for the Steelers.

q: Jack Tatum played for the Raiders.
In symbolic form, the statement is p ∨ q.
We are given that ~p ∨ q ⇔ (p → q), so
p ∨ q ⇔ (~p → q). Thus an equivalent
statement is: If Lynn Swann did not play
for the Steelers then Jack Tatum played for
the Raiders.

37. p: Altec Lansing only produces speakers.

q: Harmon Kardon only produces stereo receivers.
The symbolic form is ~ (p ∨ q).
Using De Morgan's Laws, we get
~ (p ∨ q) ⇔ ~ p ∧ ~ q.
Altec Lansing does not produce only speakers and
Harmon Kardon does not produce only stereo receivers.

38. p: Travis Tritt won an Academy Award.

q: Randy Jackson does commercials for
   Milk Bone dog biscuits.
The symbolic form is ~ p ∧ ~ q.
Using De Morgan's Laws, we get
~ p ∧ ~ q ⇔ ~ (p ∨ q). It is false
that Travis Tritt won an Academy
Award or Randy Jackson does
commercials for Milk Bone dog
biscuits.

39. p: The temperature is above 32 degrees Fahrenheit.
q: We will go ice fishing at O'Leary's Lake.
The symbolic form is ~ p → q.
The temperature is above 32 degrees Fahrenheit or
we will go ice fishing at O'Leary's Lake.

40. Converse: If you know Jay Stu, then you liten to
   Jim Rome.
Inverse: If you do not listen to Jim Rome, then
   you do not know Jay Stu.
Contrapositive: If you do not know Jay Stu,
   then you do not listen to Jim Rome.

41. Converse: If we are going to learn the table's value then we take the table to *Antiques Roadshow*.

    Inverse: If we do not take the table to *Antiques Roadshow*, then we will not learn the table's value.

    Contrapositive: If we are not going to learn the table's value then we do not take the table to *Antiques Roadshow*.

42. Converse: If you do not sell more doughnuts, then you do not advertise.

    Inverse: If If you advertise, then you sell more doughnuts.

    Contrapositive: If you sell more doughnuts, then you advertise.

43. Converse: If we do not buy a desk at Miller's Furniture, then the desk is made by Winner's Only and is in the Rose catalog.

    Inverse: If the desk is not made by Winner's Only or is not in the Rose catalog, then we will buy a desk at Miller's Furniture.

    Contrapositive: If we will buy a desk at Miller's Furniture, then the desk is not made by Winner's Only or it is not in the Rose catalogue.

44. Converse: If I let you attend the prom, then you get straight A's on your report card.

    Inverse: If you do not get straight A's on your report card, then I will not let you attend the prom.

    Contrapositive: If I do not let you attend the prom, then you do not get straight A's on your report card.

45. p: You swim everyday.

    q: You lose five pounds.

    In symbolic form, the statements are: a) $p \rightarrow q$, b) $\sim p \vee q$, and c) $\sim (p \wedge \sim q)$. Using the fact that $p \rightarrow q$ is equivalent to $\sim p \vee q$, statements (a) and (b) are equivalent. Using DeMorgan's Laws on statement (b) we get $\sim (p \wedge \sim q)$.

46. p: The screwdriver is on the workbench.

    q: The screwdriver is on the counter.

    In symbolic form, the statements are: a) $p \leftrightarrow \sim q$, b) $\sim q \rightarrow \sim p$, and c) $\sim (q \wedge \sim p)$. Looking at the truth tables for statements (a), (b), and (c) we can conclude that none of the statements are equivalent.

| | | a)<br>$p \leftrightarrow \sim q$ | | | b)<br>$\sim q \rightarrow \sim p$ | | | c)<br>$\sim (q \wedge \sim p)$ | | | |
|---|---|---|---|---|---|---|---|---|---|---|---|
| p | q | | | | | | | | | | |
| T | T | T | F | F | F | T | F | T | T | F | F |
| T | F | T | T | T | T | F | F | T | F | F | F |
| F | T | F | T | F | F | T | T | F | T | T | T |
| F | F | F | F | T | T | T | T | T | F | F | T |
| | | 1 | 3 | 2 | 1 | 3 | 2 | 4 | 1 | 3 | 2 |

47. p:  $2 + 3 = 6$.

    q:  $3 + 1 = 5$.

    In symbolic form, the statements are: a) $p \rightarrow q$,

    b) $p \leftrightarrow \sim q$, and c) $\sim q \rightarrow \sim p$.

    Statement (c) is the contrapositive of statement

    (a).  Therefore statements (a) and (c) are equivalent.
    For p and q false, (a) and (c) are true but (b) is false,
    so (b) is not equivalent to (a) and (c).

48. p:  The sale is on Tuesday.

    q:  I have money.

    r :  I will go to the sale.

    In symbolic form the statements are: a) $(p \wedge q) \rightarrow r$,

    b) $r \rightarrow (p \wedge q)$, and c) $r \vee (p \wedge q)$.  The truth table for
    statements (a), (b), and (c) shows that none of the
    statements are equivalent.

| p | q | r | $(p \wedge q) \rightarrow r$ | | | $r \rightarrow (p \wedge q)$ | | | $r \vee (p \wedge q)$ | | |
|---|---|---|---|---|---|---|---|---|---|---|---|
| T | T | T | T | T T | | T T | T | | T T | T | |
| T | T | F | T | F F | | F T | T | | F T | T | |
| T | F | T | F | T T | | T F | F | | T T | F | |
| T | F | F | F | T F | | F T | F | | F F | F | |
| F | T | T | F | T T | | T F | F | | T T | F | |
| F | T | F | F | T F | | F T | F | | F F | F | |
| F | F | T | F | T T | | T F | F | | T T | F | |
| F | F | F | F | T F | | F T | F | | F F | F | |
| | | | 1 | 3 2 | | 1 3 | 2 | | 1 3 | 2 | |

49. 

| p | q | $[(p \rightarrow q) \wedge \sim p] \rightarrow q$ | | | | |
|---|---|---|---|---|---|---|
| T | T | T | F F | T T | | |
| T | F | F | F F | T F | | |
| F | T | T | T T | T T | | |
| F | F | T | T T | F F | | |
| | | 1 | 3 2 | 5 4 | | |

The argument is invalid.

50. 

| p | q | r | $[(p \wedge q) \wedge (q \rightarrow r)] \rightarrow (p \rightarrow r)$ | | | | |
|---|---|---|---|---|---|---|---|
| T | T | T | T | T T | T | T | |
| T | T | F | T | F F | T | F | |
| T | F | T | F | F T | T | T | |
| T | F | F | F | F T | T | F | |
| F | T | T | F | F T | T | T | |
| F | T | F | F | F F | T | T | |
| F | F | T | F | F T | T | T | |
| F | F | F | F | F T | T | T | |
| | | | 1 | 3 2 | 5 | 4 | |

The argument is valid.

51. p: Jose Macias is the manager.
    q: Kevin Geis is the coach.
    r: Tim Weisman is the umpire

    p → q
    q → r
    ∴ p → r

    This argument is in the form of the law of syllogism so it is valid.

52. p: The astronaut visits the space station.
    q: The astronaut uses the space shuttle.
    r: The astronaut uses the Soyuz spacecraft.

    p → q
    q ∨ r
    ∴ ~ r

    If p is F, q is T, and r is either T or F, the premises are both true but the conclusion is false, so the argument is invalid.

53. Invalid

54. Invalid

55.

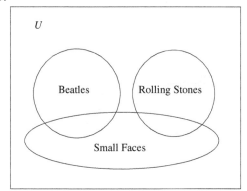

Invalid

56.

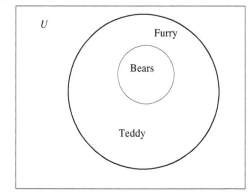

Invalid

57. a) $p \wedge [(q \wedge r) \vee \bar{p}]$

    b) For the bulb to be on, the first switch on the left must be closed, so p is T. The eliminates the bottom branch of the parallel portion, so both switches on the top branch must be closed. Thus the bulb lights exactly when p, q, and r are all T

58.

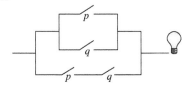

59. Symbolically the two circuits are $(p \vee q) \wedge (\overline{q} \vee \overline{p})$ and $(p \wedge \overline{q}) \vee (q \wedge \overline{p})$.

| $p$ | $q$ | $\overline{p}$ | $\overline{q}$ | $(p \vee q)$ | $\wedge$ | $(\overline{q} \vee \overline{p})$ | $p$ | $q$ | $\overline{p}$ | $\overline{q}$ | $(p \wedge \overline{q})$ | $\vee$ | $(q \wedge \overline{p})$ |
|---|---|---|---|---|---|---|---|---|---|---|---|---|---|
| T | T | F | F | T | F | F | T | T | F | F | F | F | F |
| T | F | F | T | T | T | T | T | F | F | T | T | T | F |
| F | T | T | F | T | T | T | F | T | T | F | F | T | T |
| F | F | T | T | F | F | T | F | F | T | T | F | F | F |

The next-to last columns of these truth tables are identical, so the circuits are equivalent.

## Chapter Test

1. $(p \wedge r) \vee \sim q$

2. $(r \to q) \vee \sim p$

3. $\sim (r \leftrightarrow \sim q)$

4. Phobos is not a moon of Mars and Rosalind is a moon of Uranus, if and only if Callisto is not a moon of Jupiter.

5. If Phobos is a moon of Mars or Callisto is not a Moon of Jupiter, then Rosalind is a moon of Uranus.

6.

| p | q | r | [~ (p → r)] ∧ q | | | |
|---|---|---|---|---|---|---|
| T | T | T | F | T | F | T |
| T | T | F | T | F | T | T |
| T | F | T | F | T | F | F |
| T | F | F | T | F | F | F |
| F | T | T | F | T | F | T |
| F | T | F | F | T | F | T |
| F | F | T | F | T | F | F |
| F | F | F | F | T | F | F |
| | | | 2 | 1 | 4 | 3 |

7.

| p | q | r | (q ↔ ~ r) ∨ p | | | | |
|---|---|---|---|---|---|---|---|
| T | T | T | T | F | F | T | T |
| T | T | F | T | T | T | T | T |
| T | F | T | F | T | F | T | T |
| T | F | F | F | F | T | T | T |
| F | T | T | T | F | F | F | F |
| F | T | F | T | T | T | T | F |
| F | F | T | F | T | F | T | F |
| F | F | F | F | F | T | F | F |
| | | | 1 | 3 | 2 | 5 | 4 |

8. p: $2 + 6 = 8$
   q: $7 - 12 = 5$

   $p \vee q$
   $T \vee F$
   $\quad T$

9. p:  A scissors can cut paper.
   q:  A dime equals 2 nickels.
   r :  Louisville is a city in Kentucky.

   $(p \vee q) \leftrightarrow r$
   $(T \vee T) \leftrightarrow T$
   $\quad T \;\; \leftrightarrow T$
   $\qquad T$

10. $(r \vee q) \leftrightarrow (p \wedge \sim q)$
    $(T \vee F) \leftrightarrow (T \wedge T)$
    $\quad T \quad \leftrightarrow \quad T$
    $\qquad T$

11. $[\sim(r \to \sim p)] \wedge (q \to p)$
    $[\sim(T \to F \;)] \wedge (F \to T)$
    $[\; \sim (F) \quad ] \wedge \quad T$
    $\qquad T \qquad \wedge \quad T$
    $\qquad\qquad T$

12. By DeMorgan's Laws ,
    $\sim p \vee q \Leftrightarrow \sim (\sim (\sim p) \wedge \sim q)$.
    and this is equivalent to
    $\sim(p \wedge \sim q)$.

13. p:  The bird is red.
    q:  It is a cardinal.
    In symbolic form the statements
    are: a) $p \to q$, b) $\sim p \vee q$,
    and c) $\sim p \to \sim q$.
    Statement (c) is the inverse of
    statement (a) and thus they cannot
    be equivalent.  Using the fact that
    $p \to q \Leftrightarrow \sim p \vee q$, to rewrite
    statement (a) we get $\sim p \vee q$.
    (a) and (b) are equivalent.

14. p: The test is today.  q: The concert is tonight.  In symbolic form the statements are: a) ~ (p ∨ q),  b) ~ p ∧ ~ q, and ~ p → ~ q. Applying DeMorgan's Law to statement (a) we get: ~ p ∧ ~ q. Therefore statements (a) and (b) are equivalent.  When we compare the truth tables for statements (a), (b), and (c) we see that only statements (a) and (b) are equivalent.

| p | q | ~ (p ∨ q) | | ~ p ∧ ~ q | | | ~ p → ~ q | | |
|---|---|---|---|---|---|---|---|---|---|
| T | T | F | T | F | F | F | F | T | F |
| T | F | F | T | F | F | T | F | T | T |
| F | T | F | T | T | F | F | T | F | F |
| F | F | T | F | T | T | T | T | T | T |
| | | 2 | 1 | 1 | 3 | 2 | 1 | 3 | 2 |

15. s: The soccer team won the game.
f: Sue played fullback.
p: The team is in second place.
This argument is the law of syllogism and therefore it is valid.

$$s \rightarrow f$$
$$\underline{f \rightarrow p}$$
$$s \rightarrow p$$

This argument is the law of syllogism and therefore it is valid.

16.

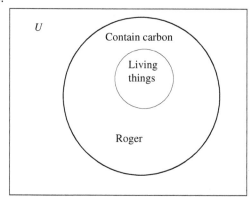

Fallacy

17. Some highways are not roads

18. Nick did not play football or Max did not play baseball.

19. Converse:  If today is Saturday, then the
garbage truck comes.
    Inverse:  If the garbage truck does not
come today, then today is not Saturday.
    Contrapositive:  If today is not Saturday,
then the garbage truck does not come.

20.

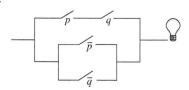

# CHAPTER NINE

## GEOMETRY

**Exercise Set 9.1**

1. Parallel

3. Angle

5. Supplementary

7. Straight

9. Obtuse

11. Vertical

13. Ray, $\overrightarrow{AB}$

15. Half line, $\overset{\circ}{\overrightarrow{BA}}$

17. Ray, $\overrightarrow{BA}$

19. Half open line segment, $\overset{\circ}{AB}$

21. $\overline{AD}$

23. $\overset{\circ}{\overrightarrow{BD}}$

25. $\{B, F\}$

27. $\{C\}$

29. $\measuredangle CBF$ or $\measuredangle FBC$

31. $\overleftrightarrow{BC}$

33. $\overrightarrow{DE}$

35. $\overrightarrow{BC}$

37. $\measuredangle ABE$

39. $\overline{BF}$

41. $\overset{\circ\circ}{AC}$

43. $\overset{\circ}{\overrightarrow{BE}}$

45. Right

47. Straight

49. Obtuse

51. None of these

53. $90° - 10° = 80°$

55. $90° - 32\frac{3}{4}° = 57\frac{1}{4}°$

57. $90° - 64.7° = 25.3°$

59. $180° - 80° = 100°$

61. $180° - 20.5° = 159.5°$

63. $180° - 43\frac{5}{7}° = 136\frac{2}{7}°$

65. f

67. b

69. a

**193**

71.  Let $x$ = measure of $\measuredangle\,2$

$5x$ = measure of $\measuredangle\,1$

$$x + 5x = 90$$
$$6x = 90$$
$$x = \frac{90}{6} = 15°,\ m\measuredangle 2$$
$$5x = (5)(15) = 75°,\ m\measuredangle 1$$

73.     Let $x$ = measure of $\measuredangle\,1$

$180 - x$ = measure of $\measuredangle\,2$

$$x - (180 - x) = 88$$
$$x - 180 + x = 88$$
$$2x - 180 = 88$$
$$2x = 268$$
$$x = \frac{268}{2} = 134°,\ m\measuredangle 1$$
$$180 - x = 180 - 134 = 46°,\ m\measuredangle 2$$

75.  $m\measuredangle\,1 + 125° = 180°$

$m\measuredangle\,1 = 55°$

$m\measuredangle\,2 = m\measuredangle\,1$ (vertical angles)

$m\measuredangle\,3 = 125°$ (vertical angles)

$m\measuredangle\,5 = m\measuredangle\,2$ (alternate interior angles)

$m\measuredangle\,4 = m\measuredangle\,3$ (alternate interior angles)

$m\measuredangle\,7 = m\measuredangle\,4$ (vertical angles)

$m\measuredangle\,6 = m\measuredangle\,5$ (vertical angles)

Measures of angles 3, 4, and 7 are each 125°.

Measures of angles 1, 2, 5, and 6 are each 55°.

77.  $m\measuredangle\,3 + 30° = 180°$

$m\measuredangle\,3 = 150°$

$m\measuredangle\,1 = 30°$ (vertical angles)

$m\measuredangle\,2 = m\measuredangle\,3$ (vertical angles)

$m\measuredangle\,4 = m\measuredangle\,1$ (corresponding angles)

$m\measuredangle\,7 = m\measuredangle\,4$ (vertical angles)

$m\measuredangle\,6 = m\measuredangle\,3$ (alternate interior angles)

$m\measuredangle\,5 = m\measuredangle\,6$ (vertical angles)

Measures of angles 1, 4, and 7 are each 30°.

Measures of angles 2, 3, 5, and 6 are each 150°.

79.  $$x + 2x + 12 = 90$$
$$3x + 12 = 90$$
$$3x = 78$$
$$x = \frac{78}{3} = 26°,\ m\measuredangle 2$$
$$90 - x = 90 - 26 = 64°,\ m\measuredangle 1$$

81.  $$x + 2x - 9 = 90$$
$$3x - 9 = 90$$
$$3x = 99$$
$$x = \frac{99}{3} = 33°,\ m\measuredangle 1$$
$$90 - x = 90 - 33 = 57°,\ m\measuredangle 2$$

83.  $$x + 3x - 4 = 180$$
$$4x - 4 = 180$$
$$4x = 184$$
$$x = \frac{184}{4} = 46°,\ m\measuredangle 2$$
$$180 - x = 180 - 46 = 134°,\ m\measuredangle 1$$

85.  $$x + 5x + 6 = 180$$
$$6x + 6 = 180$$
$$6x = 174$$
$$x = \frac{174}{6} = 29°,\ m\measuredangle 1$$
$$180 - x = 180 - 29 = 151°,\ m\measuredangle 2$$

For Exercises 87 - 93, the answers given are one of many possible answers.

87.  Plane $ABG$ and plane $JCD$

89.  $\overleftrightarrow{BG}$ and $\overleftrightarrow{DG}$

91.  Plane $AGB \cap$ plane $ABC \cap$ plane $BCD = \{B\}$

93.  $\overleftrightarrow{BC} \cap$ plane $ABG = \{B\}$

95. a) Undefined terms, definitions, postulates (axioms), and theorems

b) First, Euclid introduced **undefined terms**. Second, he introduced certain **definitions**. Third, he stated primitive propositions called **postulates (axioms)** about the undefined terms and definitions. Fourth, he proved, using deductive reasoning, other propositions called **theorems**.

97. a) An infinite number of lines can be drawn through a given point.

b) An infinite number of planes can be drawn through a given point.

99. An infinite number of planes can be drawn through a given line.

101. Always true. If any two lines are parallel to a third line, then they must be parallel to each other.

103. Sometimes true. Vertical angles are only complementary when each is equal to 45°.

105. Sometimes true. Alternate interior angles are only complementary when each is equal to 45°.

107. Answers will vary.

109. No. Line $l$ and line $n$ may be parallel or skew.

111.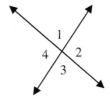

$$m\angle 1 + m\angle 2 = 180°$$
$$m\angle 3 + m\angle 4 = 180°$$
$$180° + 180° = 360°$$

**Exercise Set 9.2**

1. Polygon

3. Proportion

5. Congruent

7. a) Octagon
   b) Regular

9. a) Triangle
   b) Regular

11. a) Parallelogram
    b) Not regular

13. a) Heptagon
    b) Not regular

15. a) Right
    b) Acute

17. a) Isosceles
    b) Acute

19. a) Scalene
    b) Acute

21. a) Scalene
    b) Right

23. Trapezoid

25. Square

27. Rhombus

29. The measures of the other two angles of the triangle are 37° and 180° − 133° (supplementary angles). The measure of the third angle of the triangle is 180° − (37°) − (180° − 133°) = 96. Since angle $x$ is a vertical angle with the 96° angle, the measure of angle $x$ is 96°.

31. The measure of one angle of the triangle is 27° (by vertical angles). The measure of another angle of the triangle is 180° - 57° = 123°. The measure of the third angle of the triangle is 180° - 27° - 123° = 30°. The measure of angle $x$ is 180° - 30° = 150° (The 30° angle and angle $x$ form a straight angle.).

33.

| Angle | Measure | Reason |
|---|---|---|
| 1 | 90° | ∠1 and ∠7 are vertical angles |
| 2 | 50° | ∠2 and ∠4 are corresponding angles |
| 3 | 130° | ∠3 and ∠4 form a straight angle |
| 4 | 50° | Vertical angle with the given 50° angle |
| 5 | 50° | ∠2 and ∠5 are vertical angles |
| 6 | 40° | Vertical angle with the given 40° angle |
| 7 | 90° | ∠2, ∠6, and ∠7 form a straight angle |
| 8 | 130° | ∠3 and ∠8 are vertical angles |
| 9 | 140° | ∠9 and ∠10 form a straight angle |
| 10 | 40° | ∠10 and ∠12 are vertical angles |
| 11 | 140° | ∠9 and ∠11 are vertical angles |
| 12 | 40° | ∠6 and ∠12 are corresponding angles |

35. $n = 5$
$(5 - 2) \times 180° = 3 \times 180° = 540°$

37. $n = 9$
$(9 - 2) \times 180° = 7 \times 180° = 1260$

39. $n = 20$
$(20 - 2) \times 180° = 18 \times 180° = 3240°$

41. a) The sum of the measures of the interior angles of a triangle is 180°. Dividing by 3, the number of angles, each interior angle measures 60°.
b) Each exterior angle measures $180° - 60° = 120°$.

43. a) The sum of the measures of the interior angles of an octagon is $(8 - 2) \times 180° = 6 \times 180° = 1080°$. dividing by 8, the number of angles, each interior angle measures 135°.
b) Each exterior angle measures $180° - 135° = 45°$.

45. a) The sum of the measures of the interior angles of a decagon is $(10 - 2) \times 180° = 8 \times 180° = 1440°$. Dividing by 10, the number of angles, each interior angle measures 144°.
b) Each exterior angle measures $180° - 144° = 36°$.

47. Let $x = A'C'$
$$\frac{A'C'}{AC} = \frac{A'B'}{AB}$$
$$\frac{x}{5} = \frac{1}{2.5}$$
$$2.5x = 5$$
$$x = 2$$

Let $y = B'C'$
$$\frac{B'C'}{BC} = \frac{A'B'}{AB}$$
$$\frac{y}{4} = \frac{1}{2.5}$$
$$2.5y = 4$$
$$y = \frac{4}{2.5} = 1.6$$

49. Let $x = DC$

$$\frac{DC}{D'C'} = \frac{AB}{A'B'}$$

$$\frac{x}{6} = \frac{4}{10}$$

$$10x = 24$$

$$x = \frac{24}{10} = \frac{12}{5}$$

Let $y = B'C'$

$$\frac{B'C'}{BC} = \frac{A'B'}{AB}$$

$$\frac{y}{3} = \frac{10}{4}$$

$$4y = 30$$

$$y = \frac{30}{4} = \frac{15}{2}$$

51. Let $x = D'C'$

$$\frac{D'C'}{DC} = \frac{A'D'}{AD}$$

$$\frac{x}{16} = \frac{22.5}{18}$$

$$18x = 360$$

$$x = 20$$

Let $y = A'B'$

$$\frac{A'B'}{AB} = \frac{A'D'}{AD}$$

$$\frac{y}{17} = \frac{22.5}{18}$$

$$18y = 382.5$$

$$y = 21.25$$

53. Let $x = BC$

$$\frac{BC}{EC} = \frac{AB}{DE}$$

$$\frac{x}{1} = \frac{3}{1}$$

$$x = 3$$

55. $AD = AC - DC = 5 - \dfrac{5}{3} = \dfrac{15}{3} - \dfrac{5}{3} = \dfrac{10}{3}$

57. $AC = A'C' = 14$

59. $B'C' = BC = 15$

61. $m\angle ACB = m\angle A'C'B' = 28°$

63. $AD = A'D' = 9$

65. $A'B' = AB = 10$

67. $m\angle A'D'C' = m\angle ADC = 70°$

69. $180° - 125° = 55°$

71. $180° - 90° - 55° = 35°$

73. Let $x =$ height of silo

$$\frac{x}{6} = \frac{105}{9}$$

$$9x = 630$$

$$x = 70 \text{ ft}$$

75. a) $\dfrac{44 \text{ mi}}{0.875 \text{ in.}} = \dfrac{\text{SP-A}}{2.25 \text{ in.}}$

$\text{SP-A} = \dfrac{(44)(2.25)}{0.875} \text{ mi} = 113.14 \text{ mi}$

b) $\dfrac{44 \text{ mi}}{0.875 \text{ in.}} = \dfrac{\text{SP-R}}{1.5 \text{ in.}}$

$\text{SP-R} = \dfrac{(44)(1.5)}{0.875} \text{ mi} = 75.43 \text{ mi}$

**77.** The different types of triangles are acute, obtuse, right, isosceles, equilateral, and scalene. Descriptions will vary.

**79.**

$\dfrac{DE}{D'E'} = 3$

$\dfrac{12}{D'E'} = 3$

$3D'E' = 12$

$\overline{D'E'} = 4$

$\dfrac{EF}{E'F'} = 3$

$\dfrac{15}{E'F'} = 3$

$3E'F' = 15$

$\overline{E'F'} = 5$

$\dfrac{DF}{D'F'} = 3$

$\dfrac{9}{D'F'} = 3$

$3D'F' = 9$

$\overline{D'F'} = 3$

**81.  a)**  $m\angle HMF = m\angle TMB,\ m\angle HFM = m\angle TBM,\ m\angle MHF = m\angle MTB$

Let  $x =$ height of the wall

$\dfrac{x}{20} = \dfrac{5.5}{2.5}$

$2.5x = 110$

$x = \dfrac{110}{2.5} = 44$ ft

**Exercise Set 9.3**

Throughout this section, on exercises involving $\pi$, we used the $\pi$ key on a scientific calculator to determine the answer.  If you use 3.14 for $\pi$, your answers may vary slightly.

**1.**  1. a) Perimeter
   b) Area
**3.** Circle

**5.**  $A = \dfrac{1}{2}bh = \dfrac{1}{2}(6)(4) = 12$ cm$^2$

**7.**  $A = \dfrac{1}{2}bh = \dfrac{1}{2}(7)(5) = 17.5$ cm$^2$

**9.**  $A = lw = 10(5) = 50$ ft$^2$

**11.**  3 m $= 3(100) = 300$ cm

$A = bh = 300(20) = 6000$ cm$^2$

$P = 2l + 2w = 2(300) + 2(27) = 654$ cm

**13.**  2 ft $= 2(12) = 24$ in.

$A = \dfrac{1}{2}h(b_1 + b_2) = \dfrac{1}{2}(24)(5+19) = 288$ in.$^2$

$P = s_1 + s_2 + b_1 + b_2 = 25 + 25 + 5 + 19 = 74$ in.

**15.**  $A = \pi r^2 = \pi(5)^2 = 25\pi \approx 78.54$ m$^2$

$C = 2\pi r = 2\pi(5) = 10\pi \approx 31.42$ m

17.   $r = \dfrac{13}{2} = 6.5$ ft

   $A = \pi r^2 = \pi(6.5)^2 = 42.25\pi \approx 132.73$ ft$^2$

   $C = \pi d = \pi(13) \approx 40.84$ ft

19.   a) $c^2 = 15^2 + 8^2$

   $c^2 = 225 + 64$

   $c^2 = 289$

   $c = \sqrt{289} = 17$ yd

   b) $P = s_1 + s_2 + s_3 = 8 + 15 + 17 = 40$ yd

   c) $A = \dfrac{1}{2}bh = \dfrac{1}{2}(8)(15) = 60$ yd$^2$

21.   a) $b^2 + 5^2 = 13^2$

   $b^2 + 25 = 169$

   $b^2 = 144$

   $c = \sqrt{144} = 12$ km

   b) $P = s_1 + s_2 + s_3 = 5 + 12 + 13 = 30$ km

   c)

   $A = \dfrac{1}{2}bh = \dfrac{1}{2}(5)(12) = 30$ km$^2$

23.   Area of square: $(6)^2 = 36$ ft$^2$

   Area of circle: $\pi(3)^2 = 9\pi = 28.27433388$ ft$^2$

   Shaded area:

   $36 - 28.27433388 = 7.72566612 \approx 7.73$ ft$^2$

25.   Use the Pythagorean Theorem to find the length of a side of the shaded square.

   $x^2 = 2^2 + 2^2$

   $x^2 = 4 + 4$

   $x^2 = 8$

   $x = \sqrt{8}$

   Shaded area: $\sqrt{8}\left(\sqrt{8}\right) = 8$ in.$^2$

27.   Find area of trapezoid minus area of unshaded triangle.

   Trapezoid:   $18\left(\dfrac{9+11}{2}\right) = 180$

   Triangle:    $\dfrac{1}{2}(18)(10) = 90$

   Shaded area:   $180 - 90 = 90$ yd$^2$

29.   Area of trapezoid:

   $\dfrac{1}{2}(8)(9+20) = \dfrac{1}{2}(8)(29) = 116$ in.$^2$

   Area of circle: $\pi(4)^2 = 16\pi = 50.26548246$ in.$^2$

   Shaded area:

   $116 - 50.26548246 = 65.73451754 \approx 65.73$ in.$^2$

31.   Radius of larger circle: $\dfrac{12}{2} = 6$ mm

   Area of large circle:

   $\pi(6)^2 = 36\pi = 113.0973355$ mm$^2$

   Radius of each smaller circle: $\dfrac{6}{2} = 3$ mm

   Area of each smaller circle:

   $\pi(3)^2 = 9\pi = 28.2743388$ mm$^2$

   Shaded area:

   $113.0973355 - 28.2743388 - 28.2743388$

   $= 56.5486579 \approx 56.55$ mm$^2$

33. $\dfrac{1}{x} = \dfrac{9}{72}$

$9x = 72$

$x = \dfrac{72}{9} = 8 \text{ yd}^2$

35. $\dfrac{1}{14.7} = \dfrac{9}{x}$

$x = 14.7(9) = 132.3 \text{ ft}^2$

37. $\dfrac{1}{5} = \dfrac{10,000}{x}$

$x = 5(10,000) = 50,000 \text{ cm}^2$

39. $\dfrac{1}{x} = \dfrac{10,000}{8625}$

$10,000x = 8625$

$x = \dfrac{8625}{10,000} = 0.8625 \text{ m}^2$

41. Area of living/dining room: $25(22) = 550 \text{ ft}^2$

a) $550(9.99) = \$5494.50$

b) $550(11.99) = \$6594.50$

43. 43.  Area of kitchen: $12(14) = 168 \text{ ft}^2$

Area of first floor bathroom: $6(10) = 60 \text{ ft}^2$

Area of second floor bathroom: $8(14) = 112 \text{ ft}^2$

Area of kitchen and both bathrooms: $340 \text{ ft}^2$

Cost: $340(\$8.99) = \$3056.60$

45. Area of bedroom 1: $10(14) = 140 \text{ ft}^2$

Area of bedroom 2: $10(20) = 200 \text{ ft}^2$

Area of bedroom 3: $10(14) = 140 \text{ ft}^2$

Total area: $140 + 200 + 140 = 480 \text{ ft}^2$

Cost: $480(\$7.99) = \$3835.20$

47. Area of entire lawn if all grass:

$400(300) = 120,000 \text{ ft}^2$

Area of house: $\dfrac{1}{2}(50)(100 + 150) = 6250 \text{ ft}^2$

Area of goldfish pond:

$\pi(20)^2 = 400\pi = 1256.637061 \text{ ft}^2$

Area of privacy hedge: $200(20) = 4000 \text{ ft}^2$

Area of garage: $70(30) = 2100 \text{ ft}^2$

Area of driveway: $40(25) = 1000 \text{ ft}^2$

Area of lawn:

$120,000 - 6250 - 1256.637061 - 4000 - 2100 - 1000$

$= 105,393.3629 \text{ ft}^2 = \dfrac{105,393.3629}{9}$

$= 11,710.37366 \text{ yd}^2$

Cost:

$11,710.37366(\$0.02) = \$234.2074732 \approx \$234.21$

49. a) Perimeter $= 2(94) + 2(50) = 288$ ft
    b) Area $= (94)(50) = 4700$; 4700 tiles

51. Let $a =$ height on the wall the ladder reaches
$$a^2 + 20^2 = 29^2$$
$$a^2 + 400 = 841$$
$$a^2 = 441$$
$$a = \sqrt{441} = 21 \text{ ft}$$

53. Let $d$ be the distance.
$$d^2 = 37^2 + 310^2$$
$$d^2 = 97494$$
$$d = \sqrt{97494} \approx 312 \text{ ft}$$

55. a) $A = s^2$
    b) $A = (2s)^2 = 4s^2$
    c) The area of the square in part b) is four times larger than the area of the square in part a).

57. $s = \dfrac{1}{2}(a+b+c) = \dfrac{1}{2}(8+6+10) = 12$
$$A = \sqrt{12(12-8)(12-6)(12-10)}$$
$$= \sqrt{12(4)(6)(2)} = \sqrt{576} = 24 \text{ cm}^2$$

## Exercise Set 9.4

In this section, we use the $\pi$ key on the calculator to determine answers in calculations involving $\pi$. If you use 3.14 for $\pi$, your answers may vary slightly.

1. Volume
3. Platonic
5. Right

7. a) $V = lwh = (8)(2)(4) = 64$ ft$^3$
   b) $SA = 2lw + 2wh + 2lh$
   $SA = 2(8)(2) + 2(2)(4) + 2(8)(4) = 112$ ft$^2$

9. a) $V = s^3$; $V = 2^3 = 8$ yd$^3$
   b) $SA = 6s^2$; $SA = 6(2^2) = 24$ yd$^2$

11. a) $V = \pi r^2 h = \pi(2^2)(12) = 48\pi$
    $V \approx 150.80$ in.$^3$
    b) $SA = 2\pi r^2 + 2\pi rh$
    $SA = 2\pi(2^2) + 2\pi(2)(12) = 56\pi$
    $SA \approx 175.93$ in$^2$

13. a) $V = \dfrac{1}{3}\pi r^2 h = \dfrac{1}{3}\pi(3^2)(14) = 42\pi$
    $V \approx 131.95$ cm$^3$
    b)
    $SA = \pi r^2 + \pi r\sqrt{r^2 + h^2}$
    $SA = \pi(3^2 + 3\sqrt{3^2 + 14^2}) = \pi(9 + 3\sqrt{205})$
    $SA \approx 163.22$ cm$^2$

15. a) $r = \dfrac{9}{2} = 4.5 \text{ cm}$

$V = \dfrac{4}{3}\pi r^3$

$V = \dfrac{4}{3}\pi\left(4.5^3\right) = \dfrac{4}{3}\pi(91.125) \approx 381.70 \text{ cm}^3$

b) $SA = 4\pi r^2$

$SA = 4\pi\left(4.5^2\right) = 4\pi(20.25) \approx 254.47 \text{ cm}^2$

19. Area of the base: $B = s^2 = 12^2 = 144 \text{ cm}^2$

$V = \dfrac{1}{3}Bh = \dfrac{1}{3}(144)(15) = 720 \text{ cm}^3$

23. $V = 2(\text{volume of one small trough})$

depth of trough $= 7$

area of triangular ends $= \dfrac{1}{2}(4)(7) = 14$

$V = 2(14)(14) = 392 \text{ ft}^3$

27. $V = $ volume of rect. solid $-$ volume of pyramid

$= 3(3)(4) - \dfrac{1}{3}\left(3^2\right)(4) = 36 - 12 = 24 \text{ ft}^3$

31. $153 \text{ ft}^3 = \dfrac{153}{27} = 5.\overline{6} \approx 5.67 \text{ yd}^3$

35. $7{,}500{,}000 \text{ cm}^3 = \dfrac{7{,}500{,}000}{1{,}000{,}000} = 7.5 \text{ m}^3$

39. $SA = 2lw + 2wh + 2lh$

$SA = 2(142)(125) + 2(125)(10) + 2(10)(142)$

$SA = 40{,}840 \text{ mm}^2$

41. $V = 12(4)(3) = 144 \text{ in.}^3$

$144 \text{ in.}^3 = 144(0.01736) = 2.49984 \approx 2.50 \text{ qt}$

17. Area of the base:

$B = \dfrac{1}{2}bh = \dfrac{1}{2}(10)(10) = 50 \text{ m}^2$

$V = Bh = 50(15) = 750 \text{ m}^3$

21. $V = $ vol. of large prism $-$ vol. of small prism

$V = (8)(8)(16) - (4)(4)(16) = (64 - 16)(16)$

$V = (48)(16) = 768 \text{ ft}^3$

25. $V = $ volume of cylinder $-$ volume of 3 spheres

$= \pi(3.5)^2(20.8) - 3\left[\dfrac{4}{3}\pi(3.45)^3\right]$

$= 254.8\pi - 164.2545\pi = 90.5455\pi$

$V \approx 284.46 \text{ cm}^3$

29. $3 \text{ yd}^3 = 3(27) = 81 \text{ ft}^3$

33. $0.56 \text{ m}^3 = 0.56(1{,}000{,}000) = 560{,}000 \text{ cm}^3$

37. a) $V = lwh = (20)(15)\left(\dfrac{9}{12}\right) = 225 \text{ ft}^3$

b) $\text{Cost} = (\$11)(225) = \$2475$

43. a) $V = 80(50)(30) = 120{,}000 \text{ cm}^3$

b) $120{,}000 \text{ m}\ell$

c) $120{,}000 \text{ m}\ell = \dfrac{120{,}000}{1000} = 120 \text{ }\ell$

45. $r = \dfrac{3.875}{2} = 1.9375$ in.

Volume of each cylinder:

$\pi r^2 h = \pi (1.9375)^2 (3)$

$= 11.26171875\pi = 35.37973289$

Total volume:

$8(35.37973289) = 283.0378631 \approx 283.04$ in.$^3$

49. $V = \dfrac{1}{3}\pi r^2 h = \dfrac{1}{3}\pi \left(\dfrac{3}{2}\right)^2 (6) = 4.5\pi$

$= 14.13716694 \approx 14.14$ in.$^3$

53. $x - 8 + 4 = 2$

$x - 4 = 2$

$x = 6$ vertices

47. $5.5 \text{ ft} = 5.5(12) = 66$ in.

$r = \dfrac{2.5}{2} = 1.25$ in.

$V = \pi r^2 h = \pi (1.25)^2 (66) = 103.125\pi$

$= 323.9767424 \approx 323.98$ in.$^3$

b) $\dfrac{323.98}{1728} = 0.187488426 \approx 0.19$ ft$^3$

51. $8 - x + 4 = 2$

$12 - x = 2$

$-x = -10$

$x = 10$ edges

55. $7 - 12 + x = 2$

$-5 + x = 2$

$x = 7$ faces

57. $r_E = \dfrac{12,756.3}{2} = 6378.15$ km

$r_M = \dfrac{3474.8}{2} = 1737.4$ km

a) $SA_E = 4\pi (6378.15^2) \approx 5.11 \times 10^8$ km$^2$

b) $SA_M = 4\pi (1737.4^2) \approx 3.79 \times 10^7$ km$^2$

c) $\dfrac{SA_E}{SA_M} = \dfrac{5.11 \times 10^8}{3.79 \times 10^7} \approx 13$

d) $V_E = \dfrac{4}{3}\pi (6378.15^3) \approx 1.09 \times 10^{12}$ km$^3$

e) $V_M = \dfrac{4}{3}\pi (1737.4^3) \approx 2.20 \times 10^{10}$ km$^3$

f) $\dfrac{V_E}{V_M} = \dfrac{1.09 \times 10^{12}}{2.20 \times 10^{10}} \approx 50$

59. a) – e) Answers will vary.

f) If we double the length of each edge of a cube, the new volume will be eight times the original volume.

61. a) Find the volume of each numbered region. Since the length of each side is $a + b$, the sum of the volumes of each region will equal $(a+b)^3$.

b) $V_1 = a(a)(a) = a^3$      $V_2 = a(a)(b) = a^2 b$      $V_3 = a(a)(b) = a^2 b$      $V_4 = a(b)(b) = ab^2$

$V_5 = a(a)(b) = a^2 b$      $V_6 = a(b)(b) = ab^2$      $V_7 = b(b)(b) = b^3$

c) The volume of the piece not shown is $ab^2$.

**Exercise Set 9.5**

1. Rigid

3. Axis

5. Vector

7. Rotation

9. Glide

11. Reflective

13.  Tessellation

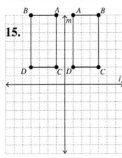

**15.**

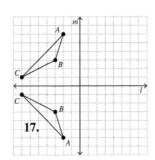

**17.**

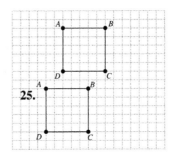

**19.**

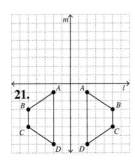

**21.**

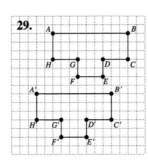

**23.**

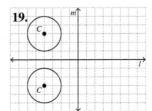

**25.**

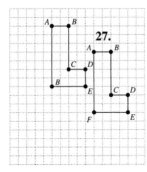

**27.**

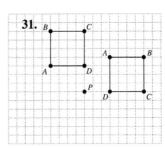

**29.**

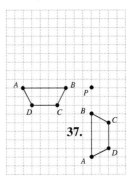

**31.**

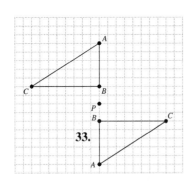

**33.**

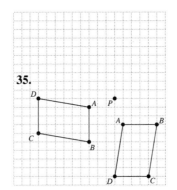

**35.**

**37.**

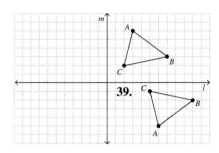

 **39.**

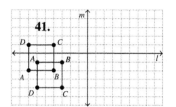

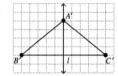

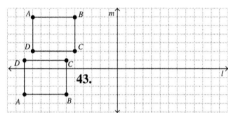 **43.**

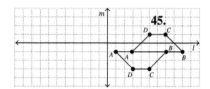

47. a)

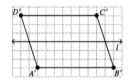

b) Yes

c) Yes

49. a)

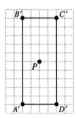

b) No

c) No

51. a)

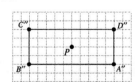

b) No

c) No

d)

53.  a) – c)

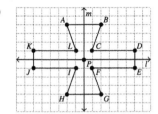

  d)  No.  Any 90° rotation will result in the figure being in a different position than the starting position.

55.  a) – b)

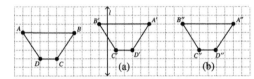

  c)  No

  d)  The order in which the translation and the reflection are performed is important.  The figure obtained in part b) is the glide reflection.

57.  Answers will vary.

59.  a) Answers will vary.

   b) A regular pentagon cannot be used as a tessellating shape.

61.  Although answers will vary depending on the font, the following capital letters have reflective symmetry about a

   vertical line drawn through the center of the letter: A, H, I, M, O, T, U, V, W, X, Y.


**Exercise Set 9.6**
1.  Rubber
3.  Klein
5.  Jordan
7.  One
9.  7 – Green; 1, 3, 5 – Yellow; 2, 4, 6 – Red. AWV
11.  1, 2, 4, 5, 7, 9 – Red; 3, 6, 8 – Green. AWV

13.  TX, KS, MS, KY, SC, FL – Red
   OK, LA, TN – Green
   MO, GA, VA – Blue
   AR, AL, NC – Yellow, AWV

15.  YT, NU, AB, ON – Red
   NT, QC – Blue
   BC, SK – Green
   MB – Yellow. AWV

17.  Outside; a straight line from point *A* to a point clearly outside the curve crosses the curve a n even number of times.

19.  Outside; a straight line from point *A* to a point clearly outside the curve crosses the curve an even number of times.

21.  Inside; a straight line from point *C* to a point clearly outside the curve crosses the curve an odd number of times.

23.  1
27.  Larger than 5

25.  5
29.  5

31. 0

33. larger than 5

35. a) - d) Answers will
    vary.

37. One

39. Two

41. a) No, it has an inside and an outside.

    b) Two        c) Two

    d) Two strips, one inside the other

43. Answers will vary.

45. Answers will vary.

**Exercise Set 9.7**

1. Parallel

3. Two

5. Sphere

7. Geodesic

9.

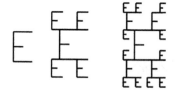

11.

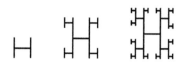

13. a)

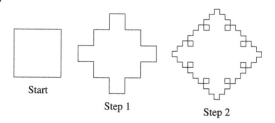

    b) Infinite.

    c) Finite since it covers a finite or closed area.

15. Each type of geometry can be used in its own frame of reference.

17. Coastlines, trees, mountains, galaxies, polymers, rivers, weather patterns, brains, lungs, blood supply

19. Benoit Mandelbrot – first to use the word fractal to describe shapes that had several common characteristics, including some form of "self-similarity"

21. Nikolay Ivanovich Lobachevsky - discovered hyperbolic geometry

23. Janos Bolyai - discovered hyperbolic geometry

**Review Exercises**

In the Review Exercises and Chapter Test questions, the $\pi$ key on the calculator is used to determine answers in calculations involving $\pi$. If you use 3.14 for $\pi$, your answers may vary slightly.

1. $\overrightarrow{BF}$

2. $\overline{AD}$

3. $\triangle BFC$

4. $\overleftrightarrow{BH}$

5. $\{F\}$

6. $\{\ \}$

7. $90° - 35.4° = 54.6°$

8. $180° - 100.5° = 79.5°$

9. Let $x = BC$

$$\frac{BC}{B'C} = \frac{AC}{A'C}$$

$$\frac{x}{3.4} = \frac{12}{4}$$

$$4x = 40.8$$

$$x = \frac{40.8}{4} = 10.2 \text{ in.}$$

10. Let $x = A'B'$

$$\frac{A'B'}{AB} = \frac{A'C}{AC}$$

$$\frac{x}{6} = \frac{4}{12}$$

$$12x = 24$$

$$x = \frac{24}{12} = 2 \text{ in.}$$

11. $m\angle ABC = m\angle A'B'C$

$m\angle A'B'C = 180° - 88° = 92°$

Thus, $m\angle ABC = 92°$

$m\angle BAC = 180° - 30° - 92° = 58°$

12. $m\angle ABC = m\angle A'B'C$

$m\angle A'B'C = 180° - 88° = 92°$

Thus, $m\angle ABC = 92°$

13. $m\angle 1 = 45°$

$m\angle 6 = 180° - 115° = 65°$

$m\angle 2 = m\angle 1 + m\angle 6 = 110°$

$m\angle 3 = m\angle 2 = 110°$

$m\angle 4 = m\angle 6 = 65°$

$m\angle 5 = 180° - m\angle 4 = 180° - 65° = 115°$

14. $n = 8$

$(n-2)180° = (8-2)180° = 6(180°) = 1080°$

15. a) $A = lw = 11(9) = 99 \text{ mi}^2$

b) $P = 2l + 2w = 2(11) + 2(9) = 40 \text{ mi}$

16. a) $A = \frac{1}{2}h(b_1 + b_2) = \frac{1}{2}(2)(4+9) = 13 \text{ in.}^2$

b) $P = 3.2 + 4 + 3.2 + 9 = 19.4 \text{ in.}$

17. a) $A = bh = 12(7) = 84 \text{ in.}^2$

b) $P = 2(9) + 2(12) = 42 \text{ in.}$

18. a) $A = \frac{1}{2}bh = \frac{1}{2}(3)(4) = 6 \text{ km}^2$

b) $P = 3 + 4 + \sqrt{3^2 + 4^2} = 7 + \sqrt{25} = 12 \text{ km}$

19. a) $A = \pi r^2 = \pi(7)^2 \approx 153.94 \text{ ft}^2$

b) $C = 2\pi r = 2\pi(7) = 14\pi \approx 43.98 \text{ ft}$

20.    $A$ = area of rectangle $-$ 3(area of one circle)

   Length of rectangle = 3(diameter of circle)

$$= 3(10) = 30$$

   Area of rectangle: $(10)(30) = 300$

   Area of circle: $\pi\left(5^2\right) = 25\pi$

   Shaded area: $300 - 3(25\pi) \approx 64.38$ m$^2$

22.    $A = lw = 14(16) = 224$ ft$^2$

   Cost: $224(\$5.25) = \$1176$

23.  a) $V = lwh = 10(3)(4) = 120$ cm$^3$

   b) $SA = 2lw + 2wh + 2lh$

$$SA = 2(10)(3) + 2(3)(4) + 2(10)(4) = 164 \text{ cm}^2$$

25.    a)  $r = \dfrac{12}{2} = 6$ mm

$$V = \frac{1}{3}\pi r^2 h = \frac{1}{3}\pi\left(6^2\right)(16) = 192\pi$$

   $V \approx 603.19$ mm$^3$

   b)  $SA = \pi r^2 + \pi r\sqrt{r^2 + h^2}$

$$SA = \pi\left(6^2 + 6\sqrt{6^2 + 16^2}\right) = \pi\left(36 + 6\sqrt{292}\right)$$

   $SA \approx 435.20$ mm$^2$

27.  $B = \dfrac{1}{2}bh = \dfrac{1}{2}(9)(12) = 54$ m$^2$

$$V = Bh = 54(8) = 432 \text{ m}^3$$

29.   $V$ = volume of cylinder $-$ volume of cone

$$= \pi(2)^2(9) - \frac{1}{3}\pi(2)^2(9) = 36\pi - 12\pi = 24\pi$$

$$= 75.39822369 \approx 75.40 \text{ cm}^3$$

21. Shaded area is the area of an 12 by 12 square

   minus the four corner squares (each 3 by 3)

   and minus the area of a circle of diameter 6.

   Shaded area = $(12)(12) - 4(3)(3) - \pi\left(3^2\right)$

$$= 108 - 9\pi \approx 79.73 \text{ yd}^2$$

24.    a) $V = \pi r^2 h = \pi\left(6^2\right)(18) = 648\pi \approx 2035.75$ in$^3$

   b) $SA = 2\pi r^2 + 2\pi rh$

$$SA = 2\pi\left(6^2\right) + 2\pi(6)(18) = 288\pi$$

$$SA \approx 904.78 \text{ in}^2$$

26.    a) $V = \dfrac{4}{3}\pi r^3$

$$V = \frac{4}{3}\pi\left(7^3\right) = \frac{4}{3}\pi(343) \approx 1436.76 \text{ yd}^3$$

   b)  $SA = 4\pi r^2$

$$SA = 4\pi\left(7^2\right) = 4\pi(49) \approx 615.75 \text{ yd}^2$$

28.    If $h$ represents the height of the triangle which
   is the base of the pyramid, then

$$h^2 + 3^2 = 5^2$$
$$h^2 + 9 = 25$$
$$h^2 = 16$$
$$h = \sqrt{16} = 4 \text{ ft}$$

$$B = \frac{1}{2}bh = \frac{1}{2}(6)(4) = 12 \text{ ft}^2$$

$$V = \frac{1}{3}Bh = \frac{1}{3}(12)(7) = 28 \text{ ft}^3$$

30.    $V$ = vol. of large sphere $-$ vol. of sm. sphere

$$= \frac{4}{3}\pi(5)^3 - \frac{4}{3}\pi(2.5)^3 = 166.6667\pi - 20.8333\pi$$

$$= 145.8334\pi \approx 458.15 \text{ in.}^3$$

31.
$$h^2 + 1^2 = 3^2$$
$$h^2 + 1 = 9$$
$$h^2 = 8$$
$$h = \sqrt{8}$$

$$A = \frac{1}{2}h(b_1 + b_2) = \frac{1}{2}(\sqrt{8})(2+4) = 8.485281374 \text{ ft}^2$$

a)   $V = Bh = 8.485281374(8)$
$$= 67.88225099 \approx 67.88 \text{ ft}^3$$

31. b)  Weight:
$$67.88(62.4) + 375 = 4610.7 \text{ lb}$$
Yes, it will support the trough filled with water.

c)   $(4610.7 - 375) = 4235.7$ lb of water

$$\frac{4235.7}{8.3} = 510.3253 \approx 510.3 \text{ gal}$$

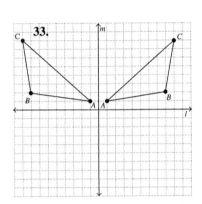

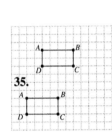

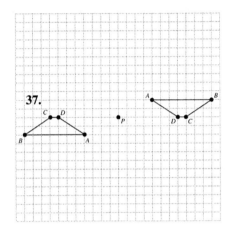

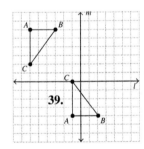

41. Yes              42. No              43. No              44. Yes

45. a) – d) Answers will vary.

46. 1, 3, 7 – Red; 2, 6, 8 – Blue; 4,5 – Green. AWV

47. Outside; a straight line from point A to a point clearly outside the curve crosses the curve an even number of times.

48. Euclidean: Given a line and a point not on the line, one and only one line can be drawn parallel to the given line through the given point.

Elliptical: Given a line and a point not on the line, no line can be drawn through the given point parallel to the given line.

Hyperbolic: Given a line and a point not on the line, two or more lines can be drawn through the given point parallel to the given line.

49.

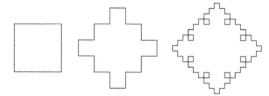

50.

**Chapter Test**

1.  $\overset{\circ}{\overset{\circ}{EF}}$

2.  $\triangle BCD$

3.  $\{D\}$

4.  $\overleftrightarrow{AC}$

5.  $90° - 74.9° = 15.1°$

6.  $180° - 10.4° = 169.6°$

7.  One angle of the triangle is $50°$ (by vertical angles) and $180° - 115° = 65°$. Thus, the measure of angle $x = 180° - 50° - 65° = 65°$.

8.  $n = 5$

$$(n-2)180° = (5-2)180° = 3(180°) = 540°$$

9.  Let $x = B'C'$

$$\frac{B'C'}{BC} = \frac{A'C'}{AC}$$

$$\frac{x}{7} = \frac{5}{13}$$

$$13x = 35$$

$$x = \frac{35}{13} = 2.692307692 \approx 2.69 \text{ cm}$$

10. a)
$$x^2 + 5^2 = 13^2$$
$$x^2 + 25 = 169$$
$$x^2 = 144$$
$$x = \sqrt{144} = 12 \text{ in.}$$

   b)  $P = 5 + 13 + 12 = 30$ in.

   c)  $A = \frac{1}{2}bh = \frac{1}{2}(5)(12) = 30$ in.$^2$

11. $r = \frac{14}{2} = 7$ cm

   a)  $V = \frac{4}{3}\pi r^3 = \frac{4}{3}\pi(7^3) \approx 1436.76$ cm$^3$

   b)  $SA = 4\pi r^2$

   $SA = 4\pi(7^2) = 4\pi(49) \approx 615.75$ cm$^2$

12. Shaded volume =

   volume of prism − volume of cylinder

   Volume of prism: $V = lwh = (6)(4)(3) = 72$ m$^3$

   Volume of cylinder: $V = \pi r^2 h = \pi(1^2)4 = 4\pi$ m$^3$

   Shaded volume $= 72 - 4\pi \approx 59.43$ m$^3$

13. $B = lw = 4(7) = 28$ ft$^2$

   $V = \frac{1}{3}Bh = \frac{1}{3}(28)(12) = 112$ ft$^3$

14.

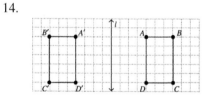

15.

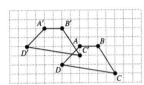

16.

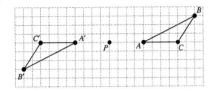

17.

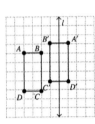

18.  a)  No

     b)  Yes

19.  A **Möbius strip** is a surface with one side and one edge.

20.  a) and b) Answers will vary.

# CHAPTER TWELVE

## PROBABILITY

**Exercise Set 12.1**

1. Experiment

3. Event

5. Empirical

7. AWV

9. AWV

11. Of 30 boats:    14 sunfish    10 kayaks    6 rowboats
   a) P(s) = 14/30 = 7/15    b) P(k) = 10/30 = 1/3    c) P(r) = 6/30 = 1/5

13. Of 105 animals:    45 are dogs.    40 are cats    15 are birds    5 are rabbits

   a) P(dog) = 45/105 = 3/7    b) P(cat) = 8/21    c) P(rabbit) = 5/105 = 1/21

15. a) $\dfrac{13,674}{153,468} \approx 0.0891$    b) $\dfrac{27,362}{153,468} \approx 0.1783$    c) $\dfrac{11,140}{153,468} \approx 0.0884$

17. a) $\dfrac{16,600,000}{66,950,000} \approx 0.2479$

   b) $\dfrac{8,870,000}{66,950,000} \approx 0.1325$

   c) $\dfrac{18,880,000}{66,950,000} \approx 0.2820$

19. Of 80 votes:    22 for Allison    18 for Emily    20 for Kimberly    14 for Johanna    6 for others
   a) P(A) = 22/80 = 11/40    b) P(E) = 18/80 = 9/40    c) P(K) = 20/80 = 1/4    d) P(J) = 14/80 = 7/40
   e) P(others) = 6/80 = 3/40

21. a) P(bulls-eye) = $\dfrac{6}{20} = \dfrac{3}{10}$

   b) P(not bulls-eye) = $\dfrac{14}{20} = \dfrac{7}{10}$

   c) P(at least 20 pts.) = $\dfrac{14}{20} = \dfrac{7}{10}$

   d) P(does not score) = $\dfrac{2}{20} = \dfrac{1}{10}$

23. a) P(affecting circular) = $\dfrac{0}{150} = 0$

   b) P(affecting elliptical) = $\dfrac{50}{250} = 0.2$

   c) P(affecting irregular) = $\dfrac{100}{100} = 1$

25. a) P(white flowers) = $\dfrac{224}{929} = 0.24$      b) P(purple flowers) = $\dfrac{705}{929} = 0.76$

27. Not necessarily, but it does mean that if a coin was flipped many times, about one-half of the tosses would land heads up.

29. a) Roll a die 100 times and determine the number of times that a 5 occurs out of 100.

  b) Answers will vary (AWV).      c) AWV

31. Answers will vary.

**Exercise Set 12.2**

1. Equally

3. 1

5. 1

7. $\dfrac{4}{7}$

9. 0.1

11. a) P(correct) = 1/5      b) P(correct) = 1/4

13. P(you win) = $\dfrac{\text{one choice}}{40 \text{ possible choices}} = \dfrac{1}{40}$

15. P(5) = $\dfrac{4}{52} = \dfrac{1}{13}$

17. P(not 5) = $\dfrac{48}{52} = \dfrac{12}{13}$

19. P(black) = $\dfrac{13+13}{52} = \dfrac{26}{52} = \dfrac{1}{2}$

21. P(red or black) = $\dfrac{26+26}{52} = \dfrac{52}{52} = \dfrac{1}{1} = 1$

23. P(>3 and <8) = P(4,5,6,7) = $\dfrac{16}{52} = \dfrac{4}{13}$

25. a) P(red) = $\dfrac{1}{4}$      b) P(green) = $\dfrac{1}{2}$

  c) P(yellow) = $\dfrac{1}{4}$      d) P(blue) = 0

27. a) P(red) = $\dfrac{4}{8} = \dfrac{1}{2}$      b) P(green) = $\dfrac{1}{8}$

  c) P(yellow) = $\dfrac{1}{8}$      d) P(blue) = $\dfrac{2}{8} = \dfrac{1}{4}$

Of 100 cans:   30 are cola (c)   40 are orange (o)   10 are ginger ale (ga)   20 are root beer (rb)

29.  P(rb) = $\dfrac{20}{100} = \dfrac{1}{5}$

31.  P(c, rb, o) = $\dfrac{90}{100} = \dfrac{9}{10}$

33.  P(600) = $\dfrac{1}{12}$

35.  P(lose/bankrupt) = $\dfrac{2}{12} = \dfrac{1}{6}$

Of 30 basketballs:   10 are Wilson (w)   15 are Spalding (s)   5 are other (o)

37.  P(s) = $\dfrac{15}{30} = \dfrac{1}{2}$

39.  P(not w) = $\dfrac{20}{30} = \dfrac{2}{3}$

For a traffic light:   25 seconds on red (r)   5 seconds on yellow (y)   55 seconds on green (g)

41.  P(g) = $\dfrac{55}{85} = \dfrac{11}{17}$

43.  P(not r) = $\dfrac{60}{85} = \dfrac{12}{17}$

Of 11 letters:   1 = T   3 = A   2 = E   2 = L   1 = H   2 = S

45.  P(S) = $\dfrac{2}{11}$

47.  P(consonant) = $\dfrac{6}{11}$

49.  P(W) = 0

51.  $\dfrac{1}{10}$

53.  $\dfrac{1}{5}$

55.  P(15) = $\dfrac{1}{26}$

57.  P($\geq$ 22) = $\dfrac{5}{26}$

59.  $P(car) = \dfrac{85}{130} = \dfrac{17}{26}$

61.  $P(GM) = \dfrac{83}{130}$

63.  $P(GM\ car) = \dfrac{55}{130} = \dfrac{11}{26}$

65.  $P(Ort) = \dfrac{10}{42} = \dfrac{5}{21}$

67.  $P(mild) = \dfrac{11}{42}$

69.  $P(TB\ medium) = \dfrac{8}{42} = \dfrac{4}{21}$

71.  P(red) = $\dfrac{2}{18} + \dfrac{1}{12} + \dfrac{1}{6} = \dfrac{4}{36} + \dfrac{3}{36} + \dfrac{6}{36} = \dfrac{13}{36}$

73.  P(yellow) = $\dfrac{1}{6} + \dfrac{1}{12} + \dfrac{1}{12} = \dfrac{2}{12} + \dfrac{2}{12} = \dfrac{4}{12} = \dfrac{1}{3}$

75.  P(yellow or green) = $\dfrac{1}{3} + \dfrac{11}{36} = \dfrac{23}{36}$

77. a)  P(CC) = 0    b)  P(CC) = 1

79. a)  P(R/R) = $\dfrac{2}{4} \cdot \dfrac{2}{4} = \dfrac{4}{16} = \dfrac{1}{4}$

b)  P(G/G) = $\dfrac{2}{4} \cdot \dfrac{2}{4} = \dfrac{4}{16} = \dfrac{1}{4}$

c)  P(R/G) = $\dfrac{2}{4} \cdot \dfrac{2}{4} = \dfrac{4}{16} = \dfrac{1}{4}$

81.  $4 \cdot 7 + 1 = 29$

**Exercise Set 12.3**

1.  Against

3.  $3 : 1$

5.  $2 : 1$

7.  $\dfrac{1}{4}$

9.  a)  P(shoes go well) $= \dfrac{5}{12}$

   b)  P(shoes do not go well) $= \dfrac{7}{12}$

   c)  odds against shoes going well $=$

   $\dfrac{\text{P(shoes do not go well)}}{\text{P(shoes go well)}} = \dfrac{{}^{7}\!/_{12}}{{}^{5}\!/_{15}} = \dfrac{7}{5}$ or $7 : 5$

   d)  odds in favor of them going well are $5 : 7$

11.  Against:  $6 : 1$;  in favor: $1 : 6$

13.  Since there is only one 2, the odds against a 2 are $5 : 1$.

15.  odds against rolling less than 3 $=$
   $\dfrac{\text{P(3 or greater)}}{\text{P(less than 3)}} =$

   $\dfrac{4/6}{2/6} = \dfrac{4}{6} \cdot \dfrac{6}{2} = \dfrac{4}{2} = \dfrac{2}{1}$  or  $2:1$

17.  odds against a king $=$
   $\dfrac{\text{P(failure to pick a king)}}{\text{P(pick a king)}} =$

   $\dfrac{48/52}{4/52} = \dfrac{48}{52} \cdot \dfrac{52}{4} = \dfrac{48}{4} = \dfrac{12}{1}$  or $12:1$

   Therefore, odds in favor of picking a king are $1:12$.

19.  odds against a picture card $=$
   $\dfrac{\text{P(failure to pick a picture)}}{\text{P(pick a picture)}} = \dfrac{40/52}{12/52} = \dfrac{40}{12} = \dfrac{10}{3}$
   or  $10:3$
   Therefore, odds in favor of picking a picture card are $3:10$.

21.  odds against red $=$
   $\dfrac{\text{P(not red)}}{\text{P(red)}} = \dfrac{1/2}{1/2} = \dfrac{1}{2} \cdot \dfrac{2}{1} = \dfrac{2}{2} = \dfrac{1}{1}$  or  $1:1$

23.  odds against red $= \dfrac{\text{P(not red)}}{\text{P(red)}} = \dfrac{5/8}{3/8} = \dfrac{5}{8} \cdot \dfrac{8}{3} = \dfrac{5}{3}$
   or  $5:3$

25. a) odds against selecting female =

$$\frac{\text{P(failure to select female)}}{\text{P(select female)}} = \frac{16/30}{14/30} = \frac{16}{14} = \frac{8}{7}$$

or 8 : 7 .

   b) odds against selecting male =

$$\frac{\text{P(failure to select male)}}{\text{P(select male)}} = \frac{14/30}{16/30} = \frac{14}{16} = \frac{7}{8}$$

or 7 : 8 .

29. odds in favor of even are $\dfrac{\text{P(even)}}{\text{P(not even)}} =$

$$\frac{7/15}{8/15} = \frac{7}{15} \cdot \frac{15}{8} = \frac{7}{8} \text{ or } 7{:}8$$

33. a) $\dfrac{8}{10} = \dfrac{4}{5}$

   b) 1 : 4

37. a) P(Wendy wins) = $\dfrac{7}{7+4} = \dfrac{7}{11}$

   b) P(Wendy loses) = $\dfrac{4}{7+4} = \dfrac{4}{11}$

41. P(G) = $\dfrac{15}{75} = \dfrac{1}{5}$

45. Odds against B9 =

$$\frac{\text{P(not B9)}}{\text{P(B9)}} = \frac{74/75}{1/75} = \left(\frac{74}{75}\right)\left(\frac{75}{1}\right) = \frac{74}{1} \text{ or } 74{:}1$$

49. $\dfrac{66}{34} = \dfrac{33}{17}$ or 33 : 17

53. If P(fixing the car) = $0.9 = \dfrac{9}{10}$, then

P(not fixing the car) = $1 - \dfrac{9}{10} = \dfrac{1}{10}$.

The odds against fixing the car = $\dfrac{1/10}{9/10} = \dfrac{1}{9}$ or 1:9.

27. odds against a stripe = $\dfrac{\text{P(not a stripe)}}{\text{P(stripe)}} =$

$$\frac{8/15}{7/15} = \frac{8}{15} \cdot \frac{15}{7} = \frac{8}{7} \text{ or } 8{:}7$$

31. odds against a ball with 9 or greater are

$$\frac{\text{P(less than 9)}}{\text{P(9 or greater)}} = \frac{8/15}{7/15} = \frac{8}{15} \cdot \frac{15}{7} = \frac{8}{7} \text{ or } 8{:}7$$

35. The odds against testing negative =

$$\frac{\text{P(test positive)}}{\text{P(test negative)}} = \frac{5/85}{80/85} = \frac{5}{80} = \frac{1}{16} \text{ or } 1{:}16$$

39. Odds against   4 : 11   P(accepted) = $\dfrac{11}{4+11} = \dfrac{11}{15}$

43. Odds in favor of G = $\dfrac{\text{P(G)}}{\text{P(not G)}} = \dfrac{1/5}{4/5} = \dfrac{1}{4}$ or 1:4

47. P(A+) = $\dfrac{34}{100} = 0.34$

51. P(O or O-) = $\dfrac{43}{100} = \dfrac{43}{43+57}$ or 43 : 57

55. If P(all parts are present) = $\dfrac{7}{8}$, then the odds in favor of all parts being present are 7 : 1 .

57. a) $P(\text{birth defect}) = \dfrac{1}{33}$

    b) Number without birth defect: $33 - 1 = 32$
       Odds against birth defect: $32 : 1$

59. $P(\#\ 1\ \text{wins}) = \dfrac{2}{9}$     $P(\#\ 2\ \text{wins}) = \dfrac{1}{3}$

    $P(\#\ 3\ \text{wins}) = \dfrac{1}{16}$     $P(\#\ 4\ \text{wins}) = \dfrac{5}{12}$

    $P(\#\ 5\ \text{wins}) = \dfrac{1}{2}$

61. If multiple births are 3% of births, then single births are 97% of births, and the odds against a multiple birth are 97 : 3.

## Exercise Set 12.4

1. Expected

3. Positive

5. $E = P_1A_1 + P_2A_2 = 0.30(60{,}000) + 0.70(21{,}000) = 32{,}700$ people

7. $E = P_1A_1 + P_2A_2 = 0.50(78) + 0.50(62) = 39 + 31 = 70$ points

9. $E = P_1A_1 + P_2A_2 = 0.40(1.2\ \text{M}) + 0.60(1.6\ \text{M}) = .48\ \text{M} + .96\ \text{M} = 1.44\ \text{M}$ viewers

11. $E = P_1A_1 + P_2A_2 = (.70)(10000) + (.10)(0) + (.20)(-7500) = 7000 + 0 + -1500 = \$5500$

13. $E = P_1A_1 + P_2A_2 + P_3A_3 = P(\$1\ \text{off})(\$1) + P(\$2\ \text{off})(\$2) + P(\$5\ \text{off})(\$5)$

    $E = (1/10)(1) + (2/10)(2) + (1/10)(5) = 7/10 + 4/10 + 5/10 = 16/10 = \$1.60$ off

15. a) $(3/6)(5) + (2/6)(2) + (1/6)(-15) \approx -\$0.17$

    b) Gabriel's expectation is the negative of Alyssa's, or $0.17.

17. a) $(1/5)(5) + (0)(0) + (4/5)(-1) = 1 - 4/5 = 1/5$

        Yes, positive expectations = 1/5

    b) $(1/4)(5) + (0)(0) + (3/4)(-1) = 5/4 - 3/4 = 1/2$

        Yes, positive expectations = 1/2

19. Fair Price = expected value + cost to play

    Fair Price = -$2.00 + $5.00 = $3.00

21. a) $\left(\dfrac{1}{500}\right)(497) + \left(\dfrac{499}{500}\right)(-3) = \dfrac{497 - 1497}{500} =$

    $\dfrac{-1000}{500} = -\$2.00$

    b) Fair price = -2.00 + 3.00 = $1.00

23. a)

$\left(\dfrac{1}{2000}\right)(997) + \left(\dfrac{2}{2000}\right)(497) + \left(\dfrac{1997}{2000}\right)(-3) = \dfrac{997 + 994 - 5991}{2000} = \dfrac{-4000}{2000} = -\$2.00$

    b) Fair price = -2.00 + 3.00 = $1.00

25. a) $\dfrac{1}{2}(1) + \dfrac{1}{2}(5) = \dfrac{1}{2} + \dfrac{5}{2}$

    $= 3 = \$3.00$

27. $\dfrac{1}{2}(10) + \dfrac{1}{4}(-5) + \dfrac{1}{4}(-20) = 5 - 1.25 - 5 = -\$1.25$

29. $(500)\left(\dfrac{3}{6}\right) + (1000)\left(\dfrac{3}{6}\right) = \$750$

31. $(100 + 200 + 300 + 400 + 500 + 1000)\left(\dfrac{1}{6}\right) = \$416.67$

33. a) $(8)\left(\dfrac{1}{2}\right) + (-1)\left(\dfrac{1}{2}\right) = \$3.50$

   b) Fair price = $\$3.50 + 2.00 = \$5.50$

35. a) $(8)\left(\dfrac{1}{4}\right) + (3)\left(\dfrac{1}{4}\right) + (-1)\left(\dfrac{1}{2}\right) = \$2.25$

   b) Fair price = $2.25 + 2.00 = \$4.25$

37. $(10 - 15)\left(\dfrac{2}{4}\right) + (25 - 15)\left(\dfrac{2}{4}\right) = \$2.50$

39.
$(0 - 15)\left(\dfrac{1}{4}\right) + (2 - 15)\left(\dfrac{1}{4}\right) + (5 - 15)\left(\dfrac{1}{4}\right) + (20 - 15)\left(\dfrac{1}{4}\right) = -\$8.25$

41. $E = P_1A_1 + P_2A_2 + P_3A_3 + P_4A_4 + P_5A_5$
=

    $0.17(1) + 0.10(2) + 0.02(3) + 0.08(4) +$
$0.63(0) =$

    0.75  base

43. $E = P_1A_1 + P_2A_2 + P_3A_3$

   $= \dfrac{3}{10}(4) + \dfrac{5}{10}(3) + \dfrac{2}{10}(1) = 1.2 + 1.5 + 0.2$

   $= 2.9$ points

45. $E = (0.65)(75) + (0.35)(20) = 55.75$
    Expected number of new employees is 56.

47. $E = (0.75)(20,000) + (0.1)(0) + (0.15)(-3,000)$
    $= \$14,550$

49. $E = P(1)(1) + P(2)(2) + P(3)(3) + P(4)(4) + P(5)(5)$
    $+ P(6)(6)$

    $= \dfrac{1}{6}(1) + \dfrac{1}{6}(2) + \dfrac{1}{6}(3) + \dfrac{1}{6}(4) + \dfrac{1}{6}(5) + \dfrac{1}{6}(6)$

    $= \dfrac{21}{6} = 3.5$ points

51. $E = P_1A_1 + P_2A_2 + P_3A_3$

    $= \dfrac{200}{365}(110) + \dfrac{100}{365}(160) + \dfrac{65}{365}(210)$

    $= 60.27 + 43.84 + 37.40 = 141.51$ calls/day

53. a) $P(1) = \dfrac{1}{2} + \dfrac{1}{16} = \dfrac{8}{16} + \dfrac{1}{16} = \dfrac{9}{16}$,

    $P(10) = \dfrac{1}{4} = \dfrac{4}{16}$,

    $P(\$20) = \dfrac{1}{8} = \dfrac{2}{16}$,   $P(\$100) = \dfrac{1}{16}$

   b) $E = P_1A_1 + P_2A_2 + P_3A_3 + P_4A_4$

    $= \dfrac{9}{16}(\$1) + \dfrac{4}{16}(\$10) + \dfrac{2}{16}(\$20) + \dfrac{1}{16}(\$100)$

    $= \dfrac{9}{16} + \dfrac{40}{16} + \dfrac{40}{16} + \dfrac{100}{16} = \dfrac{189}{16} = \$11.81$

55. $E = P(\text{insured lives})(\text{cost}) + P(\text{insured dies})(\text{cost} -$
    $\$40,000)$
    $= 0.97(\text{cost}) + 0.03(\text{cost} - 40,000)$
    $= 0.97(\text{cost}) + 0.03(\text{cost}) - 1200$
    $= 1.00(\text{cost}) - 1200$
   Thus, in order for the company to make a profit,
   the cost must exceed $\$1,200$

57. $E = P(\text{win})(\text{amount won}) + P(\text{lose})(\text{amount lost})$

    $= \left(\dfrac{1}{38}\right)(35) + \left(\dfrac{37}{38}\right)(-1) = \dfrac{35}{38} - \dfrac{37}{38} = -\dfrac{2}{38}$

    $= -\$0.053$

59. a) $E = \dfrac{1}{12}(100) + \dfrac{1}{12}(200) + \dfrac{1}{12}(300) + \dfrac{1}{12}(400) + \dfrac{1}{12}(500) + \dfrac{1}{12}(600) + \dfrac{1}{12}(700) + \dfrac{1}{12}(800) + \dfrac{1}{12}(900)$

$$\frac{1}{12}(1000) = \left(\frac{5500}{12}\right) = \$458.33$$

b) $E = \frac{1}{12}(5500) + \frac{1}{12}(-1800) = \frac{3700}{12} = \$308.33$

## Exercise Set 12.5

1. Sample

3. 14

5. a) $(50)(50) = 2500$     b) $(50)(49) = 2450$

7. a) $(6)(6)(6) = 216$     b) $(6)(5)(4) = 120$

9. a) $(2)(2) = 4$ points

b)

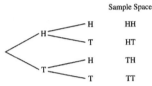

c) P(no heads) = 1/4

d) P(exactly one head) = 2/4 = 1/2

e) P(two heads) = 1/4

11. a) $(3)(3) = 9$ points

b)

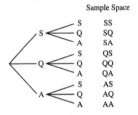

c) P(two apples) = 1/9

d) P(sun and then question mark) = 1/9

e) P(at least one apple) = 5/9

13. a) $(4)(3) = 12$ points

b)

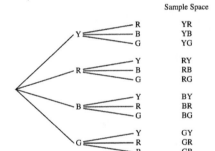

c) P(exactly one red) = 6/12 = ½

d) P(at least one is not red) = 12/12 = 1

e) P(no green) = 6/12 = 1/2

15. a)  (3)(3) = 9 points
    b)

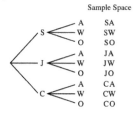

    c)  P(Java) = 1/3
    d)  P(Java and Oyster) = 1/9
    e)  P(paint other than Java) = 2/3

17. a)  (6)(6) = 36 points
    b)

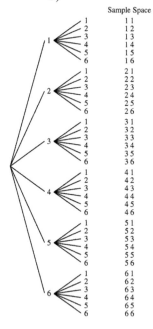

    c)  P(double) = 6/36 = 1/6
    d)  P(sum of 8) = 5/36
    e)  P(sum of 2) = 1/36
    f)  No;  the P(sum of 2) < P(sum of 8)

19. a)  (2)(2)(3) = 12
    b)

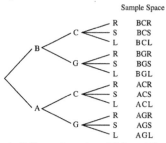

    c)  P(bruschetta) = 6/12 = 1/2
    d)  P(greens and lasagna) = 2/12 = 1/6
    e)  P(not ravioli) = 8/12 = 2/3

21. a)  (3)(2)(3) = 18 points

    b)

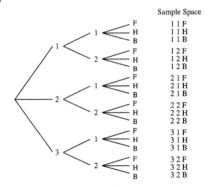

    c)  P(two bedroom) = 6/18 = 1/3
    d)  P(two bedroom, fireplace) = 2/18 = 1/9
    e)  P(no balcony) = 12/18 = 2/3

23. a)  (3)(3)(3) = 27
    b) Art

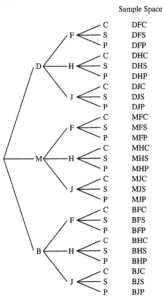

    c)  P(M) = 9/27 = 1/3
    d)  P(D and H) = 3/27 = 1/9
    e)  P(L other than S) = 18/27 = 2/3

25. a)  (2)(4)(3) = 24 sample points
    b)

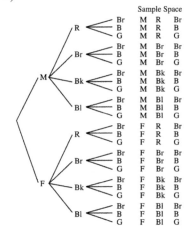

    c)  P(M, black, blue) = 1/24
    d)  P(F, blonde) = 3/24 = 1/8

27. a)  P(white) = 1/3
    b)  P(red) = 2/3
    c)  No;  P(white) < P(red)
    d)

Sample Space

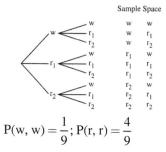

$$P(w, w) = \frac{1}{9}; P(r, r) = \frac{4}{9}$$

29.  1 red, 1 blue, and 1 brown
31. a)  120    b)  CHAIR

**Exercise Set 12.6**
1. Compound
3. And
5. Independent
7. Independent

9.  P(A) + P(B) – P(A and B)

11.  P(A or B) = P(A) + P(B) – P(A and B)
     = 0.8 + 0.4 – 0.5  = 1.2 – 0.5 = 0.7

13.  P(B) = P(A or B) + P(A and B) – P(A)
     = 0.7 + 0.3 – 0.6 = 0.4

15.  P(M and E) = 0.55
     P(M or E) = P(M) + P(E) – P(M and E)
     = 0.7 + 0.6 – 0.55= 1.3 – 0.55 = 0.75

17.  P(2 or 6) = 1/6 + 1/6 = 2/6 = 1/3

19.  P(greater than 4 or less than 2) = P(5, 6. or 1) =
     2/6 + 1/6 = 3/6 = 1/2

21.  Since these events are mutually exclusive,
     P(ace or 4) = P(ace) + P(4) =
     $$= \frac{4}{52} + \frac{4}{52} = \frac{8}{52} = \frac{2}{13}$$

23.  Since it is possible to obtain a card that is a picture
     card and a black card, these events are not mutually
     exclusive.
     P(picture or black)
     = P(pict.) + P(black) – P(pict. & black)
     $$= \frac{12}{52} + \frac{26}{52} - \frac{6}{52} = \frac{32}{52} = \frac{8}{13}$$

25.  Since it is possible to obtain a card less than 6 that
     is a club, these events are not mutually exclusive.
     $$P( < 6 \text{ or club}) = \frac{20}{52} + \frac{13}{52} - \frac{7}{52} = \frac{28}{52} = \frac{7}{13}$$

27. a)  a)  P(lion and lion ) =
     $$\frac{5}{20} \cdot \frac{5}{20} = \frac{1}{4} \cdot \frac{1}{4} = \frac{1}{16}$$
     b)  P(lion and lion ) =
     $$\frac{5}{20} \cdot \frac{4}{19} = \frac{1}{4} \cdot \frac{4}{19} = \frac{1}{19}$$

29. a) P(monkey and bird) = $\dfrac{5}{20} \cdot \dfrac{5}{20} = \dfrac{1}{4} \cdot \dfrac{1}{4} = \dfrac{1}{16}$

    b) P(monkey and bird) = $\dfrac{5}{20} \cdot \dfrac{5}{19} = \dfrac{1}{4} \cdot \dfrac{5}{19} = \dfrac{5}{76}$

31. a) P(yellow bird and frog) =

     $\dfrac{2}{20} \cdot \dfrac{5}{20} = \dfrac{2}{20} \cdot \dfrac{1}{4} = \dfrac{2}{80} = \dfrac{1}{40}$

    b) P(yellow bird and frog) =

     $\dfrac{2}{20} \cdot \dfrac{5}{19} = \dfrac{10}{380} = \dfrac{1}{38}$

33. a) P(odd and odd) = $\dfrac{12}{20} \cdot \dfrac{12}{20} = \dfrac{3}{5} \cdot \dfrac{3}{5} = \dfrac{9}{25}$

    b) P(odd and odd) = $\dfrac{12}{20} \cdot \dfrac{11}{19} = \dfrac{3}{5} \cdot \dfrac{11}{19} = \dfrac{33}{95}$

35. P(monkey or even) = $\dfrac{5}{20} + \dfrac{8}{20} - \dfrac{2}{20} = \dfrac{11}{20}$

37. P(lion or a 2) = $\dfrac{5}{20} + \dfrac{4}{20} - \dfrac{1}{20} = \dfrac{8}{20} = \dfrac{2}{5}$

39. P(2 reds) = $\dfrac{1}{2} \cdot \dfrac{1}{2} = \dfrac{1}{4}$

41. P(red and green) = $\dfrac{1}{4} \cdot \dfrac{1}{2} = \dfrac{1}{8}$

43. P(2 yellows) = P(yellow and yellow)

     $= \dfrac{3}{8} \cdot \dfrac{3}{8} = \dfrac{9}{64}$

45. P(2 reds) = $\dfrac{1}{2} \cdot \dfrac{1}{4} = \dfrac{1}{8}$

47. P(both not red) = $\dfrac{1}{2} \cdot \dfrac{3}{4} = \dfrac{3}{8}$

49. P(yellow or blue) = 3/7

51. P(both red) = (3/7)(3/7) = 9/49

53. P(all red) = (3/7)(2/6)(1/5) = 1/35

55. P(R, B, B) = (3/7)(2/6)(1/5) = 1/35

57. P(3 girls) = P(1st girl) • P(2nd girl) • P(3rd girl)

     $= \dfrac{1}{2} \cdot \dfrac{1}{2} \cdot \dfrac{1}{2} = \dfrac{1}{8}$

59. P(G,G,B) = P(1st girl) • P(2nd girl) • P(3rd boy)

     $= \dfrac{1}{2} \cdot \dfrac{1}{2} \cdot \dfrac{1}{2} = \dfrac{1}{8}$

61. a) P(5 boys) = P(b) • P(b) • P(b) • P(b) • P(b)

     $= \dfrac{1}{2} \cdot \dfrac{1}{2} \cdot \dfrac{1}{2} \cdot \dfrac{1}{2} \cdot \dfrac{1}{2} = \dfrac{1}{32}$

    b) P(next child is a boy) = $\dfrac{1}{2}$

63. a) P(mystery/biography) = $\dfrac{4}{7} \cdot \dfrac{1}{7} = \dfrac{4}{49}$

    b) P(mystery/biography) = $\dfrac{4}{7} \cdot \dfrac{1}{6} = \dfrac{4}{42} = \dfrac{2}{21}$

65. a) P(at least 1 science fiction) =

     $\dfrac{2}{7} \cdot \dfrac{5}{7} + \dfrac{5}{7} \cdot \dfrac{2}{7} + \dfrac{2}{7} \cdot \dfrac{2}{7} = \dfrac{24}{49}$

    b) P(at least 1 science fiction )=

     $\dfrac{2}{7} \cdot \dfrac{5}{6} + \dfrac{5}{7} \cdot \dfrac{2}{6} + \dfrac{2}{7} \cdot \dfrac{1}{6} = \dfrac{11}{21}$

67. P(neither had trad. ins.) = $\dfrac{48}{75} \cdot \dfrac{47}{74} = \dfrac{2256}{5550} = \dfrac{376}{925}$

69. P(at least one trad.) = 1 − P(neither trad.) =

    $1 - \dfrac{376}{925} = \dfrac{549}{925}$ (see Exercise 67)

71. P(all recommended) = $\dfrac{23}{40} \cdot \dfrac{22}{39} \cdot \dfrac{21}{38} = \dfrac{1771}{9880}$

73.  P(no/no/not sure) = $\dfrac{7}{40} \cdot \dfrac{6}{39} \cdot \dfrac{10}{38} = \dfrac{7}{988}$

75.  The probability that any individual reacts favorably is 70/100 or 0.7.
P(Mrs. Rivera reacts favorably) = 0.7

77.  P(all 3 react favorably) = 0.7•0.7•0.7 = 0.343

79.  Since each question has four possible answers of which only one is correct, the probability of guessing correctly on any given question is 1/4.
P(correct answer on any one question) = ¼

81.  P(only the 3$^{rd}$ and 4$^{th}$ questions correct) =
$\left(\dfrac{3}{4}\right)\left(\dfrac{3}{4}\right)\left(\dfrac{1}{4}\right)\left(\dfrac{1}{4}\right)\left(\dfrac{3}{4}\right) = \dfrac{27}{1024}$

83.  P(none of the 5 questions correct) =
$\left(\dfrac{3}{4}\right)\left(\dfrac{3}{4}\right)\left(\dfrac{3}{4}\right)\left(\dfrac{3}{4}\right)\left(\dfrac{3}{4}\right) = \dfrac{243}{1024}$

85.  P(orange on 1$^{st}$ reel) = 5/22

87.  P(no bar/no bar/no bar) =
$\left(\dfrac{20}{22}\right)\left(\dfrac{20}{22}\right)\left(\dfrac{21}{22}\right) = \dfrac{1050}{1331}$

89.  P(blue/blue) = $\left(\dfrac{2}{8}\right)\left(\dfrac{2}{12}\right) = \dfrac{4}{96} = \dfrac{1}{24}$

91.  P(not red on outer and not red on inner) =
$\dfrac{8}{12} \cdot \dfrac{5}{8} = \dfrac{5}{12}$

93.  P(no hit/no hit) = (0.6)(0.6) = 0.36

95.  P(both hit) = (0.4)(0.9) = 0.36

97.  a) No; The probability of the 2nd depends on the outcome of the first.
b)  P(one afflicted) = .001
c)  P(both afflicted) = (.001)(.04) = .00004
d)  P(afflicted/not afflicted) = (0.001)(.96) = 0.00096
e)  P(not afflicted/afflicted) = (.999)(.001) = .000999
f)  P(not affl/not affl) = (.999)(.999) = .998001

99.  P(audit this year) = $\dfrac{36}{1000} = \dfrac{9}{250}$

101.  P(audit/no audit) = $\dfrac{9}{250} \cdot \dfrac{241}{250} = \dfrac{2169}{62,500}$

103.  P(2 - same color) = P(2 r) + P(2 b) + P(2 y)
$= \left(\dfrac{5}{10}\right)\left(\dfrac{4}{9}\right) + \left(\dfrac{3}{10}\right)\left(\dfrac{2}{9}\right) + \left(\dfrac{2}{10}\right)\left(\dfrac{1}{9}\right)$
$= \left(\dfrac{20}{90}\right) + \left(\dfrac{6}{90}\right) + \left(\dfrac{2}{90}\right) = \dfrac{28}{90} = \dfrac{14}{45}$

105.  P(no diamonds) = $\left(\dfrac{39}{52}\right)\left(\dfrac{38}{51}\right) = \dfrac{1482}{2652} = .56$

The game favors the dealer since the probability of no diamonds is greater than 1/2.

107.  P(2/2) = (2/6)(2/6) = 4/36 = 1/9

109.  P(even or < 3) = 2/6 + 3/6 – 2/6 = 3/6 = 1/2

## Exercise Set 12.7

1. Conditional

3.  $\dfrac{1}{3}$

5.  P(3 │ orange) = 1/3

7.  P(even │ not orange) = 2/3

9.  P(red │ orange) = 2/3

11.  P(triangle │ even) = 2/3

13.  P(red │ even) = 2/3

15.  P(circle or square │ < 4) = 2/3

17.  P(2 │ purple) = 1/5

19.  P(purple │ odd) = 2/6 = 1/3

21. $P(> 4 \mid \text{purple}) = 3/5$

23. $P(\text{gold} \mid > 5) = 1/7$

25. $P(1 \text{ and } 1) = (1/4)(1/4) = 1/16$

27. $P(5 \mid \text{at least a } 5) = 1/7$

29. $P(\text{sum} = 7) = 1/6$

31. $P(7 \mid 3) = 1/6$

33. $P(> 7 \mid 2^{\text{nd}} \text{ die} = 5) = 4/6 = 2/3$

35. $P(\text{C4}) = 2/9$

37. $P(\text{at least } \$20\text{B} \mid \text{C3}) = 2/4 = 1/2$

39. $P(\text{C5} \mid \text{at least } \$25\text{B}) = 1/2$

41. $P(\text{car}) = \dfrac{1462}{2461} = 0.5941$

43. $P(\text{E-Z} \mid \text{car}) = \dfrac{527}{1462} = 0.3605$

45. $P(\text{car} \mid \text{E-Z}) = \dfrac{527}{843} = 0.6251$

47. $P(\text{agg}) = \dfrac{350}{650} = \dfrac{7}{13}$

49. $P(\text{no sale} \mid \text{pass}) = \dfrac{80}{300} = \dfrac{4}{15}$

51. $P(\text{sale} \mid \text{pass}) = \dfrac{220}{300} = \dfrac{11}{15}$

53. $P(\text{same county}) = \dfrac{12{,}393}{19{,}556} \approx 0.6337$

55. $P(\text{diff. state} \mid \text{grad. deg.}) = \dfrac{461}{1875} \approx 0.2459$

57. $P(\text{high. sch.} \mid \text{s. state, d. count.}) =$

    $\dfrac{1074}{3707} \approx 0.2897$

59. $P(\text{good}) = \dfrac{300}{330} = \dfrac{10}{11}$

61. $P(\text{defective} \mid 20 \text{ watts}) = \dfrac{15}{95} = \dfrac{3}{19}$

63. $P(\text{good} \mid 50 \text{ or } 100 \text{ watts}) = \dfrac{220}{235} = \dfrac{44}{47}$

65. $P(\text{ABC or NBC}) = \dfrac{110}{270} = \dfrac{11}{27}$

67. $P(\text{ABC or NBC} \mid \text{man}) = \dfrac{50}{145} = \dfrac{10}{29}$

69. $P(\text{ABC, NBC, or CBS} \mid \text{man}) = \dfrac{55}{145} = \dfrac{11}{29}$

71. $P(\text{large company stock}) = 93/200$

73. $P(\text{blend} \mid \text{medium co. stock}) = 15/52$

75. a) $n(A) = 140$     b) $n(B) = 120$

    c) $P(A) = 140/200 = 7/10$

    d) $P(B) = 120/200 = 6/10 = 3/5$

    e) $P(A \mid B) = \dfrac{n(B \text{ and } A)}{n(B)} = \dfrac{80}{120} = \dfrac{2}{3}$

    f) $P(B \mid A) = \dfrac{n(A \text{ and } B)}{n(B)} = \dfrac{80}{140} = \dfrac{4}{7}$

    g) $P(A) \bullet P(B) = \left(\dfrac{7}{10}\right)\left(\dfrac{3}{5}\right) = \dfrac{21}{50}$

       $P(A \mid B) \quad P(A) \bullet P(B) \qquad \dfrac{2}{3} \neq \dfrac{21}{50}$

    A and B are not independent events.

77. a) $P(A \mid B) = \dfrac{P(A \text{ and } B)}{P(B)} = \dfrac{0.15}{0.5} = 0.3$

    b) $P(B \mid A) = \dfrac{P(A \text{ and } B)}{P(A)} = \dfrac{0.15}{0.3} = 0.5$

    c) Yes, $P(A) = P(A \mid B)$ and $P(B) = P(B \mid A)$.

79. $P(+ \mid \text{orange circle}) = \tfrac{1}{2}$

81. $P(\text{green} + \mid +) = 1/3$

83. $P(\text{orange circle w/green} + \mid +) = 1/3$

**Exercise Set 12.8**

1. Counting

3. n!

5. $\dfrac{n!}{(n-r)!}$

7. $_5P_3$

9. $5! = 120$

11. $_4P_2 = \dfrac{4!}{2!} = 4 \cdot 3 = 12$

13. $0! = 1$

15. $_8P_0 = \dfrac{8!}{8!} = 1$

17. $_9P_5 = \dfrac{9!}{4!} = 9 \cdot 8 \cdot 7 \cdot 6 \cdot 5 = 15,120$

19. $_8P_3 = \dfrac{8!}{5!} = 8 \cdot 7 \cdot 6 = 336$

21. $(10)(10)(10)(10) = 10000$

23. $(3)(4)(2) = 24$

25. a) $5^5 = 3125$

    b) $\dfrac{1}{3125} = 0.00032$

27. a) $(26)(26)(10)(10)(10)(26)(26) = 456,976,000$

    b) $(26)(25)(10)(9)(8)(24)(23) = 258,336,000$

29. $(7)(4)(3)(4) = 336$

31. a) $6! = 720$     b) $5! = 120$

    c) $4! = 24$     d) $5! \bullet 5 = 600$

33. $_{10}P_3 = \dfrac{10!}{(10-3)!} = \dfrac{10!}{7!} = \dfrac{10 \cdot 9 \cdot 8 \cdot 7!}{7!} = 720$

35. a) There are 12 individuals and they can be arranged in $12! = 479,001,600$ ways

    b) $10! = 3,628,800$ different ways

    c) $5! \cdot 5! = 14,400$ different ways

37. $(26)(25)(24)(10)(9)(8)(7) = 78,624,000$

39. $(26)(10)(9)(8)(7) = 131,040$

41. $(10)(10)(10)(26)(26) = 676,000$

43. $(5)(4)(8)(26)(25) = 104,000$

45. a) $(8)(10)(10)(10)(10)(10)(10) = 8,000,000$

    b) $(8)(10)(10)(8,000,000) = 6,400,000,000$

    c) $(8)(10)(10)(8)(10^7) = (64)(10^9)$

         $= 64,000,000,000$

47. $(16)(15)(14)(13)(12) = 524,160$

49. $_7P_7 = \dfrac{7!}{0!} = \dfrac{7!}{1} = 7! = 5,040$

51. $(5)(4)(7)(2) = 280$ systems

53. $_9P_9 = \dfrac{9!}{0!} = 9! = 362,880$

55. $\dfrac{9!}{4!2!2!} = 3780$

57. $\dfrac{7!}{2!2!2!} = 630$

    (There are 2 6's, 2 7's, and 2 8's.)

59. The order of the flags is important. Thus, it is a permutation problem.

$$_9P_5 = \dfrac{9!}{(9-5)!} = \dfrac{9!}{4!} = (9)(8)(7)(6)(5) = 15,120$$

61. a) Since the pitcher must bat last, there is only one possibility for the last position. $--------\underline{1}$
   There are 8 possible batters left for the 1st position. Once the 1st batter has been selected, there are
   7 batters left for the 2$^{nd}$ position, 6 for the third, etc.    $\underline{(8)}\,\underline{(7)}\,\underline{(6)}\,\underline{(5)}\,\underline{(4)}\,\underline{(3)}\,\underline{(2)}\,\underline{(1)}\,\underline{(1)} = 40{,}320$
   b) $9! = (9)(8)(7)(6)(5)(4)(3)(2)(1) = 362{,}880$

63. a) $5^5 = 3125$ different keys
   b) $400{,}000 \div 3{,}125 = 128$ cars

   c) $\dfrac{1}{3125} = 0.00032$

65. $_7P_5 = \dfrac{7!}{2!} = \dfrac{7\cdot6\cdot5\cdot4\cdot3\cdot2!}{2!} = 2{,}520$ different

   letter permutations;  $2500 \times \dfrac{1}{12} = 210$ minutes

   or $3\dfrac{1}{2}$ hours

67. No, Ex.  $_3P_2 \neq {}_3P_{(3\text{-}2)}$

   $\dfrac{3!}{1!} \neq \dfrac{3!}{2!}$  because  $6 \neq 3$

69. $(25)(24) = 600$ tickets

71. a) $\dfrac{7!}{2!} = 2520$     b) SCROOGE


## Exercise Set 12.9

1. Combination

3. Permutations

5. $_7C_3$

7. $_6C_2 = \dfrac{6!}{(6-2)!2!} = \dfrac{(6)(5)}{(2)(1)} = 15$

9. a) $_8C_4 = \dfrac{8!}{4!4!} = \dfrac{(8)(7)(6)(5)}{(4)(3)(2)(1)} = 70$

   b) $_8P_4 = \dfrac{8!}{(8-4)!} = \dfrac{8!}{4!} = (8)(7)(6)(5) = 1680$

11. a) $_8C_0 = \dfrac{8!}{8!0!} = 1$

   b) $_8P_0 = \dfrac{8!}{(8-0)!} = \dfrac{8!}{8!} = 1$

13. a) $_{10}C_3 = \dfrac{10!}{7!3!} = \dfrac{(10)(9)(8)(7!)}{(7!)(3)(2)(1)} = 120$

   b) $_{10}P_3 = \dfrac{10!}{(10-3)!} = \dfrac{(10)(9)(8)(7!)}{7!} = 720$

15. $\dfrac{_5C_3}{_5P_3} = \dfrac{\tfrac{5!}{2!3!}}{\tfrac{5!}{2!}} = \left(\dfrac{5!}{2!3!}\right)\left(\dfrac{2!}{5!}\right) = \dfrac{1}{3!} = \dfrac{1}{6}$

17. $\dfrac{_6C_4}{_6C_3} = \dfrac{\tfrac{6!}{2!4!}}{\tfrac{6!}{3!3!}} = \left(\dfrac{6!}{2!4!}\right)\left(\dfrac{3!3!}{6!}\right) = \dfrac{3}{4}$

19. $\dfrac{_9P_4}{_{10}C_5} = \dfrac{\tfrac{9!}{5!}}{\tfrac{10!}{5!5!}} = \dfrac{(9)(8)(7)(6)}{\dfrac{(10)(9)(8)(7)(6)}{(5)(4)(3)(2)(1)}} = \dfrac{3024}{252} = 12$

21. $_{12}C_4 = \dfrac{12!}{8!4!} = \dfrac{(12)(11)(10)(9)}{(4)(3)(2)(1)} = 495$ ways

23. $_5C_4 = \dfrac{5!}{1!4!} = 5$

25. $_8C_3 = \dfrac{8!}{5!3!} = \dfrac{(8)(7)(6)}{(3)(2)(1)} = 56$

27. $_7C_4 = \dfrac{7!}{3!4!} = \dfrac{(7)(6)(5)}{(3)(2)(1)} = 35$

29. $_{12}C_8 = \dfrac{12!}{4!8!} = \dfrac{(12)(11)(10)(9)}{(4)(3)(2)(1)} = 495$

31. $_{10}C_4 = \dfrac{10!}{6!4!} = \dfrac{(10)(9)(8)(7)}{(4)(3)(2)(1)} = 210$

33. $_9C_3 \bullet \, _6C_2 =$

$\left(\dfrac{9!}{6!3!}\right)\left(\dfrac{6!}{4!2!}\right) = \left(\dfrac{(9)(8)(7)}{(3)(2)(1)}\right)\left(\dfrac{(6)(5)}{(2)(1)}\right) = 1260$

35. $_{12}C_3 \bullet \, _8C_2 =$

$\left(\dfrac{12!}{9!3!}\right)\left(\dfrac{8!}{6!2!}\right)$

$= \left(\dfrac{(12)(11)(10)}{(3)(2)(1)}\right)\left(\dfrac{(8)(7)}{(2)(1)}\right) = 6160$

37. Red:  $_{10}C_4 = \dfrac{10!}{6!4!} = \dfrac{(10)(9)(8)(7)}{(4)(3)(2)(1)} = 210$

White.  $_8C_2 = \dfrac{8!}{6!2!} = \dfrac{(8)(7)}{(2)(1)} = 28$

$(210)(28) = 5880$ different choices

39. Regular:  $_{10}C_5 =$

$\dfrac{10!}{5!5!} = \dfrac{(10)(9)(8)(7)(6)}{(5)(4)(3)(2)(1)} = 252$

Diet:  $_7C_3 =$

$\dfrac{7!}{3!4!} = \dfrac{(7)(6)(5)}{(3)(2)(1)} = 35$

$(252)(35) = 8820$ ways to select the sodas

41. $_8C_4 \bullet \, _5C_2 =$

$\left(\dfrac{8!}{4!4!}\right)\left(\dfrac{5!}{3!2!}\right) = \left(\dfrac{(8)(7)(6)(4)}{(4)(3)(2)(1)}\right)\left(\dfrac{(5)(4)}{(2)(1)}\right) = 700$

43. $_6C_2 \bullet \, _5C_2 \bullet \, _4C_3 =$

$\left(\dfrac{6!}{4!2!}\right)\left(\dfrac{5!}{3!2!}\right)\left(\dfrac{4!}{1!3!}\right) =$

$\left(\dfrac{(6)(5)}{(2)(1)}\right)\left(\dfrac{(5)(4)}{(2)(1)}\right)\left(\dfrac{(4)}{(1)}\right) = 600$

45. a) $_{10}C_8 = \dfrac{10!}{2!8!} = \dfrac{(10)(9)}{(2)(1)} = 45$

b) $_{10}C_9 = \dfrac{10!}{1!9!} = \dfrac{(10)(9!)}{(1)(9!)} = 10$

$_{10}C_{10} = \dfrac{10!}{10!} = 1$

$_{10}C_8 + {}_{10}C_9 + {}_{10}C_{10} = 45 + 10 + 1 = 56$

47. a)
```
                1
             1     1
          1     2     1
       1     3     3     1
    1     4     6     4     1
```

b)  1     5     10     10     5     1

49. a) $4! = 24$     b) $4! = 24$

51. $(15)(14) \cdot {}_{13}C_3 = (15)(14)\left(\dfrac{13!}{10!3!}\right)$

$= (15)(14)\left(\dfrac{(13)(12)(11)}{(3)(2)(1)}\right) = 60{,}060$

**Exercise Set 12.10**

1. $P(\text{4 red balls}) = \dfrac{\text{no. of 4 red ball comb.}}{\text{no. of 4 ball comb.}} = \dfrac{_{10}C_4}{_{14}C_4}$

3. $P(\text{3 vowels}) = \dfrac{\text{no. of 3 vowel comb.}}{\text{no. of 3 letter comb.}} = \dfrac{_5C_3}{_{26}C_3}$

5. $P(\text{all 5 yellow Labs}) =$

$\dfrac{\text{no. of 5 yellow Lab comb.}}{\text{no. of 5 puppy comb.}} = \dfrac{_8C_5}{_{15}C_5}$

7. $P(\text{each of the 5 has a criminal justice degree}) =$

$\dfrac{\text{no. of 5 crim. just. combo.}}{\text{no. of student comb.}} = \dfrac{_{23}C_5}{_{120}C_5}$

9. $_3C_2 = \dfrac{3!}{1!2!} = 3$

$_{10}C_2 = \dfrac{10!}{8!2!} = \dfrac{(10)(9)}{(2)(1)} = 45$

$P(\text{2 defective}) = \dfrac{3}{45} = \dfrac{1}{15}$

11. $_8C_5 = \dfrac{8!}{3!5!} = \dfrac{(8)(7)(6)}{(3)(2)(1)} = 56$

$_{14}C_5 = \dfrac{14!}{5!9!} = \dfrac{(14)(13)(12)(11)(10)}{(5)(4)(3)(2)(1)} = 2002$

$P(\text{5 men's names}) = \dfrac{56}{2002} = \dfrac{4}{143}$

13. $_4C_3 = \dfrac{4!}{1!3!} = \dfrac{(4)}{(1)} = 4$

$_{10}C_3 = \dfrac{10!}{7!3!} = \dfrac{(10)(9)(8)}{(3)(2)(1)} = 120$

$P(\text{3 greater than 5}) = \dfrac{4}{120} = \dfrac{1}{30}$

15. $_6C_2 = \dfrac{6!}{4!2!} = \dfrac{(6)(5)}{(2)(1)} = 15$

$_2C_1 = 2$

$_{11}C_3 = \dfrac{11!}{8!3!} = \dfrac{(11)(10)(9)}{(3)(2)(1)} = 165$

$P(\text{2 from mfg, 1 from acct.}) = \dfrac{(15)(2)}{165} = \dfrac{2}{11}$

17. $_{46}C_6 = \dfrac{46!}{40!6!} = 9{,}366{,}819 \quad _6C_6 = 1$

$P(\text{win grand prize}) = \dfrac{1}{9{,}366{,}819}$

19. $_3C_2 = \dfrac{3!}{1!2!} = 3 \quad _5C_2 = \dfrac{5!}{3!2!} = \dfrac{(5)(4)}{(2)(1)} = 10$

$P(\text{no cars}) = \dfrac{3}{10}$

21. $P(\text{at least 1 car}) = 1 - P(\text{no cars}) =$

$1 - 1 - \dfrac{3}{10} = \dfrac{7}{10}$

23. $_6C_3 = \dfrac{6!}{3!3!} = \dfrac{(6)(5)(4)}{(3)(2)(1)} = 20$

$_{25}C_3 = \dfrac{25!}{3!22!} = \dfrac{(25)(24)(23)}{(3)(2)(1)} = 2300$

$P(\text{3 infielders}) = \dfrac{20}{2300} = \dfrac{1}{115}$

25. $_{10}C_2 = \dfrac{10!}{8!2!} = 45 \quad _6C_1 = \dfrac{6!}{5!1!} = 6$

$P(\text{2 pitchers and 1 infielder}) = \dfrac{(45)(6)}{2300} = \dfrac{27}{230}$

For problems 27–29, use the fact that $_{25}C_6 = \dfrac{25!}{19!6!} = 177,100$

27. $_{10}C_6 = \dfrac{10!}{4!6!} = 210$

$P(\text{all mid}) = \dfrac{210}{177,100} = 0.0012$

29. $_{10}C_3 = \dfrac{10!}{7!3!} = 120$

$_{15}C_3 = \dfrac{15!}{12!3!} = 455$

$P(\text{2 mid/4 compact}) = \dfrac{(120)(455)}{117,100} = 0.3083$

For problems 31–33, use the fact that $_{12}C_4 = \dfrac{12!}{8!4!} = 495$

31. $_4C_2 = \dfrac{4!}{2!2!} = 6 \qquad _3C_2 = \dfrac{3!}{1!2!} = 3$

$P(\text{2 in FL, 2 in TX}) = \dfrac{(6)(3)}{495} = \dfrac{2}{55}$

33. $_4C_1 = 4$

$_5C_1 = 5$

$_3C_2 = 3$

$P(\text{1 in FL, 1 in CA, 2 in TX}) =$

$\dfrac{(4)(5)(3)}{495} = \dfrac{4}{33}$

For problems 35 – 37, use the fact that $_{11}C_5 = \dfrac{11!}{6!5!} = \dfrac{(11)(10)(9)(8)(7)}{(5)(4)(3)(2)(1)} = 462$

35. $_6C_5 = \dfrac{6!}{1!5!} = 6$

$P(\text{5 women first}) = \dfrac{6}{462} = \dfrac{1}{77}$

37. Any one of the 6 women can sit in any one of the five seats - 30 possibilities.

$P(\text{exactly 1 woman}) = \dfrac{30}{462} = \dfrac{5}{77}$

39. $_{24}C_3 = \dfrac{24!}{21!3!} = 2024$

$_{10}C_3 = \dfrac{10!}{7!3!} = 120$

$P(\text{all 3 are cashiers}) = \dfrac{120}{2024} = \dfrac{15}{253}$

41.  a) $P(\text{royal spade flush}) = \dfrac{_{47}C_2}{_{52}C_7} = \dfrac{1}{123760}$

b) $P(\text{any royal flush}) = \dfrac{4}{123760} = \dfrac{1}{30,940}$

43. a) $\left( \dfrac{(_4C_2)(_4C_2)(_{44}C_1)}{_{52}C_5} \right) = \dfrac{1584}{2598960} = \dfrac{33}{54,145}$

$P(\text{2 aces/2 8's/other card} \quad \text{ace or 8}) = \dfrac{33}{54,145}$

b) $P$(aces of spades and clubs/8's of spades and clubs/9 of diamonds) =

$\dfrac{1}{_{52}C_5} = \dfrac{1}{2,598,960}$

45. a) $\left(\dfrac{1}{15}\right)\left(\dfrac{1}{14}\right)\left(\dfrac{1}{13}\right)\left(\dfrac{5}{12}\right)\left(\dfrac{4}{11}\right)\left(\dfrac{3}{10}\right)\left(\dfrac{2}{9}\right)\left(\dfrac{1}{8}\right)$

$= \dfrac{120}{259459200} = \dfrac{1}{2,162,160}$

b) $P(\text{any 3 of 8 for officers}) = \dfrac{(8)(7)(6)}{2162160} = \dfrac{1}{6435}$

47. 1; Since there are more people than hairs, 2 or more people must have the same number of hairs.

**Exercise Set 12.11**

1. Probability

3. Success

5. $P(3) = {}_4C_3(0.1)^3(0.9)^{4-3}$

$= \dfrac{4!}{1!3!}(0.001)(0.9) = 0.0036$

7. $P(2) = {}_5C_2(0.4)^2(0.6)^{5-2}$

$= \dfrac{5!}{2!3!}(0.16)(0.216) = 0.3456$

9. $P(0) = {}_6C_0(0.5)^0(0.5)^{6-0}$

$= \dfrac{6!}{0!6!}(1)(.0156252) = 0.015625$

11. $p = 0.14, \ q = 1 - p = 1 - 0.14 = 0.86$

a) $P(x) = {}_nC_x(0.14)^x(0.86)^{n-x}$

b) $n = 12, \ x = 2, \ p = 0.14, \ q = 0.86$

$P(2) = {}_{12}C_2(0.14)^2(0.86)^{12-2}$

13. $P(5) = {}_8C_5(0.6)^5(0.4)^{8-5}$

$= \dfrac{8!}{3!5!}(0.07776)(0.064) = 0.27869$

15. $P(6) = {}_{10}C_6(0.77)^6(0.23)^{10-6}$

$= \dfrac{10!}{4!6!}(0.20842238)(0.0027984) = 0.12248$

17. $P(4) = {}_6C_4(0.92)^4(0.08)^{6-4}$

$= \dfrac{6!}{4!2!}(.7164)(.0064) = 0.06877$

19. $P(4) = {}_5C_4(.8)^4(.2)^{5-4}$

$= \dfrac{5!}{1!4!}(.4096)(.2) = 0.4096$

21. a) $P(\text{all five}) = {}_5C_5(0.25)^5(0.75)^{5-5}$

$= \dfrac{5!}{5!}(0.0009765625)(1) \approx 0.00098$

b) $P(\text{exactly three}) = {}_5C_3(0.25)^3(0.75)^{5-3}$

$= \dfrac{5!}{2!3!}(0.015625)(0.5625) \approx 0.08789$

c) $P(\text{at least } 3) = P(3) + P(4) + P(5)$

$P(4) = {}_5C_4(0.25)^4(0.75)^{5-1}$

$= \dfrac{5!}{1!4!}(0.00390625)(0.75) \approx 0.01465$

$P(\text{at least } 3) = 0.08789 + 0.01465 + 0.00098$

$= 0.10352$

23. a) $P(3) = {}_6C_3\left(\dfrac{12}{52}\right)^3\left(\dfrac{40}{52}\right)^3$

$\dfrac{6!}{3!3!}(.01229)(.45517) = 0.11188$

b) $P(2) = {}_6C_2\left(\dfrac{13}{52}\right)^2\left(\dfrac{39}{52}\right)^4$

$= \dfrac{6!}{2!4!}(.0625)(.3164) = 0.29663$

25. The probability that the sun would be shining would equal 0 because 72 hours later would occur at midnight.

**Review Exercises**

1. Relative frequency over the long run can accurately be predicted, not individual events or totals.

2. Roll the die many times then compute the relative frequency of each outcome and compare with the expected probability of 1/6.

3. $P(\text{SUV}) = \dfrac{8}{40} = \dfrac{1}{5}$

4. Answers will vary.

5. $P(\text{watches ABC}) = \dfrac{80}{250} = \dfrac{8}{25}$

6. $P(\text{even}) = \dfrac{5}{10} = \dfrac{1}{2}$

7. $P(\text{odd or} > 3) = \dfrac{5}{10} + \dfrac{6}{10} - \dfrac{3}{10} = \dfrac{8}{10} = \dfrac{4}{5}$

8. $P(> 3 \text{ or} < 6) = \dfrac{6}{10} + \dfrac{6}{10} - \dfrac{2}{10} = \dfrac{10}{10} = 1$

9. $P(\text{even and} > 4) = \dfrac{2}{10} = \dfrac{1}{5}$

10. $P(\text{Strawberry}) = \dfrac{18}{50} = \dfrac{9}{25}$

11. $P(\text{Blueberry}) = \dfrac{11}{50}$

12. $P(\text{Strawberry or Raspberry}) =$

$\dfrac{18}{50} + \dfrac{14}{50} = \dfrac{32}{50} = \dfrac{16}{25}$

13. $P(\text{not Banana crème pie}) = \dfrac{50 - 7}{50} = \dfrac{43}{50}$

14. a) 4:1      b) 1:4

15. 5:3

16. $P(\text{wins Triple Crown}) = \dfrac{3}{85}$

17. 17:3

18. a) E = P(win $200)•$198 + P(win $100)•$98
   + P(lose)•(–$2)
   = (.003)(198) + (.002)(98) – (.995)(2)
   = .594 + .196 – 1.990 = – 1.200 → -$1.20

   b) The expectation of a person who purchases three tickets would be 3(–1.20) = –$3.60.

   c) Expected value = Fair price – Cost
   –1.20 = Fair price – 2.00     $.80 = Fair price

19. a) $E_{\text{Cameron}}$ = P(pic. card)($9) +
   P(not pic. card)(–$3)

   $= \left(\dfrac{12}{52}\right)(9) - \left(\dfrac{40}{52}\right)(3) = \approx -\$0.23$

   b) $E_{\text{Lindsey}}$ = P(pic. card)(–$9) + P(not pic. card)($3)

   $= \dfrac{-27}{13} + \dfrac{30}{13} = \dfrac{3}{13} \approx \$0.23$

   c) Cameron can expect to lose $(100)\left(\dfrac{3}{13}\right) \approx \$23.08$

20. E = P(sunny)(1000) + P(cloudy)(500) + P(rain)(100) = 0.4(1000) + 0.5(500) + 0.1(100) =
   400 + 250+10 = 660 people

21. FP = EV + CP
   FP = -$2.50 + $6.50 = $4.00

22. FP = EV + CP
   FP = -$1.50 + $5.00 = $3.50

23. a)

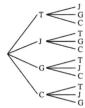

   b) Sample space:
   {TJ,TG,TC,JT,JG,JC,GT,GJ,GC,CT,CJ,CG}

   c) P(Gina is Pres. and Jake V.P.) = 1/12

24. a)

   b) Sample space:
   {H1,H2,H3,H4,T1,T2,T3,T4}

   c) P(heads and odd) = (1/2)(2/4) = 2/8 = ¼

   d) P(heads or odd) = (1/2)(2/4) + (1/2)(2/4)
   = 4/8 + 2/8 = 6/8 = 3/4

25. P(even and even) = (4/8)(4/8) = 16/64 = 1/4

26. P(outer is greater than 5 and inner is greater than 5)

   $= P(\text{outer is} > 5) \cdot P(\text{inner is} > 5) = \dfrac{3}{8} \cdot \dfrac{3}{8} = \dfrac{9}{64}$

27. P(outer odd and inner < 6)

$= \text{P(outer odd) P(inner < 6)} = \dfrac{4}{8} \cdot \dfrac{5}{8} = \dfrac{1}{2} \cdot \dfrac{5}{8} = \dfrac{5}{16}$

28. P(outer is even or less than 6)

$= \text{P(even)} + \text{P(< 6)} - \text{P(even and < 6)}$

$= \dfrac{4}{8} + \dfrac{5}{8} - \dfrac{2}{8} = \dfrac{7}{8}$

29. P(inner even and not green) =

$\dfrac{1}{2} + \dfrac{6}{8} - \dfrac{2}{8} = \dfrac{1}{2} + \dfrac{4}{8} = 1$

30. P(outer gold and inner not gold)

$= \left(\dfrac{2}{8}\right)\left(\dfrac{6}{8}\right) = \left(\dfrac{1}{4}\right)\left(\dfrac{3}{4}\right) = \dfrac{3}{16}$

31. P(all 3 are G) $= \dfrac{5}{12} \cdot \dfrac{4}{11} \cdot \dfrac{3}{10} = \dfrac{60}{1320} = \dfrac{1}{22}$

32. P(none are P) =

$\dfrac{8}{12} \cdot \dfrac{7}{11} \cdot \dfrac{6}{10} = \dfrac{336}{1320} = \dfrac{14}{55}$

33. P(at least one is P) = 1 – P(none are Powerade)

$= 1 - \dfrac{14}{55} = \dfrac{55}{55} - \dfrac{14}{55} = \dfrac{41}{55}$

34. P(G, G, AS)

$= \dfrac{5}{12} \cdot \dfrac{4}{11} \cdot \dfrac{3}{10} = \dfrac{60}{1320} = \dfrac{1}{22}$

35. P(yellow) = 1/4

36. Odds against yellow  3:1
    Odds for yellow  1:3

37. $5 for red; $10 for yellow; $20 for green
    P(green) = ½;  P(yellow) = ¼;  P(red) = ¼
    EV = (1/4)(5) + (1/4)(10) + (1/2)(20) = $13.75

38. P(red, then green) = P(red)P(green)
    = (1/4)(1/2) = 1/8

39. P(not green) = 1/4 + 1/4 + 1/8 = 5/8
    = (3/8)(10) + (1/2)(5) – (1/8)(20)
    = (15/4) + (10/4) – (10/4) = 15/4  →  $3.75

40. Odds in favor of green  3:5
    Odds against green  5:3

41. E = P(green)($10) + P(red)($5) +
    P(yellow)(–$20)
    = (3/8)(10) + (1/2)(5) – (1/8)(20)
    = (15/4) + (10/4) – (10/4) = 15/4  →  $3.75

42. P(at least one red) = 1 – P(none are red)
    = 1 – (1/2)(1/2)(1/2) = 1-1/8 = 7/8

43. P(rated good) = 150/170 = 15/17

44. P(good | breakfast) = 85/95 = 17/19

45. P(poor | lunch) = 10/75 = 2/15

46. P(breakfast | poor) = 10/20 = 1/2

47. P(right handed) $= \dfrac{230}{400} = \dfrac{23}{40}$

48. P(left brained | left handed) $= \dfrac{30}{170} = \dfrac{3}{17}$

49. P(right handed | no predominance) $= \dfrac{60}{80} = \dfrac{3}{4}$

50. P(right brained | left handed) $= \dfrac{120}{170} = \dfrac{12}{17}$

51. a)  4! = (4)(3)(2)(1) = 24
    b)  E = (1/4)(10K) + (1/4)(5K) + (1/4)(2K)
        + (1/4)(1K) = (1/4)(18K) = $4,500.00

52. # of possible arrangements = $(_5C_2)(_3C_2)(_1C_1)$

$= \left(\dfrac{5!}{3!2!}\right)\left(\dfrac{3!}{1!2!}\right)\left(\dfrac{1!}{1!}\right) = \dfrac{(5)(4)(3)}{(2)(1)} = 30$

53. $_{10}P_3 = \dfrac{10!}{7!} = (10)(9)(8) = 720$

54. $_9P_3 = \dfrac{9!}{6!} = \dfrac{(9)(8)(7)(6!)}{6!} = (9)(8)(7) = 504$

55. $_6C_3 = \dfrac{6!}{3!3!} = \dfrac{(6)(5)(4)}{(3)(2)(1)} = 20$

   b) P(Big game win) = P(match 5 #s and Big #)

     = P(match 5 #s) • P(match Big #)

$$= \left(\dfrac{1}{3,819,816}\right)\left(\dfrac{1}{46}\right) = \dfrac{1}{175,711,536}$$

56. a) $_{15}C_{10} = \dfrac{15!}{5!10!} = \dfrac{(15)(14)(13)(12)(11)}{(5)(4)(3)(2)(1)} = 3003$

   b) number of arrangements = 10! = 3,628,800

57. a) P(match 5 numbers) = $\dfrac{1}{_{56}C_5}$

$$= \dfrac{1}{\dfrac{56!}{51!5!}} = \dfrac{51!5!}{56!} = \dfrac{1}{3,819,816}$$

   b) P(Big game win) = P(match 5 #s and Big #)

     = P(match 5 #s) • P(match Big #)

$$= \left(\dfrac{1}{3,819,816}\right)\left(\dfrac{1}{46}\right) = \dfrac{1}{175,711,536}$$

58. $(_{10}C_2)(_{12}C_5) =$

$$\left(\dfrac{10!}{8!2!}\right)\left(\dfrac{12!}{7!5!}\right)$$

$$= \dfrac{(10)(9)(12)(11)(10)(9)(8)}{(2)(1)(5)(4)(3)(2)(1)}$$

$$= 35,640 \text{ possible committees}$$

59. $(_8C_3)(_5C_2) =$

$$\left(\dfrac{8!}{5!3!}\right)\left(\dfrac{5!}{2!3!}\right) = \dfrac{(8)(7)(6)(5)(4)}{(3)(2)(1)(2)(1)} = 560$$

60. P(two aces) = $\dfrac{_4C_2}{_{52}C_2} = \dfrac{\dfrac{4!}{2!2!}}{\dfrac{52!}{50!2!}}$

$$= \left(\dfrac{4!}{2!2!}\right)\left(\dfrac{50!2!}{52!}\right) = \dfrac{1}{221}$$

61. P(all three are red) = $\left(\dfrac{5}{10}\right)\left(\dfrac{4}{9}\right)\left(\dfrac{3}{8}\right) = \dfrac{1}{12}$

62. P(1st 2 are red/3rd is blue) = $\left(\dfrac{5}{10}\right)\left(\dfrac{4}{9}\right)\left(\dfrac{2}{8}\right) = \dfrac{1}{18}$

63. P(1st red, 2nd white, 3rd blue)

$$= \left(\dfrac{5}{10}\right)\left(\dfrac{3}{9}\right)\left(\dfrac{2}{8}\right) = \dfrac{1}{24}$$

64. P(at least one red) = 1 − P(none are red)

$$= 1 - \left(\dfrac{5}{10}\right)\left(\dfrac{4}{9}\right)\left(\dfrac{3}{8}\right) = 1 - \dfrac{1}{12} = \dfrac{11}{12}$$

65. P(3 N&WRs) =

$$\dfrac{_5C_3}{_{14}C_3} = \dfrac{\dfrac{5!}{3!2!}}{\dfrac{14!}{3!11!}} = \dfrac{5!3!11!}{3!2!14!} = \dfrac{(5)(4)(3)}{(14)(13)(12)} = \dfrac{5}{182}$$

66. P(2 NWs & 1 Time) =

$$\dfrac{(_6C_2)(_3C_1)}{_{14}C_3} = \dfrac{\left(\dfrac{6!}{2!4!}\right)\left(\dfrac{3!}{1!2!}\right)}{\dfrac{14!}{3!11!}}$$

$$= \dfrac{(6)(5)(3)(3)(2)(1)}{(2)(1)(14)(13)(12)} = \dfrac{45}{364}$$

67. $\dfrac{_8C_3}{_{14}C_3} = \dfrac{\dfrac{8!}{3!5!}}{\dfrac{14!}{3!11!}} = \dfrac{8!3!11!}{3!5!14!}$

$= \dfrac{(8)(7)(6)}{(14)(13)(12)} = \dfrac{336}{2184} = \dfrac{2}{13}$

68. $1 - \dfrac{2}{13} = \dfrac{11}{13}$

69. a) $P(x) = {_nC_x}\,(0.6)^x\,(0.4)^{n-x}$

b) $P(75) = {_{100}C_{75}}\,(0.6)^{75}\,(0.4)^{25}$

70. $n = 5$, $x = 3$, $p = 1/5$, $q = 4/5$

$P(3) = {_5C_3}\left(\dfrac{1}{5}\right)^3\left(\dfrac{4}{5}\right)^2 = 10\cdot\left(\dfrac{1}{5}\right)^3\left(\dfrac{4}{5}\right)^2 =$
0.0512

71. a) $n = 5$, $p = 0.6$, $q = 0.4$

$P(0) = {_5C_0}\,(0.6)^0\,(0.4)^5$

$= (1)(1)(0.4)^5 = 0.01024$

b) P(at least 1) = 1 – P(0) = 1 – 0.01024 = 0.98976

**Chapter Test**

1. $P(\text{roses}) = \dfrac{14}{50} = \dfrac{7}{25}$

2. $(P > 4) = \dfrac{5}{9} \approx 0.56$

3. $P(\text{even}) = \dfrac{4}{9} \approx 0.44$

4. $P(\text{even or} \geq 5) = \dfrac{6}{9} = \dfrac{2}{3} \approx 0.67$

5. $P(\text{both} > 5) = \dfrac{4}{9}\cdot\dfrac{3}{8} = \dfrac{12}{72} = \dfrac{1}{6}$

6. $P(\text{1st odd, 2nd even}) = \dfrac{5}{9}\cdot\dfrac{4}{8} = \dfrac{5}{9}\cdot\dfrac{1}{2} = \dfrac{5}{18}$

7. $P(\text{neither} > 6) = \dfrac{6}{9}\cdot\dfrac{5}{8} = \dfrac{1\cdot 5}{3\cdot 4} = \dfrac{5}{12}$

8. P(red or picture)
= P(red) + P(picture) – P(red and picture)
$= \dfrac{26}{52} + \dfrac{12}{52} - \dfrac{6}{52} = \dfrac{32}{52} = \dfrac{8}{13}$

9. 1 die   (6)(3) = 18

10.

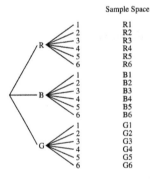

11. P(green and 2) = $\dfrac{1}{18}$

12. P(red or 1) = $\dfrac{6}{18} + \dfrac{3}{18} - \dfrac{1}{18} = \dfrac{8}{18} = \dfrac{4}{9}$

13. P(not red or even) = $\dfrac{12}{18} + \dfrac{9}{18} - \dfrac{6}{18} = \dfrac{15}{18} = \dfrac{5}{6}$

14. Number of codes = (26)(9)(10)(26)(26)
    = 1,581,840

15. a) 5:4        b) 5:4

16. E = P(club) ($8) + P(heart) ($4)
         + P(spade or diamond) (–$6)

     = $\left(\dfrac{1}{4}\right)(8) + \left(\dfrac{1}{4}\right)(4) + \left(\dfrac{2}{4}\right)(-6)$

     = $\dfrac{8}{4} + \dfrac{4}{4} - \dfrac{12}{4} = \$0.00$

17. a) P(car) = $\dfrac{214}{456} = \dfrac{107}{228}$

   b) P(George Washington) = $\dfrac{226}{456} = \dfrac{113}{228}$

   c) P(SUV | George Washington) = $\dfrac{106}{226} = \dfrac{53}{113}$

   d) P(GG Bridge | car) = $\dfrac{94}{214} = \dfrac{47}{107}$

18. $_6P_3 = \dfrac{6!}{(6-3)!} = \dfrac{6!}{3!} = 6 \cdot 5 \cdot 4 = 120$

19. a) P(neither is good) = $\dfrac{6}{20} \cdot \dfrac{5}{19} = \dfrac{3}{38}$

   b) P($\geq$ 1 good) = 1 – P(neither -good) =
    $1 - \dfrac{3}{38} = \dfrac{35}{38}$

20. (0.6)(0.6)(0.4)(0.4)(0.4 = 0.02304

     $_5C_3 = \dfrac{5!}{3!2!} = \dfrac{(5)(4)}{(2)(1)} = 10$

     (10)(.02304) = 0.2304

# CHAPTER THIRTEEN

## STATISTICS

### Exercise Set 13.1
1.  Statistics
3.  Descriptive
5.  Sample
7.  Random
9.  Cluster
11. Unbiased
13. Stratified sample

15. Cluster sample
19. Convenience sample
17. Systematic sample
21. Random sample
23. a) – c) Answers will vary.
25. President; four out of 44 U.S. presidents have been assassinated (Lincoln, Garfield, McKinley, Kennedy).

### Exercise Set 13.2
1.  The patients may have improved on their own without taking honey.
3.  Mama Mia's may have more empty spaces and more cars in the parking lot than Shanghi's due to a larger parking lot or because more people may walk to Mama Mia's than to Shanghi's.
5.  More people drive on Saturday evening. Thus, one might expect more accidents.
7.  Most driving is done close to home. Thus, one might expect more accidents close to home.
9.  We don't know how many of each professor's students were surveyed. Perhaps more of Professor Malone's students than Professor Wagner's students were surveyed. Also, because more students prefer a teacher does not mean that he or she is a better teacher. For example, a particular teacher may be an easier grader and that may be why that teacher is preferred.
11. Just because they are more expensive does not mean they will last the longer.
13. There may be deep sections in the pond, so it may not be safe to go wading.
15. a)

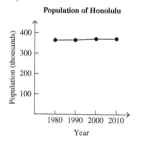

b)

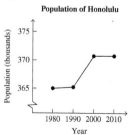

17. a)
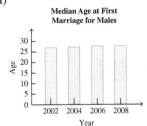

b)
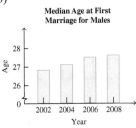

19. a)
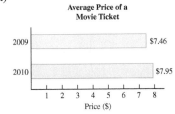

b) Answers will vary.

21.    Yes, the sum of its parts is 121%. The sum of the parts of a circle graph should be 100%. When the total percent of responses is more than 100%, a circle graph is not an appropriate graph to display the data. A bar graph is more appropriate in this situation.

23. A decimal point

**Exercise Set 13.3**

1. Frequency

3. Mark

5. Histogram

7. Stem

9. a) Number of observations = sum of frequencies = 20

   b) Width = $16 - 9 = 7$

   c) $\dfrac{16 + 22}{2} = \dfrac{38}{2} = 19$

   d) The modal class is the class with the greatest frequency. Thus, the modal class is 16 - 22.

   e) Since the class widths are 7, the next class would be 51 - 57.

11.

| Number of Visits | Number of Students |
|---|---|
| 0 | 3 |
| 1 | 8 |
| 2 | 3 |
| 3 | 5 |
| 4 | 2 |
| 5 | 7 |
| 6 | 2 |
| 7 | 3 |
| 8 | 4 |
| 9 | 1 |
| 10 | 2 |

13.

| Circulation (ten thousands) | Number of Magazines |
|---|---|
| 173 - 322 | 33 |
| 323 - 472 | 10 |
| 473 - 622 | 1 |
| 623 - 772 | 1 |
| 773 - 922 | 1 |

15.

| Circ. (ten thou) | No. of Mag. |
|---|---|
| 173 - 272 | 28 |
| 273 - 372 | 10 |
| 373 - 472 | 5 |
| 473 - 572 | 1 |
| 573 - 672 | 0 |
| 673 – 772 | 1 |
| 773 – 872 | 1 |

17.

| Population (millions) | No. of Cities |
|---|---|
| 7.0 – 7.9 | 6 |
| 8.0 – 8.9 | 4 |
| 9.0 – 9.9 | 1 |
| 10.0 –10.9 | 3 |
| 11.0 –11.9 | 1 |
| 12.0 –12.9 | 2 |
| 13.0 –13.9 | 3 |

19.

| Population (millions) | Number of Cities |
|---|---|
| 6.5 – 7.5 | 3 |
| 7.6 – 8.6 | 4 |
| 8.7 – 9.7 | 4 |
| 9.8 – 10.8 | 3 |
| 10.9 – 11.9 | 1 |
| 12.0 – 13.0 | 3 |
| 13.1 – 14.1 | 2 |

21.

| Percent | Number of States |
|---|---|
| 6.4 – 8.3 | 2 |
| 8.4 – 10.3 | 13 |
| 10.4 – 12.3 | 14 |
| 12.4 – 14.3 | 9 |
| 14.4 – 16.3 | 9 |
| 16.4 – 18.3 | 1 |
| 18.4 – 20.3 | 1 |
| 20.4 – 22.3 | 1 |

23.

| Percent | Number of States |
|---|---|
| 6.4 – 7.8 | 1 |
| 7.9 – 9.3 | 7 |
| 9.4 – 10.8 | 12 |
| 10.9 – 12.3 | 9 |
| 12.4 – 13.8 | 7 |
| 13.9 – 15.3 | 8 |
| 15.4 – 16.8 | 4 |
| 16.9 – 18.3 | 1 |
| 18.4 – 19.8 | 0 |
| 19.9 – 21.3 | 1 |

25.  1 | 2  represents 12

```
0 | 4  6  7  8
1 | 2  2  3  5  6  7  8  9
2 | 1  2  3  5  7
3 | 3  4
4 | 0
```

27.  a)

| Salaries (in $1000) | Number of Social Workers |
|---|---|
| 27 | 1 |
| 28 | 7 |
| 29 | 4 |
| 30 | 3 |
| 31 | 2 |
| 32 | 3 |
| 33 | 3 |
| 34 | 2 |

b) and c)

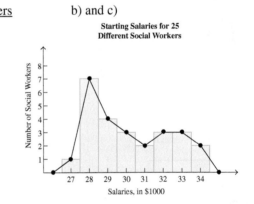

Starting Salaries for 25
Different Social Workers

d)  2 | 8  represents 28

```
2 | 7  8  8  8  8  8  8  8  9  9  9  9
3 | 0  0  0  1  1  2  2  2  3  3  3  4  4
```

29.  a)

| Total Gross (millions) | Number of Tours |
|---|---|
| 80 - 91 | 12 |
| 92 - 103 | 4 |
| 1040 - 115 | 3 |
| 116 - 127 | 2 |
| 128 - 139 | 3 |
| 140 - 151 | 0 |
| 152 - 163 | 1 |

b) and c)

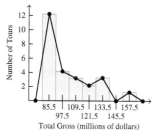

Top 25 Grossing North American
Concert Tours, 1985–2008

31.  a) $2+4+8+6+4+3+1=28$

   b) 4

   c) 2

   d) $2(0)+1(4)+2(8)+6(3)+4(4)+3(5)+1(6)=75$

e)

| Number of TVs | Number of homes |
|:---:|:---:|
| 0 | 2 |
| 1 | 4 |
| 2 | 8 |
| 3 | 6 |
| 4 | 4 |
| 5 | 3 |
| 6 | 1 |

33.  a)  7 messages

   b)  Adding the number of people who sent 6, 5, 4, or 3 messages gives: 4 + 7 + 3 + 2 = 16 people

   c)  The total number of people in the survey: 2 + 3 + 7 + 4 + 3 + 8 + 6 + 3 = 36

   d)

| Number of Messages | Number of People |
|:---:|:---:|
| 3 | 2 |
| 4 | 3 |
| 5 | 7 |
| 6 | 4 |
| 7 | 3 |
| 8 | 8 |
| 9 | 6 |
| 10 | 3 |

   e)

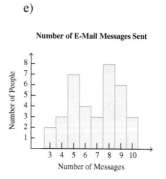

Number of E-Mail Messages Sent

35.  Tuition:  $0.345(14,570)=\$5026.65$

   Room:  $0.364(14,570)=\$5303.48$

   Board:  $0.229(14,570)=\$3336.53$

   Computer:  $0.062(14,570)=\$903.34$

37.  a) – e)  Answers will vary.

39.  a) – e)  Answers will vary.

## Exercise Set 13.4

1. Average
3. Mean
4. Mode
7. Quartiles
9. a) $\bar{x}$
   b) $\mu$

| | mean | median | mode | midrange |
|---|---|---|---|---|
| 11. | $\dfrac{129}{9} = 14$ | 13 | 13 | $\dfrac{8+26}{2} = 17$ |
| 13. | $\dfrac{555}{7} \approx 79.3$ | 82 | none | $\dfrac{52+100}{2} = 76$ |
| 15. | $\dfrac{64}{8} = 8$ | $\dfrac{7+9}{2} = 8$ | none | $\dfrac{1+15}{2} = 8$ |
| 17. | $\dfrac{118}{9} \approx 13.1$ | 11 | 1 | $\dfrac{1+36}{2} = 18.5$ |
| 19. | $\dfrac{95}{8} \approx 11.9$ | $\dfrac{12+13}{2} = 12.5$ | 13 | $\dfrac{6+17}{2} = 11.5$ |
| 21. | $\dfrac{1987}{10} = 198.7$ | $\dfrac{195+200}{2} = 197.5$ | none | $\dfrac{132+285}{2} = 208.5$ |
| 23. a) | $\dfrac{34}{7} \approx 4.9$ | 5 | 5 | $\dfrac{1+11}{2} = 6$ |
| b) | $\dfrac{37}{7} \approx 5.3$ | 5 | 5 | $\dfrac{1+11}{2} = 6$ |
| c) | Only the mean | | | |
| d) | $\dfrac{33}{7} \approx 4.7$ | 5 | 5 | $\dfrac{1+10}{2} = 5.5$ |

The mean and the midrange

25. A 79 mean average on 10 quizzes gives a total of 790 points. An 80 mean average on 10 quizzes requires a total of

800 points. Thus, Jim missed a B by 10 points not 1 point.

27. a) Mean: $\dfrac{229.7}{10} \approx 23$     b) Median: $\dfrac{22.3+22.7}{2} = 22.5$

    c) Mode: 18.5

    d) Midrange: $\dfrac{18.5+31.7}{2} \approx 25$

29. a) Mean: $\dfrac{\$45.7 \text{ billion}}{10} \approx \$4.6 \text{ billion}$     b) Median: $\dfrac{\$3.2+\$3.4}{2} \approx \$3.3 \text{ billion}$

    c) Mode: none

    d) Midrange: $\dfrac{1.9+14.8}{2} \approx \$8.4 \text{ billion}$

31. Let $x =$ the sum of his scores

    $\dfrac{x}{6} = 92$

    $$x = 92(6) = 552$$

33. One example is 72, 73, 74, 76, 77, 78.

Mean: $\dfrac{450}{6}=75$, Median: $\dfrac{74+76}{2}=75$, Midrange: $\dfrac{72+78}{2}=75$

35. a) Yes
    b) Cannot be found since we do not know the middle two numbers in the ranked list
    c) Cannot be found without knowing all of the numbers
    d) Yes

37. a) For a mean average of 60 on 7 exams, she must have a total of $60\times7=420$ points. Sheryl presently has $51+72+80+62+57+69=391$ points. Thus, to pass the course, her last exam must be $420-391=29$ or greater.
    b) A C average requires a total of $70\times7=490$ points. Sheryl has 391. Therefore, she would need $490-391=99$ or greater on her last exam.
    c) For a mean average of 60 on 6 exams, she must have a total of $60\times6=360$ points. If the lowest score on an exam she has already taken is dropped, she will have a total of $72+80+62+57+69=340$ points. Thus, to pass the course, her last exam must be $360-340=20$ or greater.
    d) For a mean average of 70 on 6 exams, she must have a total of $70\times6=420$ points. If the lowest score on an exam she has already taken is dropped, she will have a total of 340 points. Thus, to obtain a C, her last exam must be $420-340=80$ or greater.

39. One example is 1, 2, 3, 3, 4, 5 changed to 1, 2, 3, 4, 4, 5.

First set of data: Mean: $\dfrac{18}{6}=3$, Median: $\dfrac{3+3}{2}=3$, Mode: 3

Second set of data: Mean: $\dfrac{19}{6}=3.1\overline{6}$, Median: $\dfrac{3+4}{2}=3.5$, Mode: 4

41. No, by changing only one piece of the six pieces of data you cannot alter both the median and the midrange.

43. The data must be arranged in either ascending or descending order.

45. He is taller than approximately 35% of all kindergarten children.

47. a) $Q_2=$ Median $=\$23$
    b) $Q_1=$ Median of the first 10 data values $=\$20$
    c) $Q_3=$ Median of the last 10 data values $=\$34$

49. Second quartile, median

51. a) \$580     b) \$590     c) 25%     d) 25%     e) 17%     f) $100\times\$600=\$60,000$

53. a) Ruth: $\approx0.290,\ 0.359,\ 0.301,\ 0.272,\ 0.315$
    Mantle: $\approx0.300,\ 0.365,\ 0.304,\ 0.275,\ 0.321$
    b) Mantle's is greater in every case.
    c) Ruth: $\dfrac{593}{1878}\approx0.316$; Mantle: $\dfrac{760}{2440}\approx0.311$; Ruth's is greater.
    d) Answers will vary.
    e) Ruth: $\dfrac{1.537}{5}\approx0.307$; Mantle: $\dfrac{1.565}{5}=0.313$; Mantle's is greater.
    f) and g) Answers will vary.

55. $\Sigma xw=84(0.40)+94(0.60)=33.6+56.4=90$

$\Sigma w=0.40+0.60=1.00$

weighted average $=\dfrac{\Sigma xw}{\Sigma w}=\dfrac{90}{1.00}=90$

57. a) – c) Answers will vary.

**Exercise Set 13. 5**

1. Variation

3. Standard deviation

5. Sample

7. Range = $17 - 6 = 11$

$$\overline{x} = \frac{55}{5} = 11$$

| $x$ | $x - \overline{x}$ | $(x - \overline{x})^2$ |
|---|---|---|
| 11 | 0 | 0 |
| 9 | −2 | 4 |
| 6 | −5 | 25 |
| 12 | 1 | 1 |
| 17 | 6 | 36 |
|  | 0 | 66 |

9. Range = $136 - 130 = 6$

$$\overline{x} = \frac{931}{7} = 133$$

| $x$ | $x - \overline{x}$ | $(x - \overline{x})^2$ |
|---|---|---|
| 130 | −3 | 9 |
| 131 | −2 | 4 |
| 132 | −1 | 1 |
| 133 | 0 | 0 |
| 134 | 1 | 1 |
| 135 | 2 | 4 |
| 136 | 3 | 9 |
|  | 0 | 28 |

$$\frac{28}{6} \approx 4.67, s = \sqrt{4.67} \approx 2.16$$

11. Range = $15 - 4 = 11$

$$\overline{x} = \frac{60}{6} = 10$$

| $x$ | $x - \overline{x}$ | $(x - \overline{x})^2$ |
|---|---|---|
| 4 | −6 | 36 |
| 8 | −2 | 4 |
| 9 | −1 | 1 |
| 11 | 1 | 1 |
| 13 | 3 | 9 |
| 15 | 5 | 25 |
|  | 0 | 76 |

$$\frac{76}{5} = 15.2, \ s = \sqrt{15.2} \approx 3.90$$

13. Range = $12 - 7 = 5$

$$\overline{x} = \frac{63}{7} = 9$$

| $x$ | $x - \overline{x}$ | $(x - \overline{x})^2$ |
|---|---|---|
| 7 | −2 | 4 |
| 9 | 0 | 0 |
| 7 | −2 | 4 |
| 9 | 0 | 0 |
| 9 | 0 | 0 |
| 10 | 1 | 1 |
| 12 | 3 | 9 |
|  | 0 | 18 |

15. Range = $300 - 95 = \$205$

$$\overline{x} = \frac{1360}{8} = \$170$$

| $x$ | $x - \overline{x}$ | $(x - \overline{x})^2$ |
|---|---|---|
| 158 | −12 | 144 |
| 95 | −75 | 5625 |
| 175 | 5 | 25 |
| 180 | 10 | 100 |
| 95 | −75 | 5625 |
| 129 | −41 | 1681 |
| 228 | 58 | 3364 |
| 300 | 130 | 16900 |
|  | 0 | 33,464 |

$$\frac{18}{6} = 3, s = \sqrt{3} \approx 1.73$$

$$\frac{33,464}{7} \approx 4780.57, s = \sqrt{4780.57} \approx \$69.14$$

17. Range = 250 – 60 = $190

$$\bar{x} = \frac{1044}{9} = \$116$$

| $x$ | $x - \bar{x}$ | $(x - \bar{x})^2$ |
|---|---|---|
| 109 | –7 | 49 |
| 60 | –56 | 3136 |
| 80 | –36 | 1296 |
| 60 | –56 | 3136 |
| 210 | 94 | 8836 |
| 60 | –56 | 3136 |
| 100 | –16 | 256 |
| 115 | $\underline{-1}$ | $\underline{1}$ |
|  | 0 | 37,802 |

$$\frac{37,802}{8} = 4725.25, \quad s = \sqrt{4725.25} \approx \$68.74$$

19. Where one expects to find a large variability such as test scores

21. The first set of data will have the greater standard deviation because the scores have a greater spread about the mean.

23. The sum of the values in the (Data – Mean)$^2$ column will always be greater than or equal to 0.

25. a) Range = 68 - 5 = $63

$$\bar{x} = \frac{204}{6} = \$34$$

| $x$ | $x - \bar{x}$ | $(x - \bar{x})^2$ |
|---|---|---|
| 32 | –2 | 4 |
| 60 | 26 | 676 |
| 14 | –20 | 400 |
| 25 | –9 | 81 |
| 5 | –29 | 841 |
| 68 | $\underline{34}$ | $\underline{1156}$ |
|  | 0 | 3158 |

$$\frac{3158}{5} = 631.6, s = \sqrt{631.6} \approx \$25.13$$

b) New data: 42, 70, 24, 35, 15, 78

The range and standard deviation will be the same. If each piece of data is increased by the same number, the range and standard deviation will remain the same.

c)  Range = 78 - 15 = $63

$$\bar{x} = \frac{264}{6} = \$44$$

| $x$ | $x-\bar{x}$ | $(x-\bar{x})^2$ |
|---|---|---|
| 42 | −2 | 4 |
| 70 | 26 | 676 |
| 24 | −20 | 400 |
| 35 | −9 | 81 |
| 15 | −29 | 841 |
| 78 | 34 | 1156 |
|  | 0 | 3158 |

$$\frac{3158}{5} = 631.6, s = \sqrt{631.6} \approx \$25.13$$    The answers remain the same.

27.  a) - c) Answers will vary.

d)  If each number in a distribution is multiplied by $n$, both the mean and standard deviation of the new distribution will be $n$ times that of the original distribution.

e)  The mean of the second set is $4\times5=20$, and the standard deviation of the second set is $2\times5=10$.

29.  a)  The standard deviation increases.  There is a greater spread from the mean as they get older.

b)  $\approx 133$ lb

c)  $\frac{175-90}{4} = 21.25 \approx 21$ lb

d)  The mean weight is about 100 pounds and the normal range is about 60 to 140 pounds.

e)  The mean height is about 62 inches and the normal range is about 53 to 68 inches.

f)  100% - 95% = 5%

31.  a)

East

| Number of oil changes made | Number of days |
|---|---|
| 15-20 | 2 |
| 21-26 | 2 |
| 27-32 | 5 |
| 33-38 | 4 |
| 39-44 | 7 |
| 45-50 | 1 |
| 51-56 | 1 |
| 57-62 | 2 |
| 63-68 | 1 |

West

| Number of oil changes made | Number of days |
|---|---|
| 15-20 | 0 |
| 21-26 | 0 |
| 27-32 | 6 |
| 33-38 | 9 |
| 39-44 | 4 |
| 45-50 | 6 |
| 51-56 | 0 |
| 57-62 | 0 |
| 63-68 | 0 |

b)

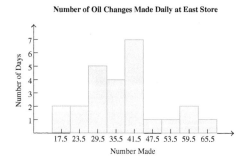

c)  They appear to have about the same mean since they are both centered around 38.

d)  The distribution for East is more spread out.  Therefore, East has a greater standard deviation.

e)  East: $\dfrac{950}{25} = 38$ , West: $\dfrac{950}{25} = 38$

31..    f)

| East | | | | West | | |
|---|---|---|---|---|---|---|
| $x$ | $x - \overline{x}$ | $(x - \overline{x})^2$ | | $x$ | $x - \overline{x}$ | $(x - \overline{x})^2$ |
| 33 | −5 | 25 | | 38 | 0 | 0 |
| 30 | −8 | 64 | | 38 | 0 | 0 |
| 25 | −13 | 169 | | 37 | −1 | 1 |
| 27 | −11 | 121 | | 36 | −2 | 4 |
| 40 | 2 | 4 | | 30 | −8 | 64 |
| 44 | 6 | 36 | | 45 | 7 | 49 |
| 49 | 11 | 121 | | 28 | −10 | 100 |
| 52 | 14 | 196 | | 47 | 9 | 81 |
| 42 | 4 | 16 | | 30 | −8 | 64 |
| 59 | 21 | 441 | | 46 | 8 | 64 |
| 19 | −19 | 361 | | 38 | 0 | 0 |
| 22 | −16 | 256 | | 39 | 1 | 1 |
| 57 | 19 | 361 | | 40 | 2 | 4 |
| 67 | 29 | 841 | | 34 | −4 | 16 |
| 15 | −23 | 529 | | 31 | −7 | 49 |
| 41 | 3 | 9 | | 45 | 7 | 49 |
| 43 | 5 | 25 | | 29 | −9 | 81 |
| 27 | −11 | 121 | | 38 | 0 | 0 |
| 42 | 4 | 16 | | 38 | 0 | 0 |
| 43 | 5 | 25 | | 39 | 1 | 1 |
| 37 | −1 | 1 | | 37 | −1 | 1 |
| 38 | 0 | 0 | | 42 | 4 | 16 |
| 31 | −7 | 49 | | 46 | 8 | 64 |
| 32 | -6 | 36 | | 31 | −7 | 49 |
| 35 | −3 | 9 | | 48 | 10 | 100 |
| | 0 | 3832 | | | 0 | 858 |

$\dfrac{3832}{24} \approx 159.67, \quad s = \sqrt{159.67} \approx 12.64$

$\dfrac{858}{24} = 35.75, \quad s = \sqrt{35.75} \approx 5.98$

33.  6, 6, 6, 6, 6

**Exercise Set 13.6**

1.  Rectangular

3.  Right

5.  Bimodal

7.  Standard

9.  Below

11. a) 68%  b) 95%  c) 99.7%

13. The distribution of outcomes from the roll of a die

15. J shaped right – consumer price index; J shaped left – value of the dollar

17. Normal

19. Skewed right

21. 0.5000

23. (area to the left of 1) – (area to the left of $-2$)

$= 0.8413 - 0.0228 = 0.8185$

25. area to the right of 1.53

$= 1 - (\text{area to the left of } 1.53)$

$= 1 - 0.9370 = 0.0630$

27. area to the left of $-1.78$

0.0375

29. area between $-1.32$ and $-1.64$

$0.0934 - 0.0505 = 0.0429$

31. area to the left of $-2.13$

0.0166

33. $0.7611 = 76.11\%$

35. (area to the left of 2.24) – (area to the left of $-1.34$)

$= 0.9875 - 0.0901 = 0.8974 = 89.74\%$

37. area greater than $-1.90$

$= \text{area less than } 1.90 = 0.9713 = 97.13\%$

39. area less than $1.96 = 0.9750 = 97.50\%$

41. (area to the left of 2.14) – (area to the left of 0.72)

$= 0.9838 - 0.7642 = 0.2196 = 21.96\%$

43. a) Emily, Sarah, and Carol are taller than the mean because their z-scores are positive.

b) Jenny and Shenice are at the mean because their z-scores are zero.

c) Sadaf, Heather, and Kim are shorter than the mean because their z-scores are negative.

45. $0.5000 = 50\%$

47. $z_{58,750} = \dfrac{58,750 - 50,000}{7000} = \dfrac{8750}{7000} = 1.25$

$1.000 - 0.8944 = 0.1056 = 10.56\%$

49. $z_{550} = \dfrac{550 - 500}{100} = \dfrac{50}{100} = 0.50$

area less than $0.5 = 0.6915 = 69.15\%$

51. $z_{550} = \dfrac{550 - 500}{100} = \dfrac{50}{100} = 0.50$

$z_{650} = \dfrac{650 - 500}{100} = \dfrac{150}{100} = 1.50$

area between 1.5 and 0.5

$= 0.9332 - 0.6915 = 0.2417 = 24.17\%$

53. $z_{525} = \dfrac{525 - 500}{100} = \dfrac{25}{100} = 0.25$

$z_{400} = \dfrac{400 - 500}{100} = \dfrac{-100}{100} = -1.00$

area between $-1.00$ and 0.25

$= 0.5987 - 0.1587 = 0.4400 = 44.00\%$

55. $z_{7.4} = \dfrac{7.4 - 7.6}{0.4} = \dfrac{-0.2}{0.4} = -0.50$

$z_{7.7} = \dfrac{7.7 - 7.6}{0.4} = \dfrac{0.1}{0.4} = 0.25$

$0.5987 - 0.3085 = 0.2902 = 29.02\%$

57. $z_{7.7} = \dfrac{7.7 - 7.6}{0.4} = \dfrac{0.1}{0.4} = 0.25$

$0.5987 = 59.87\%$

59. $0.5000 = 50.00\%$

61. $z_{56} = \dfrac{56 - 62}{5} = \dfrac{-6}{5} = -1.20$

$0.1151 = 11.51\%$

63. 11.51% of cars are traveling slower than 56 mph.  (See Exercise 67.)

$(0.1151)(200) \approx 23$ cars

65. $z_{15.83} = \dfrac{15.83 - 16}{0.1} = -1.70$

$z_{16.32} = \dfrac{16.32 - 16}{0.1} = 3.2$

$0.9993 - 0.0446 = 0.9547 = 95.47\%$

67. $z_{15.83} = \dfrac{15.83 - 16}{0.1} = -1.70$

$1 - 0.9554 = 0.0446$

$(0.0446)(300,000) = 13,380$ boxes

67. $z_{7250} = \dfrac{7250 - 8000}{1500} = \dfrac{-750}{1500} = -0.50$

area greater than $-0.50$ = area less than $0.50$

$0.6915 = 69.15\%$

69. $z_{7250} = \dfrac{7250 - 8000}{1500} = \dfrac{-750}{1500} = -0.50$

area greater than $-0.50$ = area less than $0.50$

$0.6915 = 69.15\%$

71. $z_{11,750} = \dfrac{11,750 - 8000}{1500} = \dfrac{3750}{1500} = 2.5$

$1 - 0.9938 = 0.0062 = 0.62\%$

73. 69.15% of the families pay more than $7250 annually.

(See Exercise 69.)

$(0.6915)(120) \approx 83$ children

75. We need the percentage of customers with a weight loss of less than 5 lb.

$z_5 = \dfrac{5 - 6.7}{0.81} = \dfrac{-1.7}{0.81} = -2.10$

$1 - 0.9821 = 0.0179 = 1.79\%$

77. The standard deviation is too large. There is too much variation.

79. a) $B$    b) $C$    c) $A$

81. The mode is the lowest value, the median is greater than the mode, and the mean is greater than the median. The greatest frequency appears on the left side of the curve. Since the mode is the value with the greatest frequency, the mode would appear on the left side of the curve (where the lowest values are). Every value in the set of data is considered in determining the mean. The values on the far right of the curve would increase the value of the mean. Thus, the value of the mean would be farther to the right than the mode. The median would be between the mode and the mean.

83. Answers will vary.

85. a) Katie: $z_{28,408} = \dfrac{28,408 - 23,200}{2170} = \dfrac{5208}{2170} = 2.4$

Stella: $z_{29,510} = \dfrac{29,510 - 25,600}{2300} = \dfrac{3910}{2300} = 1.7$

b) Katie. Her z-score is higher than Stella's z-score. This means her sales are further above the mean than Stella's sales.

87. Answers will vary.

89. Using Table 13.7, the answer is −1.18.

91. $\dfrac{0.77}{2} = 0.385$

Using the table in Section 13.7, an area of 0.385 has a z-score of 1.20.

$$z = \frac{x - \bar{x}}{s}$$

$$1.20 = \frac{14.4 - 12}{s}$$

$$1.20 = \frac{2.4}{s}$$

$$\frac{1.20s}{1.20} = \frac{2.4}{1.20}$$

$$s = 2$$

**Exercise Set 13.7**

1. Coefficient

3. 1

5. 0

7. Positive

9. Fit

11. No correlation

13. Strong positive

15. Yes, $|\,0.82\,| > 0.684$

17. Yes, $|\,-0.73\,| > 0.707$

19. No, $|-0.23| < 0.254$

21. No, $|0.75| < 0.917$

23. a)

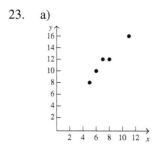

b)

| x | y | $x^2$ | $y^2$ | xy |
|---|---|---|---|---|
| 5 | 8 | 25 | 64 | 40 |
| 6 | 10 | 36 | 100 | 60 |
| 7 | 12 | 49 | 144 | 84 |
| 8 | 12 | 64 | 144 | 96 |
| 11 | 16 | 121 | 256 | 176 |
| 37 | 58 | 295 | 708 | 456 |

$$r = \frac{5(456) - 37(58)}{\sqrt{5(295) - 1369}\sqrt{5(708) - 3364}} \approx 0.981$$

c) Yes, $|0.981| > 0.878$

d) Yes, $|0.981| > 0.959$

25. a)

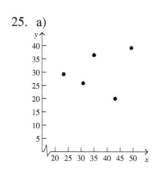

b)

| x | y | $x^2$ | $y^2$ | xy |
|---|---|---|---|---|
| 23 | 29 | 529 | 841 | 667 |
| 35 | 37 | 1225 | 1369 | 1295 |
| 31 | 26 | 961 | 676 | 806 |
| 43 | 20 | 1849 | 400 | 860 |
| 49 | 39 | 2401 | 1521 | 1911 |
| 181 | 151 | 6965 | 4807 | 5539 |

$$r = \frac{5(5539) - 181(151)}{\sqrt{5(6965) - 32,761}\sqrt{5(4807) - 22,801}} = \frac{364}{\sqrt{2064}\sqrt{1234}} \approx 0.228$$

c) No, $|0.228| < 0.878$

d) No, $|0.228| < 0.959$

27. a)

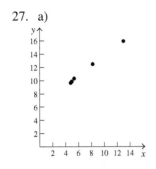

b)

| $x$ | $y$ | $x^2$ | $y^2$ | $xy$ |
|------|------|--------|--------|--------|
| 5.3 | 10.3 | 28.09 | 106.09 | 54.59 |
| 4.7 | 9.6 | 22.09 | 92.16 | 45.12 |
| 8.4 | 12.5 | 70.56 | 156.25 | 105 |
| 12.7 | 16.2 | 161.29 | 262.44 | 205.74 |
| 4.9 | 9.8 | 24.01 | 96.04 | 48.02 |
| 36 | 58.4 | 306.04 | 712.98 | 458.47 |

$$r = \frac{5(458.47) - 36(58.4)}{\sqrt{5(306.04) - 1296}\sqrt{5(712.98) - 3410.56}} = \frac{189.95}{\sqrt{234.2}\sqrt{154.34}} \approx 0.999$$

c) Yes, $|0.999| > 0.878$                    d) Yes, $|0.999| > 0.959$

29. a)

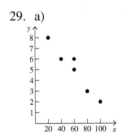

b)

| $x$ | $y$ | $x^2$ | $y^2$ | $xy$ |
|------|------|--------|--------|--------|
| 100 | 2 | 10,000 | 4 | 200 |
| 80 | 3 | 6400 | 9 | 240 |
| 60 | 5 | 3600 | 25 | 300 |
| 60 | 6 | 3600 | 36 | 360 |
| 40 | 6 | 1600 | 36 | 240 |
| 20 | 8 | 400 | 64 | 160 |
| 360 | 30 | 25,600 | 174 | 1500 |

$$r = \frac{6(1500) - 360(30)}{\sqrt{6(25,600) - 129,600}\sqrt{6(174) - 900}} = \frac{-1800}{\sqrt{24,000}\sqrt{144}} \approx -0.968$$

31. From # 23:    $m = \dfrac{5(456) - 37(58)}{5(295) - 1369} = \dfrac{67}{53} \approx 1.26$

$$b = \frac{58 - \left(\dfrac{67}{53}\right)(37)}{5} \approx 2.25, \quad y = 1.26x + 2.25$$

33. From # 25: $m = \dfrac{5(5539) - 181(151)}{5(6965) - 32,761} = \dfrac{364}{2064} \approx 0.18$

$b = \dfrac{151 - \dfrac{364}{2064}(181)}{5} \approx 23.82, \quad y = 0.18x + 23.82$

35. From # 27: $m = \dfrac{5(458.47) - 36(58.4)}{5(306.04) - 1296} = \dfrac{189.95}{234.2} \approx 0.81$

$b = \dfrac{58.4 - \dfrac{189.95}{234.2}(36)}{5} \approx 5.84, \quad y = 0.81x + 5.84$

37. From # 29: $m = \dfrac{6(1500) - 360(30)}{6(25,600) - 129,600} = \dfrac{-1800}{24,000} \approx -0.08$

$b = \dfrac{30 - \dfrac{-1800}{24,000}(360)}{6} \approx 9.50, \quad y = -0.08x + 9.50$

39.    a)

| $x$ | $y$ | $x^2$ | $y^2$ | $xy$ |
|---|---|---|---|---|
| 50 | 40 | 2500 | 1600 | 2000 |
| 53 | 42 | 2809 | 1764 | 2226 |
| 60 | 45 | 3600 | 2025 | 2700 |
| 35 | 25 | 1225 | 625 | 875 |
| 43 | 34 | 1849 | 1156 | 1462 |
| 62 | 45 | 3844 | 2025 | 2790 |
| 303 | 231 | 15827 | 9195 | 12053 |

$r = \dfrac{6(12053) - (303)(231)}{\sqrt{6(15827) - 91809}\sqrt{6(9195) - 53361}} \approx 0.974$

b) Yes, $\mid 0.974 \mid > 0.811$

c) $m = \dfrac{6(12053) - (303)(231)}{(6)(15827) - 91809} = \dfrac{775}{1051} \approx 0.74$,

$b = \dfrac{231 - \dfrac{775}{1051}(303)}{6} \approx 1.26, \quad y = 0.74x + 1.26$

41. a)

| $x$ | $y$ | $x^2$ | $y^2$ | $xy$ |
|---|---|---|---|---|
| 20 | 40 | 400 | 1600 | 800 |
| 40 | 45 | 1600 | 2025 | 1800 |
| 50 | 70 | 2500 | 4900 | 3500 |
| 60 | 76 | 3600 | 5776 | 4560 |
| 80 | 92 | 6400 | 8464 | 7360 |
| 100 | 95 | 10,000 | 9025 | 9500 |
| 350 | 418 | 24,500 | 31,790 | 27,520 |

$$r = \frac{6(27,520) - 350(418)}{\sqrt{6(24,500) - 122,500}\sqrt{6(31,790) - 174,724}} = \frac{18,820}{\sqrt{24,500}\sqrt{16,016}} \approx 0.950$$

b) Yes, $|0.950| > 0.917$

c) $m = \dfrac{6(27,520) - 350(418)}{6(24,500) - 122,500} = \dfrac{18,820}{24,500} \approx 0.77$, $\quad b = \dfrac{418 - \frac{18,820}{24,500}(350)}{6} \approx 24.86$, $\quad y = 0.77x + 24.86$

43. a)

| $x$ | $y$ | $x^2$ | $y^2$ | $xy$ |
|---|---|---|---|---|
| 110 | 70 | 12100 | 4900 | 7700 |
| 153 | 110 | 23409 | 12100 | 16830 |
| 120 | 80 | 14400 | 6400 | 9600 |
| 143 | 98 | 20449 | 9604 | 14014 |
| 100 | 70 | 10000 | 4900 | 7000 |
| 112 | 75 | 12544 | 5625 | 8400 |
| 738 | 503 | 92902 | 43529 | 63544 |

$$r = \frac{6(63544) - (738)(503)}{\sqrt{6(92902) - 544644}\sqrt{6(43529) - 253009}} = 0.98432 \approx 0.984$$

b) Yes, $|0.984| > 0.811$

c) $m = \dfrac{6(63544) - (738)(503)}{6(92902) - 544644} = 0.78712 \approx 0.79$,

$b = \dfrac{503 - (0.78712)(738)}{6} \approx -12.98$, $\quad y = 0.79x - 12.98$

d) $y = 0.79(115) - 12.98 \approx 78$

45. a)

| $x$ | $y$ | $x^2$ | $y^2$ | $xy$ |
|---|---|---|---|---|
| 27 | 23 | 729 | 529 | 621 |
| 31 | 22 | 961 | 484 | 682 |
| 35 | 20 | 1225 | 400 | 700 |
| 32 | 21 | 1024 | 441 | 672 |
| 30 | 24 | 900 | 576 | 720 |
| 30 | 22 | 900 | 484 | 660 |
| 185 | 132 | 5739 | 2914 | 4055 |

$$r = \frac{6(4055) - (185)(132)}{\sqrt{6(5739) - 34225}\sqrt{6(2914) - 17424}} \approx -0.804$$

b) No, $|-0.804| < 0.917$

c) $m = \dfrac{6(4055) - (185)(132)}{6(5739) - 34225} = -0.43063 \approx -0.43$

$b = \dfrac{132 - (-0.43063)(185)}{6} \approx 35.28, \quad y = -0.43x + 35.28$

Note, however, that since we have not found a significant correlation between $x$ and $y$, the line of best fit may not be very useful for predicting $y$ given $x$.

d) $y = -0.43(33) + 35.28 \approx 21.1$ mpg

47. a)

| $x$ | $y$ | $x^2$ | $y^2$ | $xy$ |
|---|---|---|---|---|
| 1 | 80.0 | 1 | 6400.0 | 80.0 |
| 2 | 76.2 | 4 | 5806.4 | 152.4 |
| 3 | 68.7 | 9 | 4719.7 | 206.1 |
| 4 | 50.1 | 16 | 2510.0 | 200.4 |
| 5 | 30.2 | 25 | 912.0 | 151.0 |
| 6 | 20.8 | 36 | 432.6 | 124.8 |
| 21 | 326 | 91 | 20,780.7 | 914.7 |

$$r = \frac{6(914.7) - 21(326)}{\sqrt{6(91) - 441}\sqrt{6(20,780.7) - 106,276}} = \frac{-1357.8}{\sqrt{105}\sqrt{18,408.2}} \approx -0.977$$

b) Yes, $|-0.977| > 0.917$

c) $m = \dfrac{6(914.7) - 21(326)}{6(91) - 441} = \dfrac{-1357.8}{105} \approx -12.93$, $b = \dfrac{326 - \frac{-1357.8}{105}(21)}{6} \approx 99.59$, $y = -12.93x + 99.59$

d) $y = -12.93(4.5) + 99.59 \approx 41.4\%$

49. a) and b) Answers will vary.

c)

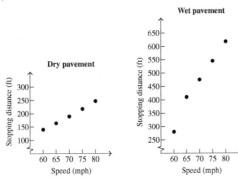

d) The values in the last row of the calculation table are:

$\Sigma x = 350$, $\Sigma y = 959$, $\Sigma x^2 = 24750$, $\Sigma y^2 = 191129$, $\Sigma xy = 68470$

$$r = \frac{5(68470) - (350)(959)}{\sqrt{5(24750) - (350)^2}\sqrt{5(191129) - (959)^2}} \approx 0.999$$

e) The values in the last row of the calculation table are:

$\Sigma x = 350$, $\Sigma y = 2328$, $\Sigma x^2 = 24750$, $\Sigma y^2 = 1151074$, $\Sigma xy = 167015$

$$r = \frac{5(167015) - (350)(2328)}{\sqrt{5(24750) - (350)^2}\sqrt{5(1151074) - (2328)^2}} \approx 0.990$$

f) Answers will vary.

g) $m = \dfrac{5(68470) - (350)(959)}{5(24750) - (350)^2} = 5.36$

$b = \dfrac{959 - (5.36)(350)}{5} = -183.40$

$y = 5.36x - 183.40$

h) $m = \dfrac{5(167015) - (350)(2328)}{5(24750) - (350)^2} = 16.22$

$b = \dfrac{2328 - (16.22)(350)}{5} = -669.80$

$y = 16.22x - 699.80$

i) Dry: $y = 5.36(77) - 183.40 \approx 229.3$ ft

Wet: $y = 16.22(77) - 669.80 = 579.1$ ft

51. Answers will vary.

53. a) The values in the last row of the calculation table are:

$\Sigma x = 12045$, $\Sigma y = 1252.1$, $\Sigma x^2 = 24180355$, $\Sigma y^2 = 261689.89$, $\Sigma xy = 2513671.1$

$$r = \frac{6(2197621) - (12045)(1252.1)}{\sqrt{6(24180355) - (12045)^2}\sqrt{6(261689.89) - (1252.1)^2}} \approx 0.963$$

b) Should be the same.

c) The values in the last row of the calculation table are:

$$\Sigma x = 15,\ \Sigma y = 1252.1,\ \Sigma x^2 = 55,\ \Sigma y^2 = 261689.89,\ \Sigma xy = 3210.6$$

$$r = \frac{6(3210.6) - (15)(1252.1)}{\sqrt{6(55) - (15)^2}\ \sqrt{6(261689.89) - (1252.1)^2}} \approx 0.963$$

### Review Exercises

1. a) A **population** consists of all items or people of interest.

   b) A **sample** is a subset of the population.

2. A **random sample** is one where every item in the population has the same chance of being selected.

3. The candy bars may have lots of calories, or fat, or sodium.  Therefore, it may not be healthy to eat them.

4. Sales may not necessarily be a good indicator of profit.  Expenses must also be considered.

5. a)

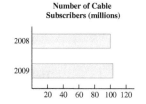

   b)

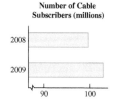

6. a)

| Class | Frequency |
|---|---|
| 35 | 1 |
| 36 | 3 |
| 37 | 6 |
| 38 | 2 |
| 39 | 3 |
| 40 | 0 |
| 41 | 4 |
| 42 | 1 |
| 43 | 3 |
| 44 | 1 |
| 45 | 1 |

b) and c)

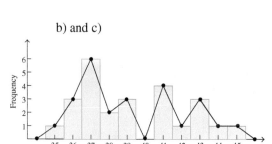

7. a)

| High Temperature | Number of Cities |
|---|---|
| 58 - 62 | 1 |
| 63 - 67 | 4 |
| 68 - 72 | 9 |
| 73 - 77 | 10 |
| 78 - 82 | 11 |
| 83 - 87 | 4 |
| 88 - 92 | 1 |

b) and c)

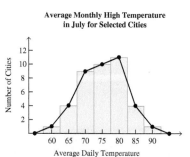

d)  6 | 5 represents 65

```
5| 8
6| 3 6 6 7 8 8 9
7| 0 1 1 1 2 2 3 3 3 4 5 5 5 6 6 7 9 9 9
8| 0 0 0 0 1 2 2 2 3 4 4 7
9| 1
```

8.  $\bar{x} = \dfrac{480}{6} = 80$

9.  $\dfrac{79+83}{2} = 81$

10.  None

11.  $\dfrac{67+93}{2} = 80$

12.  $93 - 67 = 26$

13.

| $x$ | $x-\bar{x}$ | $(x-\bar{x})^2$ |
|---|---|---|
| 67 | −13 | 169 |
| 74 | −6 | 36 |
| 79 | −1 | 1 |
| 83 | 3 | 9 |
| 84 | 4 | 16 |
| 93 | 13 | 169 |
|  | 0 | 400 |

$\dfrac{400}{5} = 80,\ s = \sqrt{80} \approx 8.94$

14.  $\bar{x} = \dfrac{156}{12} = 13$

15.  $\dfrac{12+14}{2} = 13$

16.  12 and 7

17.  $\dfrac{4+23}{2} = 13.5$

18.  $23 - 4 = 19$

19.

| $x$ | $x-\bar{x}$ | $(x-\bar{x})^2$ |
|---|---|---|
| 4 | -9 | 81 |
| 5 | -8 | 64 |
| 7 | -6 | 36 |
| 7 | -6 | 36 |
| 12 | -1 | 1 |
| 12 | -1 | 1 |
| 14 | 1 | 1 |
| 15 | 2 | 4 |
| 17 | 4 | 16 |
| 19 | 6 | 36 |
| 21 | 8 | 64 |
| 23 | 10 | 100 |
|  | 0 | 440 |

$\dfrac{440}{11} = 40,\ s = \sqrt{40} \approx 6.32$

20. $z_7 = \dfrac{7-9}{2} = \dfrac{-2}{2} = -1.00$

$z_{11} = \dfrac{11-9}{2} = \dfrac{2}{2} = 1.00$

$0.8413 - 0.1587 = 0.6826 = 68.26\%$

21. $z_5 = \dfrac{5-9}{2} = \dfrac{-4}{2} = -2.00$

$z_{13} = \dfrac{14-9}{2} = \dfrac{4}{2} = 2.00$

$0.9772 - 0.0228 = 0.9544 = 95.44\%$

22. $z_{12.2} = \dfrac{12.2-9}{2} = \dfrac{3.2}{2} = 1.6$

$0.9452 = 94.52\%$

23. Subtract the answer for Exercise 22 from 1:

$1 - 0.9452 = 0.0548 = 5.48\%$

24. $z_{7.8} = \dfrac{7.8-9}{2} = -\dfrac{1.2}{2} = -0.6$

$1 - 0.2743 = 0.7257 = 72.57\%$

25. $z_{20} = \dfrac{20-20}{5} = \dfrac{0}{5} = 0$

$z_{25} = \dfrac{25-20}{5} = \dfrac{5}{5} = 1.00$

$0.341 = 34.1\%$

26. $z_{18} = \dfrac{18-20}{5} = \dfrac{-2}{5} = -0.40$

$0.500 - 0.155 = 0.345 = 34.5\%$

27. $z_{22} = \dfrac{22-20}{5} = \dfrac{2}{5} = 0.40$

$z_{28} = \dfrac{28-20}{5} = \dfrac{8}{5} = 1.60$

$0.445 - 0.155 = 0.29 = 29.0\%$

28. $z_{30} = \dfrac{30-20}{5} = \dfrac{10}{5} = 2.00$

$0.500 - 0.477 = 0.023 = 2.3\%$

29. a)

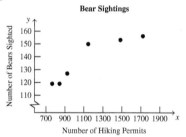

b) Yes, positive

c)

| $x$ | $y$ | $x^2$ | $y^2$ | $xy$ |
|---|---|---|---|---|
| 765 | 119 | 585,225 | 14,161 | 91,035 |
| 926 | 127 | 857,476 | 16,129 | 117,602 |
| 1145 | 150 | 1,311,025 | 22,500 | 171,750 |
| 842 | 119 | 708,964 | 14,161 | 100,198 |
| 1485 | 153 | 2,205,225 | 23,409 | 227,205 |
| 1702 | 156 | 2,896,804 | 24,336 | 265,512 |
| 6865 | 824 | 8,564,719 | 114,696 | 973,302 |

$$r = \dfrac{6(973,302) - 6865(824)}{\sqrt{6(8,564,719) - 47,128,225}\,\sqrt{6(114,696) - 678,976}} = \dfrac{183,052}{\sqrt{4,260,089}\,\sqrt{9200}} \approx 0.925$$

d) Yes, $|\,0.925\,| > 0.811$

e)    $m = \dfrac{6(973,302) - 6865(824)}{6(8,564,719) - 47,128,225} = \dfrac{183,052}{4,260,089} \approx 0.04$ ,

$b = \dfrac{824 - \dfrac{183,052}{4,260,089}(6865)}{6} \approx 88.17, \quad y = 0.04x + 88.17$

f)    $y = 0.04(1500) + 88.17 = 148.17 \approx 148$ bears

30.  a)

**Daily Sales**

Number Sold / Price (dollars)

b)    Yes; negative because generally as the price increases, the number sold decreases.

c)

| $x$ | $y$ | $x^2$ | $y^2$ | $xy$ |
|---|---|---|---|---|
| 0.75 | 200 | 0.5625 | 40,000 | 150 |
| 1.00 | 160 | 1 | 25,600 | 160 |
| 1.25 | 140 | 1.5625 | 19,600 | 175 |
| 1.50 | 120 | 2.25 | 14,400 | 180 |
| 1.75 | 110 | 3.0625 | 12,100 | 192.5 |
| 2.00 | 95 | 4 | 9025 | 190 |
| 8.25 | 825 | 12.4375 | 120,725 | 1047.5 |

$$r = \dfrac{6(1047.5) - 8.25(825)}{\sqrt{6(12.4375) - 68.0625}\sqrt{6(120,725) - 680,625}} = \dfrac{-521.25}{\sqrt{6.5625}\sqrt{43,725}} \approx -0.973$$

d) Yes, $|-0.973| > 0.811$

e)    $m = \dfrac{6(1047.5) - 8.25(825)}{6(12.4375) - 68.0625} = \dfrac{-521.25}{6.5625} \approx -79.4$

$b = \dfrac{825 - \dfrac{-521.25}{6.5625}(8.25)}{6} \approx 246.7, \quad y = -79.4x + 246.7$

f)    $y = -79.4(1.60) + 246.7 = 119.66 \approx 120$ sold

31.  180 lb
33.  25%
35.  14%

32.  185 lb
34.  25%
36.  $(100)(192) = 19,200$ lb

37.  $192 + (2)(23) = 238\,\text{lb}$

38.  $192 - (1.8)(23) = 150.6\,\text{lb}$

39.  $\bar{x} = \dfrac{152}{42} \approx 3.53$

40.  2

41.  $\dfrac{3+3}{2} = 3$

42.  $\dfrac{0+14}{2} = 7$

43.  14 - 0 = 14

44.

| $x$ | $x-\bar{x}$ | $(x-\bar{x})^2$ | $x$ | $x-\bar{x}$ | $(x-\bar{x})^2$ | $x$ | $x-\bar{x}$ | $(x-\bar{x})^2$ |
|---|---|---|---|---|---|---|---|---|
| 0 | −3.5 | 12.25 | 2 | −1.5 | 2.25 | 4 | 0.5 | 0.25 |
| 0 | −3.5 | 12.25 | 2 | −1.5 | 2.25 | 5 | 1.5 | 2.25 |
| 0 | −3.5 | 12.25 | 2 | −1.5 | 2.25 | 5 | 1.5 | 2.25 |
| 0 | −3.5 | 12.25 | 3 | −0.5 | 0.25 | 5 | 1.5 | 2.25 |
| 0 | −3.5 | 12.25 | 3 | −0.5 | 0.25 | 6 | 2.5 | 6.25 |
| 0 | −3.5 | 12.25 | 3 | −0.5 | 0.25 | 6 | 2.5 | 6.25 |
| 1 | −2.5 | 6.25 | 3 | −0.5 | 0.25 | 6 | 2.5 | 6.25 |
| 1 | −2.5 | 6.25 | 3 | −0.5 | 0.25 | 6 | 2.5 | 6.25 |
| 2 | −1.5 | 2.25 | 3 | −0.5 | 0.25 | 6 | 2.5 | 6.25 |
| 2 | −1.5 | 2.25 | 4 | 0.5 | 0.25 | 7 | 3.5 | 12.25 |
| 2 | −1.5 | 2.25 | 4 | 0.5 | 0.25 | 8 | 4.5 | 20.25 |
| 2 | −1.5 | 2.25 | 4 | 0.5 | 0.25 | 10 | 6.5 | 42.25 |
| 2 | −1.5 | 2.25 | 4 | 0.5 | 0.25 | 14 | 10.5 | 110.25 |
| 2 | −1.5 | 2.25 | 4 | 0.5 | 0.25 | | | 334.75 |
| 2 | −1.5 | 2.25 | 4 | 0.5 | 0.25 | | | |

$$\dfrac{334.75}{42} \approx 7.97, \quad s = \sqrt{7.97} \approx 2.823$$

45.

| # of Children | # of Presidents |
|---|---|
| 0 - 1 | 8 |
| 2 - 3 | 15 |
| 4 - 5 | 10 |
| 6 - 7 | 6 |
| 8 - 9 | 1 |
| 10 - 11 | 1 |
| 12 - 13 | 0 |
| 14 - 15 | 1 |

46. and 47.

Number of Children of U.S. Presidents

48.  No, it is skewed to the right.

49.  No, some families have no children, more have one child, the greatest percent may have two children, fewer have three children, etc.

50.  No, the number of children per family has decreased over the years.

## Chapter Test

1.  $\bar{x} = \dfrac{210}{5} = 42$

2.  43

3.  43

4.  $\dfrac{27+52}{2} = 39.5$

5.  $52 - 27 = 25$

6.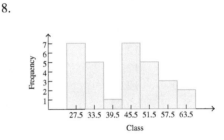

| $x$ | $x - \bar{x}$ | $(x-\bar{x})^2$ |
|---|---|---|
| 27 | −15 | 225 |
| 43 | 1 | 1 |
| 43 | 1 | 1 |
| 45 | 3 | 9 |
| 52 | 10 | 100 |
| | 0 | 336 |

$$\frac{336}{4} = 84, \ s = \sqrt{84} \approx 9.17$$

7.

| Class | Frequency |
|---|---|
| 25 - 30 | 7 |
| 31 - 36 | 5 |
| 37 - 42 | 1 |
| 43 - 48 | 7 |
| 49 - 54 | 5 |
| 55 - 60 | 3 |
| 61 - 66 | 2 |

8.

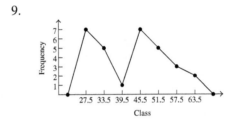

9.

10.  Mode = $735

11.  Median = $710

12.  $100\% - 25\% = 75\%$

13.  79%

14.  $100(740) = \$74{,}000$

15.  $\$740 + 1(\$40) = \$780$

16.  $z_{36} = \dfrac{36 - 42}{5} = \dfrac{-6}{5} = -1.20$

$z_{53} = \dfrac{53 - 42}{5} = \dfrac{11}{5} = 2.20$

17.  $z_{35.75} = \dfrac{35.75 - 42}{5} = -1.25$

$1 - 0.1056 = 0.8944 = 89.44\%$

18.  $z_{48.25} = \dfrac{48.25 - 42}{5} = 1.25$

19.  $z_{50} = \dfrac{50 - 42}{5} = 1.6$

$0.9452 = 94.52\%$

20. a)

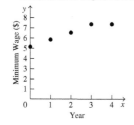

**Hourly Minimum Wage in the U.S.**

b)   Yes

c)   The values in the last row of the calculation
table are:

$\Sigma x = 10, \ \Sigma y = 32.05, \ \Sigma x^2 = 30, \ \Sigma y^2 = 208.77, \ \Sigma xy = 69.7$

$r = \dfrac{5(69.7) - (10)(32.05)}{\sqrt{5(30) - (10)^2}\sqrt{5(208.77) - (32.05)^2}} \approx 0.970$

d)   Yes, $\ |\ 0.970\ | > 0.878$

e)   $m = \dfrac{5(69.7) - (10)(32.05)}{5(30) - (10)^2} = 0.56$

$b = \dfrac{32.05 - (0.56)(10)}{5} = 5.29, \quad y = 0.56x + 5.29$

f)   $y = 0.56(8) + 5.29 = \$9.77$